CALCULUS ON MANIFOLDS

$F_X: \mathscr{D}_X \subset M \times \mathbf{R} \to M$	integral of vectorfield	41
$\mathbf{L}_X$	Lie derivative	51
$[X, Y]$	Lie bracket	47
$\mathbf{d}$	exterior derivative	61
$\mathbf{i}_X$	inner product	65
Ω	volume n form	70
μ_Ω	measure of Ω	81
$\operatorname{div}_\Omega X$	divergence of a vectorfield	77
$\det_\Omega f$	determinant of a mapping	75
ω	symplectic form	85, 95
$X^\flat = 2\omega_\flat(X)$	lowering action	86, 92
$\alpha^\sharp = \frac{1}{2}\omega_\sharp(\alpha)$	raising action	86, 92
$X_H = (dH)^\sharp$	Hamiltonian vectorfield	99
$S_p(E, \omega)$	symplectic group	88
$-\theta_0$	canonical 1-form on T^*M	96
$\omega_0 = -d\theta_0$	canonical 2-form on T^*M	96
$\{f, g\}$	Poisson bracket of functions	98
$\{\alpha, \beta\}$	Poisson bracket of 1-forms	99
$\mathscr{X}_{\mathscr{L}\mathscr{H}}$	locally Hamiltonian vectorfields	107
$\mathscr{X}_{\mathscr{H}}$	globally Hamiltonian vectorfields	109
Σ_e	energy surface	111
$\mathbf{F}L$	Legendre transformation	115
ω_L	pullback of ω_0 by FL	116
$\tilde{\omega}$	pullback of ω to $\mathbf{R} \times M$	134
$X: \mathbf{R} \times M \to TM$	time-dependent vectorfield	135
$\tilde{X}: \mathbf{R} \times M \to T(\mathbf{R} \times M)$	vectorfield associated to X	135
$\underline{t}$	unit time vectorfield on $\mathbf{R} \times M$	134
$\omega_H = \tilde{\omega} + dH \wedge dt$	Cartan form	136
$F: \mathbf{R} \times M \to \mathbf{R} \times M$	canonical transformation	138
$K_F: \mathbf{R} \times M \to \mathbf{R}$	generating function of F	138
$j^t: M \to \mathbf{R} \times M$	embedding at time t	139

QUALITATIVE THEORY OF VECTORFIELDS

Γ_X	critical elements of X	156
S	local transversal section	158
Θ	Poincaré mapping in S	159
$\omega^\sigma(m)$	σ-limit set of m; $\sigma = +, -,$ or $\pm$	162
$S^\pm$	local stable (unstable) manifold	166
$CS^\pm$	center stable (unstable) manifold	166
C	center manifold	166

(continued inside back cover)

FOUNDATIONS OF MECHANICS

THE MATHEMATICAL PHYSICS MONOGRAPH SERIES

A. S. Wightman, Editor
Princeton University

Ralph Abraham (*Princeton University*)	FOUNDATIONS OF MECHANICS
Freeman J. Dyson (*The Institute for Advanced Study*)	SYMMETRY GROUPS IN NUCLEAR AND PARTICLE PHYSICS
Robert Hermann (*Argonne National Laboratory*)	LIE GROUPS FOR PHYSICISTS
Rudolph C. Hwa (*State University of New York at Stony Brook*) and Vigdor L. Teplitz (*Massachusetts Institute of Technology*)	HOMOLOGY AND FEYNMAN INTEGRALS
André Lichnerowicz (*Collège de France*)	RELATIVISTIC HYDRODYNAMICS AND MAGNETO-HYDRODYNAMICS
George W. Mackey (*Harvard University*)	THE MATHEMATICAL FOUNDATIONS OF QUANTUM MECHANICS
Roger G. Newton (*Indiana University*)	THE COMPLEX *j*-PLANE
R. F. Streater (*Imperial College of Science and Technology*) and A. S. Wightman (*Princeton University*)	PCT, SPIN AND STATISTICS, AND ALL THAT

FOUNDATIONS OF MECHANICS

A mathematical exposition of classical mechanics with an introduction to the qualitative theory of dynamical systems and applications to the three-body problem

RALPH ABRAHAM

with the assistance of

JERROLD E. MARSDEN

Princeton University

W. A. BENJAMIN, INC.

New York Amsterdam 1967

FOUNDATIONS OF MECHANICS

Library of Congress Catalog Card Number 67-16671
Manufactured in the United States of America

*The manuscript was put into production on July 27, 1966;
this volume was published on May 31, 1967*

W. A. BENJAMIN, INC.
New York, New York 10016

PREFACE

In the Spring of 1966, I gave a series of lectures in the Princeton University Department of Physics, aimed at recent mathematical results in mechanics, especially the work of Kolmogorov, Arnold, and Moser and its application to Laplace's question of the stability of the solar system. Mr. Marsden's notes of the lectures, with some revision and expansion by both of us, became this book.

Although the lectures were attended equally by mathematicians and physicists, our goal was to make the subject available to the nonspecialists. Therefore, the mathematical background assumed was dictated by the physics graduate students in the audience. Hoping this would be typical of the people interested in this subject, I have made the same assumptions in the book.

Thus, we take for granted basic undergraduate calculus and linear algebra, and a limited amount of classical analysis, point set topology, and elementary mechanics. Then we begin with modern advanced calculus, and go on to a complete and self-contained treatment of graduate level classical mechanics. The later chapters, dealing with the recent results, require an ever-increasing adeptness in general topology, and we have collected the topological topics required in Appendix A.

To further aid the nonmathematician, the proofs are unusually detailed, and the text is replete with cross-references to earlier definitions and propositions, all of which are numbered for this purpose. The extent of these is testimony of Mr. Marsden's patience.

As our goal is to make a concise exposition, we prove propositions only if the proofs are easy, or are not to be found readily in the literature. This results in an irregular collection of proofs—in the first four chapters nearly everything is proved, being easy, and in the last three chapters there are several longer proofs included and many omitted. Some of those included are necessary because the propositions are original, and can be omitted in a first reading or an elementary course.

For the mathematical reader, the proofs we have omitted can easily be found in books or journals, and we give complete references for each. (References in square brackets refer to the Bibliography.) For this reason, the book, although not self-contained, gives a complete exposition.

In this connection we are grateful to Al Kelley for the opportunity of publishing two research articles of his, as Appendixes B and C, which have not appeared elsewhere. In each of these he proves an original theorem which is important to our development of the subject. As Kolmogorov's address at the 1954 International Congress of Mathematicians (in Russian), which inspired the most important of the recent results, has not been available in English, we include a translation of it in Appendix D. The exercises at the end of each section are nearly all used in a later section, and may be read as part of the text.

I am indebted to Arthur Wightman for his enthusiasm in making arrangements for my lectures and the publication of the book, to René Thom for discussions on structural stability and a preliminary manuscript of part of his book on that subject, to Jerrold Marsden for his energetic collaboration in the writing of this book, and to many colleagues for valuable suggestions. Some of these are acknowledged in the Notes at the end of each chapter, which also give general historical and bibliographical information.

We are both happy to express our gratitude to June Clausen for editing and typing the bulk of the manuscript, and to Patricia Clark, Bonnie Kearns, Elizabeth Epstein, Elizabeth Margosches, and Jerilynn Christiansen for their valuable assistance.

RALPH ABRAHAM

Princeton, New Jersey
June 1966

CONTENTS

MUSEUM

GALILEO GALILEI, 1590
Le Opere di Galileo Galilei,
Barbèra, Firenze, 1890.

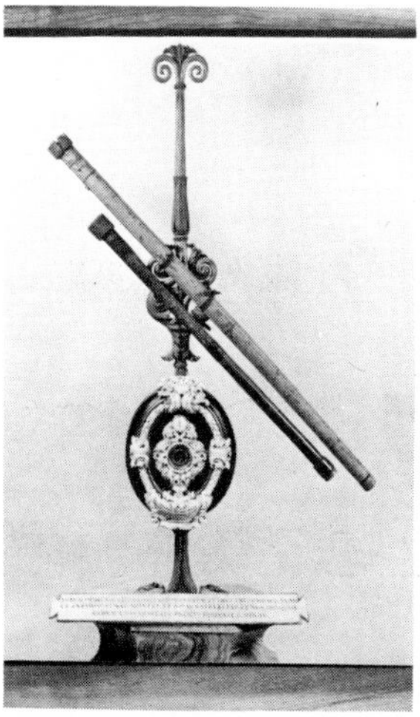

GALILEO'S FIRST TELESCOPE, 160
M. L. Bonelli,
Mostra di documenti e cimeli Galileiana,
Barbèra, Firenze (1964).

JOHANNES KEPLER, 1609
Kepler, Gesammelte Werke,
Beck, München (1960).

ISAAC NEWTON, 1665
E. T. Bell, Men of Mathematics,
Simon and Schuster, New York (1937).

GOTTFRIED WILHELM LEIBNITZ, 1675
E. T. Bell, op. cit.

PIERRE LOUIS MOREAU DE MAUPERTUIS, 1744
Courtesy of the Bibliothèque Nationale, Paris.

LEONHARD EULER, 1736
E. T. Bell, op. cit.

JOSEPH-LOUIS LAGRANGE, 1764
E. T. Bell, op. cit.

PIERRE-SIMON DE LAPLACE, 1773
Oeuvres complètes de Laplace,
Gauthier-Villars, Paris (1878).

SIMEON-DENIS POISSON, 1808
Courtesy of the Bibliothèque Nationale, Paris.

WILLIAM ROWAN HAMILTON, 1834
R. P. Graves, Life of Sir William Rowan Hamilton, Vol. II, frontispiece, Hodges, Figgis and Co., Dublin (1882).

FRAGMENT OF "THE JUDGMENT OF THE ANGELS"

WILLIAM ROWAN HAMILTON

'And through the maze of satellites involved,
And to the farthest planet, and beyond;
Till on the verge of the bottomless abyss
He stood awhile in horror. Radiant sweat
Burst from his limbs angelic: nathless soon
He entered that dark region. The array
Of fallen Powers around their gloomy King,
Innumerable, stretching far and wide,
Throne above Throne, an ordered multitude,
Seemed to expect defiance against heaven,
And words of rage and pride; when suddenly
They saw the flashing of the sword once given
To Michael from the armoury of God
Wave in the Seraph's hand: awe from above
Quell'd every empty gesture of revenge,
And threatening impotent, and show of war.
Their King himself in chains, and all the rest
Through the wide upper tract trail'd after him,
The Angel now returned; and with the hail,
"Well done, thou faithful servant!" took his post
Upon the north side of the Hill of God.

'September 21, 1883'

POEM BY HAMILTON
R. P. Graves, op. cit., p. 64.

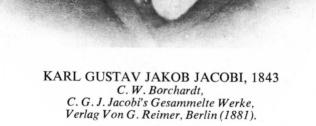

KARL GUSTAV JAKOB JACOBI, 1843
C. W. Borchardt,
C. G. J. Jacobi's Gesammelte Werke,
Verlag Von G. Reimer, Berlin (1881).

JOSEPH LIOUVILLE, 1849
L. J. Gino, Liouville and his work,
Scripta math. **4,** *p. 147-154, 257-262 (1936).*

KING OSCAR II OF SWEDEN, 1887
Courtesy of the Kungl. Biblioteket, Stockholm.

HENRI POINCARE, 1880
E. T. Bell, op. cit.

ALEKSANDR MIKHAILOVICH LIAPOUNOV, 1892
Akademija Nauk, SSSR (1954).

JACQUES HADAMARD, 1896
Selecta, Jubilé scientifique de M. Jacques Hadamard, Gauthier-Villars, Paris (1935).

PIERRE MAURICE MARIE DUHEM, 1906
E. Picard, La vie et l'oeuvre de Pierre Duhem, Gauthier-Villars, Paris (1922).

GEORGE DAVID BIRKHOFF, 1914
G. D. Birkhoff, Collected Mathematical Papers, Amer. Math. Soc., New York (1950).

ELIE JOSEPH CARTAN, 1920
Selecta, Jubilé scientifique de M. Elie Cartan, Gauthier-Villars, Paris (1939).

CARL LUDWIG SIEGEL, 1936
C. L. Siegel Gesammelte Abhandlungen,
Springer-Verlag, Berlin (1966).

ANDREI NIKOLAEVIC KOLMOGOROV, 1953
Photograph by Jürgen Moser.

JURGEN MOSER, 1953
Photograph by Caroline Abraham.

MAURICIO MATOS PEIXOTO, 1959
Photograph by Caroline Abraham.

RENE THOM, 1960

STEPHEN SMALE, 1960
Photograph by Caroline Abraham.

VLADIMIR I. ARNOL'D, 1961
Photograph by Jürgen Moser.

RICHARD F. ARENSTORF, 1963

CHARLES PUGH, 1964
Photograph by Thomas F. Pugh.

AL KELLEY, 1965

INTRODUCTION

Mechanics begins with a long tradition of qualitative investigation culminating with KEPLER and GALILEO. Following this is the period of quantitative theory (1687–1889) characterized by concomitant developments in mechanics, mathematics, and the philosophy of science that are epitomized by the works of NEWTON, EULER, LAGRANGE, LAPLACE, HAMILTON, and JACOBI. Both of these periods are thoroughly described in DUGAS [1].

Throughout these periods, the distinguished special case of *celestial mechanics* had a dominant role (see MOULTON [1] for additional historical details). Formalized in the quantitative period as the *n-body problem*, it recurs in the writings of all of the great figures of the time. The question of *stability* was one of main concerns, and was analyzed with series expansion techniques by LAPLACE (1773), LAGRANGE (1776), POISSON (1809), DIRICHLET (1858), and HARETU (1878), all of whom claimed to have proved that the solar system was stable.

As DIRICHLET died before writing down his proof, KING OSCAR of Sweden offered a prize for its discovery, which was given to POINCARÉ in 1889. The results of POINCARÉ, showing that the series expansions of LAPLACE *et al.* diverged, and the discovery by BRUNS (1887) that no quantitative methods other than series expansions could resolve the n-body problem brought the quantitative period to an end. For celestial mechanics this situation represented a great dilemma, comparable to the crises associated with relativity and quantum theory in other aspects of mechanics. The resolution we owe to the genius of POINCARÉ, who resurrected the qualitative point of view, accompanied by completely new mathematical methods. The inventions of POINCARÉ, culminating in modern differential geometry and topology, constitute a recent and lesser known example of concomitant development of mathematics and mechanics, comparable to calculus, differential equations, and variational theory.

The neoqualitative period in mechanics, that is, from POINCARÉ to the present, consists primarily in the amplification of the qualitative, geometric methods of POINCARÉ, the application of these methods to the qualitative questions of the previous period—for example, stability in the n-body problem—and the consideration of new qualitative questions that could not previously be asked.

POINCARÉ's methods are characterized first of all by the global geometric point of view. He visualized a dynamical system as a field of vectors on phase space, in which a solution is a smooth curve tangent at each of its points to the vector based at that point. The qualitative theory is based on geometrical properties of the *phase portrait*: the family of solution curves, which fill up the entire phase space. For questions such as stability, it is necessary to study the entire phase portrait, including the behavior of solutions for all values of the time parameter. Thus it was essential to consider the entire phase space at once as a geometric object. Doing so, POINCARÉ found the prevailing mathematical model for mechanics inadequate, for its underlying space was Euclidean, or a domain of several real variables, whereas for a mechanical problem with angular variables or constraints, the phase space might be a more general, nonlinear space, such as a generalized cylinder. Thus the global view in the qualitative theory led POINCARÉ to the notion of a *differentiable manifold* as the phase space in mechanics. In mechanical systems, this manifold always has a special geometric property, pertaining to the occurrence of phase variables in canonically conjugate pairs, called *symplectic structure*. Thus the new mathematical model for mechanics consists of a *symplectic manifold*, together with a *Hamiltonian vectorfield*, or global system of first order differential equations preserving the symplectic structure.

This model offers no natural system of coordinates. Indeed a manifold admits a coordinate system only locally, so it is most efficient to use the intrinsic calculus of CARTAN rather than the conventional calculus of NEWTON in the analysis of this model. The complete description of this model for mechanics comes quite a bit after POINCARÉ, as the intrinsic calculus was not fully developed until quite recently. One advantage of this model is that by suppressing unnecessary coordinates the full generality of the theory becomes evident.

The second characteristic of the qualitative theory is the replacement of analytical methods by differential-topological ones in the study of the phase portrait. For many questions, for example the stability of the solar system, one is interested finally in qualitative information about the phase portrait. In earlier times, the only techniques available were analytical. By obtaining a complete or approximate quantitative solution, qualitative or geometric properties could be deduced. It was POINCARÉ's idea to proceed directly to qualitative information by qualitative, that is, geometric, methods. Thus POINCARÉ, BIRKHOFF, and MOSER show the existence of periodic solutions in the three-body problem by applying differential-topological theorems to the phase portraits. No analytical description of these orbits has been given. In some cases the orbits have been plotted approximately by computers, but of course the computer cannot decide whether these solutions are periodic.

A third aspect of the qualitative point of view is a new question that emerges in it—the problem of *structural stability*, the most comprehensive of many different notions of stability. This problem, first posed in 1937 by ANDRONOV-PONTRIAGIN, asks: If a dynamical system X has a known phase portrait P, and is then perturbed to a slightly different system X' (for example, changing the coefficients in its differential equation slightly), then is the new phase portrait P' close to P in some topological sense? This problem has an obvious importance, as in practice the qualitative information obtained for P is to be applied not to X, but to some nearby system X', because the coefficients of the equation are to be determined experimentally, and therefore approximately.

The traditional mutuality of mechanics and philosophy has declined in recent years, perhaps because of the justifiable interest in the problems posed by relativity and quantum theory. But current problems in mechanics give new insight into the structure of physical theories.

At the turn of this century a simple description of physical theory evolved, especially among continental physicists—DUHEM, POINCARÉ, MACH, EINSTEIN, HADAMARD, HILBERT—which may still be quite close to the views of many mathematical physicists. This description—most clearly enunciated by DUHEM [1]—consisted of an *experimental domain*, a *mathematical model*, and a *conventional interpretation*. The model, being a mathematical system, embodies the logic, or axiomatization, of the theory. The interpretation is an agreement connecting the parameters and therefore the conclusions of the model and the observables in the domain.

Traditionally, the philosopher-scientists judge the usefulness of a theory by the criterion of *adequacy*, that is, the verifiability of the predictions, or the quality of the agreement between the interpreted conclusions of the model and the data of the experimental domain. To this DUHEM adds, in a brief example [1, pp. 138 ff.], the criterion of *stability*.

This criterion, suggested to him by the earliest results of qualitative mechanics (HADAMARD), refers to the stability or continuity of the predictions, or their adequacy, when the model is slightly perturbed. The general applicability of this type of criterion has been suggested by RENÉ THOM [1].

This stability concerns variation of the model only, the interpretation and domain being fixed. Therefore, it concerns mainly the model, and is primarily a mathematical or logical question. It has been studied to some extent in a general logical setting by the physicologicians BOULIGAND [1] and DESTOUCHES [1], but probably it is safe to say that a clear enunciation of this criterion in the correct generality has not yet been made. Certainly all of the various notions of stability in qualitative mechanics and ordinary differential equations are special cases of this notion, including LAPLACE'S problem of the stability of the solar system and structural stability, as well as THOM's stability of biological systems.

Also, although this criterion has not been discussed very explicitly by physicists, it has functioned as a tacit assumption, which may be called the *dogma of stability*. For example, in a model with differential equations, in which stability may mean structural stability, the model depends on parameters, namely the coefficients of the equation, each value of which corresponds to a different model. As these parameters can be determined only approximately, the theory is useful only if the equations are structurally stable, which cannot be proved at present in many important cases. Probably the physicist must rely on faith at this point, analogous to the faith of a mathematician in the consistency of set theory.

An alternative to the dogma of stability has been offered by THOM [1]. He suggests that stability, precisely formulated in a specific theory, be added to the model as an additional hypothesis. This formalization, despite the risk of an inconsistent axiomatic system, reduces the criterion of stability to an aspect of the criterion of adequacy, and in addition may admit additional theorems or predictions in the model. As yet no implications of this axiom are known for celestial mechanics, but THOM has described some conclusions in his model for biological systems.

A careful statement of this notion of stability in the general context of physical theory and epistemology could be quite useful in technical applications of mechanics as well as in the formation of new qualitative theories in physics, biology, and the social sciences.

Most of this book is devoted to a precise statement of mathematical models for mechanical systems and to precise definitions of various types of stability in this narrow context. These are illustrated by a single specific example, the restricted three-body problem, in the final chapter. In the Conclusion the present discussion, facilitated by this precise example, is resumed.

CHAPTER I

DIFFERENTIAL THEORY

In recent years, calculus has evolved considerably. The categories of differentiable manifolds and vector bundles provide a context for the generalized differential and integral calculus which is basic to the new qualitative results in mechanics. In this chapter we give a survey of these categories.

§1. FINITE-DIMENSIONAL BANACH SPACES

We shall be dealing almost exclusively with *finite-dimensional real* vector spaces, denoted $\mathbf{E}, \mathbf{F}, \ldots$. However, much of the following carries over to Banach spaces (Dieudonné [1]). In this section we review the basic properties without proofs.

1.1. Definition. *A* **norm** *on a vector space* $\mathbf{E}$ *is a mapping from* $\mathbf{E}$ *into the real numbers* $n: \mathbf{E} \to \mathbf{R}$, *such that*

(N1) $n(\mathbf{e}) \geq 0$ *for all* $\mathbf{e} \in \mathbf{E}$ *and* $n(\mathbf{e}) = 0$ *if and only if* $\mathbf{e} = \mathbf{0}$;
(N2) $n(\lambda\mathbf{e}) = |\lambda| n(\mathbf{e})$ *for all* $\mathbf{e} \in \mathbf{E}$ *and* $\lambda \in \mathbf{R}$;
(N3) $n(\mathbf{e}_1 + \mathbf{e}_2) \leq n(\mathbf{e}_1) + n(\mathbf{e}_2)$ *for all* $\mathbf{e}_1, \mathbf{e}_2 \in \mathbf{E}$.

If n is a norm on $\mathbf{E}$, $\mathbf{E}$ becomes a **metric space**. That is, the map $d: \mathbf{E} \times \mathbf{E} \to \mathbf{R}$ defined by $d(\mathbf{e}, \mathbf{f}) = n(\mathbf{e} - \mathbf{f})$ satisfies (M1), (M2), and (M3) of §A2.1 (Appendix A). Consequently, a norm on a vector space $\mathbf{E}$ defines a topology on $\mathbf{E}$.

1.2. Definition. *Two norms* n_1 *and* n_2 *on a space* $\mathbf{E}$ *are* **equivalent** *iff they induce the same topology on* $\mathbf{E}$.

1.3. Theorem. *Let* $\mathbf{E}$ *be a* **finite-dimensional real** *vector space. Then*

(*i*) $\mathbf{E}$ *possesses a norm,*
(*ii*) *all norms on* $\mathbf{E}$ *are equivalent,*
(*iii*) *all norms on* $\mathbf{E}$ *are complete.*

For a proof, see Dieudonné [1, §5.9]. Regarding (*iii*), recall that $(\mathbf{E}, n)$ is complete iff every Cauchy sequence converges (§A2).

We emphasize *finite-dimensional* and *real*, for it is false in the general case. For example, the rationals are not complete relative to the absolute value norm. For the necessity of finite dimension, the continuous functions on $[0, 1]$ have two inequivalent norms (Dieudonné [1, p. 102]).

Since we are dealing with finite-dimensional real vector spaces, theorem 1.3 tells us that a unique topology is determined by norms. Also, a mapping $f: A \subset \mathbf{E} \to \mathbf{F}$ is continuous (that is, inverse images of open sets are open) iff for all $\mathbf{e}_0 \in A$ and any $\varepsilon > 0$ and norm n on $\mathbf{F}$, there is a $\delta > 0$ and a norm m on $\mathbf{E}$ such that $f(D_{\delta,m}(\mathbf{e}_0) \cap A) \subset D_{\varepsilon,n}(f(\mathbf{e}_0))$, where

$$D_{\delta,m}(\mathbf{e}_0) = \{\mathbf{e} \in \mathbf{E} | m(\mathbf{e} - \mathbf{e}_0) < \delta\}$$

Recall that $f: \mathbf{E}_1 \times \mathbf{E}_2 \times \cdots \times \mathbf{E}_k \to \mathbf{F}$ is multilinear iff it is linear in each variable separately. Note that this does *not mean* f is linear on the product vector space.

1.4. Theorem. *For finite-dimensional real vector spaces, linear and multilinear maps are continuous.*

Again, we do not need to specify the norm because of 1.3. The proof is a consequence of Dieudonné [1, p. 99].

The following is an immediate corollary of this, but is also true more generally (Dieudonné [1, p. 89]).

1.5. Corollary. *Addition and scalar multiplication in a (normed) vector space are continuous maps from* $\mathbf{E} \times \mathbf{E} \to \mathbf{E}$ *and* $\mathbf{R} \times \mathbf{E} \to \mathbf{E}$ *respectively.*

1.6. Definition. *Given* $\mathbf{E}, \mathbf{F}$ *we let* $L(\mathbf{E}, \mathbf{F})$ *denote the set of all linear maps from* $\mathbf{E}$ *into* $\mathbf{F}$ *together with the natural structure of finite-dimensional real vector space. Similarly,* $L^k(\mathbf{E}, \mathbf{F})$ *denotes the space of multilinear maps from* $\mathbf{E} \times \cdots \times \mathbf{E}$ *(k copies) into* $\mathbf{F}$, $L_s^k(\mathbf{E}, \mathbf{F})$ *the subspace of symmetric elements of* $L^k(\mathbf{E}, \mathbf{F})$; *(that is, if* π *is any permutation we have* $f(\mathbf{e}_1, \ldots, \mathbf{e}_k) = f(\mathbf{e}_{\pi(1)}, \ldots, \mathbf{e}_{\pi(k)})$*) and* $L_a^k(\mathbf{E}, \mathbf{F})$ *the subspace of skew symmetric elements of* $L^k(\mathbf{E}, \mathbf{F})$; *(that is, if* π *is any permutation we have* $f(\mathbf{e}_1, \ldots, \mathbf{e}_k) = (\text{sign } \pi) f(\mathbf{e}_{\pi(1)}, \ldots, \mathbf{e}_{\pi(k)})$ *where sign* π *is* ± 1 *according as* π *is an even or odd permutation.)*

1.7. Theorem. *There is a natural isomorphism*

$$L(\mathbf{E}, L^k(\mathbf{E}, \mathbf{F})) \approx L^{k+1}(\mathbf{E}, \mathbf{F})$$

Proof. For $\varphi \in L(\mathbf{E}, L^k(\mathbf{E}, \mathbf{F}))$ we define $\tilde{\varphi} \in L^{k+1}(\mathbf{E}, \mathbf{F})$ by

$$\tilde{\varphi}(\mathbf{e}_1, \ldots, \mathbf{e}_{k+1}) = \varphi(\mathbf{e}_{k+1})(\mathbf{e}_1, \ldots, \mathbf{e}_k)$$

It is easy to check that the association $\varphi \rightsquigarrow \tilde{\varphi}$ is an isomorphism (that is, a linear map which is bijective, or one-to-one and onto). ∎

In a similar way we can identify $L(\mathbf{R}, \mathbf{F})$ with $\mathbf{F}$: to $\varphi \in L(\mathbf{R}, \mathbf{F})$ we associate $\varphi(1) \in \mathbf{F}$.

It is important to realize that although $L(\mathbf{E}, \mathbf{R})$ and $\mathbf{E}$ have the same dimension, and are therefore isomorphic, any such isomorphism requires a basis for its description. Hence we regard $\mathbf{E}$ and $L(\mathbf{E}, \mathbf{R})$ as distinct; they are not *naturally* isomorphic.

Exercises

1A. Let $f \in L(\mathbf{E}, \mathbf{F})$, so that f is continuous. Show that there is a constant K such that $\|f(\mathbf{e})\| \leq K\|\mathbf{e}\|$ for all $\mathbf{e} \in \mathbf{E}$. Define $\|f\|$ as the greatest lower bound of such K. Show that this is a norm on $L(\mathbf{E}, \mathbf{F})$ and that the isomorphism in 1.7 preserves this norm.

1B. Suppose $f \in L(\mathbf{E}, \mathbf{F})$ and $\dim \mathbf{E} = \dim \mathbf{F}$. Then f is an isomorphism iff it is a monomorphism (one-to-one) and iff it is surjective (onto).

1C. Complete the proof of 1.7.

§2. LOCAL DIFFERENTIAL CALCULUS

The usual approach to elementary calculus is not suitable for generalization to manifolds. Thus, in this section, we reinterpret the differentiation process in a way that will be useful for manifolds.

For a differentiable function $f: U \subset \mathbf{R} \to \mathbf{R}$, the usual interpretation of the derivative at $u_0 \in U$ is the slope of the line tangent to the graph of f at u_0. The idea which generalizes is to interpret $Df(u_0) = f'(u_0)$ as a linear map acting on the vector $(u - u_0)$. Then we can say that $Df(u_0)$ is the unique linear map from $\mathbf{R}$ into $\mathbf{R}$ such that the mapping

$$g: U \to \mathbf{R}: u \rightsquigarrow g(u) = f(u_0) + Df(u_0)\cdot(u - u_0)$$

is tangent to f at u_0 (see Fig. 2-1). This motivates the following.

2.1. Definition. *Let* $\mathbf{E}, \mathbf{F}$ *be two (finite-dimensional, real) vector spaces with maps*

$$f, g: U \subset \mathbf{E} \to \mathbf{F}$$

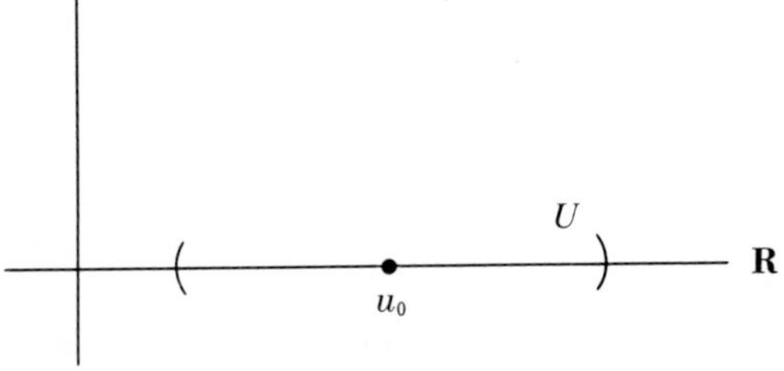

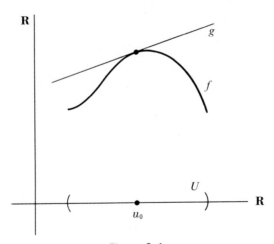

Figure 2-1

where U is open in $\mathbf{E}$. *We say f and g are* **tangent** *at $u_0 \in U$ iff*

$$\operatorname*{limit}_{u \to u_0} \frac{\| f(u) - g(u) \|}{\| u - u_0 \|} = 0$$

where $\| \cdot \|$ represents any norm on the appropriate space.

2.2. *Theorem.* *For $f\colon U \subset \mathbf{E} \to \mathbf{F}$, and $u_0 \in U$ there is* **at most one** *$L \in L(\mathbf{E}, \mathbf{F})$ so that the map $g_L\colon U \subset \mathbf{E} \to \mathbf{F}$ given by $g_L(u) = f(u_0) + L(u - u_0)$ is tangent to f at u_0.*

We leave the proof as an easy exercise on limits.

2.3. *Definition.* *If, in 2.2, there is such an $L \in L(\mathbf{E}, \mathbf{F})$ we say f is* **differentiable at** *u_0, and define $Df(u_0) = L$. If f is differentiable at each $u_0 \in U$, the map*

$$Df\colon U \to L(\mathbf{E}, \mathbf{F})\colon u \rightsquigarrow Df(u)$$

is the **derivative** *of f. Moreover, if Df is a continuous map we say f is* **of class C^1** *(or is* **continuously differentiable***).*

2.4. *Definition.* *Suppose f is of class $C^1\colon U \subset \mathbf{E} \to \mathbf{F}$. Define the* **tangent** *of f to be the map*

$$Tf\colon U \times \mathbf{E} \to \mathbf{F} \times \mathbf{F}$$

given by

$$Tf(u, \mathbf{e}) = (f(u), Df(u) \cdot \mathbf{e})$$

where $Df(u) \cdot \mathbf{e}$ is $Df(u)$ applied to $\mathbf{e} \in \mathbf{E}$ as a linear map.

From a general point of view, T is more natural than D. One reason for this is the behavior of T under composition, as given in the next theorem. Indeed, this theorem expresses the fact that T is a *covariant functor.*

2.5. *Theorem (C^1 composite mapping theorem).* *Suppose $f\colon U \subset \mathbf{E} \to V \subset \mathbf{F}$ and $g\colon V \subset \mathbf{F} \to \mathbf{G}$ are C^1 maps. Then the composite, $g \circ f\colon U \subset \mathbf{E} \to \mathbf{G}$ is also C^1 and*

$$T(g \circ f) = Tg \circ Tf$$

In terms of D, this formula is equivalent to the "chain rule"

$$D(g \circ f)(u) \cdot \mathbf{e} = Dg(f(u)) \cdot (Df(u) \cdot \mathbf{e})$$

For a proof, see Dieudonné [1, p. 145].

We will now show how the derivative Df is related to the usual directional derivative.

A **curve** in $\mathbf{E}$ is a C^1 map from I into $\mathbf{E}$, where I is an open interval of $\mathbf{R}$. Thus, for $t \in I$ we have $Dc(t) \in L(\mathbf{R}, \mathbf{E})$, by definition 2.3. We identify $L(\mathbf{R}, \mathbf{E})$ with $\mathbf{E}$ by associating, in this case, $Dc(t)$ with $Dc(t) \cdot 1$ $(1 \in \mathbf{R})$. Let

$$\frac{dc}{dt}(t) = Dc(t) \cdot 1$$

Now for $f: U \subset \mathbf{E} \to \mathbf{F}$ of class C^1 we consider $f \circ c$ where $c: I \to U$. It follows at once from 2.5 that

$$Df(u) \cdot \mathbf{e} = \frac{d}{dt}\{f(u + t\mathbf{e})\}|_{t=0}$$

For let c be defined by

$$c(t) = u + t\mathbf{e} \qquad (u, \mathbf{e} \in \mathbf{E}, t \in \mathbf{R})$$

for suitable $I = (-\lambda, \lambda)$, and apply the "chain rule" to $f \circ c$. Indeed, on Euclidean space the d/dt defined this way coincides with the usual directional derivative.

More specifically, suppose we have $f: U \subset \mathbf{R}^m \to \mathbf{R}^n$ of class C^1. Now $Df(u)$ is a linear map from $\mathbf{R}^m \to \mathbf{R}^n$ and so it is represented by its components relative to the standard basis $\mathbf{e}_1, \ldots, \mathbf{e}_m$ of $\mathbf{R}^m$. By the above formula we see

$$Df(u) \cdot \mathbf{e}_i = \left(\frac{\partial f^1}{\partial x^i}(u), \ldots, \frac{\partial f^n}{\partial x^i}(u)\right)$$

Thus $Df(u)$ is represented by the usual Jacobian matrix.

We shall now define derivatives of higher order. For $f: U \subset \mathbf{E} \to \mathbf{F}$ of class C^1 we have $Df: U \subset \mathbf{E} \to L(\mathbf{E}, \mathbf{F})$. If $D^2 f$ is continuous we say f is of class C^2. Moreover, we identify $L(\mathbf{E}, L(\mathbf{E}, \mathbf{F}))$ with $L^2(\mathbf{E}, \mathbf{F})$. Proceeding inductively, we define

$$D^r f = D(D^{r-1} f): U \subset \mathbf{E} \to L^r(\mathbf{E}, \mathbf{F})$$

if it exists. If $D^r f$ exists and is continuous we say f is **of class C^r**. The symmetry of second partial derivatives appears here in the following form.

2.6. *Theorem.* *If $f: U \subset \mathbf{E} \to \mathbf{F}$ is C^r, then*

(*i*) $D^r f(u) \in L^r_s(\mathbf{E}, \mathbf{F})$;
(*ii*) *f is C^q, $q = 0, \ldots, r$.* $\qquad$ (*C^0 = continuous.*)

For a proof of this, see Dieudonné [1, p. 176].

In a similar way we can define $T^r f$, and by induction on the C^1 composite mapping theorem we obtain

2.7. Theorem (C^r composite mapping theorem). *Let $f: U \subset \mathbf{E} \to V \subset \mathbf{F}$ and $g: V \subset \mathbf{F} \to \mathbf{G}$ be C^r maps. Then $g \circ f$ is C^r and*

$$T^r(g \circ f) = T^r g \circ T^r f$$

Note that a corresponding statement in terms of D is a good deal more complicated.

For computation of higher derivatives we have, by repeated application of the computational rule for $Df(u) \cdot \mathbf{e}$,

$$D^r f(u)(\mathbf{e}_1, \ldots, \mathbf{e}_r) = \frac{d}{dt_r} \cdots \frac{d}{dt_1}\left\{f\left(u + \sum_{i=1}^{r} t_i \mathbf{e}_i\right)\right\}\Bigg|_{t_1 = \cdots = t_r = 0}$$

In particular, for $f\colon U \subset \mathbf{R}^m \to \mathbf{R}^n$ the components of $D^r f(u)$ in terms of the standard basis are

$$\frac{\partial^r f^\alpha(u)}{\partial x^{i_1} \cdots \partial x^{i_r}} \qquad \begin{matrix} \alpha = 1, \ldots, n \\ i_k = 1, \ldots, m \qquad \Sigma i_k = r \end{matrix}$$

Thus f is of class C^r iff all its rth-order partial derivatives exist and are continuous.

Suppose $U \subset \mathbf{E}$ is an open set. Then as $+ : \mathbf{E} \times \mathbf{E} \to \mathbf{E}$ is continuous, there exists an open set $\tilde{U} \subset \mathbf{E} \times \mathbf{E}$ with (i) $U \times \{\mathbf{0}\} \subset \tilde{U}$, (ii) $u + h \in U$ for all $(u, h) \in \tilde{U}$, and (iii) $(u, h) \in \tilde{U}$ implies $u \in U$. For example, let

$$\tilde{U} = \{+^{-1}(U)\} \cap \{U \times \mathbf{E}\}$$

Let us call such a set $\tilde{U}$, temporarily, a **thickening** of U.

2.8. Theorem (Taylor's theorem). *A map $f\colon U \subset \mathbf{E} \to \mathbf{F}$ is of class C^r iff there are continuous mappings*

$$\varphi_p\colon U \subset \mathbf{E} \to L_s^p(\mathbf{E}, \mathbf{F}) \qquad p = 1, \ldots, r$$

$$R\colon \tilde{U} \to L_s^r(\mathbf{E}, \mathbf{F})$$

where $\tilde{U}$ is a thickening of U, such that, for all $(u,h) \in \tilde{U}$,

$$f(u + h) = f(u) + \frac{\varphi_1(u)}{1!} \cdot h + \frac{\varphi_2(u)}{2!} \cdot h^2 + \cdots + \frac{\varphi_r(u)}{r!} \cdot h^r + R(u, h)h^r$$

where $h^r = (h, \ldots, h)$ (r times) and $R(u, 0) = 0$.

For the *only if* part see Dieudonné [1, p. 185] with $\varphi_p(u) = D^p f(u)$. For the converse, see Abraham–Robbin [1, §2].

If f is C^∞ (that is, is C^r for all r) then we may be able to extend the above formula into a convergent power series. If we can, we say f is of class C^ω, or **analytic**. The standard example of a C^∞ function that is not analytic is, in $\mathbf{R}^n$,

$$\theta(x) = \begin{cases} \exp\{-1/(1 - |x|^2)\} & |x| < 1 \\ 0 & |x| \geq 1 \end{cases}$$

This function is C^∞, but vanishes everywhere except inside the unit sphere, and so cannot be analytic.

2.9. Definition. *A map $f\colon U \subset \mathbf{E} \to V \subset \mathbf{F}$ (U, V open) is a* **C^r diffeomorphism** *iff f is of class C^r, is a bijection (that is, one-to-one and onto V), and f^{-1} is also of class C^r.*

The following theorem is often useful for testing for a C^r diffeomorphism.

2.10. Theorem (Inverse mapping theorem). *Let $f\colon U \subset \mathbf{E} \to \mathbf{F}$ be of class C^r, $r \geq 1$, $u_0 \in U$, and suppose $Df(u_0)$ is a linear isomorphism. Then f is a C^r diffeomorphism of some neighborhood of u_0 onto some neighborhood of $f(u_0)$.*

For a proof, see Dieudonné [1, p. 268].

Leibnitz' rule for derivatives has the following general form.

2.11. Proposition. *For $f: U \subset \mathbf{E} \to \mathbf{E}'$ and $g: U \subset \mathbf{E} \to \mathbf{F}'$ of class C^1 define $f \times g: U \to \mathbf{E}' \times \mathbf{F}'$ by $(f \times g)(u) = (f(u), g(u))$. Suppose $B: \mathbf{E}' \times \mathbf{F}' \to \mathbf{G}$ is a bilinear map, and $f \cdot g = B \circ (f \times g)$. Then $f \cdot g$ is of class C^1 and $D(f \cdot g) = f \cdot Dg + Df \cdot g: U \to L(\mathbf{E}, \mathbf{G})$ (where $(f \cdot Dg)(u) \cdot \mathbf{e} = B(f(u), Dg(u) \cdot \mathbf{e})$).*

This follows easily by the composite mapping theorem, and the fact that the derivative of B at $(\mathbf{e}'_0, \mathbf{f}'_0)$ is $(\mathbf{e}', \mathbf{f}') \rightsquigarrow B(\mathbf{e}', \mathbf{f}'_0) + B(\mathbf{e}'_0, \mathbf{f}')$. See Dieudonné [1, p. 144]. In the case $\mathbf{E}' = \mathbf{F}' = \mathbf{R}$ and B is multiplication, 2.11 reduces to the usual product rule for derivatives.

It will also be convenient to consider partial derivatives in this context.

2.12. Definition. *Let $U \subset \mathbf{E}$, $V \subset \mathbf{F}$ be open, and suppose $f: U \times V \to \mathbf{G}$, and f is differentiable. Then the* **partial derivative** *of f with respect to the first factor $\mathbf{E}$, denoted, $D_1 f$, is defined by*

$$D_1 f(u, v): \mathbf{E} \to \mathbf{G}: \mathbf{e} \rightsquigarrow D_1 f(u, v) \cdot \mathbf{e} = Df(u, v) \cdot (\mathbf{e}, \mathbf{0})$$

We similarly define $D_2 f$.

Thus, if we identify $\mathbf{E} \times \mathbf{F}$ with $\mathbf{E} \oplus \mathbf{F}$, $(\mathbf{e}, \mathbf{0})$ with $\mathbf{e}$, we may write

$$Df = D_1 f + D_2 f$$

Exercises

2A. Prove Theorem 2.2.

2B. For $f: U \subset \mathbf{E} \to \mathbf{F}$, show that

$$T^2 f: (U \times \mathbf{E}) \times (\mathbf{E} \times \mathbf{E}) \to (\mathbf{F} \times \mathbf{F}) \times \mathbf{F} \times \mathbf{F}$$

$$: (u, \mathbf{e}_1, \mathbf{e}_2, \mathbf{e}_3) \rightsquigarrow (f(u), Df(u) \cdot \mathbf{e}_1, Df(u) \cdot \mathbf{e}_2, D^2 f(u) \cdot (\mathbf{e}_2, \mathbf{e}_3) + Df(u) \cdot \mathbf{e}_3)$$

2C. Prove the *if* part of 2.8 for $r = 2$.

§3. MANIFOLDS AND MAPPINGS

The basic idea of a manifold is to introduce a local object that will support a differentiation process and then to patch these local structures together smoothly.

Before giving the formal definitions it is good to have in mind an example. In $\mathbf{R}^{n+1}$ consider the n-sphere S^n; that is, all $x \in \mathbf{R}^{n+1}$ such that $\|x\| = 1$ ($\| \ \|$ is the usual Euclidean norm). We can construct, locally, bijections from S^n to $\mathbf{R}^n$. One way is to project stereographically from the south pole onto a hyperplane tangent to the north pole. This is a bijection from S^n, with the south pole removed, onto $\mathbf{R}^n$. Similarly we can interchange the roles of the poles to obtain another bijection. (See Figure 3-1.)

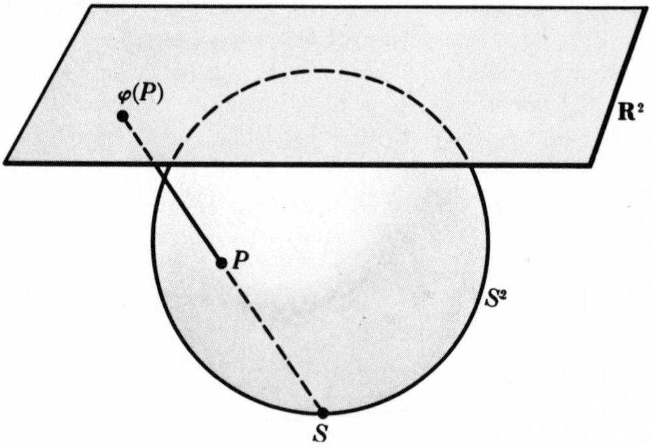

Figure 3-1

In this way we can assign coordinate systems to S^n. Note, however, that no single bijection can be used between S^n and $\mathbf{R}^n$, but we can cover S^n using two of them. We demand that these be compatible; that is, in a region covered by both coordinate systems we must be able to change coordinates smoothly.

For some studies of the sphere, two coordinate systems will not suffice. We thus allow all other coordinate systems compatible with these.

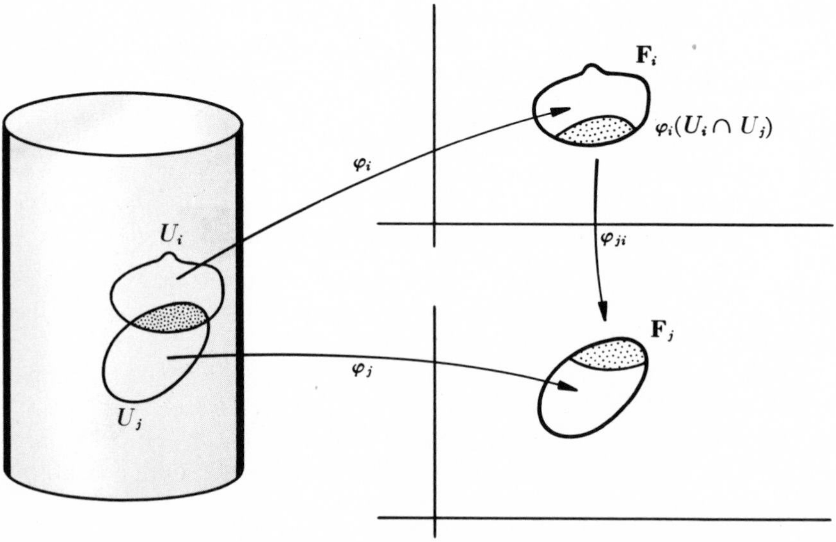

Figure 3-2

3.1. Definition. *Let S be a set. A* **local chart** *on S is a bijection φ from a subset U of S to an open subset of some (finite-dimensional, real) vector space* **F**. *We sometimes denote φ by (U, φ), to indicate the domain U of φ;* **F** *also may depend on φ. An* **atlas** *on S is a family $\mathscr{A}$ of charts $\{(U_i, \varphi_i): i \in I\}$, such that*

(MA1) $S = \bigcup\{U_i | i \in I\}$;

(MA2) *The overlap maps between members of $\mathscr{A}$ are C^∞ diffeomorphisms: for two charts (U_i, φ_i) and (U_j, φ_j) with $U_i \cap U_j \neq \phi$ we form the overlap maps: $\varphi_{ji} = \varphi_j \circ \varphi_i^{-1} | \varphi_i(U_i \cap U_j)$ where $\varphi_i^{-1} | \varphi_i(U_i \cap U_j)$ means the restriction of φ_i^{-1} to the set $\varphi_i(U_i \cap U_j)$. We require that $\varphi_i(U_i \cap U_j)$ is open in $\mathbf{F}_i$, and that φ_{ji} be a C^∞ diffeomorphism.*

Two atlases $\mathscr{A}_1$ and $\mathscr{A}_2$ are **equivalent** *iff $\mathscr{A}_1 \cup \mathscr{A}_2$ is an atlas. A* **differentiable structure** *$\mathscr{S}$ on S is an* **equivalence class of atlases on** *S. The union of the atlases in $\mathscr{S}$, $\mathscr{A}_{\mathscr{S}} = \bigcup\{\mathscr{A} | \mathscr{A} \in \mathscr{S}\}$ is the* **maximal atlas** *of $\mathscr{S}$, and a chart $(U, \varphi) \in \mathscr{A}_{\mathscr{S}}$ is an* **admissible local chart**.

A **differentiable manifold** *M is a pair $(S, \mathscr{S})$ where S is a set and $\mathscr{S}$ is a differentiable structure on S.*

We shall often identify M with the underlying set S.

The reader might wish to compare these definitions with others, such as those of Sternberg [2, p. 35]. The principal difference is that S is usually taken as a topological space with the domain of a chart as an open subset. However, we can induce a topology with the same end result.

3.2. Definition. *Let M be a differentiable manifold. A subset $A \subset M$ is* **open** *iff for each $a \in A$ there is an admissible local chart (U, φ) such that $a \in U$ and $U \subset A$.*

A differentiable manifold M is an **n-manifold** *iff for every point $a \in M$ there exists an admissible local chart (U, φ) with $a \in U$ and $\varphi(U) \subset \mathbf{R}^n$.*

A **manifold** *will always mean a Hausdorff, second countable, differentiable n-manifold* (§A1).

3.3. Examples

A. S^n with a maximal atlas generated by the atlas described previously makes S^n into an n-manifold. The topology resulting is the same as that induced on S^n as a subset of $\mathbf{R}^{n+1}$.

B. A set can have more than one differentiable structure. For example, **R** regarded as a set has the following incompatible charts

$$(U_1, \varphi_1): U_1 = \mathbf{R} \qquad \varphi_1(r) = r^3 \in \mathbf{R}$$

$$(U_2, \varphi_2): U_2 = \mathbf{R} \qquad \varphi_2(r) = r \in \mathbf{R}$$

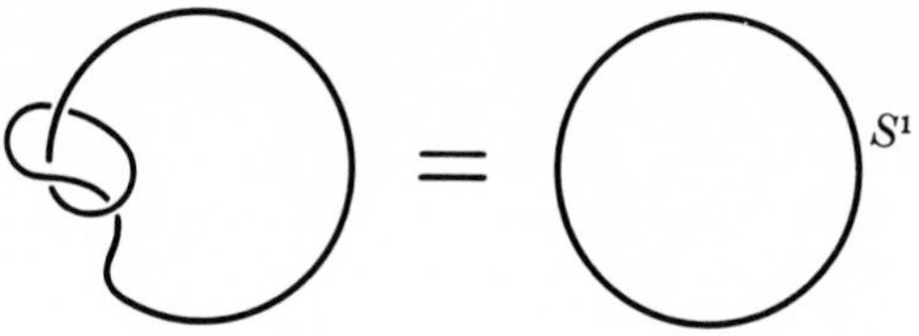

Figure 3-3

They are not compatible since $\varphi_2 \circ \varphi_1^{-1}$ is not differentiable at the origin.

Nevertheless, these two resulting structures turn out to be essentially the same (diffeomorphic), but two structures can be different on more complicated sets (e.g., S^7).

C. Essentially the only one-dimensional connected manifolds are $\mathbf{R}$ and S^1. This means that all others are diffeomorphic to $\mathbf{R}$ or S^1 (diffeomorphic will be precisely defined later). For example, the circle with a knot is diffeomorphic to S^1. (See Figure 3-3.)

A very general two-dimensional connected manifold is the sphere with "handles" (see Figure 3-4). This includes, for example, the torus.

3.4. *Definition.* *Let $(S_1, \mathscr{S}_1)$ and $(S_2, \mathscr{S}_2)$ be two manifolds. The* **product manifold** *$(S_1 \times S_2, \mathscr{S}_1 \times \mathscr{S}_2)$ consists of the set $S_1 \times S_2$ together with the differentiable structure $\mathscr{S}_1 \times \mathscr{S}_2$ generated by the atlas $\{(U_1 \times U_2, \varphi_1 \times \varphi_2) | (U_i, \varphi_i)$ is a chart of $(S_i, \mathscr{S}_i)\}$.*

That this is an atlas is immediate, for if $\psi_1 : U \subset \mathbf{E}_1 \to V_1 \subset \mathbf{F}_1$;

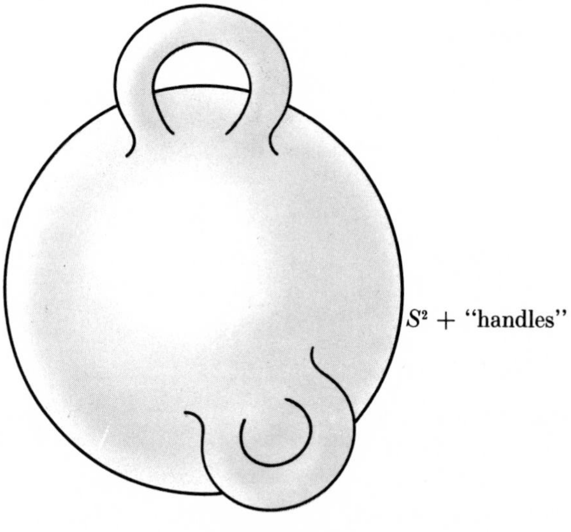

Figure 3-4

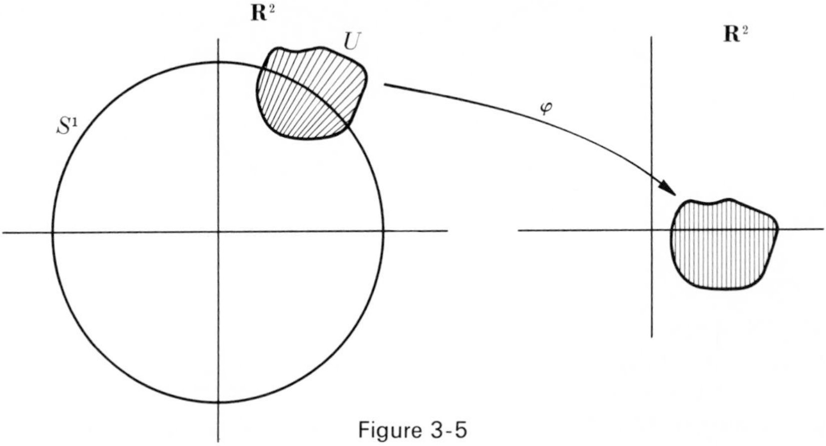

Figure 3-5

$\psi_2: U_2 \subset \mathbf{E}_2 \to V_2 \subset \mathbf{F}_2$ then $\psi_1 \times \psi_2$ is a diffeomorphism iff ψ_1 and ψ_2 are, and in this case $(\psi_1 \times \psi_2)^{-1} = \psi_1^{-1} \times \psi_2^{-1}$. Note that, from Ex. 2D $D(\psi_1 \times \psi_2) = D\psi_1 \times D\psi_2$.

It is also clear that the topology on the product manifold is the product topology (§A1).

If M is a manifold and $A \subset M$ is an open subset of M, the differentiable structure of M naturally induces one on A. We call A an **open submanifold** of M.

Further, we would like to say that S^n is a submanifold of $\mathbf{R}^{n+1}$, although it is a closed subset. To motivate the general definition notice that there are charts in $\mathbf{R}^{n+1}$ in which S^n appears as $\mathbf{R}^n$, locally. (See Figure 3-5.)

3.5. Definition. *A* **submanifold** *of a manifold M is a subset $B \subset M$ with the property that for each $b \in B$ there is an admissible chart (U, φ) in M with $b \in U$ which has the* **submanifold property**, *namely*

(SM) $\varphi: U \to \mathbf{E} \times \mathbf{F}$, *and* $\varphi(U \cap B) = \varphi(U) \cap (\mathbf{E} \times \{\mathbf{0}\})$

An open subset of M is a submanifold in this sense. Here we merely take $\mathbf{F} = \{\mathbf{0}\}$. Indeed if M is an n-manifold, an open subset is an n-submanifold.

Let B be a submanifold of a manifold M. Then B becomes a manifold with differentiable structure generated by the atlas

$$\{(U \cap B, \varphi | U \cap B): (U, \varphi)$$

is an admissible chart in M having property (SM) for $B\}$.

Thus the topology on B is the relative topology (§A1).

Now $S^n \subset \mathbf{R}^{n+1}$ is, in this sense, a submanifold of $\mathbf{R}^{n+1}$. Indeed, it is true that any n-manifold can be realized (embedded) as a closed (in the topological sense) submanifold of $\mathbf{R}^{2n+1}$. For the proof, see Sternberg [2, p. 63].

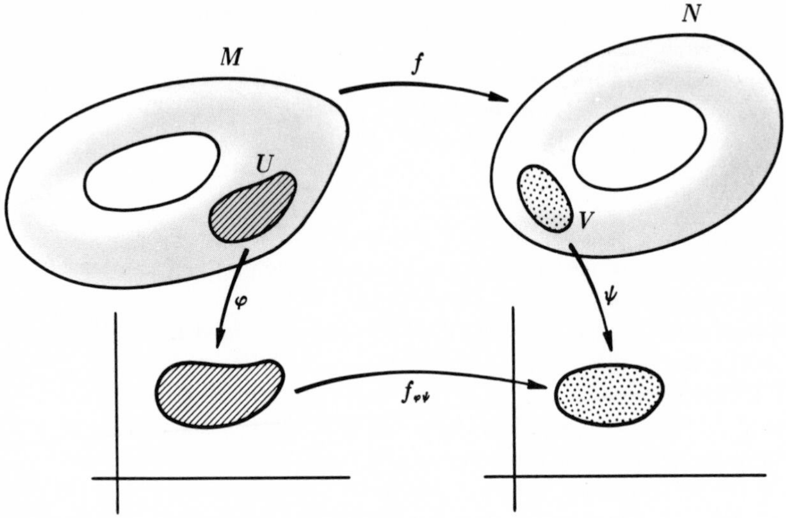

Figure 3-6

3.6. Definition. *Suppose we have $f: M \to N$ where M and N are manifolds (that is, f maps the underlying set of M into that of N.) We say f is* **of class C^r** *iff for each x in M and admissible chart (V, ψ) of N with $f(x) \in V$, there is a chart (U, φ) of M with $x \in U$ and $f(U) \subset V$ and the* **local representative** *of f, $f_{\varphi\psi} = \psi \cdot f \cdot \varphi^{-1}$, is of class C^r* (§2) (*see Figure* 3-6).

Note that we have consistency of this for $r = 0$ with the definition of continuity of f, regarded as a map between topological spaces (with the manifold topologies). If f is continuous, the requirement $f(U) \subset V$ can always be satisfied. The importance of property (MA2) for the differentiable structure is seen from the following.

3.7. Proposition. *Given $f: M \to N$ where M and N are manifolds, we have:*

(i) If (U, φ) and (U, φ') are charts in M while (V, ψ) and (V, ψ') are charts in N with $f(U) \subset V$, then $f_{\varphi\psi}$ is of class C^r if and only if $f_{\varphi'\psi'}$ is of class C^r;

(ii) If (U, φ) and (V, ψ) are charts in M and N with $f(U) \subset V$ and if φ'' (and ψ'') are restrictions of φ (and ψ) to open subsets of U (and V) then $f_{\varphi\psi}$ is of class C^r implies $f_{\varphi''\psi''}$ is of class C^r;

(iii) If f is of class C^r on open subsets of M (as submanifolds) it is of class C^r on their union.

The proof of this is completely straightforward, from the smoothness of the overlap maps and the C^r composite mapping theorem (§2). We leave the details as an exercise.

Note that 3.7(i) implies that if $f_{\varphi\psi}$ is not C^r, then f is not C^r, while without (MA2) this might not be the case.

3.8. Definition. *A map $f: M \to N$ where M and N are manifolds is called a (C^∞)* **diffeomorphism** *iff f is of class C^∞, is a bijection, and $f^{-1}: N \to M$ is of class C^∞.*

Exercises

3A. Show that the open sets on a manifold (3.2) is a topology (§A1) and with this topology, the manifold is second countable iff it has an atlas with a countable family of local charts. (See §A1.)

3B. Prove that S^1 is a submanifold of $\mathbf{R}^2$. Complete the details of examples 3.3A and 3.3B.

3C. Prove 3.7 and show that (i) if (U, φ) is a chart of M and $\psi: \varphi(U) \to V \subset \mathbf{F}$ is a diffeomorphism then $(U, \psi \circ \varphi)$ is an admissible chart of M and (ii) admissible local charts are diffeomorphisms (in the manifold sense).

§4. VECTOR BUNDLES

Roughly speaking, a vector bundle is a manifold with a vector space attached at each point. During the formal definitions we may keep in mind the example of the n-sphere $S^n \subset \mathbf{R}^{n+1}$. The collection of tangent planes to S^n (regarded as vector spaces) form a vector bundle. Similarly, the collection of normal lines to S^n form a vector bundle.

The definitions will follow the pattern of those for a manifold. Namely, we obtain a vector bundle by smoothly patching together local vector bundles.

4.1. Definition. *Let $\mathbf{E}$ and $\mathbf{F}$ be (finite-dimensional, real) vector spaces with U an open subset of $\mathbf{E}$. We call the Cartesian product $U \times \mathbf{F}$ a* **local vector bundle**. *We call U the* **base space**, *which can be identified with $U \times \{\mathbf{0}\}$, the* **zero section**. *For $u \in U$, $\{u\} \times \mathbf{F}$ is called the* **fiber** *over u, which we can endow with the vector space structure of $\mathbf{F}$. Also, the map $\pi: U \times \mathbf{F} \to U$ given by $\pi(u, f) = u$ is called the* **projection** *of $U \times \mathbf{E}$. (Thus, for $u \in U$, the fiber over u is $\pi^{-1}(u)$. Also note that $U \times \mathbf{F}$ is an open subset of $\mathbf{E} \times \mathbf{F}$ and so is a local manifold.)*

Suppose we have a map $\varphi: U \times \mathbf{F} \to U' \times \mathbf{F}'$ where $U \times \mathbf{F}$ and $U' \times \mathbf{F}'$ are local vector bundles. We say that φ is a **local vector bundle isomorphism** *iff φ is a C^∞ diffeomorphism, and φ has the form $\varphi(u, f) = (\varphi_1(u), \varphi_2(u) \cdot f)$ where $\varphi_2(u)$ is a linear isomorphism for each $u \in U$. (See Figure 4-1.)*

4.2. Definition. *Let S be a set. A* **local bundle chart** *of S is a pair (U, φ) where $U \subset S$ and $\varphi: U \subset S \to U' \times \mathbf{F}'$ is a bijection onto a local bundle $U' \times \mathbf{F}'$. (U', $\mathbf{F}'$ depend on φ.) A* **vector bundle atlas**

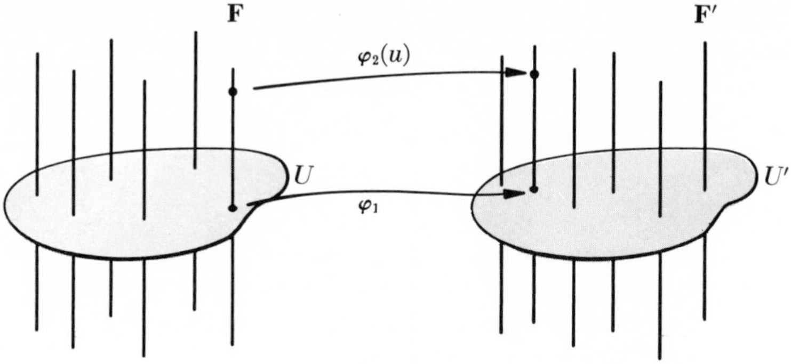

Figure 4-1

on S is a family $\mathscr{B} = \{(U_i, \varphi_i)\}$ *of local bundle charts satisfying* (VBA1) = (MA1 *of* 3.1) (*it covers S*) *and, in addition,* (VBA2) *for any two local bundle charts* (U_i, φ_i) *and* (U_j, φ_j) *in* $\mathscr{B}$ *with* $U_i \cap U_j \neq \phi$, $\varphi_i(U_i \cap U_j) = U_i'' \times \mathbf{F}_i'$, *and the overlap map* $\psi_{ji} = \varphi_j \cdot \varphi_i^{-1} | \varphi_i(U_i \cap U_j)$ *is a local vector bundle isomorphism. If* $\mathscr{B}_1$ *and* $\mathscr{B}_2$ *are two vector bundle atlases on S, we say they are* **VB-equivalent** *iff* $\mathscr{B}_1 \cup \mathscr{B}_2$ *is a vector bundle atlas. A* **vector bundle structure** *on S is an equivalence class of vector bundle atlases. A* **vector bundle** *E is a pair* $(S, \mathscr{V})$ *where S is a set and* $\mathscr{V}$ *is a vector bundle structure on S. A chart in an atlas of* $\mathscr{V}$ *is an* **admissible local bundle chart** *of E.*

As in §3 *we will often identify E with the underlying set S. Also, for a vector bundle structure* $\mathscr{V}$ *on S,* (MA1) *and* (MA2) *hold, so* $\mathscr{V}$ *induces a differentiable structure on S. In addition, we shall assume that the differentiable structure on a vector bundle gives rise to a Hausdorff, second countable topology and that the induced manifold is of constant dimension.*

For a vector bundle $E = (S, \mathscr{V})$ *we define the* **zero section** *by*

$$E_0 = \{e \in E \mid \exists (U, \varphi) \in \mathscr{V} \text{ with } e = \varphi^{-1}(u', 0)\}$$

Hence E_0 *is the union of all the zero sections of the local vector bundles (identifying U with a local vector bundle via* $\varphi : U \to U' \times \mathbf{F}'$*).*

If $(U, \varphi) \in \mathscr{V}$ *is a vector bundle chart, and* $e_0 \in U$ *with* $\varphi(e_0) = (u', 0)$, *let* $E_{e_0, \varphi}$ *denote the subset* $\varphi^{-1}(\{u'\} \times \mathbf{F}')$ *of S together with the structure of a real vector space induced by the bijection* φ.

The next few propositions derive basic properties of vector bundles which are sometimes included in the definition.

4.3. Proposition. (i) *If* e_0 *lies in the domains of two local bundle charts* φ_1 *and* φ_2, *then* $E_{e_0, \varphi_1} = E_{e_0, \varphi_2}$ *where the equality means equality as sets, and also as real vector spaces.*

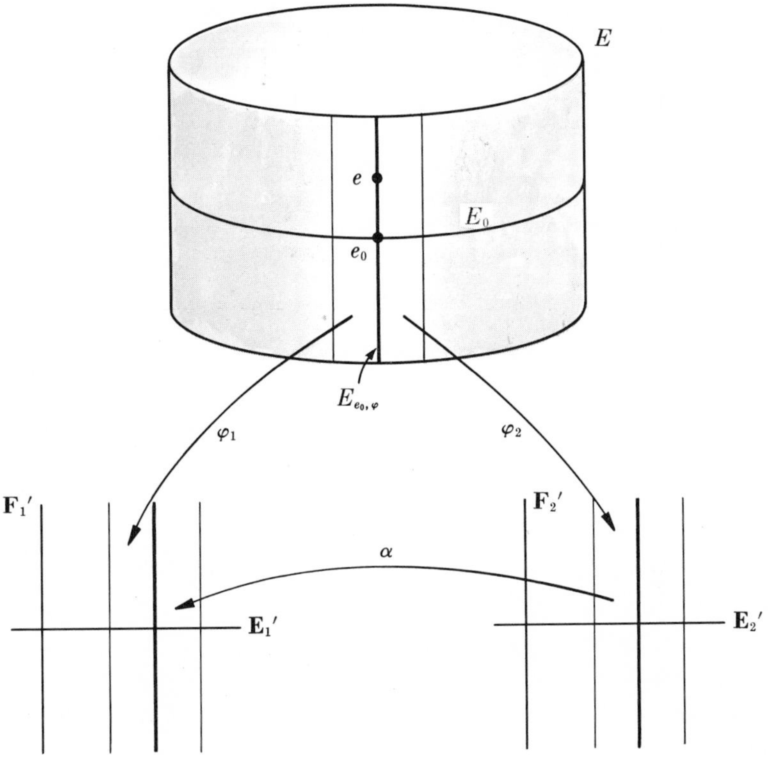

Figure 4-2

(*ii*) *For* $e \in E$, *there is exactly one* $e_0 \in E_0$ *such that* $e \in E_{e_0,\varphi_1}$, *for some* (U, φ_1).

(*iii*) E_0 *is a submanifold of* E.

(*iv*) *The map* $\boldsymbol{\pi}$, *defined by* $\boldsymbol{\pi}: E \to E_0$, $\boldsymbol{\pi}(e) = e_0$ (*in* (*ii*)) *is surjective and* C^∞.

Proof. (i) Suppose $\varphi_1(e_0) = (u_1', 0)$ and $\varphi_2(e_0) = (u_2', 0)$. We may assume the domains of φ_1 and φ_2 are identical for $E_{e_0,\varphi}$ is unchanged if we restrict φ to any local bundle chart containing e_0. Then $\alpha = \varphi_1 \circ \varphi_2^{-1}$ is a local vector bundle isomorphism. But we have

$$E_{e_0,\varphi_1} = \varphi_1^{-1}(\{u_1'\} \times \mathbf{F}_1') = \varphi_2^{-1} \circ \alpha^{-1}(\{u_1'\} \times \mathbf{F}_1') = \varphi_2^{-1}(\{u_2'\} \times \mathbf{F}_2')$$

Hence $E_{e_0,\varphi_1} = E_{e_0,\varphi_2}$ as sets, and it is easily seen that addition and scalar multiplication in E_{e_0,φ_1} and E_{e_0,φ_2} are identical. (See Figure 4-2.)

For (*ii*) note that if $e \in E$, $\varphi_1(e) = (u_1, \mathbf{f}_1)$, $\varphi_2(e) = (u_2, \mathbf{f}_2)$, $e_1 = \varphi_1^{-1}(u_1, \mathbf{0})$, and $e_2 = \varphi_2^{-1}(u_2, \mathbf{0})$, then $\alpha(u_2, \mathbf{f}_2) = (u_1, \mathbf{f}_1)$, so α gives a linear isomorphism

$\{u_2\} \times \mathbf{F}'_2 \to \{u_i\} \times \mathbf{F}'_1$, and therefore $\varphi_1(e_2) = \alpha(u_2, \mathbf{0}) = (u_1, \mathbf{0}) = \varphi_1(e_1)$, or $e_2 = e_1$.

To prove (*iii*) we must verify that for $e_0 \in E_0$ there is an admissible chart with the submanifold property (3.5). For such a manifold chart we choose an admissible vector bundle chart, (U, φ), $e_0 \in U$. Then $\varphi(U \cap E_0) = U' \times \{\mathbf{0}\} = \varphi(U) \cap (\mathbf{E}' \times \{\mathbf{0}\})$ (see Figure 4-2).

Finally, for (*iv*), from proposition 3.7 we see that it is enough to check that π is C^∞ using local bundle charts. But this is clear, for such a representative is of the form $(u'_1, f') \to (u'_1, 0)$. That π is onto should be clear. ∎

The following summarizes the basic properties of a vector bundle.

4.4. Theorem. *Let E be a vector bundle. The* **zero section** *of E, E_0, is a submanifold of E and there is a map $\pi : E \to E_0$ called the* **projection** *which is of class C^∞, and is surjective (onto). Moreover, for each $e_0 \in E_0$, $\pi^{-1}(e_0)$, called the* **fiber** *over e_0, has a (finite dimensional, real) vector space structure induced by any admissible local bundle chart.*

Because of these properties we sometimes write "the vector bundle $\pi: E \to \mathbf{E}_0$" instead of "the vector bundle $(E, \mathscr{V})$." We now define vector bundle mappings analogously.

4.5. Definition. *A map $\varphi: U \times \mathbf{F} \to U' \times \mathbf{F}'$ between local vector bundles is called a* **local vector bundle mapping** *when φ is of class C^∞ and has the form $\varphi(u, \mathbf{f}) = (\varphi_1(u), \varphi_2(u) \cdot \mathbf{f})$ where $\varphi_1: U \to U'$, and $\varphi_2: U \to L(\mathbf{F}, \mathbf{F}')$.*

Let E and E′ be two vector bundles. A map $f: E \to E'$ (that is, between the underlying sets) is called a **vector bundle mapping** *when for each $e \in E$ and each admissible local bundle chart (V, ψ) of E′ with $f(e) \in V$ there is an admissible local bundle chart (U, φ) with $f(U) \subset V$ so that the local representative $f_{\varphi,\psi} = \psi \circ f \circ \varphi^{-1}$ is a local vector bundle mapping.*

Note that this definition makes sense only for local vector bundle charts, and not for all manifold charts. Also, such a U is not guaranteed by the continuity of f, nor does it imply it. However, if we first check that f is *fiber preserving* (which it must be) and is continuous, then such an open set U is guaranteed.

This fiber preserving character is made more explicit in the following.

4.6. Proposition. *Suppose $f: E \to E'$ is a vector bundle map. Then*

(*i*) *f preserves the zero section*

$$f(E_0) \subset E'_0$$

(*ii*) *f induces a unique mapping $f_0 : E_0 \to E'_0$ such that the following diagram commutes,*

$$\begin{array}{ccc} E & \xrightarrow{\ f\ } & E' \\ \pi \big\downarrow & & \big\downarrow \pi' \\ E_0 & \xrightarrow[\ f_0\ ]{} & E_0' \end{array}$$

that is, $\pi' \circ f = f_0 \circ \pi$. (Here, π and π' are the projection maps.)

(iii) A C^∞ map $g : E \to E'$ is a vector bundle map iff there is a map $g_0 : E_0 \to E_0'$ such that $\pi' \circ g = g_0 \circ \pi$ and g restricted to each fiber is a linear map into a fiber.

Proof. (*i*) Suppose $e_0 \in E_0$. We must show $f(e_0) \in E_0'$. That is, for a vector bundle chart (V, ψ) and $f(e_0) \in V$ we must show $\psi f(e_0) = (v', \mathbf{0})$. But we have a chart (U, φ) so $e_0 \in U$, $f(U) \subset V$. Here $\varphi(e_0) = (u', \mathbf{0})$. Hence $\psi f(e_0) = \psi \circ f \circ \varphi^{-1}(u', \mathbf{0})$. But this is of the form $(v', \mathbf{0})$ since $f_{\varphi\psi}$ is linear on each fiber.

For (*ii*) let $f_0 = f|E_0 : E_0 \to E_0'$. With the notations above, then

$$\psi \circ \pi' \circ f(e) = \psi \circ f_0 \circ \pi(e)$$

Also, if $f_{\varphi\psi} = (\alpha_1, \alpha_2)$, then $(f_0)_{\varphi\psi} = \alpha_1$, so f_0 is C^∞.

One half of (*iii*) is clear from (*i*) and (*ii*). For the converse we easily see that g has the form, in local representation,

$$\begin{aligned} g_{\varphi\psi}(u', \mathbf{e}') &= (\alpha_1(u'), \alpha_2(u')\mathbf{e}') \\ &= \psi \circ g \circ \varphi^{-1}(u', \mathbf{f}') \end{aligned}$$

where

$$u' = \varphi \circ \pi(u), \quad \alpha_1 = \psi \circ g_0 \circ \varphi^{-1} \quad \text{and} \quad \alpha_2(u') = (\psi \circ g \circ \varphi^{-1})|\{u'\} \times \mathbf{E}')$$

is obviously linear. Thus, the local representatives of g with respect to admissible local bundle charts are local bundle mappings. ∎

We shall now define a second generalization of a local C^r mapping, $f : U \subset \mathbf{E} \to \mathbf{F}$, which globalizes not f but rather its graph mapping $\gamma_f : U \to U \times \mathbf{F} : u \rightsquigarrow (u, f(u))$.

4.7. Definition. *Let $\pi : E \to B$ be a vector bundle. A C^r* **section** *of π is a map $\xi : B \to E$ of class C^r such that for each $b \in B$, $\pi(\xi(b)) = b$. Let $\Gamma^r(\pi)$ denote the set of all C^r sections of π, together with the obvious real (infinite-dimensional) vector space structure.*

The condition on ξ merely says that $\xi(e_0)$ lies in the fiber over e_0.

As a generalization of local C^r mappings, the C^r sections still form a linear function space suitable for global linear analysis. This differs from the more general class of global C^r maps from one manifold to another, which is a nonlinear function space.

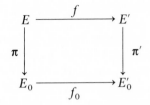

Exercises

4A. (i) Give a precise definition of the Möbius band as a vector bundle, and construct a vector bundle atlas. (A cylinder with a half twist, see Figure 11-1. Compare with the torus, §A9.)

(ii) Complete the details of 4.3 and show that the differentiable structure on a vector bundle is larger than the vector bundle structure.

4B. Find an example of a fiber preserving diffeomorphism between vector bundles that is not a vector bundle isomorphism.

4C. Let $\pi : E \to B$ and $\pi' : E' \to B'$ be two vector bundles. Define the *sum* as $\pi \times \pi' : E \times E' \to B \times B'$. Show that this is a vector bundle in a natural way, and construct a vector bundle atlas.

§5. THE TANGENT FUNCTOR

Recall that for $f : U \subset \mathbf{E} \to V \subset \mathbf{F}$ of class C^{r+1} we define $Tf : TU \to TV$ by $TU = U \times \mathbf{E}$, $TV = V \times \mathbf{F}$, and $Tf(u, \mathbf{e}) = (f(u), Df(u) \cdot \mathbf{e})$. Hence, Tf is a local vector bundle mapping of class C^r. Also $T(f \circ g) = Tf \circ Tg$ (T is a covariant functor).

Moreover, for each open set U in some vector space $\mathbf{E}$ let $\tau_U : TU \to U$ be the projections (as in §4 we identify U with the zero section $U \times \{\mathbf{0}\}$). Then the diagram

$$\begin{array}{ccc} TU & \xrightarrow{\;Tf\;} & TV \\ {\scriptstyle \tau_U}\downarrow & & \downarrow{\scriptstyle \tau_V} \\ U & \xrightarrow[\;f\;]{} & V \end{array}$$

is commutative, that is, $f \circ \tau_U = \tau_U \circ Tf$.

We will now extend the tangent functor T from this local context to the category of differentiable manifolds and mappings. During the definitions it may be helpful to keep in mind the example of the family of tangent spaces of the sphere $S^n \subset \mathbf{R}^{n+1}$.

5.1. *Definition.* *Let M be a manifold and $m \in M$. A* **curve at** m *is a C^1 map $c : I \to M$ from an open interval $I \subset \mathbf{R}$ into M with $0 \in I$ and $c(0) = m$. Let c_1 and c_2 be curves at m and (U, φ) be an admissible chart with $m \in U$. Then we say c_1 and c_2 are* **tangent at** m **with respect to** φ *if and only if $\varphi \circ c_1$ and $\varphi \circ c_2$ are tangent at 0 (in the sense of §2; we may restrict the domain of c_i such that $\varphi \circ c_i$ is defined, see Figure 5-1).*

5.2. *Proposition.* *Let c_1 and c_2 be two curves at $m \in M$. Suppose (U_β, φ_β) is an admissible chart with $m \in U_\beta$, $\beta = 1, 2$. Then*

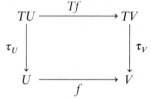

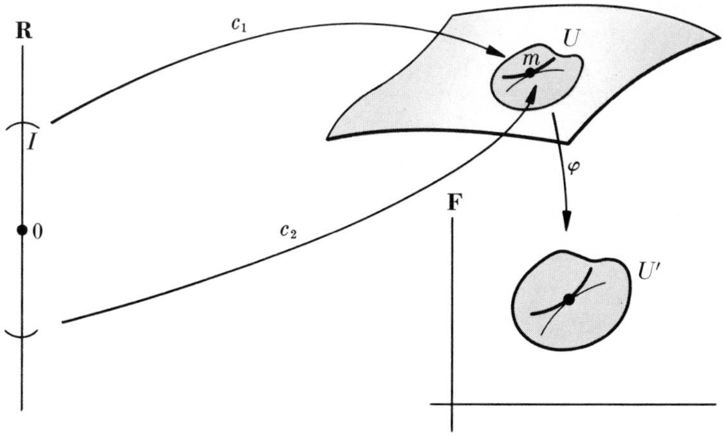

Figure 5-1

c_1 and c_2 are tangent at m with respect to φ_1 if and only if they are tangent at m with respect to φ_2.

Proof. Note c_1 and c_2 are tangent at m with respect to φ_1 iff $D(\varphi_1 \circ c_1)(0) = D(\varphi_1 \circ c_2)(0)$. By taking restrictions if necessary we may suppose $U_1 = U_2$. Hence we have $\varphi_2 \circ c_\alpha = (\varphi_2 \circ \varphi_1^{-1}) \circ (\varphi_1 \circ c_\alpha)$. From the C^1 composite mapping theorem (§2) it follows that $D(\varphi_2 \circ c_1)(0) = D(\varphi_2 \circ c_2)(0)$. ∎

Thus, proposition 5.2 guarantees that the tangency of curves at $m \in M$ is independent of the chart used. Thus we say c_1, c_2 are **tangent at** $m \in M$ iff c_1, c_2 are tangent at m with respect to φ, for any local chart φ at m. It is evident that tangency at $m \in M$ is an equivalence relation among curves at m. An **equivalence class** of such curves is denoted $[c]_m$ where c is a representative of the class.

5.3. Definition. *For a manifold M and $m \in M$ the* **tangent space of** M **at** m *is the set of equivalence classes of curves at m*

$$T_m(M) = \{[c]_m | c \text{ is a curve at } m\}$$

For a subset $A \subset M$, $TM|A = \bigcup_{m \in A} T_m(M)$. Then $TM = TM|M$ is the **tangent bundle** *of M.*

The mapping $\tau_M\colon TM \to M$ defined by $\tau_M([c]_m) = m$, is the **tangent bundle projection** *of M.*

Next we must show that the definition above corresponds to $TU = U \times \mathbf{E}$ for the case of a local manifold. We let T_2 denote T as defined in §2, so $T_2 U = U \times \mathbf{E}$, and let T_5 denote T as defined here. That $T_2(U)$ and $T_5(U)$ can be identified is justified by the following.

5.4. Proposition. *Let U be an open subset of* $\mathbf{E}$, *and c a curve at $u \in U$. Then there is a unique $\mathbf{e} \in \mathbf{E}$ such that the curve $c_{u,\mathbf{e}}$ defined* *by* $c_{u,\mathbf{e}}(t) = u + t\mathbf{e}$ *(on some interval* I *such that* $c_{u,\mathbf{e}}(I) \subset U$*) is tangent to* c *at* u.

Proof. From §2, $Dc(0)$ is the unique linear map in $L(\mathbf{R}, \mathbf{E})$ such that the curve $g\colon \mathbf{R} \to \mathbf{E}$ given by $g(t) = u + Dc(0) \cdot t$ is tangent to c at $t = 0$. If $\mathbf{e} = Dc(0) \cdot 1$, then $g = c_{u,\mathbf{e}}$. ∎

Thus define a map $i\colon T_2(U) \to T_5(U)$ by $i(u, \mathbf{e}) = [c_{u,\mathbf{e}}]_u$. Proposition 5.4 says i is a bijection. Moreover we can define a local vector bundle structure on $T_5(U)$ by means of i. For example, the fiber over $u \in U$ is $i(\{u\} \times \mathbf{F})$. Then i becomes a local vector bundle isomorphism. (See §4.) It will appear after 5.12 that this local vector bundle structure of $T_5 U$ is natural.

5.5. Proposition. *Suppose* c_1 *and* c_2 *are curves at* $m \in M$ *and are tangent at* m. *Let* $f\colon M \to N$ *be of class* C^1. *Then* $f \circ c_1$ *and* $f \circ c_2$ *are tangent at* $f(m) \in N$.

Proof. From the C^1 composite mapping theorem it follows that $f \circ c_1$ and $f \circ c_2$ are of class C^1. (See 5.7 below.) For tangency, let (V, ψ) be a chart on N with $f(m) \in V$. We must show that $(\psi \circ f \circ c_1)'(0) = (\psi \circ f \circ c_2)'(0)$. But $\psi \circ f \circ c_\alpha = (\psi \circ f \circ \varphi^{-1}) \circ (\varphi \circ c_\alpha)$ where (U, φ) is a chart on M, with $f(u) \subset V$. Hence the result follows at once from the C^1 composite mapping theorem (§2). ∎

This justifies the following.

5.6. Definition. *If* $f\colon M \to N$ *is of class* C^1 *we define* $Tf\colon TM \to TN$ *by*

$$Tf([c]_m) = [f \circ c]_{f(m)}$$

We call Tf *the* **tangent** *of* f.

Tf is well defined for if we choose any other representative from $[c]_m$, say c_1, then c and c_1 are tangent at m and hence $f \circ c$ and $f \circ c_1$ are tangent at $f(m)$. That is, $[f \circ c]_{f(m)} = [f \circ c_1]_{f(m)}$.

The basic properties of T are summarized in the following.

5.7. Theorem. (i) ***(C^1 composite mapping theorem.)*** *Suppose* $f\colon M \to N$ *and* $g\colon N \to K$ *are* C^1 *maps of manifolds. Then* $g \circ f\colon M \to K$ *is of class* C^1 *and*

$$T(g \circ f) = Tg \circ Tf$$

(ii) *If* $h\colon M \to M$ *is the identity map, then* $Th\colon TM \to TM$ *is the identity map.*

(iii) *If* $f\colon M \to N$ *is a diffeomorphism, then* $Tf\colon TM \to TN$ *is a bijection and* $(Tf)^{-1} = T(f^{-1})$.

Proof. (i) Let (U, φ), (V, ψ), (W, ρ) be charts of M, N, K, with $f(U) \subset V$ and $g(V) \subset W$ (see §3). Then we have, for the local representatives:

$$\begin{aligned}(g \circ f)_{\varphi\rho} &= \rho \circ g \circ f \circ \varphi^{-1} \\ &= \rho \circ g \circ \psi^{-1} \circ \psi \circ f \circ \varphi^{-1} \\ &= g_{\psi\rho} \circ f_{\varphi\psi}\end{aligned}$$

By the C^1 composite mapping theorem (§2) this, and hence $g \circ f$, is of class C^1. Moreover, $T(g \circ f)[c]_m = [g \circ f \circ c]_{g \circ f(m)}$ and $Tg \circ Tf[c]_m = Tg([f \circ c]_{f(m)}) = [g \circ f \circ c]_{g \circ f(m)}$. Hence $T(g \circ f) = Tg \circ Tf$.

Part (*ii*) is an immediate consequence of the definition of T. For (*iii*), we have that f and f^{-1} are diffeomorphisms with $f \circ f^{-1}$ the identity on N, while $f^{-1} \circ f$ is the identity on M. But then using (*i*) and (*ii*), $Tf \circ Tf^{-1}$ is the identity on TN while $Tf^{-1} \circ Tf$ is the identity on TM. Thus (*iii*) follows. (See Exercise AA of Appendix A.) ∎

Again, as in the case of local manifolds, these properties signify that T is a functor. The behavior of T under products is given by the following.

5.8. Proposition. *Let M and N be manifolds and $M \times N$ the product manifold. Then $T(M \times N)$ is related to $TM \times TN$ by a vector bundle isomorphism. If $f: K \to M$ and $g: K \to N$ are smooth mappings, then $T(f \times g) = Tf \times Tg$, if we identify $T(M \times N)$ and $TM \times TN$. (The functor T is natural with respect to products.)*

Proof. Let $[c]_{(m,n)} \in T(M \times N)$ (5.3). Then $c: I \to M \times N$, $c(0) = (m, n)$ has the form $c(t) = (c_M(t), c_N(t))$ where c_M is a curve in M at m and c_N is a curve in N at n. Consider the map $[c]_{(m,n)} \rightsquigarrow ([c_M]_m, [c_N]_n): T(M \times N) \to TM \times TN$. From the local representative we see that the mapping is well defined (5.2). Also, since it has an obvious inverse it is a bijection. Moreover, in local representation, it is merely the mapping $(u, v, e, f) \rightsquigarrow ((u, e), (v, f))$, which is a vector bundle isomorphism. The second part follows easily from definition 5.6. ∎

Next let us show that in the case of local manifolds, Tf as defined in §2, which we denote $T_2 f$, coincides with T as defined here, which we denote $T_5 f$, when we identify $T_2 U$ with $T_5 U$.

5.9. Proposition. *Let $U \subset \mathbf{E}$ and $V \subset \mathbf{F}$ be local manifolds (open subsets) and $f: U \to V$ be of class C^1. Let $i: T_2(U) \to T_5(U)$ be the map defined in 5.4. Then the diagram*

$$\begin{array}{ccc} T_2(U) & \xrightarrow{T_2 f} & T_2(V) \\ \downarrow i & & \downarrow i \\ T_5(U) & \xrightarrow[T_5 f]{} & T_5(V) \end{array}$$

commutes, that is, $T_5 f \circ i = i \circ T_2 f$.

Proof. For $(u, \mathbf{e}) \in T_2(U) = U \times \mathbf{E}$, we have

$$\begin{aligned} (T_5 f \circ i)(u, \mathbf{e}) &= T_5 f \circ [c_{u,\mathbf{e}}]_u \\ &= [f \circ c_{u,\mathbf{e}}]_{f(u)} \end{aligned}$$

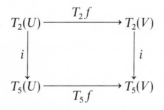

Also, $(i \circ T_2 f)(u, \mathbf{e}) = i \cdot (f(u), Df(u) \cdot \mathbf{e}) = [c_{f(u),\, Df(u) \cdot \mathbf{e}}]_{f(u)}$. These will be equal provided the curves $t \rightsquigarrow f(u + t\mathbf{e})$ and $t \rightsquigarrow f(u) + t(Df(u) \cdot \mathbf{e})$ are tangent at $t = 0$. But this is clear from the definition of the derivative and the composite mapping theorem (§2). ∎

This theorem states that if we identify $T_2(U)$ and $T_5(U)$ by means of i then we can identify $T_2 f$ and $T_5 f$. Thus we will just write T, and will formally suppress the identification.

5.10. Proposition. *If $f\colon U \subset \mathbf{E} \to V \subset \mathbf{F}$ is a diffeomorphism then $Tf\colon U \times \mathbf{E} \to V \times \mathbf{F}$ is a local vector bundle isomorphism.*

Proof. Since $Tf(u, \mathbf{e}) = (f(u), Df(u) \cdot \mathbf{e})$, Tf is a local vector bundle mapping (4.5). But as f is a diffeomorphism, $(Tf)^{-1} = T(f^{-1})$ is also a local vector bundle mapping, and hence Tf is a diffeomorphism. ∎

For a chart (U, φ) on a manifold M, we can construct $T\varphi\colon TU \to TU'$. By 5.7, $T\varphi$ is a bijection, since φ is a diffeomorphism (Exercise 3C). Hence, on TM we can regard $(TU, T\varphi)$ as a local vector bundle chart. In the target of $T\varphi$ note that we have a special local vector bundle, where the fibers have the same dimension as the base.

5.11. Theorem. *Let M be a manifold and $\mathscr{A}$ an atlas of admissible charts. Then $T\mathscr{A} = \{(TU, T\varphi)\colon (U, \varphi) \in \mathscr{A}\}$ is a vector bundle atlas of TM called a* **natural atlas**.

Proof. Since the union of chart domains of $\mathscr{A}$ is M, the union of the corresponding TU is TM. Thus we must verify VBA2 (§4). Hence, suppose we have $TU_i \cap TU_j \neq \phi$. Then $U_i \cap U_j \neq \phi$ and we can form the overlap map $\varphi_i \circ \varphi_j^{-1}$, by restriction of φ_j^{-1} to $\varphi_j(U_i \cap U_j)$, as in §3. Then we must verify $T\varphi_i \circ (T\varphi_j)^{-1} = T(\varphi_j \circ \varphi_j^{-1})$ is a local vector bundle isomorphism. But this is guaranteed by 5.10. ∎

Hence TM has a natural vector bundle structure, induced by the differentiable structure of M. If M is n-dimensional, Hausdorff, and second countable, TM will be $2n$-dimensional, Hausdorff, and second countable.

We shall now reconcile the bundle projection τ_M of 5.3 and the one given in §4 for an arbitrary vector bundle.

5.12. Proposition. *If $m \in M$, then $\tau_M^{-1}(m) = T_m M$ is a fiber of TM and $\tau_M | (TM)_0\colon TM_0 \to M$ is a diffeomorphism.*

Proof. Let (U, φ) be a local chart at $m \in M$, with $\varphi\colon U \to U' \subset \mathbf{E}$ and $\varphi(m) = u'$. Then $T\varphi\colon TM|U \to U' \times \mathbf{E}$ is a natural chart of TM, $T\varphi^{-1}(\{u'\} \times \mathbf{E}) = T\varphi^{-1}\{[c_{u', \mathbf{e}}]_{u'} | \mathbf{e} \in \mathbf{E}\}$ by definition of $T\varphi$, and this is exactly $T_m M$, by 5.7 (iii). For the second assertion, $\tau_M | (TM)_0$ is obviously a bijection, and its local representative with respect to $T\varphi$ and φ is the natural identification $U' \times \{\mathbf{0}\} \to U'$, a local diffeomorphism. ∎

We will often then identify M with the zero section of TM, and τ_M with the bundle projection onto the zero section.

5.13. Proposition. *Let M and N be manifolds, and let $f: M \to N$ be of class C^{r+1}. Then $Tf: TM \to TN$ is a vector bundle mapping of class C^r.*

Proof. By proposition 3.7 it is enough to check Tf using the natural atlas. For $u \in M$ choose (U, φ) and (V, ψ) charts of M and N so $u \in U$, $f(u) \subset V$ and $f_{\varphi\psi} = \psi \circ f \circ \varphi^{-1}$ is of class C^{r+1}. Then using $(TU, T\varphi)$ for TM and $(TV, T\psi)$ for TN, we must verify that $(Tf)_{T\varphi, T\psi}$ is a local vector bundle map of class C^r. But we have $(Tf)_{T\varphi, T\psi} = T\psi \circ Tf \circ T\varphi^{-1} = T(f_{\varphi\psi})$, and $Tf_{\varphi\psi}(u', \mathbf{e}) = (f_{\varphi\psi}(u'), Df_{\varphi\psi}(u') \cdot \mathbf{e})$ which is a local vector bundle map of class C^r. (See §4.) ∎

Now that TM has a manifold structure we can form higher tangents. Induction on 5.7 (i) yields the following.

5.14. Theorem (C^r composite mapping theorem). *Suppose $f: M \to N$ and $g: N \to K$ are C^r mappings of manifolds. Then $g \circ f$ is of class C^r and $T^r(g \circ f) = T^r g \circ T^r f$.*

As was the case for local manifolds, for $f: M \to N$ of class C^1, we have the commutative diagram

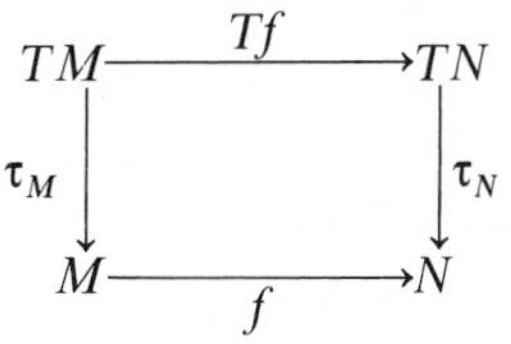

We sometimes write $\tau_f = (Tf, f): \tau_M \to \tau_N$ for this diagram. A special case is τ_M:

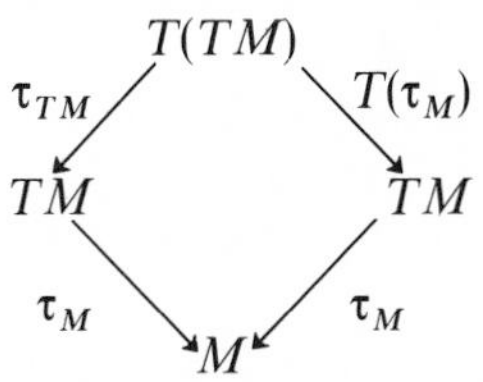

As it may be shown that the set $T(TM)$ has a vector bundle structure, in addition to the usual one, in which $T\tau_M$ is a projection, it is confusing to write $T(TM)$ alone for $(T(TM), T\mathscr{A})$. But "the bundle $\tau_{TM}: T(TM) \to TM$" is adequate to indicate which vector bundle structure is implied.

The inverse mapping theorem, 2.10, takes the following form.

5.15. Theorem. *Let M and N be manifolds and $f: M \to N$ be of class C^∞. Suppose Tf is an isomorphism on the fiber over $m \in M$. Then f is a diffeomorphism from some neighborhood of m onto some neighborhood of $f(m)$.*

This follows easily from 2.10. In fact, 5.15 is a special case of the **implicit mapping theorem**.

5.16. Theorem. *Let M and N be manifolds and $f: M \to N$ be of class C^∞. Suppose Tf restricted to the fiber T_mM is surjective. Then there are charts (U, φ) and (V, ψ) with $m \in U$, $f(U) \subset V$, $\varphi: U \to U' \times V'$, $\varphi(m) = (\mathbf{0}, \mathbf{0})$, $\psi: V \to V'$ and $f_{\varphi\psi}: U' \times V' \to V'$ is the projection onto the second factor.*

For a proof see Dieudonné [1, p. 265.]

The conditon that $T_mf = Tf|T_mM$ be surjective means, for $f: \mathbf{R}^k \to \mathbf{R}^n$, that the rank of the Jacobian matrix of f at $m \in M$ should be n $(k \geq n)$.

5.17. Definition. *Suppose M and N are manifolds with $f: M \to N$ of class C^1. A point $n \in N$ is called a* **regular value** *of f iff for each $m \in f^{-1}(\{n\})$, T_mf is surjective. Let R_f denote the set of regular values of $f: M \to N$.*

Note $N \setminus f(M) \subset R_f \subset N$. The next result will be important when we consider energy surfaces.

5.18. Proposition. *Suppose $f: M \to N$ is of class C^∞ and $n \in R_f$. Then $f^{-1}(n) = \{m | m \in M, f(m) = n\}$ is a submanifold of M.*

Proof. If $f^{-1}(n) = \phi$ the theorem is satisfied. Otherwise, for $m \in f^{-1}(n)$

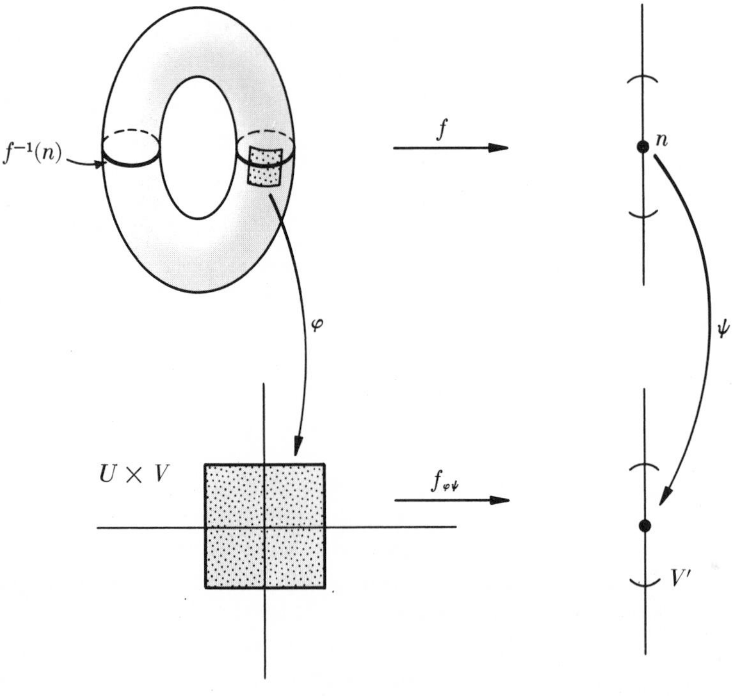

Figure 5-2

we find charts (U, φ), (V, ψ) as described in the implicit mapping theorem (5.16). Then it must be shown that the chart (U, φ) has the submanifold property (§3). But $\varphi(U \cap f^{-1}(n)) = f_{\varphi\psi}^{-1}(0) = U' \times \{0\}$. This is exactly the submanifold property. (See Figure 5-2.) ∎

The following relatively deep result is a weak form of *Sard's theorem.* See, for example, Abraham-Robbin [1, Chapter III].

5.19. Theorem (Sard). *Suppose $f: M \to N$ is of class C^∞. Then R_f is dense in N* (§A1).

Exercises

5A. Establish 5.15 and 5.16 from the corresponding local statements in Dieudonné. Deduce each of 5.15 and 5.16 from the other.

5B. Use 5.18 to given an alternative proof that S^n is a submanifold of $\mathbf{R}^{n+1}$.

5C. A **vectorfield** on a local manifold U is a C^∞ section of $TU = U \times \mathbf{E}$. Interpret geometrically and examine the conditon that a curve $c: I \to U$ is tangent to X, $Tc(t) \cdot 1 = X(c(t))$. Show also that $c'(t) = Tc(t) \cdot 1$ coincides with the usual derivative.

§6. TENSORS

Given a vector space $\mathbf{E}$ we can form a new vector space consisting of tensors on $\mathbf{E}$. When this is done on each fiber of a vector bundle, we obtain a new vector bundle structure. An important case occurs when this is applied to the tangent bundle of a manifold. Thus we begin with a review of tensors on vector spaces.

Recall from §1 that $L^k(\mathbf{E}_1, \ldots, \mathbf{E}_k; \mathbf{F})$ denotes the vector space of multilinear maps from $\mathbf{E}_1 \times \cdots \times \mathbf{E}_k$ into $\mathbf{F}$. The special case $L(\mathbf{E}, \mathbf{R})$ is denoted $\mathbf{E}^*$, the **dual space** of $\mathbf{E}$. If $\hat{\mathbf{e}} = (\mathbf{e}_1, \ldots, \mathbf{e}_n)$ is an ordered basis of $\mathbf{E}$, there is a unique ordered basis of $\mathbf{E}^*$, the **dual basis** $\hat{\mathbf{e}}^* = (\boldsymbol{\alpha}^1, \ldots, \boldsymbol{\alpha}^n)$, such that $\boldsymbol{\alpha}^j(\mathbf{e}_i) = \delta_i^j$ where $\delta_i^j = 1$ if $j = i$ and 0 otherwise. Furthermore, for each

$$\mathbf{e} \in \mathbf{E}, \quad \mathbf{e} = \sum_{i=1}^{n} \boldsymbol{\alpha}^i(\mathbf{e})\mathbf{e}_i$$

and for each

$$\boldsymbol{\alpha} \in \mathbf{E}^*, \quad \boldsymbol{\alpha} = \sum_{i=1}^{n} \boldsymbol{\alpha}(\mathbf{e}_i)\boldsymbol{\alpha}^i.$$

Employing the **summation convention**, whereby summation is implied when an index is repeated on upper and lower levels, these expressions become $\mathbf{e} = \boldsymbol{\alpha}^i(\mathbf{e})\mathbf{e}_i$ and $\boldsymbol{\alpha} = \boldsymbol{\alpha}(\mathbf{e}_i)\boldsymbol{\alpha}^i$.

We may identify $\mathbf{E}^{**} = L(\mathbf{E}^*, \mathbf{R})$ with $\mathbf{E}$ by associating with each $\mathbf{e} \in \mathbf{E}$, $\mathbf{e}^{**} \in \mathbf{E}^{**}$ given by $\mathbf{e}^{**}(\boldsymbol{\alpha}) = \boldsymbol{\alpha}(\mathbf{e})$ for all $\boldsymbol{\alpha} \in \mathbf{E}^*$. Because $\mathbf{E}$ has finite dimension, the map $\mathbf{e} \rightsquigarrow \mathbf{e}^{**}$ is an isomorphism (Exercise 1B).

6.1. Definition. *For a vector space* $\mathbf{E}$ *we put* $T^r_s(\mathbf{E}) = L^{r+s}(\mathbf{E}^*, \ldots, \mathbf{E}^*, \mathbf{E}, \ldots, \mathbf{E}; \mathbf{R})$ (r *copies of* $\mathbf{E}^*$ *and* s *copies of* $\mathbf{E}$). *Elements of* $T^r_s(\mathbf{E})$ *are called* **tensors on E**, **contravariant** *of order* r *and* **covariant** *of order* s; *or simply*, **of type** $\binom{r}{s}$.

Given $\mathbf{t}_1 \in T^{r_1}_{s_1}(\mathbf{E})$ *and* $\mathbf{t}_2 \in T^{r_2}_{s_2}(\mathbf{E})$ *the* **tensor product** *of* $\mathbf{t}_1$ *and* $\mathbf{t}_2$ *is the tensor* $\mathbf{t}_1 \otimes \mathbf{t}_2 \in T^{r_1+r_2}_{s_1+s_2}(\mathbf{E})$ *defined by*

$$\mathbf{t}_1 \otimes \mathbf{t}_2(\boldsymbol{\beta}^1, \ldots, \boldsymbol{\beta}^{r_1}, \boldsymbol{\gamma}^1, \ldots, \boldsymbol{\gamma}^{r_2}, \mathbf{f}_1, \ldots, \mathbf{f}_{s_1}, \mathbf{g}_1, \ldots, \mathbf{g}_{s_2})$$
$$= \mathbf{t}_1(\boldsymbol{\beta}^1, \ldots, \boldsymbol{\beta}^{r_1}, \mathbf{f}_1, \ldots, \mathbf{f}_{s_1})\mathbf{t}_2(\boldsymbol{\gamma}^1, \ldots, \boldsymbol{\gamma}^{r_2}, \mathbf{g}_1, \ldots, \mathbf{g}_{s_2})$$

where $\boldsymbol{\beta}^j, \boldsymbol{\gamma}^j \in \mathbf{E}^*$ *and* $\mathbf{f}_j, \mathbf{g}_j \in \mathbf{E}$. (*It is obviously multilinear.*)

Because of the identifications discussed in §1, we have $T^1_0(\mathbf{E}) \approx \mathbf{E}$, $T^0_1(\mathbf{E}) = \mathbf{E}^*$, $T^0_2(\mathbf{E}) \approx L(\mathbf{E}; \mathbf{E}^*)$, and $T^1_1(\mathbf{E}) \approx L(\mathbf{E}; \mathbf{E})$. It is easy to see that $\otimes$ is associative and bilinear.

6.2. Proposition. *If* $\dim \mathbf{E} = n$ *then* $T^r_s(\mathbf{E})$ *has the structure of a real vector space of dimension* n^{r+s}. *Indeed, for an ordered basis* $\hat{\mathbf{e}} = (\mathbf{e}_1, \ldots, \mathbf{e}_n)$ *of* $\mathbf{E}$, *a basis of* $T^r_s(\mathbf{E})$ *is given by*

$$\{\mathbf{e}_{i_1} \otimes \cdots \otimes \mathbf{e}_{i_r} \otimes \boldsymbol{\alpha}^{j_1} \otimes \cdots \otimes \boldsymbol{\alpha}^{j_s} \mid i_k, j_k = 1, \ldots, n\}$$

where $\hat{\mathbf{e}}^* = (\boldsymbol{\alpha}^1, \ldots, \boldsymbol{\alpha}^n)$ *is the dual basis of* $\hat{\mathbf{e}}$.

Proof. We must show that the elements $\mathbf{e}_{i_1} \otimes \cdots \otimes \mathbf{e}_{i_r} \otimes \boldsymbol{\alpha}^{j_i} \otimes \cdots \otimes \boldsymbol{\alpha}^{j_s}$ of $T^r_s(\mathbf{E})$ are linearly independent, and span $T^r_s(\mathbf{E})$. Suppose $t^{i_1 \cdots i_r}_{j_1 \cdots j_s}\mathbf{e}_{i_1} \otimes \times \cdots \otimes \mathbf{e}_{i_r} \otimes \boldsymbol{\alpha}^{j_1} \otimes \cdots \otimes \boldsymbol{\alpha}^{j_s} = \mathbf{0}$. Then apply this to $(\boldsymbol{\alpha}^{k_1}, \ldots, \boldsymbol{\alpha}^{k_r}, \mathbf{e}_{l_1}, \ldots, \mathbf{e}_{l_s})$ using the identification $\mathbf{e}_i(\boldsymbol{\alpha}^j) = \boldsymbol{\alpha}^j(\mathbf{e}_i)$ to give $t^{k_1 \cdots k_r}_{l_1 \cdots l_s} = 0$. Next, we easily check that for $\mathbf{t} \in T^r_s(\mathbf{E})$ we have

$$\mathbf{t} = \mathbf{t}(\boldsymbol{\alpha}^{i_r}, \ldots, \boldsymbol{\alpha}^{i_r}, \mathbf{e}_{j_1}, \ldots, \mathbf{e}_{j_s})\mathbf{e}_{i_1} \otimes \cdots \otimes \mathbf{e}_{i_r} \otimes \boldsymbol{\alpha}^{j_1} \otimes \cdots \otimes \boldsymbol{\alpha}^{j_s}. \quad \blacksquare$$

The coefficients $t^{i_1 \cdots i_r}_{j_1 \cdots j_s} = \mathbf{t}(\boldsymbol{\alpha}^{i_1}, \ldots, \boldsymbol{\alpha}^{i_r}, \mathbf{e}_{j_1}, \ldots, \mathbf{e}_{j_s})$ are called the **components of t relative to** $\hat{\mathbf{e}}$.

The classical operations of tensor algebra can be defined invariantly in this context. For example, the **Kronecker delta** is the tensor $\boldsymbol{\delta} \in T^1_1(\mathbf{E})$ associated to the identity $\mathbf{I} \in L(\mathbf{E}, \mathbf{E})$ under the canonical isomorphism $T^1_1(\mathbf{E}) \approx L(\mathbf{E}, \mathbf{E})$, that is, $\boldsymbol{\delta}(\boldsymbol{\alpha}, \mathbf{e}) = \boldsymbol{\alpha}(\mathbf{e})$ for all $\boldsymbol{\alpha} \in \mathbf{E}^*$, $\mathbf{e} \in \mathbf{E}$. Relative to any basis, the components of $\boldsymbol{\delta}$ are the usual δ^i_j.

An example of an **inner product** is the mapping $i(\mathbf{e})\colon T^1_1(\mathbf{E}) \to T^1_0(\mathbf{E})$, where $\mathbf{e} \in \mathbf{E}$, defined by $i(\mathbf{e})\mathbf{t}(\boldsymbol{\alpha}) = \mathbf{t}(\boldsymbol{\alpha}, \mathbf{e})$. This one suggests the identification $T^1_1(\mathbf{E}) \approx L(\mathbf{E}, \mathbf{E}^{**})$. Using other identifications we have more general inner products. An example of a **contraction** is the mapping $tr\colon T^1_1(\mathbf{E}) \to \mathbf{R}$ where $tr(\mathbf{t})$ is the trace of the linear mapping associated to $\mathbf{t}$ by the isomorphism $T^1_1(\mathbf{E}) \approx L(\mathbf{E}, \mathbf{E})$. More general contractions may be defined by composing a sequence of inner products with this contraction. A reader with experience in the classical tensor calculus may wish to translate other operations into this language, but we will not need the full machinery in the sequel.

If $\varphi \in L(\mathbf{E}, \mathbf{F})$ we can consider $\varphi \in L(T_0^1(\mathbf{E}), T_0^1(\mathbf{F}))$. Also we define $\varphi_* \in L(\mathbf{F}^*, \mathbf{E}^*) = L(T_1^0(\mathbf{F}), T_1^0(\mathbf{F}))$ by $\varphi_*(\boldsymbol{\beta}) \cdot \mathbf{e} = \boldsymbol{\beta}(\varphi(\mathbf{e}))$ where $\boldsymbol{\beta} \in \mathbf{F}^*$ and $\mathbf{e} \in \mathbf{E}$. Unfortunately φ_* maps in the wrong direction for our purposes, but this may be remedied if φ is an isomorphism.

6.3. Definition. *If $\varphi \in L(\mathbf{E}, \mathbf{F})$ is an isomorphism, let $T_s^r\varphi = \varphi_s^r \in L(T_s^r(\mathbf{E}), T_s^r(\mathbf{F}))$ be defined by*

$$\varphi_s^r\mathbf{t}(\boldsymbol{\beta}^1, \ldots, \boldsymbol{\beta}^r, \mathbf{f}_1, \ldots, \mathbf{f}_s) = \mathbf{t}(\varphi_*(\boldsymbol{\beta}^1), \ldots, \varphi_*(\boldsymbol{\beta}^r), \varphi^{-1}(\mathbf{f}_1), \ldots, \varphi^{-1}(\mathbf{f}_s))$$

where $\mathbf{t} \in T_s^r(\mathbf{E})$, $\boldsymbol{\beta}^1, \ldots, \boldsymbol{\beta}^r \in \mathbf{F}^*$, and $\mathbf{f}_1, \ldots, f_s \in \mathbf{F}$.

Note $\varphi_1^0 = (\varphi^{-1})_*$, which maps "forward" like φ, and we identify φ with φ_0^1. The next proposition asserts essentially that T_s^r is a covariant functor.

6.4. Proposition. *Let $\varphi : \mathbf{E} \to \mathbf{F}$ and $\psi : \mathbf{F} \to \mathbf{G}$ be isomorphisms. Then*

(i) $(\psi \cdot \varphi)_s^r = \psi_s^r \circ \varphi_s^r$;
(ii) If $\mathbf{i} : \mathbf{E} \to \mathbf{E}$ is the identity, then so is $\mathbf{i}_s^r : T_s^r(\mathbf{E}) \to T_s^r(\mathbf{E})$;
(iii) $\varphi_s^r : T_s^r(\mathbf{E}) \to T_s^r(\mathbf{F})$ is an isomorphism, and $(\varphi_s^r)^{-1} = (\varphi^{-1})_s^r$.

Proof. For (*i*), we have by 6.3

$$\begin{aligned}
&\psi_s^r(\varphi_s^r\mathbf{t})(\gamma^1, \ldots, \gamma^r, \mathbf{g}_1, \ldots, \mathbf{g}_s) \\
&= \varphi_s^r\mathbf{t}(\psi_*(\gamma^1), \ldots, \psi_*(\gamma^r), \psi^{-1}(\mathbf{g}_1), \ldots, \psi^{-1}(\mathbf{g}_s)) \\
&= \mathbf{t}(\varphi_*\psi_*(\gamma^1), \ldots, \varphi_*\psi_*(\gamma^r), \varphi^{-1}\psi^{-1}(\mathbf{g}_1), \ldots, \varphi^{-1}\psi^{-1}(\mathbf{g}_s)) \\
&= \mathbf{t}((\psi \circ \varphi)_*(\gamma^1), \ldots, (\psi \circ \varphi)_*(\gamma^r), (\psi \circ \varphi)^{-1}(\mathbf{g}_1), \ldots, (\psi \circ \varphi)^{-1}(\mathbf{g}_s)) \\
&= (\psi \circ \varphi)_s^r\mathbf{t}(\gamma^1, \ldots, \gamma^r, \mathbf{g}_1, \ldots, \mathbf{g}_s)
\end{aligned}$$

where $\gamma^1, \ldots, \gamma^r \in \mathbf{G}^*$, $\mathbf{g}_1, \ldots, \mathbf{g}_s \in \mathbf{G}$, and $\mathbf{t} \in T_s^r(\mathbf{E})$. We have used the fact that $(\psi \circ \varphi)_* = \varphi_* \circ \psi_*$ and $(\psi \circ \varphi)^{-1} = \varphi^{-1} \circ \psi^{-1}$, which the reader can easily check. Part (*ii*) is an immediate consequence of the definition and the fact that $\mathbf{i}_* = \mathbf{i}$ and $\mathbf{i}^{-1} = \mathbf{i}$. Finally, for (*iii*) we have $\varphi_s^r \circ (\varphi^{-1})_s^r = \mathbf{i}_s^r$, the identity on $T_s^r(\mathbf{F})$, by (*i*) and (*ii*). Similarly, $(\varphi^{-1})_s^r \circ \varphi_s^r = \mathbf{i}_s^r$ the identity on $T_s^r(\mathbf{E})$. Hence (*iii*) follows. Note the similarity to 5.7 ∎

The next proposition gives a connection with component notation. We shall rarely use this approach in practice. The proof is left as an easy exercise for the reader.

6.5. Proposition. *Let $\varphi \in L(\mathbf{E}, \mathbf{F})$ be an isomorphism. For ordered bases $\hat{\mathbf{e}} = (\mathbf{e}_1, \ldots, \mathbf{e}_n)$ of $\mathbf{E}$ and $\hat{\mathbf{f}} = (\mathbf{f}_1, \ldots, \mathbf{f}_n)$ of $\mathbf{F}$, suppose $\varphi(\mathbf{e}_i) = A_i^j\mathbf{f}_j$ and $(\varphi^{-1})_*(\boldsymbol{\alpha}^i) = B_j^i\boldsymbol{\beta}^j$. Then $B_i^jA_j^k = A_i^jB_j^k = \delta_i^k$, or the inverse matrix of (A_i^j) is (B_i^j), and for $\mathbf{t} \in T_s^r(\mathbf{E})$ with components $t_{j_1 \cdots j_s}^{i_1 \cdots i_r}$ relative to $\hat{\mathbf{e}}$, the components of $\varphi_s^r\mathbf{t}$ relative to $\hat{\mathbf{f}}$ are given by*

$$'t_{j_1' \cdots j_s'}^{i_1' \cdots i_r'} = t_{j_1 \cdots j_s}^{i_1 \cdots i_r} A_{i_1}^{i_1'} \cdots A_{i_r}^{i_r'} B_{j_1'}^{j_1} \cdots B_{j_s'}^{j_s}$$

In particular, if $\mathbf{E} = \mathbf{F}$ and φ is the identity, the above describes the components of $\mathbf{t}$ relative to the "new basis" $\hat{\mathbf{f}}$.

We extend the tensor algebra next to local vector bundles, and finally to vector bundles. For $U \subset \mathbf{E}$ (open) recall that $U \times \mathbf{F}$ is a local vector bundle. Then $U \times T^r_s(\mathbf{F})$ is also a local vector bundle in view of 6.2. Suppose φ: $U \times \mathbf{F} \to U' \times \mathbf{F}'$ is a local vector bundle mapping (4.5) and is an *isomorphism on each fiber*; that is, $\varphi_u = \varphi|\{u\} \times \mathbf{F} \in L(\mathbf{F}, \mathbf{F}')$ (by the identifications of §4) is an isomorphism. Also, let φ_0 denote the restriction of φ to the zero section as in §4. Then φ induces a mapping of the local tensor bundles as follows.

6.6. Definition. *If $\varphi: U \times \mathbf{F} \to U' \times \mathbf{F}'$ is a local vector bundle mapping such that for each $u \in U$, φ_u is an isomorphism, let φ^r_s: $U \times T^r_s(\mathbf{F}) \to U' \times T^r_s(\mathbf{F}')$ be defined by*

$$\varphi^r_s(u, \mathbf{t}) = (\varphi_0(u), (\varphi_u)^r_s \mathbf{t})$$

where $\mathbf{t} \in T^r_s(\mathbf{F})$.

6.7. Proposition. *If $L_{\text{iso}}(\mathbf{E}, \mathbf{F})$ denotes the set of isomorphisms from $\mathbf{E}$ onto $\mathbf{F}$, then L_{iso} is open in $L(\mathbf{E}, \mathbf{F})$.*

Proof. We may suppose $L_{\text{iso}}(\mathbf{E}, \mathbf{F}) \neq \phi$, say $\varphi_0 \in L_{\text{iso}}(\mathbf{E}, \mathbf{F})$. Then as the linear mapping: $L(\mathbf{E}, \mathbf{F}) \to L(\mathbf{E}, \mathbf{E})$: $\psi \rightsquigarrow \varphi_0^{-1} \circ \psi$ is continuous, it is sufficient to prove $L_{\text{iso}}(\mathbf{E}, \mathbf{E})$ is open in $L(\mathbf{E}, \mathbf{E})$. For $\varphi \in L_{\text{iso}}(\mathbf{E}, \mathbf{E})$ we shall prove that $\|\varphi - \psi\| < \|\varphi\|$ implies $\psi \in L_{\text{iso}}(\mathbf{E}, \mathbf{E})$, which will give the result. Since $\psi = \varphi \circ (\mathbf{I} + \varphi^{-1} \circ (\psi - \varphi))$ it is sufficient to show $\|\psi\| < 1$ implies $\mathbf{I} + \psi \in L_{\text{iso}}(\mathbf{E}, \mathbf{E})$ ($\mathbf{I}$ is the identity, and $\|\ \|$ denotes some norm). For this, consider the sequence $\psi_0 = \mathbf{I}$, $\psi_1 = \mathbf{I} - \psi$, $\psi_2 = \mathbf{I} - \psi + \psi \circ \psi$, $\psi_3 = \mathbf{I} - \psi + \psi \circ \psi - \psi \circ \psi \circ \psi, \ldots$. An easy argument shows that this is a Cauchy sequence (if $r \in \mathbf{R}$, $r < 1$ then $1, 1 - r, 1 - r + r^2, \ldots$ is Cauchy). Hence, as $L(\mathbf{E}, \mathbf{E})$ is complete, ψ_n converges. (See 1.3 and §A1.) We claim that the limit, say ρ, is the inverse of $\mathbf{I} + \psi$. In fact, $(\mathbf{I} + \psi) \circ \psi_n = (-1)^{n-1} \psi \circ \psi \circ \cdots \circ \psi + \mathbf{I}$, so that the result follows. ∎

6.8. Proposition. *Let $\mathcal{S}_*$: $L(\mathbf{E}, \mathbf{F}) \to L(\mathbf{F}^*, \mathbf{E}^*)$; $\varphi \rightsquigarrow \varphi_*$ and $\mathcal{S}^{-1}$: $L_{\text{iso}}(\mathbf{E}, \mathbf{F}) \to L_{\text{iso}}(\mathbf{F}, \mathbf{E})$; $\varphi \rightsquigarrow \varphi^{-1}$. Then $\mathcal{S}_*$ and $\mathcal{S}^{-1}$ are of class C^∞.*

Proof. The first part follows at once as $\mathcal{S}_*$ is linear. For the second part, we may assume $L_{\text{iso}}(\mathbf{E}, \mathbf{F}) \neq \phi$. In fact, let us show that $D\mathcal{S}^{-1}(\varphi) \cdot \psi = -\varphi^{-1} \circ \psi \circ \varphi^{-1}$. Then it will follow from Leibnitz' rule (§2) that $\mathcal{S}^{-1}$ is of class C^∞. Since $\psi \rightsquigarrow -\varphi^{-1}\psi\varphi^{-1}$ is linear ($\psi \in L(\mathbf{E}, \mathbf{F})$) we must show, according to 2.2,

$$\lim_{\psi \to \varphi} \frac{\|\psi^{-1} - (\varphi^{-1} - \varphi^{-1}\psi\varphi^{-1} + \varphi^{-1}\varphi\varphi^{-1})\|}{\|\psi - \varphi\|} = 0$$

Note

$$\begin{aligned} \psi^{-1} - (\varphi^{-1} - \varphi^{-1}\psi\varphi^{-1} + \varphi^{-1}\varphi\varphi^{-1}) &= \psi^{-1} - 2\varphi^{-1} + \varphi^{-1}\psi\varphi^{-1} \\ &= \psi^{-1}(\psi - \varphi)\varphi^{-1}(\psi - \varphi)\varphi^{-1} \end{aligned}$$

As $\|\beta \circ \alpha\| \leq \|\alpha\| \, \|\beta\|$ for $\alpha \in L(\mathbf{E}, \mathbf{F})$, $\beta \in L(\mathbf{F}, \mathbf{G})$,

$$\|\psi^{-1}(\psi - \varphi)\varphi^{-1}(\psi - \varphi)\varphi^{-1}\| \leq \|\psi^{-1}\| \, \|\psi - \varphi\|^2 \|\varphi^{-1}\|^2$$

With this inequality, the limit above is clearly zero. ∎

6.9. Proposition. *If $\varphi\colon U \times \mathbf{F} \to U' \times \mathbf{F}'$ is a local vector bundle map and φ_u is an isomorphism for all $u \in U$, then $\varphi^r_s\colon U \times T^r_s(\mathbf{F}) \to U' \times T^r_s(\mathbf{F}')$ is a local vector bundle map and $(\varphi_u)^r_s = (\varphi^r_s)_u$ is an isomorphism for all $u \in U$. Moreover, if φ is a local vector bundle isomorphism then so is φ^r_s.*

Proof. Isomorphism on fibers follows from the functorial property of φ^r_s (6.4) and the last assertion follows easily from the former. From 6.6 then, we need only establish that $(\varphi_u)^r_s = (\varphi^r_s)_u$ is of class C^∞. Now, φ_u is a smooth function of u, and, by 6.8, φ_{u*} and φ_u^{-1} are smooth functions of u. The Cartesian product of smooth functions is easily seen to be smooth (2.12), and $(\varphi_u)^r_s$ is a multilinear mapping on a Cartesian product of smooth functions (6.3) (this is not linearity in φ). Hence from the product formula (2.11), $(\varphi_u)^r_s$ is smooth. ∎

This smoothness can be verified also by using the standard bases in the tensor spaces as local bundle charts, and proving that the components $(\varphi^r_s t)^{i_1 \cdots i_r}_{j_1 \cdots j_s}$ are C^∞ functions. We include the intrinsic argument above in support of the view that components are rarely needed.

As in §4 we have the following commutative diagram which says that φ^r_s preserves fibers.

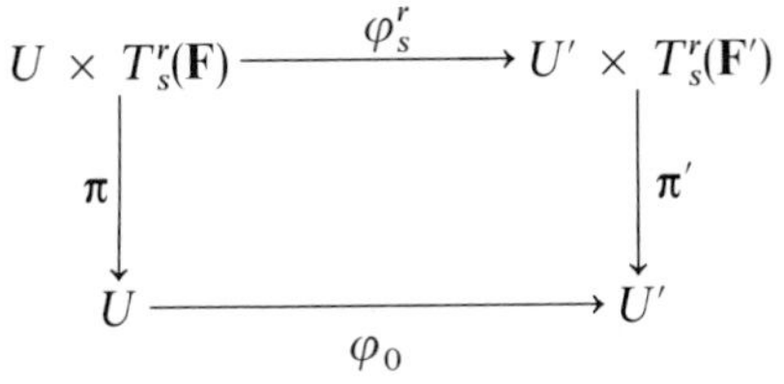

6.10. Definition. *Let $\pi\colon E \to B$ be a vector bundle with $E_b = \pi^{-1}(b)$ the fiber over $b \in B$. Define $T^r_s(E) = \bigcup_{b \in B} T^r_s(E_b)$ and $\pi^r_s\colon T^r_s(E) \to B$ by $\pi^r_s(e) = b$ iff $e \in T^r_s(E_b)$. Furthermore, for a subset A of B, we put $T^r_s(E)|A = \bigcup_{b \in A} T^r_s(E_b)$. If $\pi'\colon E' \to B'$ is another vector bundle and $(\varphi, \varphi_0)\colon \pi \to \pi'$ is a vector bundle mapping with $\varphi_b = \varphi|E_b$ an isomorphism for all $b \in B$, let $\varphi^r_s\colon T^r_s(E) \to T^r_s(E')$ be defined by $\varphi^r_s|T^r_s(E_b) = (\varphi_b)^r_s$.*

Now suppose $(E|U, \varphi)$ is an admissible local bundle chart of π, where $U \subset B$ is an open set. Then the mapping $\varphi^r_s|[T^r_s(E)|U]$ is obviously a bijection onto a local bundle, by 6.4, and thus is a local bundle chart. Further, $(\varphi^r_s)_b = (\varphi_b)^r_s$ is a linear isomorphism, so this chart preserves the linear structure of each fiber, which in this case is given an advance. We shall call such a chart a **natural chart** of $T^r_s(E)$.

6.11. Theorem. *If $\pi: E \to B$ is a vector bundle, then the set of all natural charts of π^r_s: $T^r_s(E) \to B$ is a vector bundle atlas.*

Proof. Axiom (VBA1) is obvious. For (VBA2), suppose we have two overlapping natural charts, φ^r_s and ψ^r_s. For simplicity, let them have the same domain. Then $\alpha = \psi \circ \varphi^{-1}$ is a local vector bundle isomorphism, and by 6.4, $\psi^r_s \circ (\varphi^r_s)^{-1} = \alpha^r_s$, a local vector bundle isomorphism by 6.9. ∎

This atlas of natural charts, the **natural atlas** of π^r_s, generates a vector bundle structure, and it is easily seen that the resulting vector bundle is Hausdorff, second countable, and has constant dimension. *Hereafter, π^r_s will denote all of this structure.* Note the similarity of this construction with the development of the tangent bundle (5.11).

6.12. Proposition. *If $f: E \to E'$ is a vector bundle map which is an isomorphism on each fiber then f^r_s: $T^r_s(E) \to T^r_s(E')$ is also a vector bundle map which is an isomorphism on each fiber.*

Proof. Let (U, φ) be an admissible vector bundle chart of E and (V, ψ) be one of E' so that $f(U) \subset V$ and $f_{\varphi\psi} = \psi \circ f \circ \varphi^{-1}$ is a local vector bundle mapping. Then using the natural atlas in 6.11 we see $(f^r_s)_{\varphi^r_s, \psi^r_s} = (f_{\varphi\psi})^r_s$ by 6.4. The result now follows at once from 6.9. ∎

6.13. Proposition. (*i*) *Suppose $f: E \to E'$ and $g: E' \to E''$ are vector bundle maps which are isomorphisms on each fiber. Then so is $g \circ f$, and $(g \circ f)^r_s = g^r_s \circ f^r_s$.*

(*ii*) *If $\mathbf{i}: E \to E$ is the identity then $\mathbf{i}^r_s$: $T^r_s(E) \to T^r_s(E)$ is the identity.*

(*iii*) *If $f: E \to E'$ is a vector bundle isomorphism then so is f^r_s and $(f^r_s)^{-1} = (f^{-1})^r_s$.*

Proof. For (*i*) we examine representatives of $(g \circ f)^r_s$ and $g^r_s \circ f^r_s$ as in 6.12. These representatives are the same in view of 6.4. Part (*ii*) is clear from the definition, and (*iii*) follows from (*i*) and (*ii*) by the same method as in 6.4. ∎

This proposition asserts that T^r_s is a covariant functor on vector bundles and vector bundle mappings (regular on fibers).

We now specialize to the important case where $\pi: E \to B$ is the tangent vector bundle of a manifold.

6.14. Definition. *Let M be a manifold and τ_M: $TM \to M$ its tangent bundle* (§5). *We call $T^r_s(M) = T^r_s(TM)$ the* **vector bundle of tensors of contravariant order** *r* **and covariant order** *s; or simply* **of type** $\binom{r}{s}$. *Also $T^0_1(M)$ is called the* **cotangent bundle** *and is denoted by τ^*_M: $T^*M \to M$.*

Since $\mathbf{E}^{**}$ can be identified with $\mathbf{E}$, we may identify $T^1_0(M)$ with TM, the tangent bundle.

We saw in §5 that the zero section of TM may be identified with M. Thus, from 6.11, the zero section of $T^r_s(M)$ may also be identified with M.

Recall from 4.7 that a section of a bundle assigns to each base point b a vector in the fiber over b. In the case of $T^r_s(M)$ these vectors are called **tensors**. Also, the addition and scalar multiplication of sections takes place within each fiber. The C^∞ sections of $\pi: E \to B$ were denoted $\Gamma^\infty(\pi)$, or $\Gamma^\infty(E)$.

6.15. Definition. *A* **tensorfield of type** $\binom{r}{s}$ *on a manifold M is a C^∞ section of $T^r_s(M)$. We denote by $\mathscr{T}^r_s(M)$ the set $\Gamma^\infty(T^r_s(M))$ together with its (infinite-dimensional) real vector space structure. Also we let $\mathscr{F}(M)$ denote the set of mappings from M into $\mathbf{R}$ that are of class C^∞ (the standard local manifold structure being used on $\mathbf{R}$) together with its structure as a ring; namely $f + g$, cf, fg for $f, g \in \mathscr{F}(M)$, $c \in \mathbf{R}$ are given by $(f+g)(x) = f(x) + g(x)$, $(cf)(x) = c(f(x))$ and $(fg)(x) = f(x)\cdot g(x)$. A* **vectorfield** *on M is an element of $\mathscr{X}(M) = \mathscr{T}^1_0(M)$. A* **covectorfield**, *or* **differential 1-form**, *is an element of $\mathscr{X}^*(M) = \mathscr{T}^0_1(M)$.*

Note that for the tangent bundle TM a natural chart is obtained by taking $T\varphi$, where φ is an admissible chart of M. This in turn induces a natural chart $(T\varphi)^r_s = T^r_s\varphi$ for T^r_sM. We shall call these the **natural charts** of T^r_sM. If $t \in \mathscr{T}^r_s(M)$ and $(T^r_s\varphi, \varphi_0)$ is a natural chart, we write ${}_\varphi t$ rather than $t_{T^r_s\varphi, \varphi_0}$ for the local representative. These local representatives lead to the classical notion of tensorfields if we start with a chart (U, φ) of M with range $\varphi(U) = U' \subset \mathbf{R}^n$. For if $\hat{\mathbf{e}}$ is the standard ordered basis of $\mathbf{R}^n$, then

$$ {}_\varphi t(u') = {}_\varphi t^{i_1\cdots i_r}_{j_1\cdots j_s}(u')\mathbf{e}_{i_1} \otimes \cdots \otimes \boldsymbol{\alpha}^{j_s} $$

where ${}_\varphi t^{i_1\cdots i_r}_{j_1\cdots j_s}(u') = {}_\varphi t(u')(\boldsymbol{\alpha}^{i_1}, \ldots, \mathbf{e}_{j_s})$, in the notations of 6.2. Here however, the components of ${}_\varphi t$ relative to $\hat{\mathbf{e}}$ are C^∞ functions.

Also, the algebraic operations on tensors, such as contraction and inner products, all carry over, fiberwise, to tensorfields. For example, if $\boldsymbol{\delta}_m \in T^1_1(T_mM)$ is the Kronecker delta, then $\delta: M \to T^1_1(M): m \rightsquigarrow \boldsymbol{\delta}_m$ is obviously C^∞, and $\delta \in \mathscr{T}^1_1(M)$ is also called the **Kronecker delta**. In addition, the mapping $T^r_s\varphi$ induces an action on tensorfields. We now treat the most important of these extensions explicitly.

6.16. Definition. *If $\varphi: M \to N$ is a diffeomorphism and $t \in \mathscr{T}^r_s(M)$, let $\varphi^*t = (T\varphi)^r_s \circ t \circ \varphi^{-1}$.*

6.17. Proposition. *If $\varphi: M \to N$ is a diffeomorphism, and $t \in \mathscr{T}^r_s(M)$, then (i) $\varphi^*t \in \mathscr{T}^r_s(N)$, and (ii) $\varphi^*: \mathscr{T}^r_s(M) \to \mathscr{T}^r_s(N)$ is a linear isomorphism.*

Proof. (*i*) The differentiability is evident from the composite mapping theorem, 5.7, together with 6.9. (*ii*) This follows at once from 6.4 and 6.13. ∎

6.18. Definition. *If $f \in \mathscr{F}(M)$ and $t \in \mathscr{T}^r_s(M)$, let $ft: M \to T^r_s(M): m \rightsquigarrow f(m)t(m)$. If also $X_i \in \mathscr{X}(M)$, $i = 1, \ldots, s$, $\alpha^j \in \mathscr{X}^*(M)$, $j = 1, \ldots, r$, let*

$$ t(\alpha^1, \ldots, \alpha^r, X_1, \ldots, X_s): M \to \mathbf{R}: m \rightsquigarrow t(m)(\alpha^1(m), \ldots, X_s(m)) $$

If also $t' \in \mathscr{T}^{r'}_{s'}(M)$, let $t \otimes t': M \to T^{r+r'}_{s+s'}(M): m \rightsquigarrow t(m) \otimes t'(m)$.

6.19. Proposition. *With f, t, X_i, α^j, t' as in 6.18, $ft \in \mathscr{T}^r_s(M)$, $t(\alpha^1, \ldots, X_s) \in \mathscr{F}(M)$, and $t \otimes t' \in \mathscr{T}^{r+r'}_{s+s'}$.*

Proof. The differentiability is evident in each case from the product rule 2.11, in local representation. ∎

Finally, we may describe an alternative approach to tensorfields. Suppose $\mathscr{F}(M)$ is defined as above, and $\mathscr{X}(M)$ either our way or some equivalent way (see §8, for example). Then with the "scalar multiplication" $(f, X) \rightsquigarrow fX$ defined in 6.18, $\mathscr{X}(M)$ becomes an $\mathscr{F}(M)$-module. That is, $\mathscr{X}(M)$ is essentially a vector space over $\mathscr{F}(M)$, but the "scalars" $\mathscr{F}(M)$ form only a commutative ring with identity, rather than a field, as $1/f$ may not exist, even if $f \neq 0$. We may thus define

$$L_{\mathscr{F}(M)}(\mathscr{X}(M), \mathscr{F}(M)) = \mathfrak{X}^*(M)$$

the $\mathscr{F}(M)$ linear mappings, and similarly

$$\mathfrak{T}^r_s(M) = L^{r+s}_{\mathscr{F}(M)}(\mathfrak{X}^*(M), \ldots, \mathscr{X}(M); \mathscr{F}(M))$$

the $\mathscr{F}(M)$ multilinear mappings. From 6.17, we have a natural mapping $\mathscr{T}^r_s(M) \to \mathfrak{T}^r_s(M)$, which is an $\mathscr{F}(M)$ linear isomorphism. (See 8.8.)

In any case, the direct sum $\mathscr{T}(M)$ of the $\mathscr{T}^r_s(M)$, including $\mathscr{T}^0_0(M) = \mathscr{F}(M)$, is a real vector space with $\otimes$-product, including $f \otimes t = ft$, a "bigraded $\mathscr{F}(M)$-algebra," called the **tensor algebra** of M, and if $\varphi: M \to N$ is a diffeomorphism, $\varphi^*: \mathscr{T}(M) \to \mathscr{T}(N)$ is an algebra isomorphism.

Exercises

6A. Establish the remarks at the beginning of this section. Describe a norm for $\mathbf{E}^*$; for $T^r_s(\mathbf{E})$.

6B. (i) Define, intrinsically, the contraction of $t \in \mathscr{T}^r_s(M)$ between the ith contravariant and the jth covariant indices.

(ii) Prove 6.5 and interpret in classical tensor language.

6C. Complete the details for 6.10 and 6.11.

6D. The local representative of $t \in \mathscr{T}^r_s(M)$ with respect to a chart (U, φ) if $\varphi^*(t|U)$. Complete the details of 6.17 and 6.19.

Notes

Basic differential theory in the context of Banach spaces is the subject of Dieudonné [1] and Lang [1]. Our treatment follows theirs, except that we restrict to the finite-dimensional case, and the definitions of vector bundle and the tangent functor are given in the spirit of Eilenberg–Cartan [1] for expository reasons. The same material is covered in more classical fashion in many standard references, such as Bishop–Crittenden [1], Hicks [1], Chevalley [1], Helgason [1], Sternberg [1], and Nomizu–Kobayashi [1]. Among elementary books, the definition of derivative we use is found in Lang [2] and Fleming [1].

CHAPTER II

CALCULUS ON MANIFOLDS

Certainly the mathematical topic of widest practical use is calculus. For many applications, and this book is an example, it is essential to use calculus in the large. In spite of its importance and usefulness, this subject has not yet found its way into the standard applied mathematics curriculum, and regrettably not all of its basic topics can be found in any single text. In this chapter we outline that part of the subject which is basic to the applications to mechanics of the succeeding chapters.

§7. VECTORFIELDS AS DYNAMICAL SYSTEMS

Recall (6.15) that a vectorfield on a manifold M is a mapping $M \to TM$ that assigns to each point $m \in M$ a vector in T_mM. A vectorfield may be interpreted alternatively as the right-hand side of a system of first-order ordinary differential equations in the large, a dynamical system. In this section we develop this interpretation and discuss the basic existence and uniqueness theorems for the integral of the system.

Recall that a curve c at a point m of a manifold M is a C^1 map from an open interval I of $\mathbf{R}$ into M such that $0 \in I$ and $c(0) = m$. For such a curve we may assign a tangent vector at each point $c(\lambda)$, $\lambda \in I$, by $c'(\lambda) = Tc(\lambda, 1)$ (see §5).

7.1. Definition. *Let M be a manifold and $X \in \mathscr{X}(M)$ (see §6). An* **integral curve of** X **at** $m \in M$ *is a curve c at m such that $X(c(\lambda)) = c'(\lambda)$ for each $\lambda \in I$.*

We now express the condition that c be an integral curve of X in terms of local representatives with respect to natural charts. Let (U, φ) be a chart of M and suppose the image of c is contained in U. Then the local representative of c with respect to the identity of $\mathbf{R}$ and (U, φ) is $c_\varphi = \varphi \circ c$, while the local representative of the curve c' with respect to the identity of $\mathbf{R}$ and the natural chart $(TM|U, T\varphi)$ is given by

$$\begin{aligned}(c')_\varphi(\lambda) &= T\varphi \circ c'(\lambda) = T\varphi \circ Tc(\lambda, 1)\\ &= T(\varphi \circ c)(\lambda, 1) = (c_\varphi)'(\lambda)\end{aligned}$$

by the composite mapping theorem (5.7). Also, the local representative of $X \circ c$ with respect to the identity of $\mathbf{R}$ and the natural chart $T\varphi$ is

$$T\varphi \circ X \circ c = T\varphi \circ X \circ \varphi^{-1} \circ \varphi \circ c = X_\varphi \circ c_\varphi$$

where X_φ is the local representative of X. Thus c is an integral curve of X iff $X \circ c = c'$ iff $X_\varphi \circ c_\varphi = c'_\varphi$ iff c_φ is an integral curve of X_φ. This condition takes a simple form if $\varphi(U) \subset \mathbf{R}^n$. Then we have $X_\varphi(y) = (y; X_1(y), \ldots, X_n(y))$ where $y \in \varphi(U) \subset \mathbf{R}^n$, $\{X_i(y)\}$ are the components of X_φ, $c_\varphi(\lambda) = (c_1(\lambda), \ldots, c_n(\lambda))$, $c'_\varphi(\lambda) = (c(\lambda); c'_1(\lambda), \ldots, c'_n(\lambda))$, and $X_\varphi \circ c_\varphi = c'_\varphi$ iff $c'_i(\lambda) = X_i(c(\lambda))$ for $i = 1, \ldots, n$ and all $\lambda \in I$. Thus c is an integral curve of X iff the local representatives satisfy the system of first-order ordinary differential equations

$$\begin{cases} c'_1(\lambda) = X_1(c^1(\lambda), \ldots, c^n(\lambda)) \\ \vdots \\ c'_n(\lambda) = X_n(c^1(\lambda), \ldots, c^n(\lambda)) \end{cases}$$

Note that λ does not appear explicitly on the right. Such a system of equations (a **local dynamical system**) includes regular equations of higher order (see Coddington–Levinson [1, p. 21]) and the Hamiltonian equations of motion as special cases.

For a system of ordinary differential equations there are well-known existence and uniqueness theorems. The form that we shall need is the following.

7.2. Theorem. *Let $X: U \subset \mathbf{R}^n \to \mathbf{R}^n$ be of class C^∞. For each $x_0 \in \mathbf{R}^n$, there is a curve $c: I \to U$ at x_0 such that $c'(\lambda) = X(c(\lambda))$ for all $\lambda \in I$. Any two such curves are equal on the intersection of their domains. Moreover, there is a neighborhood U_0 of $x_0 \in U$, a real number $a > 0$, and a C^∞ mapping $F: U_0 \times I \to \mathbf{R}^n$ where $I = (-a, a)$ such that $c_u = F|\{u\} \times I: I \to \mathbf{R}^n$ is a curve at $u \subset \mathbf{R}^n$ satisfying the differential equation $c'_u(\lambda) = X(c(\lambda))$ for all $\lambda \in I$.*

For a proof, see Coddington–Levinson [1, p. 22] or Dieudonné [1, p. 300].

The foregoing theorem is local, and in general does not permit global statements about the **global dynamical system** $c' = X \circ c$ on a manifold.

The mapping F gives a locally unique integral curve c_u for each $u \in U_0$, and for each $\lambda \in I$, $F_\lambda = F|(U_0 \times \{\lambda\})$ maps U_0 to some other set. It is convenient to think of each point u being allowed to "flow for time λ" along the integral curve c_u (see Figure 7-1).

This is a picture of a U_0 "flowing," and the system (U_0, a, F) is a local flow of X, or *flow box*. The analogous situation on a manifold is given by the following.

7.3. Definition. *Let M be a manifold and X a vectorfield on M. A* **flow box of** *X* **at** *$m \in M$ is a triple (U_0, a, F) where*

(i) *$U_0 \subset M$ is open, $m \in U_0$, and $a \in \mathbf{R}$, $a > 0$ or $a = +\infty$;*
(ii) *$F: U_0 \times I_a \to M$ is of class C^∞ where $I_a = (-a, a)$;*
(iii) *$F|\{u\} \times I_a: I_a \to M$ is an integral curve of X at $u \in M$ for all $u \in U_0$;*

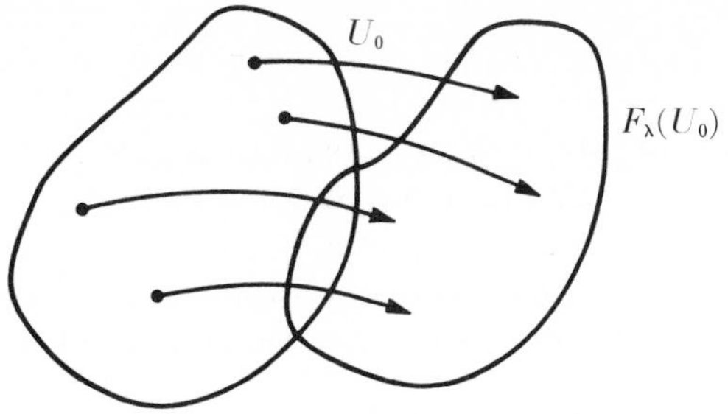

Figure 7-1

(iv) $F_\lambda = F|U_0 \times \{\lambda\}$: $U_0 \to F_\lambda(U_0) \subset M$, *for* $\lambda \in I_a$ *has* $F_\lambda(U_0)$ *open, and* F_λ *is a diffeomorphism.*

Before proving the existence of a flow box, it is convenient first to establish the following, which concerns uniqueness.

7.4. Proposition. *Suppose* c_1 *and* c_2 *are two integral curves of* X *at* $m \in M$. *Then* $c_1 = c_2$ *on the intersection of their domains.*

Proof. This does not follow at once from 7.2 for c_1 and c_2 may lie in different charts. Indeed, if the manifold is not Hausdorff, examples show that this proposition is false. Suppose $c_1 : I_1 \to M$ and $c_2 : I_2 \to M$. Let $I = I_1 \cap I_2$, and let $K = \{\lambda | \lambda \in I \text{ and } c_1(\lambda) = c_2(\lambda)\}$. From A1.7, K is closed, since M is Hausdorff. We will now show that K is open. From 7.2, K contains some neighborhood of 0. For $\lambda \in K$ consider c_1^λ and c_2^λ where $c^\lambda(t) = c(\lambda + t)$. Then c_1^λ and c_2^λ are integral curves at $c_1(\lambda) = c_2(\lambda)$. Again by 7.2 they agree on some neighborhood of 0. Thus some neighborhood of λ lies in K, and so K is open. Since I is connected, $K = I$ (§A7). ∎

The next two propositions give elementary properties of flow boxes.

7.5. Proposition. *Suppose* (U_0, a, F) *is a triple satisfying (i), (ii), and (iii) of 7.3. Then for* $\lambda, \mu, \lambda + \mu \in I_a$ *we have* $F_{\lambda+\mu} = F_\lambda \circ F_\mu = F_\mu \circ F_\lambda$, *and* F_0 *is the identity map. Moreover, if* $U_\lambda = F_\lambda(U_0)$ *and* $U_\lambda \cap U_0 \neq \phi$, *then* $F_\lambda|U_{-\lambda} \cap U_0$: $U_{-\lambda} \cap U_0 \to U_0 \cap U_\lambda$ *is a diffeomorphism and its inverse is* $F_{-\lambda}|U_0 \cap U_\lambda$.

Proof. $F_{\lambda+\mu}(u) = c_u(\lambda + \mu)$ where c_u is the integral curve defined by F at u. But $d(\lambda) = F_\lambda(F_\mu(u) = F_\lambda(c_u(\mu))$ is the integral curve through $c_u(\mu)$, and $f(t) = c_u(t + \mu)$ is also an integral curve at $c_u(\mu)$. Hence, by 7.4 we have $F_\lambda(F_\mu(u)) = c_u(\lambda + \mu) = F_{\lambda+\mu}(u)$. For $F_{\lambda+\mu} = F_\mu \circ F_\lambda$ merely note $F_{\lambda+\mu} = F_{\mu+\lambda} = F_\mu \circ F_\lambda$. By a similar uniqueness argument, F_0 is easily seen to be the identity. Finally, the last statement is an easy consequence of $F_\lambda \circ F_{-\lambda} = F_{-\lambda} \circ F_\lambda =$ identity. Note, however, that $F_\lambda(U_0) \cap U_0 = \phi$ can occur. ∎

The following will be left as an easy exercise for the reader. (It does not correspond to the reversibility of a mechanical system.)

7.6. Proposition. *If (U_0, a, F) is a flow box for X, then (U_0, a, F_-) is a flow box for $-X$, where $F_-(u, \lambda) = F(u, -\lambda)$, and $(-X)(m) = -(X(m))$.*

7.7. Theorem (Uniqueness of flow boxes). *Suppose (U_0, a, F), (U'_0, a', F') are two flow boxes at $m \in M$. Then F and F' are equal on $(U_0 \cap U'_0) \times (I_a \cap I_{a'})$.*

Proof. Again we emphasize that this does not follow at once from 7.2, for U_0, U'_0 need not be chart domains. However, for each $u \in U_0 \cap U'_0$ we have $F|\{u\} \times I = F'|\{u\} \times I$ where $I = I_a \cap I_{a'}$. This follows from 7.4 and 7.3 (*iii*). Hence $F = F'$ on $(U_0 \cap U'_0) \times I$. ∎

Clearly uniqueness depends only on (*i*) and (*iii*) of 7.3.

7.8. Theorem (Existence of flow boxes). *Let X be a vectorfield on a manifold M. For each $m \in M$ there is a flow box of X at m.*

Proof. Let (U, φ) be a chart in M with $m \in U$. It is enough to establish the result in $\varphi(U)$ by means of the local representation. That is, let (U'_0, a, F') be a flow box of X_φ at $\varphi(m)$ as given by 7.2, with

$$U'_0 \subset U' = \varphi(U) \quad \text{and} \quad F'(U'_0 \times I_a) \subset U', \quad U_0 = \varphi^{-1}(U'_0)$$

and

$$F: U_0 \times I_a \to u: (u, \lambda) \rightsquigarrow \varphi^{-1}(F'(\varphi_u, \lambda))$$

Since F is continuous $\exists b \in (0, a) \subset \mathbf{R}$ and $V_0 \subset U_0$ open, $m \in V_0$, such that $F(V_0 \times I_b) \subset U_0$. We contend that (V_0, b, F) is a flow box at m (where F is understood as the restriction of F to $V_0 \times I_b$). Only (*iv*) need be established, that is, F_λ is a diffeomorphism. From 7.5 we have that F_λ, for $\lambda \in I_b$, has a C^∞ inverse given by $F_{-\lambda}$ as $V_\lambda \cap U_0 = V_\lambda$. From the inverse mapping theorem (2.10) it follows that $F_\lambda(V_0)$ is open. And, since F_λ and $F_{-\lambda}$ are both of class C^∞, F_λ is a diffeomorphism. ∎

7.9. Theorem. *Let X be a vectorfield on a manifold M and suppose, for some $m \in M$, $X(m) \neq \mathbf{0}$. Then there is a local chart (U, φ) with $m \in U$ so that*

(*i*) *$\varphi(U) = V \times I \subset \mathbf{R}^{n-1} \times \mathbf{R}$, $V \subset \mathbf{R}^{n-1}$ open, and*

$$I = (-a, a) \subset \mathbf{R}, \qquad a > 0$$

(*ii*) *$\varphi^{-1}|\{v\} \times I: I \to M$ is an integral curve of X at $\varphi^{-1}(v)$, for all $v \in V$;*

(*iii*) *the local representative X_φ has the form $X_\varphi(y, \lambda) = (\mathbf{0}, 1)$.*

Proof. If X(m) $\neq 0$, there exists a local chart (U_0, ω) of M at m such that $X(m') \neq \mathbf{0}$ for all $m' \in U_0$, $\omega(U_0) = U'_0 \subset \mathbf{R}^n$, and $\omega(m) = \mathbf{0}$. Let α be a linear isomorphism such that $\alpha(X_\omega(m)) = (0, \ldots, 0, 1)$, where X_ω is the local representative of X relative to $(\omega, T\omega)$. Let $\psi = \alpha \circ \omega$, then (U_0, ψ) is a local chart at $m \in M$ and $X_\psi(\mathbf{0}) = (0, \ldots, 0, 1)$. Now let (U'_1, b, F) be a flow box of X_ψ at $\mathbf{0}$, where $U'_1 = V_0 \times I_c \subset \mathbf{R}^{n-1} \times \mathbf{R} \approx \mathbf{R}^n$, $I_c = (-c, c)$, $c > 0$, and $F(U'_1 \times I_b) \subset U'_0$. If $f_0 = F|(V_0 \times \{0\}) \times I_b : V_0 \times I_b \to U'_0$, we see that $Df_0(\mathbf{0}, 0)$ is a linear isomorphism because $X_\psi(\mathbf{0}) = (0, \ldots, 0, 1)$. Thus by the inverse mapping theorem (2.10) there is an open neighborhood $V \times I_a$ of $(\mathbf{0}, 0) \in V_0 \times I_b$ such that $f = f_0|V \times I_a$ is a diffeomorphism onto an open set $U' \subset U'_0$. Let $U = \psi^{-1}(U')$, and $\varphi = f^{-1} \circ \psi$. Then (U, φ) is a chart at $m \in M$ with $\varphi(U) = V \times I_a \subset \mathbf{R}^{n-1} \times \mathbf{R} \approx \mathbf{R}^n$. By construction, $\varphi^{-1} = \psi \circ f$ so $\varphi^{-1}|\{v\} \times I_a$ is an integral curve, and (*iii*) follows from (*ii*). ■

7.10. Definition. *Given a manifold M and a vectorfield X on M, let $\mathscr{D}_X \subset M \times \mathbf{R}$ be the set of $(m, \lambda) \in M \times \mathbf{R}$ such that there is an integral curve $c: I \to M$ of X at m with $\lambda \in I$. The vectorfield X is* **complete** *iff $\mathscr{D}_X = M \times \mathbf{R}$. Also, a point $m \in M$ is called* **σ complete**, *where $\sigma = +, -,$ or $\pm$, iff $\mathscr{D}_X \cap (\{m\} \times \mathbf{R})$ contains all $t > 0$, $t < 0$, or $t \in \mathbf{R}$, respectively.*

Thus, X is complete iff each integral curve can be extended so that its domain becomes $(-\infty, \infty)$.

7.11. Examples. For $M = \mathbf{R}^2$ (a local manifold) let X be the constant vectorfield $(0, 1)$. Then X is complete. However, $\mathbf{R}^2 \setminus \{\mathbf{0}\}$, with the same definition for X, is not complete. For $M = \mathbf{R}$, let X be the vectorfield for which

$$c: (-\pi/2, \pi/2) \to \mathbf{R}: \theta \rightsquigarrow c(\theta) = \tan\theta$$

is the integral curve. Then X is not complete.

7.12. Proposition. *Let M be a manifold and $X \in \mathscr{X}(M)$. Then*

(*i*) *$\mathscr{D}_X \supset M \times \{0\}$;*
(*ii*) *$\mathscr{D}_X$ is open in $M \times \mathbf{R}$;*
(*iii*) *there is a unique mapping $F_X: \mathscr{D}_X \to M$ such that the mapping $t \rightsquigarrow F_X(m, t)$ is an integral curve at m, for all $m \in M$.*

Proof. Parts (*i*) and (*ii*) follow at once from the flow box existence theorem, and (*iii*) by the uniqueness of integral curves. ■

Thus, by 7.7 F_X is smooth, and for X complete, (M, ∞, F_X) is a flow box.

7.13. Definition. *Let M be a manifold and $X \in \mathscr{X}(M)$. Then the mapping F_X defined in 7.12 is called the* **integral** *of X, and the curve $t \rightsquigarrow F_X(m, t)$ is called the* **maximal integral curve** *of X at m. In case X is complete, F_X is called the* **flow** *of X.*

Thus, from 7.5, if X is complete with flow F, then the set $\{F_t | t \in \mathbf{R}\}$ is a group of diffeomorphisms on M, sometimes called a **one-parameter group of diffeomorphisms.** The following is a useful criterion for completeness. (See §A4 for a discussion of compactness.)

7.14. Theorem. *Suppose M is a compact manifold and X is a vectorfield on M. Then X is complete.*

Proof. For $m \in M$ consider a maximal integral curve φ through m. Suppose the resultant domain is (a, b), and $b \neq +\infty$. Then find a sequence $b_n \to b$. By compactness of M some subsequence of $\varphi(b_n)$ converges, say, to c. (The limit point c is unique since M is assumed Hausdorff.) Construct a flow box about c. But for some n, $\varphi(b_n)$ lies in this flow box region. Hence φ can be extended in domain beyond b, as in 7.4. The argument for the lower limit is similar. ∎

The same argument also gives the following.

7.15. Corollary. *A vectorfield with compact support on a manifold M is complete.*

For further criteria for completeness we refer the reader to Lang [1, p. 66]. Note that compactness is not a necessary condition for completeness (7.11).

Exercises

7A. Use the example of Appendix A, Exercise D, to show that the Hausdorff assumption in 7.4 cannot be dropped.

7B. Complete the details of 7.5 and 7.12 and prove 7.6.

7C. Let M and N be manifolds and $f: M \to N$ a diffeomorphism; suppose $X \in \mathscr{X}(M)$ and $c: I \to M$ is an integral curve of X at $m \in M$. Then show $\varphi \circ c$ is an integral curve of $\varphi^* X$ at $\varphi(m)$. How are the (local) flows related?

§8. VECTORFIELDS AS DIFFERENTIAL OPERATORS

In this section we shall show how a vectorfield X on a manifold induces a differential operator $\mathbf{L}_X$ on the full tensor algebra $\mathscr{T}(M)$, called the *Lie derivative*. Our development of this aspect of vectorfields departs from the spirit of the previous sections in that it is special to the finite-dimensional case. Our definition, inspired by a theorem of Willmore, is adopted for reasons of efficiency. For the definition and the treatment of the infinite-dimensional case we refer the interested reader to Lang [1]. At the end of this section, however, we show that the two definitions coincide (in the finite-dimensional case).

We shall begin by defining $\mathbf{L}_X$ on $\mathscr{F}(M)$ and $\mathscr{X}(M)$, and then use a unique extension theorem to define $\mathbf{L}_X$ on $\mathscr{T}(M)$.

8.1. Definition. *Let $f \in \mathscr{F}(M)$ so that*

$$Tf: TM \to T\mathbf{R} = \mathbf{R} \times \mathbf{R}$$

and

$$T_m f = Tf \mid T_m M \in L(T_m M, \{f(m)\} \times \mathbf{R})$$

We then define $df: M \to T^*(M)$ by $df(m) = P_2 \circ T_m f$ where P_2 denotes the projection onto the second factor. We call df the **differential** *of f.*

For $X \in \mathscr{X}(M)$, *define* $\mathbf{L}_X f\colon M \to \mathbf{R}$ *by* $\mathbf{L}_X f(m) = df(m)[X(m)]$. *We call* $\mathbf{L}_X f$ *the* **Lie derivative of** f **with respect to** X.

8.2. Proposition. (*i*) *For* $f \in \mathscr{F}(M)$, $df \in \mathscr{X}^*(M)$, *and for* $X \in \mathscr{X}(M)$, $df(X) = P_2 \circ Tf \circ X$; *that is*, $df(X)(m) = P_2 \cdot T_m f(X(m))$.

(*ii*) *For* $f \in \mathscr{F}(M)$ *and* $X \in \mathscr{X}(M)$ *we have* $\mathbf{L}_X f \in \mathscr{F}(M)$.

Proof. For (*i*), we need only to show df is smooth. Let (U, φ) be an (admissible) chart on M so that the local representative of df in the natural charts is $(df)_\varphi = \varphi_1^0 \circ df \circ \varphi^{-1}\colon U' \to U' \times \mathbf{E}^*$, where $\varphi\colon U \subset M \to U' \subset \mathbf{E}$. Then

$$(df)_\varphi(u') \cdot \mathbf{e} = (T_u\varphi)_1^0 \circ df(u) \cdot \mathbf{e} = (T_u\varphi)_1^0 \circ P_2 \circ T_u f \cdot \mathbf{e} = P_2 \circ T_u f(T_{u'}\varphi^{-1} \cdot \mathbf{e})$$
$$= P_2 \circ T_{u'}(f \circ \varphi^{-1}) \cdot \mathbf{e} = D(f \circ \varphi^{-1})(u') \cdot \mathbf{e},$$

by 6.3, the composite mapping theorem 5.7(*i*), and 2.4. Hence $(df)_\varphi$ is of class C^∞ and (*i*) is established. Then (*ii*) follows at once for $\mathbf{L}_X f = df(X)$. (See 6.19.) ∎

8.3. Proposition. (*i*) *Suppose* $\varphi\colon M \to N$ *is a diffeomorphism* (3.8). *Then* $\mathbf{L}_X$ *is* **natural with respect to** φ^* (6.16). *That is, for each* $f \in \mathscr{F}(M)$, $\mathbf{L}_{\varphi^* X}(\varphi^* f) = \varphi^* \mathbf{L}_X f$; *or the following diagram commutes:*

$$\begin{array}{ccc} \mathscr{F}(M) & \xrightarrow{\varphi^*} & \mathscr{F}(N) \\ \Big\downarrow \mathbf{L}_X & & \Big\downarrow \mathbf{L}_{\varphi^* X} \\ \mathscr{F}(M) & \xrightarrow[\varphi^*]{} & \mathscr{F}(N) \end{array}$$

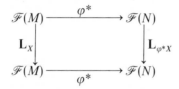

(*ii*) $\mathbf{L}_X$ *is* **natural with respect to restrictions**. *That is, for* U *open in* M *and* $f \in \mathscr{F}(M)$, $\mathbf{L}_{X|U}(f|U) = (\mathbf{L}_X f)|U$; *or, if* $|U\colon \mathscr{F}(M) \to \mathscr{F}(U)$ *denotes restriction to* U, *the following diagram commutes:*

$$\begin{array}{ccc} \mathscr{F}(M) & \xrightarrow{|U} & \mathscr{F}(U) \\ \Big\downarrow \mathbf{L}_X & & \Big\downarrow \mathbf{L}_{X|U} \\ \mathscr{F}(M) & \xrightarrow[|U]{} & \mathscr{F}(U) \end{array}$$

Proof. For (*i*), let $n = f(m)$. Then

$$\mathbf{L}_{\varphi^* X}(\varphi^* f)(n) = d(f \circ \varphi^{-1}) \cdot \varphi^* X(n) = P_2 \circ T_n(f \circ \varphi^{-1}) \circ T_m\varphi \circ X \circ \varphi^{-1}(n)$$
$$= P_2(T_m f) \cdot X \cdot \varphi^{-1}(n) = \varphi^* \mathbf{L}_X f(n)$$

by 5.7(*iii*). Then (*ii*) follows from the fact that $d(f|U) = (df)|U$, which is clear from the definition of d. ∎

To show that $\mathbf{L}_X$ has the "Leibnitz rule" of derivatives, we use 2.11.

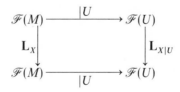

8.4. Proposition. *(i)* $\mathbf{L}_X\colon \mathscr{F}(M) \to \mathscr{F}(M)$ *is a* **derivation** *on the algebra* $\mathscr{F}(M)$. *That is,* $\mathbf{L}_X$ *is* $\mathbf{R}$ *linear and for* $f, g \in \mathscr{F}(M)$, $\mathbf{L}_X(fg) = (\mathbf{L}_X f)g + f(\mathbf{L}_X g)$.

(ii) If c is a constant function, $\mathbf{L}_X c = 0$.

Proof. By 8.3 *(ii)* it is enough to verify *(i)* in a chart (U, φ). Then the local representative of $\mathbf{L}_X(fg)$ is

$$\begin{aligned}\mathbf{L}_X(fg) \circ \varphi^{-1}(u') &= (d(fg)X) \circ \varphi^{-1}(u')\\ &= P_2 T_u(fg) T_u(\varphi^{-1}) \cdot T_u \varphi X \varphi^{-1}(u')\\ &= D_{u'}((fg) \circ \varphi^{-1}) \cdot X_\varphi(u')\end{aligned}$$

by the proof of 8.2 *(i)*. But $(fg) \circ \varphi^{-1} = (f \circ \varphi^{-1})(g \circ \varphi^{-1})$ and the result follows at once from 2.11. The result *(ii)* is a general property of derivations. Let 1 be the constant function with value 1. Then $\mathbf{L}_X(1) = \mathbf{L}_X(1^2) = 1 \cdot \mathbf{L}_X 1 + 1 \cdot \mathbf{L}_X 1$. Hence $\mathbf{L}_X(1) = 0$. Then $\mathbf{L}_X(c) = \mathbf{L}_X(c \cdot 1) = c\mathbf{L}_X(1) = 0$ by $\mathbf{R}$ linearity of $\mathbf{L}_X$. ∎

8.5. Corollary. *For* $f, g \in \mathscr{F}(M)$ *we have* $d(fg) = (df)g + f(dg)$, *and if c is constant,* $dc = 0$.

We saw that, in §6, the tensor product has a natural extension to $\mathscr{T}(M)$. Then 8.4 and 8.5 become

$$\mathbf{L}_X(f \otimes g) = \mathbf{L}_X f \otimes g + f \otimes \mathbf{L}_X g \in \mathscr{F}(M)$$

$$d(f \otimes g) = df \otimes g + f \otimes dg \in \mathscr{X}^*(M)$$

8.6. Proposition. *If* $\alpha_m \in T_m^* M$, *there is an* $f \in \mathscr{F}(M)$ *such that* $df(m) = \alpha_m$.

Proof. Let $\varphi\colon U \to U' \subset \mathbf{R}^n$ be a chart at $m \in M$ such that U' contains a sphere of radius 2 about $\varphi(m) = 0$. This clearly can be done by composing φ with a translation and a magnification if necessary. Construct the following *bump function on* $\mathbf{R}^n$.

$$h(\mathbf{x}) = \begin{cases} 1 & \|\mathbf{x}\| \le 1 \\ \theta(\|\mathbf{x}\| - 1) & 1 < \|\mathbf{x}\| < 2 \\ 0 & \|\mathbf{x}\| \ge 2 \end{cases}$$

where θ was given in 2.8. Then $h \in \mathscr{F}(\mathbf{R}^n)$. Let $\beta = \varphi^* \alpha_m$ and $g \in \mathscr{F}(U')$ be given by $g = P_2 \circ \beta | U'$ where P_2 is the projection onto the second factor. Then $dg(u') = P_2 \circ \beta$. Then let $f \in \mathscr{F}(M)$ be given by

$$f(u) = \begin{cases} [h \circ \varphi(u)] \cdot [g \circ \varphi(u)] & \text{if } u \in U \\ 0 & \text{if } u \notin U \end{cases}$$

Hence

$$\begin{aligned} df(m)\cdot\mathbf{e} &= d([h\cdot\varphi(m)][g\circ\varphi(u)])\cdot\mathbf{e} \\ &= d(g\circ\varphi(u))\cdot\mathbf{e} \qquad \text{(by 8.5)} \\ &= P_2\circ\beta\circ T_u\varphi(\mathbf{e}) \\ &= P_2\circ(\varphi^{-1})^*\beta(u)(\mathbf{e}) \\ &= \alpha_m(\mathbf{e}) \qquad \blacksquare \end{aligned}$$

Using *partitions of unity* (§11), we have the following generalization of the foregoing bump function.

8.7. Proposition. *Let M be a manifold and U, V, two open sets on M such that $U^c \subset V$ (see §A1). Then there is an $h \in \mathscr{F}(M)$ so that*

$$h(x) = \begin{cases} 1 & \text{if} \quad x \in U \\ 0 & \text{if} \quad x \notin V \end{cases}$$

For the proof, see A6.2.

We saw in §6 that tensorfields can be regarded as $\mathscr{F}(M)$ multilinear maps of $\mathscr{X}^*(M)$, $\mathscr{X}(M)$ into $\mathscr{F}(M)$. Actually, this association is an isomorphism, according to the following.

8.8. Theorem. *$\mathscr{T}^r_s(M)$ is isomorphic to the $\mathscr{F}(M)$ multilinear maps from $\mathscr{X}^*(M) \times \cdots \times \mathscr{X}(M)$ into $\mathscr{F}(M)$, regarded as $\mathscr{F}(M)$ modules or as real vector spaces.*

Proof. Being $\mathbf{R}$-isomorphic follows from being $\mathscr{F}(M)$ isomorphic. We consider then the map $\mathscr{T}^r_s(M) \to L_{\mathscr{F}(M)}(\mathscr{X}^*(M), \ldots, \mathscr{X}(M); \mathscr{F}(M))$ given by $l(\alpha^1, \ldots, \alpha^r, X_1, \ldots, X_s)(m) = l(m)(\alpha^1(m), \ldots, X_s(m))$. This map is clearly $\mathscr{F}(M)$ linear. To show it is an isomorphism, given such a multilinear map l, define t by $t(m)(\alpha^1(m), \ldots, X_s(m)) = l(\alpha^1, \ldots, X_s)(m)$. To show this is well defined we must show that, for each $v_0 \in T_m(M)$, there is an $X \in \mathscr{X}(M)$ so $X(m) = v_0$, and similarly for dual vectors. Let (U, φ) be a chart at m and let $T_m\varphi(v_0) = (m, v_0')$. Define $Y \in \mathscr{X}(U')$ by $Y(u) = (u, v_0')$, on a neighborhood V_1 of m. Extend Y to U' so Y is zero outside V_2, where $V_1 \subset V_2^c \subset U'$, by means of a bump function. Then X is defined by $X_\varphi = Y$ on U, and $X = 0$ outside U. Then $X(m) = v_0$. The construction is similar for dual vectors. Also, $t(m)$ so defined is evidently C^∞ from its local representative, for t_φ is

$$t(m)(\underline{\alpha}^{i_1}(m), \ldots, \underline{e}_{j_s}(m))\underline{e}_{i_1} \otimes \cdots \otimes \underline{\alpha}^{j_s}$$

where $\{\mathbf{e}_1, \ldots, \mathbf{e}_n\}$ is a basis of $\mathbf{R}^n \supset \varphi(U)$, $\underline{e}_i(m) = T_m\varphi^{-1}(m, \mathbf{e}_i)$ and $\underline{\alpha}^i$ is dual to $\underline{e}_i$. Finally, the above two maps are inverses and hence each is an isomorphism. $\blacksquare$

Returning to the Lie derivative, we have the following property, which is often taken as an alternative definition for $\mathscr{X}(M)$.

8.9. Proposition. *The collection of operators* $\mathbf{L}_X$ *on* $\mathscr{F}(M)$ *forms a real vector space and* $\mathscr{F}(M)$ *module, with* $(f\mathbf{L}_X)(g) = f(\mathbf{L}_X g)$, *and is isomorphic to* $\mathscr{X}(M)$ *as a real vector space and as an* $\mathscr{F}(M)$ *module. In particular,* $\mathbf{L}_X = 0$ *iff* $X = 0$; *and* $\mathbf{L}_{fX} = f\mathbf{L}_X$.

Proof. Consider the map $\sigma\colon X \leadsto \mathbf{L}_X$. It is obviously $\mathbf{R}$ and $\mathscr{F}(M)$ linear, as

$$\mathbf{L}_{X_1 + fX_2} = \mathbf{L}_{X_1} + f\mathbf{L}_{X_2}$$

(see 8.1). To show that it is one-to-one, we must show $\mathbf{L}_X = 0$ implies $X = 0$. But if $\mathbf{L}_X f(m) = 0$, then $df(m)X(m) = 0$ for all f. Hence, by 8.6 $\alpha_m X(m) = 0$ for all $\alpha_m \in T_m^*(M)$. Thus $X(m) = 0$ (§6). ∎

8.10. Theorem. *The collection of all* ($\mathbf{R}$ *linear) derivations on* $\mathscr{F}(M)$ (8.4) *form a real vector space isomorphic to* $\mathscr{X}(M)$ *as a real vector space. In particular, for each derivation* $\boldsymbol{\theta}$ *there is a unique* $X \in \mathscr{X}(M)$ *such that* $\boldsymbol{\theta} = \mathbf{L}_X$.

Proof. From 8.9 it is enough to establish the last assertion. First of all, $\boldsymbol{\theta}$ induces an $\mathbf{R}$ linear derivation on $\mathscr{F}(U)$ for any open subset U of M. This is done as follows: for $f \in \mathscr{F}(U)$ and $m \in U$, extend f to $\tilde{f}_m \in \mathscr{F}(M)$ by means of a bump function so that $\tilde{f}_m$ agrees with f on a neighborhood of m. Put $(\boldsymbol{\theta}|U)f(m) = \boldsymbol{\theta}(\tilde{f}_m)(m)$. Since $\boldsymbol{\theta}(c) = 0$, if c is constant, $\boldsymbol{\theta}|U$ is defined independent of the extension. We shall still use $\boldsymbol{\theta}$ for $\boldsymbol{\theta}|U$. Now for a chart (U, φ), $m \in U$ and $f \in \mathscr{F}(M)$, where $\varphi\colon U \to U' \subset \mathbf{R}^n$, we can write, for $\mathbf{x} \in U'$ and $\mathbf{a} = \varphi(m)$

$$(\varphi^* f)(\mathbf{x}) = (\varphi^* f)(\mathbf{a}) + \int_0^1 \frac{\partial}{\partial t}(\varphi^* f)[\mathbf{a} + t(\mathbf{x} - \mathbf{a})]\, dt$$

$$= (\varphi^* f)(\mathbf{a}) + \sum_{i=1}^{n} (x^j - a^j) \int_0^1 (\varphi^* f)_{,j}[\mathbf{a} + t(\mathbf{x} - \mathbf{a})]\, dt$$

where

$$\mathbf{x} = (x^1, \ldots, x^n), \quad \mathbf{a} = (a^1, \ldots, a^n), \quad \text{and} \quad (\varphi^* f)_{,j} = \frac{\partial(\varphi^* f)}{\partial x^j}$$

This formula holds in some neighborhood $\varphi(V)$ of $\mathbf{a}$. Hence, for $u \in V$ we have

$$f(u) = f(m) + \sum_{i=1}^{n} (\varphi^i(u) - a^i)g^i(u)$$

where $g_i \in \mathscr{F}(V)$ and

$$g_i(m) = \left.\frac{\partial(\varphi^* f)}{\partial x^i}\right|_a$$

Hence

$$\begin{aligned}\boldsymbol{\theta} f(m) &= \sum_{i=1}^{n} g_i(m)\boldsymbol{\theta}(\varphi^i)(m)\\ &= \sum_{i=1}^{n} \frac{\partial}{\partial x^i}(\varphi^* f)(a)\boldsymbol{\theta}(\varphi^i)(m)\end{aligned}$$

and this is independent of the chart. Now define X on U by its local representative

$$X_\varphi(\mathbf{x}) = (\mathbf{x}, \boldsymbol{\theta}(\varphi^1)(u), \ldots, \boldsymbol{\theta}(\varphi^n)(u))$$

where $\mathbf{x} = \varphi(u) \in U'$. We leave, as an exercise, that $X|U$ is independent of the chart φ and hence $X \in \mathscr{X}(M)$. Then, for $f \in \mathscr{F}(M)$, the local representative of $\mathbf{L}_X f$ is

$$D(f \circ \varphi^{-1})(\mathbf{x}) \cdot X_\varphi(\mathbf{x}) = \sum_{i=1}^{n} \frac{\partial}{\partial x^i}(f \circ \varphi^{-1})(u)\boldsymbol{\theta}(\varphi^i)(\mathbf{x}) = \boldsymbol{\theta} f(u)$$

(see §2). Hence $\mathbf{L}_X = \boldsymbol{\theta}$. Finally, uniqueness is contained in 8.3. ∎

From 8.10 we may say that the differential operators $\partial/\partial x^i$, in any chart (U, φ) form a basis of the space of derivations at a point m. Hence any vectorfield can be uniquely represented by

$$\mathbf{L}_X f(m) = \sum_{i=1}^{n} \left\{ \frac{\partial(f \circ \varphi^{-1})}{\partial x^i}\bigg|_{\varphi(m)} \right\} \mathbf{L}_X(\varphi^i)(m)$$

This provides another connection with the classical notion of tensor.

8.11. Proposition. *If X and Y are vectorfields on M then $[\mathbf{L}_X, \mathbf{L}_Y] = \mathbf{L}_X \circ \mathbf{L}_Y - \mathbf{L}_Y \circ \mathbf{L}_X$ is an ($\mathbf{R}$ linear) derivation on $\mathscr{F}(M)$.*

Proof. More generally, let $\boldsymbol{\theta}_1$ and $\boldsymbol{\theta}_2$ be two derivations on an algebra $\mathscr{F}$. Clearly $[\boldsymbol{\theta}_1, \boldsymbol{\theta}_2] = \boldsymbol{\theta}_1 \circ \boldsymbol{\theta}_2 - \boldsymbol{\theta}_2 \circ \boldsymbol{\theta}_1$ is linear. Also

$$\begin{aligned}[\boldsymbol{\theta}_1, \boldsymbol{\theta}_2](fg) &= \boldsymbol{\theta}_1 \circ \boldsymbol{\theta}_2(fg) - \boldsymbol{\theta}_2 \circ \boldsymbol{\theta}_1(fg)\\ &= \boldsymbol{\theta}_1((\boldsymbol{\theta}_2 f)g + f(\boldsymbol{\theta}_2 g)) - [\boldsymbol{\theta}_2(\boldsymbol{\theta}_1 f)g + f(\boldsymbol{\theta}_1 g)]\\ &= \boldsymbol{\theta}_1(\boldsymbol{\theta}_2 f)g + (\boldsymbol{\theta}_2 f)(\boldsymbol{\theta}_1 g) + (\boldsymbol{\theta}_1 f)(\boldsymbol{\theta}_2 g) + f\boldsymbol{\theta}_1(\boldsymbol{\theta}_2 g)\\ &\quad - \boldsymbol{\theta}_2(\boldsymbol{\theta}_1 f)g - (\boldsymbol{\theta}_1 f)(\boldsymbol{\theta}_2 g) - (\boldsymbol{\theta}_2 f)(\boldsymbol{\theta}_1 g) - f\boldsymbol{\theta}_2(\boldsymbol{\theta}_1 g)\\ &= ([\boldsymbol{\theta}_1, \boldsymbol{\theta}_2]f)g + f([\boldsymbol{\theta}_1, \boldsymbol{\theta}_2]g)\end{aligned}$$

The special case 8.11 follows by 8.4. ∎

Because of 8.10, then, we can state the following.

8.12. Definition. $[X, Y] = \mathbf{L}_X Y$ *is the unique vectorfield such that* $\mathbf{L}_{[X,Y]} = [\mathbf{L}_X, \mathbf{L}_Y]$. *We call* $\mathbf{L}_X Y$ *the* **Lie derivative of** Y **with respect to** X, *or* **the Lie bracket of** X **and** Y.

8.13. Proposition. *The composition* $[X, Y]$ *on* $\mathscr{X}(M)$, *together with the real vector space structure of* $\mathscr{X}(M)$, *form a* **Lie algebra**. *That is,*

(*i*) $[\,,\,]$ *is* $\mathbf{R}$ *bilinear;*

(*ii*) $[X, X] = 0$ *for all* $X \in \mathscr{X}(M)$;

(*iii*) $[X,[Y,Z]] + [Y,[Z,X]] + [Z,[X,Y]] = 0$ *for all* $X, Y, Z \in \mathscr{X}(M)$.

Proof. More generally, the derivations on an algebra $\mathscr{F}$ form a Lie algebra. For them (*i*), (*ii*), and (*iii*) are easily verified by direct computation. The special case 8.13 results from 8.10 and the definition 8.12. ∎

Note that (*i*) and (*ii*) of 8.13 imply that $[X, Y] = -[Y, X]$, for

$$[X + Y, X + Y] = 0 = [X, X] + [X, Y] + [Y, X] + [Y, Y]$$

Also, (*iii*) may be written in the following suggestive way:

$$\mathbf{L}_X[Y, Z] = [\mathbf{L}_X Y, Z] + [Y, \mathbf{L}_X Z]$$

or, $\mathbf{L}_X$ *is a Lie bracket derivation.*

From 8.10 it is easy to see in local representation,

$$X_\varphi(x) = (x, X^1(x), \ldots, X^n(x))$$

that $[X, Y]$ has components

$$X^i \frac{\partial Y^j}{\partial x^i} - Y^i \frac{\partial X^j}{\partial x^i}$$

Strictly speaking we should not use the same symbol $\mathbf{L}_X$ for both definitions 8.1 and 8.12. However, the meaning is generally clear from the context. The analogue of 8.3 on the vectorfield level is the following.

8.14. Proposition. (*i*) *Let* $\varphi: M \to N$ *be a diffeomorphism and* $X \in \mathscr{X}(M)$. *Then* $\mathbf{L}_X: \mathscr{X}(M) \to \mathscr{X}(M)$ *is* **natural with respect to** φ^*. *That is,* $\mathbf{L}_{\varphi^* X}\varphi^* Y = \varphi^* \mathbf{L}_X Y$, *or* $[\varphi^* X, \varphi^* Y] = \varphi^*[X, Y]$, *or the following diagram commutes:*

$$\begin{array}{ccc} \mathscr{X}(M) & \xrightarrow{\varphi^*} & \mathscr{X}(N) \\ {\scriptstyle \mathbf{L}_X}\downarrow & & \downarrow{\scriptstyle \mathbf{L}_{\varphi^* X}} \\ \mathscr{X}(M) & \xrightarrow[\varphi^*]{} & \mathscr{X}(N) \end{array}$$

(*ii*) $\mathbf{L}_X$ *is* **natural with respect to restrictions**. *That is, for* $U \subset M$ *open, we have* $[X|U, Y|U] = [X, Y]|U$; *or the following diagram commutes:*

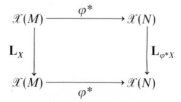

$$\begin{array}{ccc} \mathcal{X}(M) & \xrightarrow{|U} & \mathcal{X}(U) \\ \Big\downarrow \mathbf{L}_X & & \Big\downarrow \mathbf{L}_{X|U} \\ \mathcal{X}(M) & \xrightarrow[|U]{} & \mathcal{X}(U) \end{array}$$

Proof. For (*i*), let $f \in \mathcal{F}(N)$ and $\varphi(m) = n \in N$. Then

$$\begin{aligned}
[\mathbf{L}_{\varphi * X}, \mathbf{L}_{\varphi * Y}] f(n) &= \mathbf{L}_{\varphi * X} df(n) T_m\varphi \circ Y \circ \varphi^{-1}(n) - \mathbf{L}_{\varphi * Y} df(n) T_m \varphi \circ X \circ \varphi^{-1}(n) \\
&= \mathbf{L}_{\varphi * X} P_2 T_m(f \circ \varphi) \circ Y \circ \varphi^{-1}(n) \\
&\quad - \mathbf{L}_{\varphi * Y} P_2 T_m(f \circ \varphi) \circ X \circ \varphi^{-1}(n) \\
&= P_2 T_n(T_m(f \circ \varphi) \circ Y \circ \varphi^{-1}) T_m \varphi \circ X \circ \varphi^{-1}(n) \\
&\quad - P_2 T_n(T_m(f \circ \varphi) \circ X \circ \varphi^{-1}) T_m \varphi \circ Y \circ \varphi^{-1}(n) \\
&= P_2 T_m(T_m(f \circ \varphi) \circ Y) \circ X \circ \varphi^{-1}(n) \\
&\quad - P_2 T_m(T_m(f \circ \varphi) \circ Y) \circ X \circ \varphi^{-1}(n) \qquad \text{(by 5.7)} \\
&= \mathbf{L}_{[X,Y]}(f \circ \varphi)(m) = \mathbf{L}_{\varphi * [X,Y]} f(n)
\end{aligned}$$

For (*ii*) we merely note, as in 8.3, that $d(f|U) = df|U$. ∎

8.15. Proposition. *For* $X \in \mathcal{X}(M)$, $\mathbf{L}_X$ *is a derivation on* $\{\mathcal{F}(M), \mathcal{X}(M)\}$. *That is,* $\mathbf{L}_X$ *is* $\mathbf{R}$ *linear on each, and* $\mathbf{L}_X(f \otimes Y) = \mathbf{L}_X f \otimes Y + f \otimes \mathbf{L}_X Y$.

Proof. For $g \in \mathcal{F}(M)$, we have

$$\begin{aligned}
[X, fY]g &= \mathbf{L}_X(\mathbf{L}_{fY} g) - \mathbf{L}_{fY}\mathbf{L}_X g \\
&= \mathbf{L}_X(f\mathbf{L}_Y g) - f\mathbf{L}_Y\mathbf{L}_X g \\
&= (\mathbf{L}_X f)\mathbf{L}_Y g + f\mathbf{L}_X\mathbf{L}_Y g - f\mathbf{L}_Y\mathbf{L}_X g
\end{aligned}$$

by 8.4 and 8.9, so $[X, fY] = (\mathbf{L}_X f)\mathbf{L}_Y + f[X, Y]$ by 8.10. ∎

Next, we shall develop machinery for extending $\mathbf{L}_X$ to the full tensor algebra.

8.16. Definition. *A* **differential operator** *on the full tensor algebra* $\mathcal{T}(M)$ *of a manifold* M *is a collection* $\mathbf{D}^r_s(U)$ *of maps of* $\mathcal{T}^r_s(U)$ *into itself for each* $r, s \geq 0$ $(\mathcal{T}^0_0(U) = \mathcal{F}(U))$ *and each open set* $U \subset M$, *which we denote merely* $\mathbf{D}$ *(the* r, s *and* U *to be inferred from the context), such that*

(DO 1) $\mathbf{D}$ *is a* **tensor derivation**; *that is,* $\mathbf{D}$ *is* $\mathbf{R}$ *linear and for* $t_1 \in \mathcal{T}^{r_1}_{s_1}(M)$, $t_2 \in \mathcal{T}^{r_2}_{s_2}(M)$; $\mathbf{D}(t_1 \otimes t_2) = \mathbf{D}t_1 \otimes t_2 + t_1 \otimes \mathbf{D}t_2$.

(DO 2) $\mathbf{D}$ *is* **natural with respect to restrictions**. *That is, for*

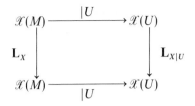

$U \subset V \subset M$ open sets, and $t \in \mathscr{T}^r_s(V)$

$$(\mathbf{D}t)|U = \mathbf{D}(t|U) \in \mathscr{T}^r_s(U)$$

or the following diagram commutes:

$$\begin{array}{ccc} \mathscr{T}^r_s(V) & \xrightarrow{\;|U\;} & \mathscr{T}^r_s(U) \\ \Big\downarrow \mathbf{D} & & \Big\downarrow \mathbf{D} \\ \mathscr{T}^r_s(V) & \xrightarrow[\;|U\;]{} & \mathscr{T}^r_s(U) \end{array}$$

(DO 3) "**D** *commutes with contractions.*" *This means that* $\mathbf{D}\delta = 0$ *where* $\delta \in \mathscr{T}^1_1(U)$ *is Kronecker's delta* (§6).

Note that we do not demand that **D** be natural with respect to diffeomorphisms (8.14). The reason is that it is not needed for the following unique extension theorem, and indeed, the latter can be used to extend the covariant derivative (with minor modifications), which is not natural with respect to diffeomorphisms.

8.17. Theorem (Willmore). *Suppose for each $U \subset M$, open, we have maps $\mathbf{E}_U$: $\mathscr{F}(U) \to \mathscr{F}(U)$ and $\mathbf{F}_U$: $\mathscr{X}(U) \to \mathscr{X}(U)$, which are* (**R** *linear*) *tensor derivations and natural with respect to restrictions. That is*

(*i*) $\mathbf{E}_U(f \otimes g) = (\mathbf{E}_U f) \otimes g + f \otimes \mathbf{E}_U g \qquad f, g \in \mathscr{F}(U);$
(*ii*) *For* $f \in \mathscr{F}(M)$, $\mathbf{E}_U(f|U) = (\mathbf{E}_M f)|U$;
(*iii*) $\mathbf{F}_U(f \otimes X) = (\mathbf{E}_U f) \otimes X + f \otimes \mathbf{F}_U X$;
(*iv*) *For* $X \in \mathscr{X}(M)$, $\mathbf{F}_U(X|U) = (\mathbf{F}_M X)|U$.

Then there is a unique differential operator **D** *on* $\mathscr{T}(M)$ *that coincides with* $\mathbf{E}_U$ *on* $\mathscr{F}(U)$ *and with* $\mathbf{F}_U$ *on* $\mathscr{X}(U)$.

Proof. Suppose that such a **D** exists. Let $\varphi: U \to U' \subset \mathbf{R}^n$ be a coordinate chart. By (DO 2) and (*ii*), (*iv*) above we may restrict attention to the chart (U, φ). (Actually, we could proceed as in 8.10 and define restrictions by means of bump functions.) Let $\mathbf{e}_i$ denote the standard basis of $\mathbf{R}^n$ and let

$$\underset{\sim}{e}_i(u) = T_{u'}\varphi^{-1}(u', \mathbf{e}_i)$$

for all $u \in U$, with $u' = \varphi(u)$. These are a basis of $T_u(M)$ (see 4.4). Let $\underset{\sim}{\alpha}^j(u)$ denote the dual basis. Note that the local representatives of $\underset{\sim}{e}_i(u)$ and $\underset{\sim}{\alpha}^j(u)$ appear as constant sections. As we saw in 6.2 we may write, for $t \in \mathscr{T}^r_s(U)$,

$$t(u) = t^{i_1 \cdots i_r}_{j_1 \cdots j_s}(u) \underset{\sim}{e}_{i_1} \otimes \cdots \otimes \underset{\sim}{e}_{i_r} \otimes \underset{\sim}{\alpha}^{j_1} \otimes \cdots \otimes \underset{\sim}{\alpha}^{j_s}(u)$$

where

$$t^{i_1 \cdots i_r}_{j_1 \cdots j_s} \in \mathscr{F}(U)$$

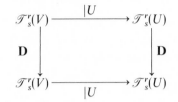

Then using **R** linearity and the derivation property of **D** we obtain a sum of terms all of which can be immediately expressed in terms of $\mathbf{E}_U, \mathbf{F}_U$ except for $\mathbf{D}\underline{\alpha}^j(u)$. However, by (DO 3),

$$\mathbf{D}\delta = 0 = \mathbf{D}(\underline{e}_j(u) \otimes \underline{\alpha}^j(u)) = (\mathbf{D}\underline{e}_j(u)) \otimes \underline{\alpha}^j(u) + e_j(u) \otimes \mathbf{D}\underline{\alpha}^j(u)$$

Applying this to $(\alpha^i(u), \underline{e}_i(u))$ gives $0 = \mathbf{F}_U(\underline{e}_i(u)) + \mathbf{D}\alpha^j(u)(\underline{e}_i(u))$. Hence $\mathbf{D}\alpha^j(u)$ is determined. Hence, such a **D**, if it exists, is unique. For existence, we define **D** as obtained in the foregoing uniqueness argument. We leave it to the reader to check that the resulting **D** is well defined and satisfies (DO 1), (DO 2), and (DO 3). ∎

Taking $\mathbf{E}_U$ and $\mathbf{F}_U$ to be $\mathbf{L}_{X|U}$ we see that the hypotheses of Willmore's theorem are satisfied (see 8.3 (*ii*), 8.4 (*i*), 8.14 (*ii*), and 8.15). Hence we can define a differential operator as follows.

8.18. Definition. *If $X \in \mathscr{X}(M)$ we let $\mathbf{L}_X$ be the unique differential operator on $\mathscr{T}(M)$, called the* **Lie derivative with respect to** *X, such that $\mathbf{L}_X$ coincides with $\mathbf{L}_X$ as given in* 8.1 *and* 8.12.

It may be instructive for the reader to examine Lie derivatives of higher order tensors in component notation, as was done in 8.10.

8.19. Proposition. *Let $\varphi\colon M \to N$ be a diffeomorphism and X a vectorfield on M. Then $\mathbf{L}_X$ is* **natural with respect to** *φ_*; that is, $\mathbf{L}_{\varphi_* X}\varphi_* t = \varphi_* \mathbf{L}_X t$ for $t \in \mathscr{T}^r_s(M)$, or the following diagram commutes:*

$$\begin{array}{ccc} \mathscr{T}^r_s(M) & \xrightarrow{\varphi_*} & \mathscr{T}^r_s(N) \\ \Big\downarrow \mathbf{L}_X & & \Big\downarrow \mathbf{L}_{\varphi_* X} \\ \mathscr{T}^r_s(M) & \xrightarrow[\varphi_*]{} & \mathscr{T}^r_s(N) \end{array}$$

Proof. For an open set $U \subset M$ define $\mathbf{D}\colon \mathscr{T}^r_s(U) \to \mathscr{T}^r_s(U)$ by $\mathbf{D}t = (\varphi_*)^{-1} \circ \mathbf{L}_{\varphi_* X|U}(\varphi_* t)$ where we use the same symbol φ for $\varphi|U$. From 8.3 (*i*) and 8.14 (*i*), **D** coincides with $\mathbf{L}_{X|U}$ on $\mathscr{F}(U)$ and $\mathscr{X}(U)$. Next, we show that **D** is a differential operator. For (DO 1) we use the fact that $\varphi_*(t_1 \otimes t_2) = \varphi_* t_1 \otimes \varphi_* t_2$, which follows on from the definitions 6.3 and 6.16. Then

$$\begin{aligned} \mathbf{D}(t_1 \otimes t_2) &= (\varphi_*)^{-1} \circ \mathbf{L}_{\varphi_* X}\varphi_*(t_1 \otimes t_2) = (\varphi_*)^{-1}\mathbf{L}_{\varphi_* X}(\varphi_* t_1 \otimes \varphi_* t_2) \\ &= (\varphi_*)^{-1}[(\mathbf{L}_{\varphi_* X}\varphi_* t_1) \otimes \varphi_* t_2] + (\varphi_*)^{-1}[\varphi_* t_1 \otimes \mathbf{L}_{\varphi_* X}\varphi_* t_2] \\ &= \mathbf{D}t_1 \otimes t_2 + t_1 \otimes \mathbf{D}t_2 \end{aligned}$$

(See 6.15.) For (DO 2) we have, if $t \in \mathscr{T}^r_s(M)$,

$$\begin{aligned} \mathbf{D}t|U &= [(\varphi_*)^{-1}\mathbf{L}_{\varphi_* X}\varphi_* t]|U = (\varphi_*)^{-1}\mathbf{L}_{\varphi_* X}\varphi_* t|U \\ &= (\varphi_*)^{-1}\mathbf{L}_{\varphi_* X|U}\varphi_* t|U \qquad \text{(by (DO 2) for } \mathbf{L}_X) \\ &= \mathbf{D}(t|U) \end{aligned}$$

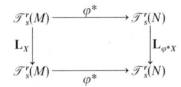

Finally, (DO 3) follows from the fact that $\varphi^*\delta = \delta$, which the reader can easily check (§6). Then we have

$$\mathbf{D}\delta = (\varphi^*)^{-1}\mathbf{L}_{\varphi^*X}\varphi^*\delta = (\varphi^*)^{-1}\mathbf{L}_{\varphi^*X}\delta = 0$$

by (DO 3) for $\mathbf{L}_X$. The result follows by Willmore's theorem (8.17). ■

We now turn to an alternate interpretation of the Lie derivative. The basic idea is that to differentiate according to §2 we need a curve in a single vector space. For $t \in \mathscr{T}^r_s(M)$ we can find a curve at $t(m)$ in the fiber over m by means of a local flow box (§7). The derivative of this curve is in fact the Lie derivative. In spirit, the flow box plays the same role as a connection (Christoffel symbols) in covariant differentiation. (See Figure 8-1.)

More precisely, for $m \in M$ and a vectorfield X on M let (U, a, F) be a flow box at m. For each $\lambda \in I_a = (-a, a)$ we can form the diffeomorphism $F_\lambda = F|U \times \{\lambda\}: U \to U_\lambda = F_\lambda(U)$. Now let $t \in \mathscr{T}^r_s(M)$ and define $t_\lambda = (F_\lambda^{-1})^*(t|U_\lambda) \in \mathscr{T}^r_s(U)$. (See 6.16 and 6.17.) Define the map $t_\sharp(m): I_a \to T^r_s T_m(M)$: $\lambda \rightsquigarrow t_\lambda(m)$. Using this notation we have the following.

8.20. Theorem. *$t_\sharp(m)$ is a curve in $T^r_s(T_m(M))$ at $t(m)$ and $\mathbf{L}_X t(m) = t_\sharp(m)'(0)$.*

Proof. For smoothness of $t_\sharp$, we have $t_\lambda(m) = (TF_\lambda^{-1}(m))^r_s t(F_\lambda(m))$. Hence we need verify only that $(TF_\lambda^{-1}(m))^r_s$ is a smooth function of λ. Consider $F: U \times I_a \to M$, which is smooth in (U, λ). Then $TF: TU \times (I_a \times \mathbf{R}) \to M$ is also smooth. For smoothness of TF_λ, note $TF_\lambda = TF|TF \times I_a \times \{0\}$. Then from 6.9 we see that $(TF_\lambda^{-1})^r_s$ is smooth in λ. Since F_0 is the identity, it is clear that $t_\sharp$ is a curve at $t(m)$.

Now define $\mathbf{\theta}_X: \mathscr{T}(M) \to \mathscr{T}(M)$ by $\mathbf{\theta}_X t(m) = t'_\sharp(m)|_{\lambda=0}$. From the flow box existence and uniqueness theorem (§7) it is clear that $\mathbf{\theta}_X$ is well defined, and from smoothness of $t_\lambda(m)$, $\mathbf{\theta}_X t(m) = Tt_\sharp(m)\cdot(0, 1) \in \mathscr{T}(M)$. Let us apply Willmore's theorem 8.17. First, $\mathbf{\theta}_X$ is $\mathbf{R}$ linear and is a derivation. This follows easily using the local representatives and 2.11. Also, $\mathbf{\theta}_X$ is natural with respect to restrictions because it is defined locally. Moreover,

$$\mathbf{\theta}_X\delta = \frac{d}{d\lambda}(F_\lambda^{-1})^*\delta = \frac{d}{d\lambda}\delta = 0$$

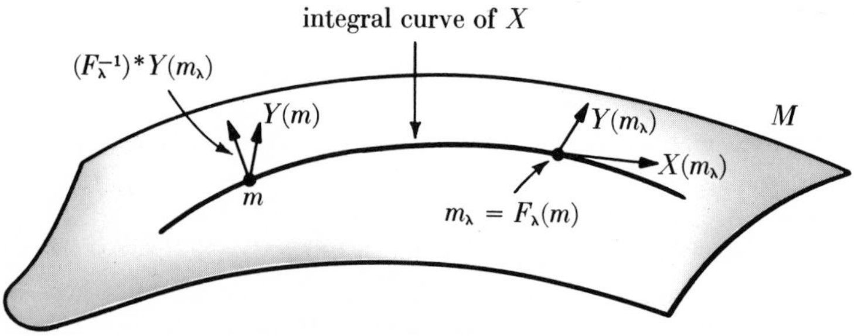

Figure 8-1

Hence $\boldsymbol{\theta}_X$ is a differential operator. It remains to show $\boldsymbol{\theta}_X$ coincides with $\mathbf{L}_X$ on $\mathscr{F}(M)$ and $\mathscr{X}(M)$. For $f \in \mathscr{F}(M)$, we have $f_\lambda(m) = f \circ F_\lambda(m)$ and

$$\frac{d}{d\lambda} f_\lambda(m)|_{\lambda=0} = P_2 T_m f \circ T_\lambda F_\lambda(m)(0, 1) = df \circ X(m) = \mathbf{L}_X f$$

Hence $\boldsymbol{\theta}_X f = \mathbf{L}_X f$. Finally we must verify that $\boldsymbol{\theta}_X Y = [X, Y] = \mathbf{L}_X Y$, or equivalently $\mathbf{L}_{\boldsymbol{\theta}_X} Y = [\mathbf{L}_X, \mathbf{L}_Y]$. First let us note that for $f \in \mathscr{F}(M)$ there is a function $g_t(u)$ so $f \circ F_\lambda = f + \lambda g_\lambda$ and $g_0 = \mathbf{L}_X f$; namely, take

$$g_\lambda(u) = \int_0^1 \frac{\partial}{\partial t} f \circ F(t\lambda, u)\, dt$$

Then

$$\begin{aligned}
\mathbf{L}_{\boldsymbol{\theta}_X Y} f(m) &= df(m)\frac{d}{d\lambda}[T_m F_{-\lambda} \circ Y \circ F_\lambda(m)]|_{\lambda=0} \\
&= \frac{d}{d\lambda}[T_m(f \circ F_{-\lambda}) \circ Y \circ F_\lambda(m)]|_{\lambda=0} \\
&= \frac{d}{d\lambda}[T_m(f - \lambda g_{-\lambda}) \circ Y \circ F_\lambda(m)]|_{\lambda=0} \\
&= \frac{d}{d\lambda} T_m f \circ Y \circ F_\lambda(m)|_{\lambda=0} - \frac{d}{d\lambda}[\lambda][T_m g_{-\lambda} \circ Y \circ F_\lambda(m)]|_{\lambda=0} \\
&= d(T_m f \circ Y) \circ F'_\lambda(m)|_{\lambda=0} - T_m g_0 \circ Y \circ F_0(m) \\
&= \mathbf{L}_X \mathbf{L}_Y f - \mathbf{L}_Y \mathbf{L}_X f
\end{aligned}$$

Hence from 8.11, $\boldsymbol{\theta}_X Y = [X, Y]$.

Finally, by Willmore's theorem, $\boldsymbol{\theta}_X = \mathbf{L}_X$ for all $t \in \mathscr{T}(M)$. ∎

8.21. Corollary. *If $t \in \mathscr{T}(M)$, $\mathbf{L}_X t = 0$ iff t is constant along the integral curves of X. That is, $t(m) = (F_\lambda^{-1})^r_s \circ t \circ F_\lambda(m)$, $\lambda \in I_a$, for any flow box F at m.*

This follows at once from 8.20.

Exercises

8A. If each point $m \in M$ has a neighborhood U such that for all $f \in \mathscr{F}(U)$, $\mathbf{L}_X f = \mathbf{L}_Y f$ (on U), show $X = Y$.

8B. Complete the details of 8.10. How may a single element of TM be regarded as a derivation?

8C. Supply the proof of 8.13 and complete the proof of 8.17.

8D. Prove that φ^* is a tensor algebra homomorphism, as indicated in the proof of 8.19. Show also $\varphi^*\delta = \delta$.

8E. (i) For functions, show that *constant* in 8.21 means constant value on the integral curves.

(ii) Interpret the more general condition $\mathbf{L}_X t = 0$. For example, on $\mathbf{R}^2$, let $X(x, y) = (x, y; y, -x)$. Find the flow of X and interpret 8.21 geometrically.

8F. (For readers with a knowledge of Riemannian geometry): Let M be a manifold with a connection, denoted ∇, so that $\nabla_X Y$ is the covariant derivative of Y in the direction X. Show that $\mathbf{L}_X Y = \nabla_X Y - \nabla_Y X$. Note, however, that $\mathbf{L}_X$ does not require a connection or metric for its definition.

§9. EXTERIOR ALGEBRA

The calculus of Cartan concerns exterior differential forms, which are sections of a vector bundle of linear exterior forms on the tangent spaces of a manifold. We begin with the exterior algebra of a vector space and extend this fiberwise to a vector bundle. As with tensorfields, the most important case is the tangent bundle of a manifold, which is considered in the next section.

9.1. Definition. *Let* $\mathbf{E}$ *be a finite-dimensional real vector space. Let* $\Omega^0(\mathbf{E}) = \mathbf{R}$, $\Omega^1(\mathbf{E}) = \mathbf{E}^*$ *and, in general,* $\Omega^k(\mathbf{E}) = L_a^k(\mathbf{E}, \mathbf{R})$, *the vector space of skew symmetric k multilinear maps* (1.7), *or* **exterior** ***k*-forms** *on* $\mathbf{E}$.

We leave as an easy exercise for the reader the fact that $\Omega^k(\mathbf{E})$ is a vector subspace of $T_k^0(\mathbf{E})$ (see 1.6).

Recall that the permutation group on k elements, denoted S_k, consists of all bijections $\varphi: \{1, \ldots, k\} \to \{1, \ldots, k\}$ together with the structure of a group under composition. Clearly, S_k has order $k!$. Letting $(\tilde{\mathbf{R}}, \times)$ denote $\mathbf{R} \setminus \{0\}$ with the multiplicative group structure, we have a homomorphism $sign: S_k \to (\tilde{\mathbf{R}}, \times)$. That is, for $\sigma, \tau \in S_k$, $sign(\sigma \circ \tau) = (sign\, \sigma)(sign\, \tau)$. The image of *sign* is the subgroup $\{-1, 1\}$, while its kernel consists of the subgroup of even permutations. One other fact we shall need is the following, which the reader can easily check: If G is a group and $g_0 \in G$, the map $R_{g_0}: G \to G$; $g \rightsquigarrow g g_0$ is a bijection.

9.2. Definition. **The alternation mapping** $\mathbf{A}: T_k^0(\mathbf{E}) \to T_k^0(\mathbf{E})$ *(as before, we do not index the* $\mathbf{A}$*) is defined by*

$$\mathbf{A}\mathbf{t}(\mathbf{e}_1, \ldots, \mathbf{e}_k) = \frac{1}{k!} \sum_{\sigma \in S_k} (sign\, \sigma)\mathbf{t}(\mathbf{e}_{\sigma(1)}, \ldots, \mathbf{e}_{\sigma(k)})$$

where the sum is over all k! elements of S_k.

9.3. Proposition. $\mathbf{A}$ *is a linear mapping onto* $\Omega^k(\mathbf{E})$, $\mathbf{A}|\Omega^k(\mathbf{E})$ *is the identity, and* $\mathbf{A} \circ \mathbf{A} = \mathbf{A}$.

Proof. Linearity of $\mathbf{A}$ follows at once. If $\mathbf{t} \in \Omega^k(\mathbf{E})$, then

$$\begin{aligned} \mathbf{A}\mathbf{t}(\mathbf{e}_1, \ldots, \mathbf{e}_k) &= \frac{1}{k!} \sum_{\sigma \in S_k} (sign\, \sigma)\mathbf{t}(\mathbf{e}_{\sigma(1)}, \ldots, \mathbf{e}_{\sigma(k)}) \\ &= \frac{1}{k!} \sum_{\sigma \in S_k} \mathbf{t}(\mathbf{e}_1, \ldots, \mathbf{e}_k) \\ &= \mathbf{t}(\mathbf{e}_1, \ldots, \mathbf{e}_k) \end{aligned}$$

since $(sign\ \sigma)^2 = 1$ and S_k has order $k!$. Second, for $\mathbf{t} \in T_k^0(\mathbf{E})$ we have

$$\begin{aligned}\mathbf{At}(\mathbf{e}_1, \ldots, \mathbf{e}_k) &= \frac{1}{k!} \sum_{\sigma \in S_k} (sign\ \sigma)\mathbf{t}(\mathbf{e}_{\sigma(1)}, \ldots, \mathbf{e}_{\sigma(k)}) \\ &= \frac{1}{k!} \sum_{\sigma \in S_k} (sign\ \sigma\tau)\mathbf{t}(\mathbf{e}_{\sigma\tau(1)}, \ldots, \mathbf{e}_{\sigma\tau(k)}) \\ &= (sign\ \tau)\mathbf{At}(\mathbf{e}_{\tau(1)}, \ldots, \mathbf{e}_{\tau(k)})\end{aligned}$$

since $\sigma \rightsquigarrow \sigma\tau$ is a bijection and *sign* is a homomorphism. This proves the first two assertions, and the last follows at once. ∎

Then we may state the following.

9.4. Definition. *If* $\boldsymbol{\alpha} \in T_k^0(\mathbf{E})$ *and* $\boldsymbol{\beta} \in T_l^0(\mathbf{E})$, *define* $\boldsymbol{\alpha} \wedge \boldsymbol{\beta} \in \boldsymbol{\Omega}^{k+1}(\mathbf{E})$ *by* $\boldsymbol{\alpha} \wedge \boldsymbol{\beta} = \mathbf{A}(\boldsymbol{\alpha} \otimes \boldsymbol{\beta})$. *(Again, we do not index* $\wedge$.*) In particular, for* $\boldsymbol{\alpha} \in T_0^0(\mathbf{E}) = \mathbf{R}$, *we put* $\boldsymbol{\alpha} \wedge \boldsymbol{\beta} = \boldsymbol{\beta} \wedge \boldsymbol{\alpha} = \boldsymbol{\alpha\beta}$.

Note that if $\boldsymbol{\alpha} \in \Omega^k(\mathbf{E})$, $\boldsymbol{\beta} \in \Omega^l(\mathbf{E})$, $\boldsymbol{\alpha} \otimes \boldsymbol{\beta}$ is not, in general, in $\Omega^{k+l}(\mathbf{E})$.

The basic properties of the composition $\wedge$ are given in the following.

9.5. Proposition. *For* $\boldsymbol{\alpha} \in T_k^0(\mathbf{E})$, $\boldsymbol{\beta} \in T_l^0(\mathbf{E})$ *and* $\boldsymbol{\gamma} \in T_m^0(\mathbf{E})$, *we have*

(*i*) $\boldsymbol{\alpha} \wedge \boldsymbol{\beta} = \mathbf{A}\boldsymbol{\alpha} \wedge \boldsymbol{\beta} = \boldsymbol{\alpha} \wedge \mathbf{A}\boldsymbol{\beta}$;
(*ii*) $\wedge$ *is bilinear;*
(*iii*) $\boldsymbol{\alpha} \wedge \boldsymbol{\beta} = (-1)^{kl}\ \boldsymbol{\beta} \wedge \boldsymbol{\alpha}$;
(*iv*) $\boldsymbol{\alpha} \wedge (\boldsymbol{\beta} \wedge \boldsymbol{\gamma}) = (\boldsymbol{\alpha} \wedge \boldsymbol{\beta}) \wedge \boldsymbol{\gamma}$.

Proof. For (*i*), first note that if $\sigma \in S_k$, and $\sigma\mathbf{t}(\mathbf{e}_1, \ldots, \mathbf{e}_k) = \mathbf{t}(\mathbf{e}_{\sigma(1)}, \ldots, \mathbf{e}_{\sigma(k)})$ then $\mathbf{A}(\sigma\mathbf{t}) = (sign\ \sigma)\mathbf{At}$, for

$$\begin{aligned}\mathbf{A}(\sigma\mathbf{t}) &= \frac{1}{k!} \sum_{\rho \in S_k} (sign\ \rho)\mathbf{t}(\mathbf{e}_{\rho\sigma(1)}, \ldots, \mathbf{e}_{\rho\sigma(k)}) \\ &= \frac{1}{k!} \sum_{\rho \in S_k} (sign\ \sigma)(sign\ \rho\sigma)\mathbf{t}(\mathbf{e}_{\rho\sigma(1)}, \ldots, \mathbf{e}_{\rho\sigma(k)}) \\ &= (sign\ \sigma)\mathbf{At}(\mathbf{e}_1, \ldots, \mathbf{e}_k)\end{aligned}$$

since $\rho \rightsquigarrow \rho\sigma$ is a bijection. Then, since $\mathbf{A}$ is linear,

$$\mathbf{A}(\mathbf{A}\boldsymbol{\alpha} \otimes \boldsymbol{\beta})(\mathbf{e}_1, \ldots, \mathbf{e}_k, \ldots, \mathbf{e}_{k+l}) = \frac{1}{k!} \sum_{\tau \in S_k} (sign\ \tau)\mathbf{A}(\tau\boldsymbol{\alpha} \otimes \boldsymbol{\beta})(\mathbf{e}_1, \ldots, \mathbf{e}_{k+l})$$

Letting $\tau' \in S_{k+l}$ be given by

$$\tau'(1, \ldots, k, \ldots, k+l) = (\tau(1), \ldots, \tau(k), k+1, \ldots, k+l)$$

we obtain for the above, since $sign\ \tau = sign\ \tau'$ and $\tau\boldsymbol{\alpha} \otimes \boldsymbol{\beta} = \tau'(\boldsymbol{\alpha} \otimes \boldsymbol{\beta})$,

$$\frac{1}{k!} \sum_{\tau \in S_k} (sign\ \tau)(sign\ \tau)\mathbf{A}(\boldsymbol{\alpha} \otimes \boldsymbol{\beta})(\mathbf{e}_1, \ldots, \mathbf{e}_{k+l}) = \mathbf{A}(\boldsymbol{\alpha} \otimes \boldsymbol{\beta})(\mathbf{e}_1, \ldots, \mathbf{e}_{k+l})$$

The other part of (*i*) is similar.

Now (*ii*) is clear since $\otimes$ is bilinear and $\mathbf{A}$ is linear.

For (*iii*), let $\sigma_0 \in S_{k+l}$ be given by $\sigma_0(1, \ldots, k + l) = (k + 1, \ldots, k + l, 1, \ldots, k)$. Then $\boldsymbol{\alpha} \otimes \boldsymbol{\beta}(\mathbf{e}_1, \ldots, \mathbf{e}_{k+l}) = \boldsymbol{\beta} \otimes \boldsymbol{\alpha}(\mathbf{e}_{\sigma_0(1)}, \ldots, \mathbf{e}_{\sigma_0(k+l)})$. Hence, by the proof of (*i*), $\mathbf{A}(\boldsymbol{\alpha} \otimes \boldsymbol{\beta}) = (\mathit{sign}\, \sigma_0)\mathbf{A}(\boldsymbol{\beta} \otimes \boldsymbol{\alpha})$. But $\mathit{sign}\, \sigma_0 = (-1)^{kl}$. Finally, (*iv*) follows from (*i*), for $\boldsymbol{\alpha} \wedge (\boldsymbol{\beta} \wedge \boldsymbol{\gamma}) = \boldsymbol{\alpha} \wedge \mathbf{A}(\boldsymbol{\beta} \otimes \boldsymbol{\gamma}) = \boldsymbol{\alpha} \wedge (\boldsymbol{\beta} \otimes \boldsymbol{\gamma}) = \mathbf{A}(\boldsymbol{\alpha} \otimes (\boldsymbol{\beta} \otimes \boldsymbol{\gamma})) = \mathbf{A}((\boldsymbol{\alpha} \otimes \boldsymbol{\beta}) \otimes \boldsymbol{\gamma}) = \mathbf{A}(\boldsymbol{\alpha} \otimes \boldsymbol{\beta}) \wedge \boldsymbol{\gamma} = (\boldsymbol{\alpha} \wedge \boldsymbol{\beta}) \wedge \boldsymbol{\gamma}$. ∎

9.6. Definition. *The direct sum of the spaces $\Omega^k(\mathbf{E})$ ($k = 0, 1, 2, \ldots$) together with its structure as a real vector space and multiplication induced by $\wedge$, is called the* **exterior algebra** *of* $\mathbf{E}$.

9.7. Proposition. *Let $n = \dim \mathbf{E}$. Then for $k > n$, $\Omega^k(\mathbf{E}) = \{\mathbf{0}\}$, while for $0 < k \le n$, $\Omega^k(\mathbf{E})$ has dimension $\binom{n}{k}$. The exterior algebra over $\mathbf{E}$ has dimension 2^n. Indeed, if $\hat{\mathbf{e}} = (\mathbf{e}_1, \ldots, \mathbf{e}_n)$ is an ordered basis of $\mathbf{E}$ and $\hat{\mathbf{e}}^* = (\boldsymbol{\alpha}^1, \ldots, \boldsymbol{\alpha}^n)$ its dual basis, a basis of $\Omega^k(\mathbf{E})$ is*

$$\{\boldsymbol{\alpha}^{i_1} \wedge \cdots \wedge \boldsymbol{\alpha}^{i_k} \mid 1 \le i_1 < i_2 < \cdots < i_k \le n\}$$

Proof. If $\mathbf{t} \in \Omega^k(\mathbf{E})$ we may write, from 6.2 and 9.3,

$$\mathbf{t} = \mathbf{t}(\mathbf{e}_{i_1}, \ldots, \mathbf{e}_{i_k})\boldsymbol{\alpha}^{i_1} \wedge \cdots \wedge \boldsymbol{\alpha}^{i_k}$$

(By 9.5, brackets are unnecessary in $\boldsymbol{\alpha}^{i_1} \wedge \cdots \wedge \boldsymbol{\alpha}^{i_k}$.) However, if $\sigma \in S_k$ and $i_1, \ldots, i_k$ are fixed, from 9.5 we see

$$\mathbf{t}(\mathbf{e}_{i_1}, \ldots, \mathbf{e}_{i_k})\boldsymbol{\alpha}^{i_1} \wedge \cdots \wedge \boldsymbol{\alpha}^{i_k} = \mathbf{t}(\mathbf{e}_{\sigma(i_1)}, \ldots, \mathbf{e}_{\sigma(i_k)})\boldsymbol{\alpha}^{\sigma(i_1)} \wedge \cdots \wedge \boldsymbol{\alpha}^{\sigma(i_k)}$$

Thus, the sum need be taken only over distinct sets $\{i_1, \ldots, i_k\}$, and with a factor $k!$

$$\mathbf{t} = k! \sum_{i_1 < \cdots < i_k} \mathbf{t}(\mathbf{e}_{i_1}, \ldots, \mathbf{e}_{i_k})\boldsymbol{\alpha}^{i_1} \wedge \cdots \wedge \boldsymbol{\alpha}^{i_k}$$

Secondly, we show

$$\{\boldsymbol{\alpha}^{i_1} \wedge \cdots \wedge \boldsymbol{\alpha}^{i_k} | i_1 < \cdots < i_k\}$$

are linearly independent. Suppose that

$$\sum_{i_1 < \cdots < i_k} t_{i_1 \cdots i_k} \boldsymbol{\alpha}^{i_1} \wedge \cdots \wedge \boldsymbol{\alpha}^{i_k} = \mathbf{0}$$

For fixed $i'_1, \ldots, i'_k$, let $j'_{k+1}, \ldots, j'_n$ denote the complementary set of indices, $j'_{k+1} < \cdots < j'_n$. Then

$$\sum_{i_1 < \cdots < i_k} t_{i_1 \cdots i_k} \boldsymbol{\alpha}^{i_1} \wedge \cdots \wedge \boldsymbol{\alpha}^{i_k} \wedge \boldsymbol{\alpha}^{j'_{k+1}} \wedge \cdots \wedge \boldsymbol{\alpha}^{j'_n} = \mathbf{0}$$

However, by 9.5, this reduces to

$$t_{i'_1 \cdots i'_k} \boldsymbol{\alpha}^1 \wedge \cdots \wedge \boldsymbol{\alpha}^n = \mathbf{0}$$

But $\boldsymbol{\alpha}^1 \wedge \cdots \wedge \boldsymbol{\alpha}^n \ne \mathbf{0}$, as $\boldsymbol{\alpha}^1 \wedge \cdots \wedge \boldsymbol{\alpha}^n(\mathbf{e}_1, \ldots, \mathbf{e}_n) = 1$ (see 9.9). Hence

$$t_{i'_1 \cdots i'_k} = 0$$

The first part of the theorem now follows easily, as $\boldsymbol{\alpha}^i \wedge \boldsymbol{\alpha}^i = \mathbf{0}$ (9.5(*iii*)). ∎

9.8. *Definition.* *The nonzero elements of the one-dimensional space* $\Omega^n(\mathbf{E})$ *are called* **volume elements**. *If* $\boldsymbol{\omega}_1$ *and* $\boldsymbol{\omega}_2$ *are volume elements, we say* $\boldsymbol{\omega}_1$ *and* $\boldsymbol{\omega}_2$ *are* **equivalent** *iff there is a* $c > 0$ *so* $\boldsymbol{\omega}_1 = c\boldsymbol{\omega}_2$. *An equivalence class of volume elements on* $\mathbf{E}$ *is called an* **orientation** *on* $\mathbf{E}$.

We shall see shortly the close relationship between volume elements and determinants.

9.9. *Proposition.* *Let* $\boldsymbol{\alpha}_1, \ldots, \boldsymbol{\alpha}_k \in \mathbf{E}^*$. *Then* $\boldsymbol{\alpha}_1, \ldots, \boldsymbol{\alpha}_k$ *are linearly dependent iff* $\boldsymbol{\alpha}_1 \wedge \cdots \wedge \boldsymbol{\alpha}_k = \mathbf{0}$.

Proof. If $\boldsymbol{\alpha}_1, \ldots, \boldsymbol{\alpha}_k$ are linearly dependent, then

$$\boldsymbol{\alpha}_i = \sum_{j \neq i} c_j \boldsymbol{\alpha}_j$$

for some i. Then, since $\boldsymbol{\alpha} \wedge \boldsymbol{\alpha} = \mathbf{0}$ (9.5(*iii*)), we see $\boldsymbol{\alpha}_1 \wedge \cdots \wedge \boldsymbol{\alpha}_k = \mathbf{0}$. Conversely, if $\boldsymbol{\alpha}_1, \ldots, \boldsymbol{\alpha}_k$ are linearly independent, extend to a basis $\boldsymbol{\alpha}_1, \ldots, \boldsymbol{\alpha}_n$. Then $\boldsymbol{\alpha}_1 \wedge \cdots \wedge \boldsymbol{\alpha}_n \neq \mathbf{0}$, by 9.7 and hence $\boldsymbol{\alpha}_1 \wedge \cdots \wedge \boldsymbol{\alpha}_k \neq \mathbf{0}$. ∎

9.10. *Proposition.* *Let* $dim(\mathbf{E}) = n$, *and* $\varphi \in L(\mathbf{E}, \mathbf{E})$. *Then there is a unique constant det* φ, *called the* **determinant** *of* φ, *such that* $\varphi_*: \Omega^n(\mathbf{E}) \to \Omega^n(\mathbf{E})$, *defined by* $\varphi_*\boldsymbol{\omega}(\mathbf{e}_1, \ldots, \mathbf{e}_n) = \boldsymbol{\omega}(\varphi(\mathbf{e}_1), \ldots, \varphi(\mathbf{e}_n))$ *satisfies* $\varphi_*\boldsymbol{\omega} = (det\ \varphi)\boldsymbol{\omega}$ *for all* $\boldsymbol{\omega} \in \Omega^n(\mathbf{E})$.

Proof. Clearly $\varphi_*: \Omega^n(\mathbf{E}) \to \Omega^n(\mathbf{E})$ is a linear mapping. But, from 9.7, $\Omega^n(\mathbf{E})$ is one-dimensional, so that if $\boldsymbol{\omega}_0$ is a basis and $\boldsymbol{\omega} = c\boldsymbol{\omega}_0$, $\varphi_*\boldsymbol{\omega} = c\varphi_*\boldsymbol{\omega}_0 = d\boldsymbol{\omega}$ for some constant d, clearly unique. ∎

It is easy to see that this definition of determinant is the usual one (Exercise 9B). However, it has the advantage of suggesting the proper global definition (§11), as well as making its basic properties trivial, as follows.

9.11. *Proposition.* *Let* $\varphi, \psi \in L(\mathbf{E}, \mathbf{E})$. *Then*

(*i*) $det\ (\varphi \circ \psi) = (det\ \varphi)(det\ \psi)$;

(*ii*) *if* φ *is the identity,* $det\ \varphi = 1$;

(*iii*) φ *is an isomorphism iff* $det\ \varphi \neq 0$, *and in this case* $det(\varphi^{-1}) = (det\ \varphi)^{-1}$.

Proof. For (*i*), $(\varphi \circ \psi)_*\boldsymbol{\omega} = det(\varphi \circ \psi)\boldsymbol{\omega}$, but $(\varphi \circ \psi)_*\boldsymbol{\omega} = \psi_* \circ \varphi_*\boldsymbol{\omega}$ as we see easily from the definitions (see 9.15 below). Hence, $(\varphi \circ \psi)_*\boldsymbol{\omega} = \psi_*(\det \varphi)\boldsymbol{\omega} = (det\ \psi)(det\ \varphi)\boldsymbol{\omega}$ and (*i*) follows. (*ii*) follows at once from the definition. For (*iii*), suppose φ is an isomorphism with inverse φ^{-1}. Then, by (*i*) and (*iii*), $1 = det(\varphi \circ \varphi^{-1}) = (det\ \varphi)(det\ \varphi^{-1})$, and in particular, $det\ \varphi \neq 0$. Conversely, if φ is not an isomorphism there is an $\mathbf{e}_1 \neq \mathbf{0}$ so $\varphi(\mathbf{e}_1) = \mathbf{0}$ (Exercise 1B). Extend to a basis $\mathbf{e}_1, \mathbf{e}_2, \ldots, \mathbf{e}_n$. Then for all n-forms $\boldsymbol{\omega}$, $\varphi_*\boldsymbol{\omega}(\mathbf{e}_1, \ldots, \mathbf{e}_n) = \boldsymbol{\omega}(0, \varphi(\mathbf{e}_2), \ldots, \varphi(\mathbf{e}_n)) = 0$. Hence, $det\ \varphi = 0$. ∎

Recall that a unique topology is determined on $L(\mathbf{E}, \mathbf{E})$ by 1.4. One convenient norm giving this topology is

$$\|\varphi\| = sup\{\|\varphi(\mathbf{e})\| \mid \|\mathbf{e}\| = 1\} = sup\left\{\frac{\|\varphi(\mathbf{e})\|}{\|\mathbf{e}\|} \mathbf{e} \neq 0\right\}$$

where $\|\mathbf{e}\|$ is a norm on $\mathbf{E}$. See Exercise 1A. Hence, for any $\mathbf{e} \in \mathbf{E}$,

$$\|\varphi(\mathbf{e})\| \leq \|\varphi\| \, \|\mathbf{e}\|$$

9.12. Proposition. *det: $L(\mathbf{E}, \mathbf{E}) \to \mathbf{R}$ is continuous.*

Proof. Note that $\|\boldsymbol{\omega}\| = sup\{|\boldsymbol{\omega}(\mathbf{e}_1, \ldots, \mathbf{e}_n)| \mid \|\mathbf{e}_1\| = \cdots = \|\mathbf{e}_n\| = 1\} = sup\{|\boldsymbol{\omega}(\mathbf{e}_1, \ldots, \mathbf{e}_n)| / \|\mathbf{e}_1\| \cdots \|\mathbf{e}_n\| \mid \mathbf{e}_1, \ldots, \mathbf{e}_n \neq 0\}$ is a norm on $\Omega^n(\mathbf{E})$ and $|\boldsymbol{\omega}(\mathbf{e}_1, \ldots, \mathbf{e}_n)| \leq \|\boldsymbol{\omega}\| \, \|\mathbf{e}_1\| \cdots \|\mathbf{e}_n\|$. Then, for $\varphi, \psi \in L(\mathbf{E}, \mathbf{E})$,

$$\begin{aligned}
|det\, \varphi - det\, \psi| \, \|\boldsymbol{\omega}\| &= \|\varphi_*\boldsymbol{\omega} - \psi_*\boldsymbol{\omega}\| \\
&= sup\{|\boldsymbol{\omega}(\varphi(\mathbf{e}_1), \ldots, \varphi(\mathbf{e}_n)) - \boldsymbol{\omega}(\psi(\mathbf{e}_1), \ldots, \psi(\mathbf{e}_n)| \mid \|\mathbf{e}_1\| = \cdots = \|\mathbf{e}_n\| = 1\} \\
&\leq sup\{|\boldsymbol{\omega}(\varphi(\mathbf{e}_1) - \psi(\mathbf{e}_1), \varphi(\mathbf{e}_2), \ldots, \varphi(\mathbf{e}_n)| + \cdots \\
&\qquad + |\boldsymbol{\omega}(\psi(\mathbf{e}_1), \psi(\mathbf{e}_2), \ldots, \varphi(\mathbf{e}_n) - \psi(\mathbf{e}_n))| \mid \|\mathbf{e}_1\| = \cdots = \|\mathbf{e}_n\| = 1\} \\
&\leq \|\boldsymbol{\omega}\| \, \|\varphi - \psi\| \{\|\varphi\|^{n-1} + \|\varphi\|^{n-2}\|\psi\| + \cdots + \|\psi\|^{n-1}\} \\
&\leq \|\boldsymbol{\omega}\| \, \|\varphi - \psi\| \, \|\varphi + \psi\|^{n-1}
\end{aligned}$$

Consequently, $|det\, \varphi - det\, \psi| \leq \|\varphi - \psi\| \, \|\varphi + \psi\|^{n-1}$ and the result follows. ∎

9.13. Proposition. *Let $L_{\mathrm{iso}}(\mathbf{E}, \mathbf{F})$ denote those $\varphi \in L(\mathbf{E}, \mathbf{F})$ which are isomorphisms. Then $L_{\mathrm{iso}}(\mathbf{E}, \mathbf{F})$ is an open subset of $L(\mathbf{E}, \mathbf{F})$.*

Proof. If $L_{\mathrm{iso}}(\mathbf{E}, \mathbf{F}) = \phi$ the conclusion is true. Otherwise, suppose $i: \mathbf{E} \to \mathbf{F}$ is an isomorphism. Then, as in 9.11, φ is an isomorphism iff $det_i \varphi \neq 0$. Hence $L_{\mathrm{iso}}(\mathbf{E}, \mathbf{F}) = (det_i)^{-1}(\mathbf{R} \setminus \{0\})$. But, by 9.12, det_i is continuous. Hence, since $\mathbf{R} \setminus \{0\}$ is open, $L_{\mathrm{iso}}(\mathbf{E}, \mathbf{F}) \subset L(\mathbf{E}, \mathbf{F})$ is open. ∎

Note that this proof is special to the finite-dimensional case, but the proposition is true more generally, as we saw in 6.7.

9.14. Definition. *Let $\varphi \in L(\mathbf{E}, \mathbf{F})$. For $\boldsymbol{\alpha} \in T_k^0(\mathbf{F})$ define $\varphi_*\boldsymbol{\alpha} \in L_k^0(\mathbf{E})$* by $\varphi_*\boldsymbol{\alpha}(\mathbf{e}_1, \ldots, \mathbf{e}_k) = \boldsymbol{\alpha}(\varphi(\mathbf{e}_1), \ldots, \varphi(\mathbf{e}_k))$. *If $\varphi \in L_{\mathrm{iso}}(\mathbf{E}, \mathbf{F})$, we denote by φ^* the map defined in 6.3.*

9.15. Proposition. *Let $\varphi \in L(\mathbf{E}, \mathbf{F})$, $\psi \in L(\mathbf{F}, \mathbf{G})$. Then*

(*i*) *$\varphi_*: T_k^0(\mathbf{F}) \to T_k^0(\mathbf{E})$ is linear, and $\varphi_*(\Omega^k(\mathbf{F})) \subset \Omega^k(\mathbf{E})$;*

(*ii*) *$(\psi \circ \varphi)_* = \varphi_* \circ \psi_*$;*

(*iii*) *If φ is the identity, so is φ_*;*

(*iv*) *If $\varphi \in L_{\mathrm{iso}}(\mathbf{E}, \mathbf{F})$ then $\varphi_* \in L_{\mathrm{iso}}(T_k^0(\mathbf{F}), T_k^0(\mathbf{E}))$, $(\varphi_*)^{-1} = (\varphi^{-1})_*$, and $\varphi_*\Omega^k(\mathbf{F}) = \Omega^k(\mathbf{E})$;*

(*v*) *If $\varphi \in L_{\mathrm{iso}}(\mathbf{E}, \mathbf{F})$ then $\varphi^* \in L_{\mathrm{iso}}(T_k^0\mathbf{E}, T_k^0\mathbf{F})$, $(\varphi^{-1})_* = \varphi^*$ and $(\varphi^*)^{-1} = (\varphi^{-1})^*$. If $\psi \in L_{\mathrm{iso}}(\mathbf{F}, \mathbf{G})$, $(\psi \circ \varphi)^* = \psi^* \circ \varphi^*$;*

(*vi*) *If $\boldsymbol{\alpha} \in \Omega^k(\mathbf{F})$, $\boldsymbol{\beta} \in \Omega^l(\mathbf{F})$, then $\varphi_*(\boldsymbol{\alpha} \wedge \boldsymbol{\beta}) = \varphi_*\boldsymbol{\alpha} \wedge \varphi_*\boldsymbol{\beta}$.*

Proof. It is evident that (*i*) follows at once from the definition. For (*ii*),

$$\begin{aligned}
(\psi \circ \varphi)_*\boldsymbol{\alpha}(\mathbf{e}_1, \ldots, \mathbf{e}_k) &= \boldsymbol{\alpha}(\psi \circ \varphi(\mathbf{e}_1), \ldots, \psi \circ \varphi(\mathbf{e}_k)) \\
&= \psi_*\boldsymbol{\alpha}(\varphi(\mathbf{e}_1), \ldots, \varphi(\mathbf{e}_k)) = \varphi_* \circ \psi_*\boldsymbol{\alpha}(\mathbf{e}_1, \ldots, \mathbf{e}_k)
\end{aligned}$$

Then (*iii*) is clear, and (*iv*) follows from (*ii*) and (*iii*) (see 5.7). For (*v*), $\varphi^*\boldsymbol{\beta}(\mathbf{f}_1,\ldots,\mathbf{f}_k) = \boldsymbol{\beta}(\varphi^{-1}\mathbf{f}_1,\ldots,\varphi^{-1}\mathbf{f}_k) = (\varphi^{-1})_*\boldsymbol{\beta}(\mathbf{f}_1,\ldots,\mathbf{f}_k)$ and $(\varphi^*)^{-1} = (\varphi^{-1})_*^{-1} = \varphi_* = (\varphi^{-1})^*$. Alternatively, this and the last assertion are a restatement of 6.4. Finally, $\varphi_*(\boldsymbol{\alpha}\wedge\boldsymbol{\beta})(\mathbf{e}_1,\ldots,\mathbf{e}_{k+l}) = \boldsymbol{\alpha}\wedge\boldsymbol{\beta}(\varphi\mathbf{e}_1,\ldots,\varphi\mathbf{e}_{k+l}) = \varphi_*\boldsymbol{\alpha}\wedge\varphi_*\boldsymbol{\beta}(\mathbf{e}_1,\ldots,\mathbf{e}_{k+l})$. ∎

As in §6, we can consider the exterior algebra on the fibers of a vector bundle as follows.

9.16. Definition. *Let $\varphi: U \times \mathbf{F} \to U' \times \mathbf{F}'$ be a local vector bundle map that is an isomorphism on each fiber. Then define $\varphi^*: U \times \Omega^k(\mathbf{F}) \to U' \times \Omega^k(\mathbf{F}')$ by $(u, \boldsymbol{\omega}) \rightsquigarrow (\varphi(u), \varphi_u^*\boldsymbol{\omega})$ where φ_u is the second factor of φ (an isomorphism for each u).*

9.17. Proposition. *If $\varphi: U \times \mathbf{F} \to U' \times \mathbf{F}'$ is a local vector bundle map that is an isomorphism on each fiber, then so is φ^*. Moreover, if φ is a local vector bundle isomorphism, so is φ^*.*

Proof. This is a special case of 6.9. ∎

9.18. Definition. *Suppose $\boldsymbol{\pi}: E \to B$ is a vector bundle. Define*

$$\omega^k(E)|A = \bigcup_{b\in A} \Omega^k(E_b)$$

where A is a subset of B and $E_b = \boldsymbol{\pi}^{-1}(b)$ is the fiber over $b \in B$ (4.4). Let $\omega^k(E)|B = \omega^k(E)$ and define $\boldsymbol{\omega}^k(\boldsymbol{\pi}): \omega^k(E) \to B$ by $\omega^k(\boldsymbol{\pi})(t) = b$ iff $t \in \Omega^k(E_b)$.

9.19. Theorem. *Suppose $\{E|U_i, \varphi_i\}$ is a vector bundle atlas of $\boldsymbol{\pi}$, where $\varphi_i: E|U_i \to U_i' \times \mathbf{F}_i'$. Then $\{\omega^k(E)|U_i, \varphi_i^*\}$ is a vector bundle atlas of $\boldsymbol{\omega}^k(\boldsymbol{\pi}): \omega^k(E) \to B$ where $\varphi_i^*: \omega^k(E)|U_i \to U_i' \times \Omega^k(\mathbf{F}_i')$ is defined by $\varphi_i^*|E_b = (\varphi_i|E_b)^*$ (as in 9.16).*

Proof. We must verify (VBA 1) and (VBA 2) of 4.2: (VBA 1) is clear; for (VBA 2) let φ_i, φ_j be two charts on $\boldsymbol{\pi}$, so that $\varphi_i \circ \varphi_j^{-1}$ is a local vector bundle isomorphism. (We may assume $U_i = U_j$.) But then from 9.15, $\varphi_i^* \circ \varphi_j^{*-1} = (\varphi_i \circ \varphi_j^{-1})^*$, which is a local vector bundle isomorphism by 9.17. ∎

Because of this theorem, the vector bundle structure of $\boldsymbol{\pi}: E \to B$ induces naturally a vector bundle structure on $\boldsymbol{\omega}^k(\boldsymbol{\pi}): \omega^k(E) \to B$, which is also Hausdorff, second countable, and of constant dimension. Hereafter $\boldsymbol{\omega}^k(\boldsymbol{\pi})$ will denote this vector bundle.

Exercises

9A. If $k!$ is omitted in the definition of $\mathbf{A}$ (9.1), show that $\wedge$ fails to be associative.

9B. Show that, in terms of components, our definition of the determinant is the usual one.

9C. Complete the details of 9.12.

§10. CARTAN'S CALCULUS OF DIFFERENTIAL FORMS

We now specialize the exterior algebra of the preceding section to tangent bundles and develop a differential calculus that is special to this case. This is basic to the dual integral calculus of §12 and to the Hamiltonian mechanics of Chapter III.

If $\tau_M: TM \to M$ is the tangent bundle of a manifold M, let $\omega^k(M) = \omega^k(TM)$, and $\boldsymbol{\omega}_M^k = \boldsymbol{\omega}^k(\tau_M)$, so $\boldsymbol{\omega}_M^k: \omega^k(M) \to M$ is the vector bundle of exterior k forms on the tangent spaces of M. Also, let $\Omega^0(M) = \mathscr{F}(M)$, $\Omega^1(M) = \mathscr{T}_1^0(M)$, and $\Omega^k(M) = \Gamma^\infty(\boldsymbol{\omega}_M^k)$, $k = 2, 3, \ldots$ (see 4.7 and 9.18).

10.1. Proposition. *Regarding $\mathscr{T}_k^0(M)$ as an $\mathscr{F}(M)$ module (§6), $\Omega^k(M)$ is an $\mathscr{F}(M)$ submodule.*

Proof. If $t_1, t_2 \in \Omega^k(M)$ and $f \in \mathscr{F}(M)$, we must show $f \otimes t_1 + t_2 \in \Omega^k(M)$. From 6.19, we have $f \otimes t_1 + t_2 \in \mathscr{T}_k^0(M)$. But, by 9.1, $f \otimes t_1 + t_2(m) \in \Omega^k(T_mM)$ and the result follows. ∎

10.2. Proposition. *If $\alpha \in \Omega^k(M)$ and $\beta \in \Omega^l(M)$; $k, l = 0, 1, \ldots, n$, define $\alpha \wedge \beta: M \to \omega^k(M)$ by $(\alpha \wedge \beta)(m) = \alpha(m) \wedge \beta(m)$. Then $\alpha \wedge \beta \in \Omega^{k+l}(M)$, and $\wedge$ is bilinear and associative.*

Proof. First, $\wedge$ is bilinear and associative by 9.5. To show $\alpha \wedge \beta$ is of class C^∞, consider the local respresentative of $\alpha \wedge \beta$ in natural charts. This is a map of the form $(\alpha \wedge \beta)_\varphi = B \circ (\alpha_\varphi \times \beta_\varphi)$, with $\alpha_\varphi, \beta_\varphi$, C^∞ and $B = \wedge$, which is bilinear. Thus $(\alpha \wedge \beta)_\varphi$ is C^∞ by Leibnitz' rule, 2.11. ∎

10.3. Definition. *Let $\Omega(M)$ denote the direct sum of $\Omega^k(M)$, $k = 0, 1, \ldots, n$, together with its structure as an (infinite dimensional) real vector space and with the multiplication $\wedge$ extended componentwise to $\Omega(M)$. We call $\Omega(M)$ the* **algebra of exterior differential forms** *on M. Elements of $\Omega^k(M)$ are called* ***k* forms**. *In particular, elements of $\mathscr{X}^*(M)$ are called* **1 forms**.

Note that we generally regard $\Omega(M)$ as a real vector space rather than an $\mathscr{F}(M)$ module (as with $\mathscr{T}(M)$). The reason is that $\mathscr{F}(M) = \Omega^0(M)$ is included in the direct sum, and $f \wedge \alpha = f \otimes \alpha = f\alpha$.

10.4. Notation. *Let (U, φ) be a chart on a manifold M with $U' = \varphi(U) \subset \mathbf{R}^n$. Let $\mathbf{e}_i$ denote the standard basis of $\mathbf{R}^n$ and let $\underline{e}_i(u) = T_{\varphi(u)}\varphi^{-1}(\varphi(u), \mathbf{e}_i)$. Similarly let $\boldsymbol{\alpha}^i$ denote the dual basis of $\mathbf{e}_i$ and $\underline{\alpha}^i(u) = (T_u\varphi)^*(\varphi(u), \boldsymbol{\alpha}^i)$. (Thus, for each $u \in U$, $\underline{e}_i(u)$ and $\underline{\alpha}^i(u)$ are dual bases of the fiber T_uM). Then if $\varphi(u) = (x^1(u), \ldots, x^n(u)) \in \mathbf{R}^n$, we define*

$$\frac{\partial f}{\partial x^i} = L_{\underline{e}_i} f = \frac{\partial f_\varphi}{\partial x^i} \circ \varphi^{-1}$$

at points $u \in U$ (8.1).

With these notations, we see $dx^i(u) = \underline{\alpha}^i(u)$, for

$$\begin{aligned} dx^i(u)(\underline{e}_j(u)) &= P_2 T_u x^i \circ T_{\varphi(u)}\varphi^{-1}(\varphi(u), \mathbf{e}_j) \\ &= P_2 T_u(x^i \circ \varphi^{-1})(\varphi(u), \mathbf{e}_j) \\ &= D(x^i \circ \varphi^{-1})(\varphi(u)) \circ \mathbf{e}_j = \delta^i_j \end{aligned}$$

Hence,

$$df(u) = df(\underline{e}_i)\,\underline{\alpha}^i(u) = \frac{\partial f}{\partial x^i}(u)\,dx^i(u)$$

Thus the components of the differential df are the usual $\partial f/\partial x^i$, where the latter are as in 10.4. Also, for each $t \in \mathcal{T}^r_s(U)$ we have

$$t(u) = t^{i_1 \cdots i_r}_{j_1 \cdots j_s}(u)\underline{e}_{i_1} \otimes \cdots \otimes \underline{e}_{i_r} \otimes dx^{j_1} \otimes \cdots \otimes dx^{j_s}$$

and for each $\omega \in \Omega^k(U)$

$$\omega(u) = k! \sum_{i_1 < \cdots < i_k} \omega_{i_1 \cdots i_k}(u)\,dx^{i_1} \wedge \cdots \wedge dx^{i_k}(u)$$

where

$$t^{i_1 \cdots i_r}_{j_1 \cdots j_r} = t(dx^{i_1}, \ldots, dx^{i_r}, \underline{e}_{j_1}, \ldots, \underline{e}_{j_s})$$

and

$$\omega_{i_1 \cdots i_k} = \omega(\underline{e}_{i_1}, \ldots, \underline{e}_{i_k})$$

The extension of d (8.1) to $\Omega^k(M)$ is given by the following.

10.5. Theorem. *Let M be a manifold. Then there is a unique family of mappings $\mathbf{d}^k(U)\colon \Omega^k(U) \to \Omega^{k+1}(U)$, $(k = 0, 1, 2, \ldots n$, and U is open in M), which we merely denote by* **d**, *called the* **exterior derivative** *on M, such that*

(*i*) **d** *is a* $\wedge$ **antiderivation**. *That is,* **d** *is* **R** *linear and for $\alpha \in \Omega^k(U)$, $\beta \in \Omega^l(U)$, $\mathbf{d}(\alpha \wedge \beta) = \mathbf{d}\alpha \wedge \beta + (-1)^k \alpha \wedge \mathbf{d}\beta$;*
(*ii*) *If $f \in \mathcal{F}(U)$, $\mathbf{d}f = df$ (8.1);*
(*iii*) $\mathbf{d} \circ \mathbf{d} = \mathbf{0}$ *(that is, $\mathbf{d}^{k+1}(U) \circ \mathbf{d}^k(U) = \mathbf{0}$);*
(*iv*) **d** *is natural with respect to restrictions; that is, if $U \subset V \subset M$ are open and $\alpha \in \Omega^k(V)$, then $\mathbf{d}(\alpha|U) = (\mathbf{d}\alpha)|U$, or the following diagram commutes:*

$$\begin{array}{ccc} \Omega^k(V) & \xrightarrow{\ |U\ } & \Omega^k(U) \\ {\scriptstyle \mathbf{d}}\downarrow & & \downarrow{\scriptstyle \mathbf{d}} \\ \Omega^{k+1}(V) & \xrightarrow[\ |U\ ]{} & \Omega^{k+1}(U) \end{array}$$

(Actually, by a method similar to that of 8.10, (*iv*) may be omitted, but we include it to simplify the proof.)

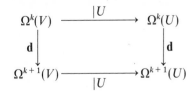

Proof. We first establish uniqueness. Using (*iv*) it is sufficient to consider the local case $\omega \in \Omega^k(U)$; $U \subset \mathbf{E}$. By $\mathbf{R}$ linearity and 9.7 it is sufficient to consider the case in which ω has the form $\omega = f_0\, df_1 \wedge \cdots \wedge df_k$ where $f_i \in \mathscr{F}(U)$. Hence, from (*i*) and (*iii*), $\mathbf{d}\omega = df_0 \wedge df_1 \wedge \cdots \wedge df_k$ and thus, by (*ii*), $\mathbf{d}\omega$ is uniquely determined.

For existence we may again suppose $\omega = f_0\, df_1 \wedge \cdots \wedge df_k$ in some chart, and define $\mathbf{d}\omega = df_0 \wedge df_1 \wedge \cdots \wedge df_k$, which is clearly independent of the chart. Then (*ii*) and (*iv*) are clear, as is $\mathbf{R}$ linearity. To prove (*i*), note that if $\rho = g_0\, dg_1 \wedge \cdots \wedge dg_l$ then

$$\begin{aligned}\mathbf{d}(\omega \wedge \rho) &= d(f_0 g_0) \wedge df_1 \wedge \cdots \wedge df_k \wedge dg_1 \wedge \cdots \wedge dg_l \\ &= g_0\, df_0 \wedge df_1 \wedge \cdots \wedge df_k \wedge dg_1 \wedge \cdots \wedge dg_l \\ &\quad + f_0\, dg_0 \wedge df_1 \wedge \cdots \wedge df_k \wedge dg_1 \wedge \cdots \wedge dg_l \\ &= \mathbf{d}\omega \wedge \rho + (-1)^k \omega \wedge \mathbf{d}\rho\end{aligned}$$

Finally, for (*iii*), it is clearly sufficient to verify $\mathbf{d} \circ \mathbf{d}f = 0$ for functions. But in a local chart $df(u) = Df(u) \cdot \mathbf{e}_i\, dx^i$ so that $\mathbf{d} \circ df(u) = DDf(u) \cdot (\mathbf{e}_i, \mathbf{e}_j)\, dx^j \wedge dx^i = 0$, as $D^2 f(u) \in L_s^2(\mathbf{E}, \mathbf{R})$ (2.6). ∎

10.6. Corollary. *Let $\omega \in \Omega^k(U)$ where $U \subset \mathbf{E}$ (open). Then*

$$\mathbf{d}\omega(u)(\mathbf{e}_0, \ldots, \mathbf{e}_k) = \sum_{i=0}^{k} (-1)^i D\omega(u) \cdot \mathbf{e}_i(\mathbf{e}_0, \ldots, \hat{\mathbf{e}}_i, \ldots, \mathbf{e}_k)$$

where $\hat{\mathbf{e}}_i$ denotes that $\mathbf{e}_i$ is deleted. Also, we denote elements $(u, \mathbf{e})$ of TU merely by $\mathbf{e}$, for brevity. (Note that $D\omega(u) \cdot \mathbf{e} \in L^k(\mathbf{E}, \mathbf{R})$.)

Proof. First note that $\mathbf{d}$ defined this way is a map $\Omega^k(U) \to \Omega^{k+1}(U)$. Then it is sufficient to verify (*i*)–(*iv*) of 10.5. But $\mathbf{R}$ linearity, (*ii*), and (*iv*) are clear, and as $\wedge$ is bilinear (9.5) we have $D(\omega \wedge \rho) = \omega \wedge D\rho + D\omega \wedge \rho$ by 2.11 from which (*i*) readily follows. Finally, (*iii*) follows as in 10.5. ∎

10.7. Definition. *Suppose $F: M \to N$ is a C^∞ mapping of manifolds. For $\omega \in \Omega^k(N)$ define $F_*\omega: M \to \omega^k(M)$ by $F_*\omega(m) = (T_m F)_* \circ \omega \circ F(m)$ (see 9.14).*

Especially, note if $g \in \Omega^0(N)$, $F_* g = g \circ F$.

10.8. Proposition. *Let $F: M \to N$ and $G: N \to W$ be C^∞ mappings of manifolds. Then*

(*i*) *$F_*: \Omega^k(N) \to \Omega^k(M)$;*
(*ii*) *$(G \circ F)_* = F_* \circ G_*$;*
(*iii*) *If $H: M \to M$ is the identity, then $H_*: \Omega^k(M) \to \Omega^k(M)$ is the identity;*
(*iv*) *If F is a diffeomorphism, then F_* is a vector bundle isomorphism and $(F_*)^{-1} = (F^{-1})_*$.*

Proof. Choose charts (U, φ), (V, ψ) of M and N so that $\varphi(U) \subset V$, then $F_{\varphi\psi} = \psi \circ F \circ \varphi^{-1}$ is of class C^∞, as is $\omega_\psi = (T\psi)^* \circ \omega \circ \psi^{-1}$. Then

$$\begin{aligned}(T_{u'}F_{\varphi\psi})_* &= (T_{u'}\varphi^{-1})_* \circ (T_u F)_* \circ (T_{f(u)}\psi)_* \qquad \text{(by 9.15)}\\ &= (T_u\varphi)^* \circ (T_u F)_* \circ (T_{f(u)}\psi)_*\end{aligned}$$

Hence the local representative of $F_*\omega$ is

$$\begin{aligned}(F_*\omega)_\varphi(u') &= \varphi^* \circ F_*\omega \circ \varphi^{-1}(u')\\ &= (T_{u'}F_{\varphi\psi})_* \circ \omega_\psi \circ F_{\varphi\psi}\end{aligned}$$

which is of class C^∞ by the composite mapping theorem; **R** linearity is clear.

For (*ii*), we merely note that it holds for the local representatives by 9.15; (*iii*) follows at once from the definition; and (*iv*) follows in the usual way from (*ii*) and (*iii*) (See 5.7). ∎

As $F_*: \Omega^k(N) \to \Omega^k(M)$ is **R** linear, it induces a mapping on the direct sums, $F_*: \Omega(N) \to \Omega(M)$, which are differential algebras with $\wedge$ and **d**.

10.9. Theorem. *Let $F: M \to N$ be of class C^∞. Then $F_*: \Omega(N) \to \Omega(M)$ is a homomorphism of differential algebras; that is,*

(*i*) *$F_*(\psi \wedge \omega) = F_*\psi \wedge F_*\omega$, and*
(*ii*) **d is natural with respect to mappings**; *that is, $F_*(\mathbf{d}\omega) = \mathbf{d}(F_*\omega)$, or the following diagram commutes:*

$$\begin{array}{ccc}\Omega^k(N) & \xrightarrow{\;F_*\;} & \Omega^k(M)\\ \mathbf{d}\big\downarrow & & \big\downarrow\mathbf{d}\\ \Omega^{k+1}(N) & \xrightarrow[\;F_*\;]{} & \Omega^{k+1}(M)\end{array}$$

Proof. We first consider $F_*(\psi \wedge \omega)$ when ψ is a function. Then

$$\begin{aligned}F_*(\psi\omega)(m) &= (T_m F)_* \circ \psi\omega \circ F(m)\\ &= (T_m F)_* \circ [(\psi \circ F) \cdot (\omega \circ F)](m)\\ &= \psi(F(m))F_*\omega(m)\end{aligned}$$

or $F_*(\psi \wedge \omega) = F_*\psi \wedge F_*\omega$, as $F_*\psi = \psi \circ F$ if $\psi \in \Omega^0(N)$. Then (*i*) follows immediately from 9.15 (*vi*). For (*ii*) we shall show in fact that if $m \in M$, there is a neighborhood U of $m \in M$ such that $\mathbf{d}(F_*\omega|U) = (F_*\mathbf{d}\omega)|U$, which is sufficient, as F_* and **d** are both natural with respect to restriction. Let (V, φ) be a local chart at $F(m)$ and U a neighborhood of $m \in M$ with $F(U) \subset V$. Then $\omega \in \Omega^k(V)$,

$$\omega = \omega_{i_1 \cdots i_k}\, dx^{i_1} \wedge \cdots \wedge dx^{i_k}$$

$$\mathbf{d}\omega = \partial_{i_0}\omega_{i_1 \cdots i_k}\, dx^{i_0} \wedge \cdots \wedge dx^{i_k}$$

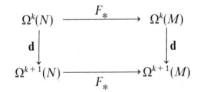

and by (*i*) above

$$F_*\omega|U = (F_*\omega_{i_1\cdots i_k})F_*dx^{i_1} \wedge \cdots \wedge F_*dx^{i_k}$$

But if $\psi \in \Omega^0(N)$, obviously $d(F_*\psi) = F_*d\psi$ by the composite mapping theorem (5.7 (*i*)), so

$$\begin{aligned} \mathbf{d}(F_*\omega|U) &= F_*(d\omega_{i_1\cdots i_k}) \wedge F_*dx^{i_1} \wedge \cdots \wedge F_*dx^{i_k} \\ &= F_*(\mathbf{d}\omega)|U \end{aligned}$$

by (*i*) above. ∎

10.10. Corollary. *The operator* $\mathbf{d}$ *is natural with respect to diffeomorphisms. That is, if* $F: M \to N$ *is a diffeomorphism, then* $F^*\mathbf{d}\omega = \mathbf{d}F^*\omega$, *or the following diagram commutes:*

$$\begin{array}{ccc} \Omega^k(M) & \xrightarrow{F^*} & \Omega^k(N) \\ \mathbf{d}\downarrow & & \downarrow\mathbf{d} \\ \Omega^{k+1}(M) & \xrightarrow[F^*]{} & \Omega^{k+1}(N) \end{array}$$

Proof. With F^* defined as in 6.16, namely $F^* = (F)^0_k$, we see that $F^* = (F^{-1})_*$ (see 10.7). The result then follows from 10.9 (*ii*). ∎

The next few propositions give some important relations between the Lie derivative and the exterior derivative.

10.11. Theorem. *Let* $X \in \mathscr{X}(M)$. *Then* $\mathbf{d}$ *is natural with respect to* $\mathbf{L}_X$. *That is, for* $\omega \in \Omega^k(M)$ *we have* $\mathbf{L}_X\omega \in \Omega^k(M)$ *and* $\mathbf{d}\mathbf{L}_X\omega = \mathbf{L}_X\mathbf{d}\omega$, *or the following diagram commutes:*

$$\begin{array}{ccc} \Omega^k(M) & \xrightarrow{\mathbf{L}_X} & \Omega^k(M) \\ \mathbf{d}\downarrow & & \downarrow\mathbf{d} \\ \Omega^{k+1}(M) & \xrightarrow[\mathbf{L}_X]{} & \Omega^{k+1}(M) \end{array}$$

Proof. If $\alpha^1, \ldots, \alpha^k \in \Omega^1(M)$ we have

$$\mathbf{L}_X(\alpha^1 \wedge \cdots \wedge \alpha^k) = \mathbf{L}_X\alpha^1 \wedge \alpha^2 \wedge \cdots \wedge \alpha^k + \cdots + \alpha^1 \wedge \cdots \wedge \mathbf{L}_X\alpha^k$$

This follows from the fact that $\mathbf{L}_X$ is $\mathbf{R}$ linear and is a tensor derivation. Since locally $\omega \in \Omega^k(M)$ is a linear combination of such products, it readily follows that $\mathbf{L}_X\omega \in \Omega^k(M)$. For the second part, let (U, a, F) be a flow box at $m \in M$, so that from 8.20,

$$\mathbf{L}_X\omega(m) = \frac{d}{d\lambda}(F_\lambda^{-1})^*\omega(m_\lambda)|_{\lambda=0}$$

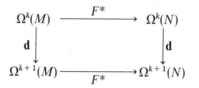

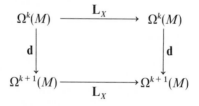

But from 10.10 we have $(F_\lambda^{-1})^*\mathbf{d}\omega = \mathbf{d}(F_\lambda^{-1})^*\omega$. Then, since $\mathbf{d}$ is linear we see $\mathbf{dL}_X\omega = \mathbf{L}_X\mathbf{d}\omega$. ∎

The foregoing proof can also be carried out in terms of local representatives, although it is longer. This is a good example of economy resulting from intrinsic proofs rather than component manipulation.

10.12. Definition. *Let M be a manifold, $X \in \mathscr{X}(M)$ and $\omega \in \Omega^{k+1}(M)$. Then define $\mathbf{i}_X\omega \in \mathscr{T}_k^0(M)$ by $\mathbf{i}_X\omega(X_1,\ldots,X_k) = (k+1)\omega(X, X_1,\ldots,X_k)$ (see 8.8). If $\omega \in \Omega^0(M)$, we put $\mathbf{i}_X\omega = \mathbf{0}$. We call $\mathbf{i}_X\omega$ the* **inner product** *of X and ω.*

10.13. Theorem. *We have $\mathbf{i}_X\colon \Omega^k(M) \to \Omega^{k-1}(M)$, $k = 1,\ldots, n$, and, for $\alpha \in \Omega^k(M)$, $\beta \in \Omega^l(M)$, $f \in \Omega^0(M)$,*

(*i*) *$\mathbf{i}_X$ is a $\wedge$ antiderivation. That is, $\mathbf{i}_X$ is $\mathbf{R}$ linear and $\mathbf{i}_X(\alpha\wedge\beta) = (\mathbf{i}_X\alpha)\wedge\beta + (-1)^k\alpha\wedge(\mathbf{i}_X\beta)$;*
(*ii*) *$\mathbf{i}_{fX}\alpha = f\mathbf{i}_X\alpha$;*
(*iii*) *$\mathbf{i}_X\,\mathbf{d}f = \mathbf{L}_Xf$;*
(*iv*) *$\mathbf{L}_X\alpha = \mathbf{i}_X\mathbf{d}\alpha + \mathbf{d}\mathbf{i}_X\alpha$;*
(*v*) *$\mathbf{L}_{fX}\alpha = f\mathbf{L}_X\alpha + \mathbf{d}f\wedge\mathbf{i}_X\alpha$.*

Proof. That $\mathbf{i}_X\omega \in \Omega^{k-1}(M)$ follows at once from 8.8. For (*i*), $\mathbf{R}$ linearity is clear. For the second part of (*i*)

$$\mathbf{i}_X(\alpha\wedge\beta)(X_2, X_3,\ldots,X_{k+l}) = (k+l)(\alpha\wedge\beta)(X, X_2,\ldots,X_{k+l})$$

and

$$\begin{aligned}\mathbf{i}_X\alpha\wedge\beta &+ (-1)^k\alpha\wedge\mathbf{i}_X\beta(X_2,\ldots,X_{k+l})\\ &= k\mathbf{A}[\alpha(X, X_2,\ldots,X_k)\beta(X_{k+1},\ldots,X_{k+l})]\\ &\quad + l(-1)^k\mathbf{A}[\alpha(X_2,\ldots,X_{k+1})\beta(X, X_{k+2},\ldots,X_{k+l})]\end{aligned}$$

But the sum over all permutations in the last term can be replaced by the sum over $\sigma\sigma_0$ where σ_0 is the permutation $(2, 3,\ldots,k+1, 1, k+2,\ldots, k+l) \rightsquigarrow (1, 2, 3,\ldots,k+l)$ whose sign is $(-1)^k$. Hence (*i*) follows. For (*ii*), we merely note $\mathbf{i}_X$ is linear on each fiber, and (*iii*) is just the definition of $\mathbf{L}_Xf$ (8.1). For (*iv*) we proceed by induction on k. First note that for $k = 0$, (*iv*) reduces to (*iii*). Now assume that (*iv*) holds for k. Then a $k+1$ form may be written as $\Sigma\,\mathbf{d}f_i\wedge\omega_i$ where ω_i is a k form, in some neighborhood of $m \in M$. But $\mathbf{L}_X(\mathbf{d}f\wedge\omega) = \mathbf{L}_X\mathbf{d}f\wedge\omega + \mathbf{d}f\wedge\mathbf{L}_X\omega$ and

$$\begin{aligned}\mathbf{i}_X\mathbf{d}(\mathbf{d}f\wedge\omega) + \mathbf{d}\mathbf{i}_X(\mathbf{d}f\wedge\omega) &= -\mathbf{i}_X(\mathbf{d}f\wedge\mathbf{d}\omega) + \mathbf{d}(\mathbf{i}_X\mathbf{d}f\wedge\omega - \mathbf{d}f\wedge\mathbf{i}_X\omega)\\ &= -\mathbf{i}_X\mathbf{d}f\wedge\mathbf{d}\omega + \mathbf{d}f\wedge\mathbf{i}_X\mathbf{d}\omega + \mathbf{d}\mathbf{i}_X\mathbf{d}f\wedge\omega\\ &\quad +\mathbf{i}_X\mathbf{d}f\wedge\mathbf{d}\omega + \mathbf{d}f\wedge\mathbf{d}\mathbf{i}_X\omega\\ &= \mathbf{d}f\wedge\mathbf{L}_X\omega + \mathbf{dL}_Xf\wedge\omega\end{aligned}$$

by our inductive assumption and (*iii*). Since $\mathbf{dL}_Xf = \mathbf{L}_X\mathbf{d}f$, the result follows.

Finally for (v) we have

$$\begin{aligned} \mathbf{L}_{fX}\omega &= \mathbf{i}_{fX}\mathbf{d}\omega + \mathbf{d}\mathbf{i}_{fX}\omega = f\mathbf{i}_X\mathbf{d}\omega + \mathbf{d}(f\mathbf{i}_X\omega) \\ &= f\mathbf{i}_X\mathbf{d}\omega + \mathbf{d}f\wedge\mathbf{i}_X\omega + f\mathbf{d}\mathbf{i}_X\omega \\ &= f\mathbf{L}_X\omega + \mathbf{d}f\wedge\mathbf{i}_X\omega \qquad \blacksquare \end{aligned}$$

The behavior of inner products under diffeomorphisms is given by the following.

10.14. Proposition. *Let M and N be manifolds and $f: M \to N$ a diffeomorphism. Let $f_* = (f^{-1})^*$, defined on $\mathscr{T}(N)$ (6.16). Then, if $\omega \in \Omega^k(N)$ and $X \in \mathscr{X}(N)$, we have*

$$\mathbf{i}_{f_*X} f_*\omega = f_*\mathbf{i}_X\omega$$

or inner products are natural with respect to diffeomorphisms, or the following diagram commutes:

$$\begin{array}{ccc} \Omega^k(N) & \xrightarrow{\quad f_* \quad} & \Omega^k(M) \\ \Big\downarrow \mathbf{i}_X & & \Big\downarrow \mathbf{i}_{f_*X} \\ \Omega^{k-1}(N) & \xrightarrow[\quad f_* \quad]{} & \Omega^{k-1}(M) \end{array}$$

Similarly for $Y \in \mathscr{X}(M)$ we have the following commutative diagram (compare 8.19):

$$\begin{array}{ccc} \Omega^k(M) & \xrightarrow{\quad f^* \quad} & \Omega^k(N) \\ \Big\downarrow \mathbf{i}_Y & & \Big\downarrow \mathbf{i}_{f^*Y} \\ \Omega^{k-1}(M) & \xrightarrow[\quad f^* \quad]{} & \Omega^{k-1}(N) \end{array}$$

Proof. Let $v_1, \ldots, v_{k-1} \in T_m(M)$ and $n = f(m)$. Then by 10.12 and 10.7

$$\begin{aligned} &\mathbf{i}_{f^*X} f_*\omega(m)\cdot(v_1, \ldots, v_{k-1}) \\ &\quad = kf_*\omega(m)\cdot(f_*X(m), v_1, \ldots, v_{k-1}) \\ &\quad = kf_*\omega(m)\cdot(Tf^{-1}\circ X(n), v_1, \ldots, v_{k-1}) \\ &\quad = k\omega(n)\cdot(Tf\circ Tf^{-1}X(n), Tfv_1, \ldots, Tfv_{k-1}) \\ &\quad = \mathbf{i}_X\omega(n)\cdot(Tfv_1, \ldots, Tfv_{k-1}) \\ &\quad = f_*\mathbf{i}_X\omega(m)\cdot(v_1, \ldots, v_{k-1}) \qquad \blacksquare \end{aligned}$$

The next proposition expresses $\mathbf{d}$ in terms of the Lie derivative.

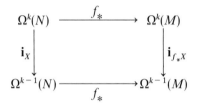

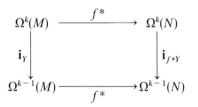

10.15. Proposition. *Let $\alpha \in \Omega^1(M)$, $X, Y \in \mathscr{X}(M)$ and $\omega \in \Omega^k(M)$. Then we have*

(*i*) $(\mathbf{L}_X\omega)(X_1,\ldots,X_k) = \mathbf{L}_X(\omega(X_1,\ldots,X_k))$

$$- \sum_{i=1}^{k} \omega(X_1,\ldots,\mathbf{L}_X X_i,\ldots,X_k)$$

(*ii*) $$\mathbf{d}\omega(X_0,X_1,\ldots,X_k) = \frac{1}{k+1}\left[\sum_{i=0}^{k}(-1)^i\mathbf{L}_{X_i}(\omega(X_0,\ldots,\hat{X}_i,\ldots,X_k)) + \sum_{0\le i<j\le k}(-1)^{i+j}\omega(\mathbf{L}_{X_i}(X_j),X_0,\ldots,\hat{X}_i,\ldots,\hat{X}_j,\ldots,X_k)\right]$$

where $\hat{X}_i$ denotes that X_i is deleted.

Proof. Part (*i*) is immediate in the notations 10.4, using 8.16 and 8.17. For (*ii*) we proceed by induction. For $k = 0$, it is merely $\mathbf{d}\omega(X_0) = \mathbf{L}_{X_0}\omega$. Assume the formula for $k - 1$. Then if $\omega \in \Omega^k(M)$, we have, by 10.13 (*iv*),

$$\begin{aligned}(k+1)\mathbf{d}\omega(X,X_1,\ldots,X_k) &= (\mathbf{i}_X\mathbf{d}\omega)(X_1,\ldots,X_k)\\ &= (\mathbf{L}_X\omega)(X_1,\ldots,X_k) - (\mathbf{d}(\mathbf{i}_X\omega))(X_1,\ldots,X_k)\\ &= \mathbf{L}_X(\omega(X_1,\ldots,X_k))\\ &\quad - \sum_{1}^{k}\omega(X_1,\ldots,\mathbf{L}_X X_i,\ldots,X_k)\\ &\quad -(\mathbf{d}\mathbf{i}_X\omega)(X_1,\ldots,X_k)\ \text{(by (}i\text{))}\end{aligned}$$

But $\mathbf{i}_X\omega \in \Omega^{k-1}(M)$ and we may apply the induction assumption. This gives, after a simple permutation and 10.12

$$\begin{aligned}(\mathbf{d}(\mathbf{i}_X\omega))(X_1,\ldots,X_k) &= \sum_{i=1}^{k}(-1)^{i-1}\mathbf{L}_{X_i}(\omega(X_1,\ldots,\hat{X}_i,\ldots,X_k)) -\\ &\quad - \sum_{1\le i<j\le k}(-1)^{i+j}\omega(\mathbf{L}_{X_i}X_j,X,X_1,\ldots,\hat{X}_i,\ldots,\hat{X}_j,\ldots,X_k)\end{aligned}$$

Substituting this into the above easily yields the result. ∎

10.16. Definition. *We call $\omega \in \Omega^k(M)$* **closed** *iff* $\mathbf{d}\omega = 0$, *and* **exact** *iff there is an $\alpha \in \Omega^{k-1}(M)$ such that $\omega = \mathbf{d}\alpha$.*

10.17. Theorem. (*i*) *Every exact form is closed.*

(*ii*) **(Poincaré lemma).** *If ω is closed, then for each $m \in M$, there is a neighborhood U of m for which $\omega|U \in \Omega^k(U)$ is exact.*

Proof. Part (*i*) is clear since $\mathbf{d}\circ\mathbf{d} = 0$ (10.5). Using a local chart and 10.9 (*ii*) together with 10.5 (*iv*), it is sufficient to consider the case $\omega \in \Omega^k(U)$, $U \subset \mathbf{E}$ a disk about $\mathbf{0} \in \mathbf{E}$, to prove (*ii*). On U we construct an $\mathbf{R}$ linear mapping $\mathbf{H}$: $\Omega^k(U) \to \Omega^{k-1}(U)$ such that $\mathbf{d}\circ\mathbf{H} + \mathbf{H}\circ\mathbf{d}$ is the identity on $\Omega^k(U)$. This will give the result, for $\mathbf{d}\omega = 0$ implies $\mathbf{d}(\mathbf{H}\omega) = \omega$.

For $\mathbf{e}_1,\ldots,\mathbf{e}_k \in \mathbf{E}$ define

$$\mathbf{H}\omega(u)(\mathbf{e}_1,\ldots,\mathbf{e}_{k-1}) = \int_0^1 t^{k-1}\omega(tu)(u,\mathbf{e}_1,\ldots,\mathbf{e}_{k-1})\,dt$$

Then, by 10.6,

$$\mathbf{dH}\omega(u)\cdot(\mathbf{e}_1,\ldots,\mathbf{e}_k) = \sum_{i=1}^{k}(-1)^{i+1}D\mathbf{H}\omega(u)\cdot\mathbf{e}_i(\mathbf{e}_1,\ldots,\hat{\mathbf{e}}_i,\ldots,\mathbf{e}_k)$$

$$= \sum_{i=1}^{k}(-1)^{i+1}\int_0^1 t^{k-1}\omega(tu)(\mathbf{e}_i,\mathbf{e}_1,\ldots,\hat{\mathbf{e}}_i,\ldots,\mathbf{e}_k)\,dt$$

$$+ \sum_{i=1}^{k}(-1)^{i+1}\int_0^1 t^k D\omega(tu)\cdot\mathbf{e}_i(u,\mathbf{e}_1,\ldots,\hat{\mathbf{e}}_i,\ldots,\mathbf{e}_k)\,dt$$

the last line following from 2.11 and the composite mapping theorem (5.7). (The interchange of D and $\int$ is permissible, as ω is smooth and bounded over $t\in[0,1]$.) However, we also have, by 10.6

$$\mathbf{Hd}\omega(u)\cdot(\mathbf{e}_1,\ldots,\mathbf{e}_k) = \int_0^1 t^k\mathbf{d}\omega(tu)(u,\mathbf{e}_1,\ldots,\mathbf{e}_k)\,dt$$

$$= \int_0^1 t^k D\omega(tu)\cdot u(\mathbf{e}_1,\ldots,\mathbf{e}_k)\,dt$$

$$+ \sum_{i=1}^{k}(-1)^{i}\int_0^1 t^k D\omega(tu)\cdot\mathbf{e}_i(u,\mathbf{e}_1,\ldots,\hat{\mathbf{e}}_i,\ldots,\mathbf{e}_k)\,dt$$

Hence

$$[\mathbf{dH}\omega(u)+\mathbf{Hd}\omega(u)](\mathbf{e}_1,\ldots,\mathbf{e}_k) = \int_0^1 kt^{k-1}\omega(tu)\cdot(\mathbf{e}_1,\ldots,\mathbf{e}_k)\,dt$$

$$+ \int_0^1 t^k D\omega(tu)\cdot u(\mathbf{e}_1,\ldots,\mathbf{e}_k)\,dt$$

$$= \int_0^1 \frac{d}{dt}[t^k\omega(tu)\cdot(\mathbf{e}_1,\ldots,\mathbf{e}_k)\,dt \qquad (5.7)$$

$$= \omega(u)\cdot(\mathbf{e}_1,\ldots,\mathbf{e}_k)$$

which proves the assertion. ∎

It will also be useful to consider a "relative" form of 10.17.

10.18. Definition. *Let M and N be manifolds and $M\times N$ the product manifold, with $\pi^2\colon M\times N\to N : (m,n)\rightsquigarrow n$. A differential form $\alpha\in\Omega^k(M\times N)$ will be called* **zero mod** *N iff for any $f\in\mathscr{F}(N)$, $\alpha\wedge\pi^2_* df = 0$ (and hence $\alpha\wedge\pi^2_*\beta = 0$ for any form $\beta\in\Omega^k(N)$, $k\geq 1$). Similarly, α is called* **closed mod** *N iff $\mathbf{d}\alpha$ is zero mod N, and α is* **exact mod** *N iff for some γ, $\alpha-\mathbf{d}\gamma$ is zero mod N. If $\alpha\in\Omega^k(M\times N)$, the* **horizontal part** *of α, denoted $h(\alpha)$, is defined as follows: at each point of*

$M \times N$, $\Omega^k(M \times N)$ splits into the direct sum of forms zero mod N and forms on M. The projection onto the second factor at each point gives the horizontal part. (It is clear from components that $h(\alpha) \in \Omega^k(M \times N)$.)

Then we have the following.

10.19. Proposition. (*i*) *If $\alpha \in \Omega^k(M \times N)$ is exact mod N, then α is closed mod N.*

(*ii*) **(Relative Poincaré lemma).** *If $\alpha \in \Omega^k(M \times N)$ is closed mod N, there is a neighborhood about each point on which α is exact mod N.*

Proof. For (*i*), if $(\alpha - \mathbf{d}\gamma) \wedge \pi_*^2 \mathbf{d}f = 0$ then by 10.6, 10.9, $\mathbf{d}\alpha \wedge \pi_*^2 \mathbf{d}f = 0$. For (*ii*), it is sufficient to consider the local case $\alpha \in \Omega^k(M \times N)$ where $M \subset \mathbf{E}$ is a disk about $0 \in \mathbf{E}$. Also, we may assume α is horizontal, for α and $h(\alpha)$ differ by a form that is zero mod N. For $n \in N$ let $j^n : M \to M \times N$; $m \rightsquigarrow (m, n)$ and $\mathbf{H}_M^n = \pi_*^1 \circ \mathbf{H} \circ j_*^n$ (10.17). Then if α is horizontal and $\mathbf{d}_M^n = \mathbf{d}_M \circ j_*^n$ ($\mathbf{d}_M$ is $\mathbf{d}$ on M), then $\mathbf{H}_M^n \circ \mathbf{d}_M^n \alpha + \mathbf{d}_M^n \mathbf{H}_M^n \alpha = j_*^n \alpha$ for each n. Finally, since $\mathbf{d}_M^n \alpha = 0$, $j_*^n \alpha = \mathbf{d}_M^n \beta$, where $\beta = \mathbf{H}_M^n \alpha$. But, for each n, $\pi_*^1 \mathbf{d}_M^n \beta$ and $\pi_*^1 \mathbf{d}\beta$ differ by a form that is zero mod N. Hence $\alpha - \mathbf{d}(\pi_*^1 \beta)$ is zero mod N, which proves the assertion. ∎

It is not true that closed forms are always exact (for example, on a sphere). In fact, the quotient groups of closed forms by exact forms (called the **de Rham cohomology groups** of M) shed light on the manifold topology.

Exercises

10A. Write out 10.5 and 10.19 in component notation. Give a coordinate free proof of 10.9 (*ii*). Prove 10.15 (*i*), using 2.11.

10B. On S^1 find a closed one-form α that is not exact. What are the cohomology groups of S^1?

10C. Show that the following properties uniquely characterize $\mathbf{i}_X$:

(i) $\mathbf{i}_X : \Omega^k(M) \to \Omega^{k-1}(M)$ is a $\wedge$ antiderivation;

(ii) $\mathbf{i}_X f = 0$; $f \in \mathscr{F}(M)$;

(iii) $\mathbf{i}_X \omega = \omega(X)$ for $\omega \in \Omega^1(M)$;

(iv) $\mathbf{i}_X$ is natural with respect to restrictions.

Hence show $\mathbf{i}_{[X,Y]} = \mathbf{L}_X \mathbf{i}_Y - \mathbf{i}_Y \mathbf{L}_X$. Finally, show $\mathbf{i}_X \circ \mathbf{i}_X = 0$.

10D. If $\omega \in \Omega^k(M)$, and if, for some $f \in \mathscr{F}(M)$, $f(m) \neq 0$ for all $m \in M$ and $f\omega$ is exact, there is a $\theta \in \Omega^1(U)$ with $\mathbf{d}\omega = \theta \wedge \omega$ and $\mathbf{d}\omega \wedge \omega = 0$. Interpret as a necessary condition for integrability of a total differential equation. Such a function f is an *integrating factor* of ω. For a partial converse, see Flanders [1, p. 94].

10E. (i) If $\mathbf{H} : \Omega^k(U) \to \Omega^{k-1}(U)$ is the operator of the Poincaré lemma (10.17), $X \in \mathscr{X}(U)$ is a constant vectorfield, $\alpha \in \Omega^k(U)$, and $\mathbf{i}_X \alpha = 0$, then $\mathbf{i}_X \mathbf{H}\alpha = 0$.

(ii) Suppose $\alpha \in \Omega^k(U \times V)$ is horizontal, $X \in \mathscr{X}(U \times V)$ is constant, and $\mathbf{i}_X \alpha = 0$. Then $\mathbf{i}_X \mathbf{H}_U \alpha = 0$ where $\mathbf{H}_U$ is the operator in the relative Poincaré lemma. Hint: Write X as a sum of vertical and horizontal components. For the vertical part use the relative Poincaré lemma and for the horizontal part use (i).

(iii) If $X \in \mathscr{X}(U)$ is constant and $\mathbf{i}_X \alpha = 0$, show $\mathbf{L}_X \mathbf{H} \alpha = 0$.

(iv) Under the hypotheses of (ii) show $\mathbf{L}_X \mathbf{H}_U \alpha = 0$.

§11. ORIENTABLE MANIFOLDS

The purpose of this section is to globalize the definitions of orientation and determinant discussed in §9. This leads naturally to the divergence of a vectorfield, which will be used in Chapter III.

First, we will discuss partitions of unity, which will be used in some proofs of this section, and which will be essential for the definition of the integral (§12).

11.1. Definitions. *If t is a tensorfield on a manifold M, the* **support** *of t is the closure* (§A1) *of the set of $m \in M$ for which $t(m) \neq 0$, and is denoted supp t. Also, we say t has* **compact support** *iff supp t is compact in M* (§A4). *(In a Hausdorff space, compact sets are closed. See* §A4.)

A collection of subsets $\{C_\alpha\}$ of a manifold M (or, more generally, a topological space) is called **locally finite** *iff for each $m \in M$ there is a neighborhood U of m such that $U \cap C_\alpha = \phi$ except for finitely many indices α.*

11.2. Definition. *A* **partition of unity** *on a manifold M is a collection $\{(U_i, \varphi_i, g_i)\}$, where*

(i) *$\{(U_i, \varphi_i)\}$ is an atlas on M;*
(ii) *$g_i \in \mathscr{F}(M)$, $g_i(m) \geq 0$ for all $m \in M$, g_i has compact support, and supp $g_i \subset U_i$ for all i;*
(iii) *$\{U_i\}$ is locally finite;*
(iv) *For each $m \in M$, $\sum_i g_i(m) = 1$.*

(By (iii), this is a finite sum.)

If $\mathscr{A}$ is an atlas on M, a **partition at unity subordinate to** *$\mathscr{A}$ is a partition at unity $\{(U_i, \varphi_i, g_i)\}$ such that each chart (U_i, φ_i) is a restriction of a chart of $\mathscr{A}$ to an open subset of its domain.*

11.3. Theorem. *If $\mathscr{A}$ is an atlas of M, there is a partition of unity subordinate to $\mathscr{A}$.*

For a proof see A6.1. (The proof consists of a skillful use of the bump functions discussed in §8.)

11.4. Definition. *A* **volume** *on an n-manifold M is an n-form $\Omega \in \Omega^n(M)$ such that $\Omega(m) \neq 0$ for all $m \in M$; M is called* **orientable** *iff there is a volume on M.*

Thus, Ω assigns an orientation, as defined in 9.8, to each fiber of TM.

11.5. Theorem. *Let M be an n-manifold. Then (i) M is orientable iff $\Omega^n(M)$, regarded as an $\mathscr{F}(M)$ module, is one-dimensional (has one generator);*

(ii) M is orientable iff M has an atlas $\{(U_i, \varphi_i)\}$ where $\varphi_i\colon U_i \to U_i' \subset \mathbf{R}^n$, such that the Jacobian determinant of the overlap maps is positive (the Jacobian determinant being the determinant of the derivative, a linear map from $\mathbf{R}^n$ into $\mathbf{R}^n$).

Proof. For (*i*) assume first that M is orientable, with a volume Ω. Let Ω' be any other element of $\Omega^n(M)$. Now each fiber of $\Omega^n(M)$ is one-dimensional, so we may define a map $f\colon M \to \mathbf{R}$ by

$$\Omega'(m) = f(m)\Omega(m)$$

We must show that $f \in \mathscr{F}(M)$. In local representation,

$$\Omega'(m) = \omega'_{i_1 \cdots i_n}(m)\, dx^{i_1} \wedge \cdots \wedge dx^{i_n}(m)$$

and $\Omega(m) = \omega_{i_1 \cdots i_n}(m)\, dx^{i_1} \wedge \cdots \wedge dx^{i_n}(m)$. But $\omega_{i_1 \cdots i_n}(m) \neq 0$ for all $m \in M$. Hence $f(m) = \omega'_{i_1 \cdots i_m}(m)/\omega_{i_1 \cdots i_m}(m)$ is of class C^∞. Conversely, if $\Omega^n(M)$ is generated by Ω, then $\Omega(m) \neq 0$ for all $m \in M$ since each fiber is one-dimensional.

To prove (*ii*), let $\{(U_i, \varphi_i)\}$ be an atlas with $U_i' \subset \mathbf{R}^n$. Also, we may assume that all U_i' are connected (see §A7) by taking restrictions if necessary. Now $\varphi_i^*\Omega = f_i\, dx^1 \wedge \cdots \wedge dx^n = f_i\Omega_0$ where Ω_0 is the standard volume element on $\mathbf{R}^n$. By means of a reflection if necessary, we may assume that $f_i(u') > 0$ ($f_i \neq 0$ since Ω is a volume). However, a continuous real valued function on a connected space which is not zero is always >0 or always <0 (A7.3). Hence, for overlap maps we have

$$(\varphi_i \circ \varphi_j^{-1})^*\, dx^1 \wedge \cdots \wedge dx^n = \varphi_i^* \circ \varphi_j^{*^{-1}}\, dx^1 \wedge \cdots \wedge dx^n$$

$$= \frac{f_i}{f_j \circ \varphi_j \circ \varphi_i^{-1}} dx^1 \wedge \cdots \wedge dx^n$$

by (10.9). But,

$$\psi_*(u)(\boldsymbol{\alpha}^1 \wedge \cdots \wedge \boldsymbol{\alpha}^n) = D\psi(u) \cdot \boldsymbol{\alpha}^1 \wedge D\psi(u) \cdot \boldsymbol{\alpha}^2 \wedge \cdots \wedge D\psi(u) \cdot \boldsymbol{\alpha}^n$$

where $D\psi(u) \cdot \boldsymbol{\alpha}^1(\mathbf{e}) = \boldsymbol{\alpha}^1(D\psi(u) \cdot \mathbf{e})$. Hence, by definition of determinant 9.11 we have

$$det(D(\varphi_j \circ \varphi_i^{-1})(u)) = \frac{f_i(u)}{f_j[\varphi_j \circ \varphi_i^{-1}(u)]} > 0$$

We leave as an exercise for the reader that the canonical isomorphism $L(\mathbf{E}; \mathbf{E}) \approx L(\mathbf{E}^*; \mathbf{E}^*)$, used above, does not affect determinants.

For the converse of (*ii*), let $\{(V_\alpha, \psi_\alpha)\}$ be an atlas with the given property, and $\{(U_i, \varphi_i, g_i)\}$ a subordinate partition of unity (11.3). Let

$$\Omega_i = \varphi_{i*}(dx^1 \wedge \cdots \wedge dx^n) \in \Omega^n(U_i)$$

and let

$$\tilde{\Omega}_i(m) = \begin{cases} g_i(m)\Omega_i(m) & \text{if} \quad m \in U_i \\ 0 & \text{if} \quad m \notin U_i \end{cases}$$

Since $supp\, g_i \subset U_i$, $\tilde{\Omega}_i \in \Omega^n(M)$. Then let

$$\Omega = \sum_i \tilde{\Omega}_i$$

Since this sum is finite in some neighborhood of each point, it is clear from local representatives that $\Omega \in \Omega^n(M)$. Finally, as the overlap maps have positive Jacobian determinant, then on $U_i \cap U_j$, $\Omega_i \neq 0$ and

$$\begin{aligned} \Omega_j = \varphi_{j*}(dx^1 \wedge \cdots \wedge dx^n) &= \varphi_{i*}(\varphi_j \circ \varphi_i^{-1})_*(dx^1 \wedge \cdots \wedge dx^n) \\ &= [det(\varphi_j \circ \varphi_i^{-1}) \circ \varphi_i]\varphi_{i_*}(dx^1 \wedge \cdots \wedge dx^n) \end{aligned}$$

Since $\Sigma_j g_j = 1$, it is clear then that $\Omega(m) \neq 0$ for each $m \in M$. ∎

Thus, if M is an orientable manifold, with volume Ω, 11.5 (*i*) defines a map from $\Omega^n(M)$ into $\mathscr{F}(M)$; namely, for each $\Omega' \in \Omega^n(M)$, there is a unique $f \in \mathscr{F}(M)$ such that $\Omega' = f\Omega$.

11.6. Definition. *Let M be an orientable manifold. Two volumes Ω_1 and Ω_2 on M are called* **equivalent** *iff there is an $f \in \mathscr{F}(M)$ with $f(m) > 0$ for all $m \in M$ such that $\Omega_1 = f\Omega_2$. (This is clearly an equivalence relation.) An* **orientation** *of M is an equivalence class $[\Omega]$ of volumes on M. An* **oriented manifold**, *$(M, [\Omega])$, is an orientable manifold M together with an orientation $[\Omega]$ on M.*

If $[\Omega]$ is an orientation of M, then $[-\Omega]$ (which is clearly another orientation) is called the **reverse orientation**.

The next proposition tells us when $[\Omega]$ and $[-\Omega]$ are the only two orientations.

11.7. Proposition. *Let M be an orientable manifold. The M is connected iff M has exactly two orientations.*

Proof. Suppose M is connected, and Ω, Ω' are two volumes with $\Omega' = f\Omega$. Since M is connected, and $f(m) \neq 0$ for all $m \in M$, $f(m) > 0$ for all m or else $f(m) < 0$ for all m (A7.3). Thus Ω' is equivalent to Ω or $-\Omega$. Conversely, if M is not connected, let $U \neq \phi$ or M be a subset that is both open and closed. If Ω is a volume on M, define Ω' by

$$\Omega'(m) = \begin{cases} \Omega(m) & m \in U \\ -\Omega(m) & -m \notin U \end{cases}$$

Obviously Ω' is a volume on M, and $\Omega' \notin [\Omega] \cup [-\Omega']$. ∎

A simple example of a nonorientable manifold is the Möbius band (see Figure 11-1).

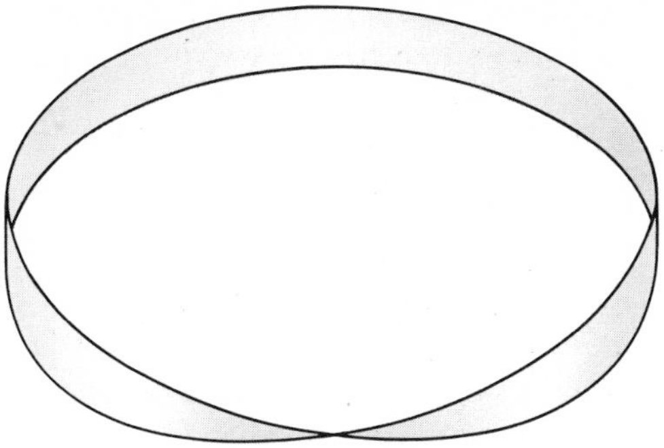

Figure 11-1

11.8. Proposition. *The equivalence relation in* 11.6 *is natural with respect to mappings and diffeomorphisms. That is, if* $f: M \to N$ *is of class* C^∞, Ω_N *and* Ω'_N *are equivalent volumes on* N, *and* $f_*(\Omega_N)$ *is a volume on* M, *then* $f_*(\Omega'_N)$ *is an equivalent volume. If* f *is a diffeomorphism and* Ω_M *and* Ω'_M *are equivalent volumes on* M, *then* $f^*(\Omega_M)$ *and* $f^*(\Omega'_M)$ *are equivalent volumes on* N.

Proof. This follows easily from the fact that

$$f_*(g\omega) = (g \circ f)f_*\omega$$

which implies

$$f^*(g\omega) = (g \circ f^{-1})f^*\omega$$

when f is a diffeomorphism. (See 10.9.) ∎

11.9. Definition. *Let* M *be an orientable manifold with orientation* $[\Omega]$. *A chart* (U, φ) *with* $\varphi(U) = U' \subset \mathbf{R}^n$ *is called* **positively oriented** *iff* $\varphi^*(\Omega|U)$ *is equivalent to the standard volume*

$$dx^1 \wedge \cdots \wedge dx^n \in \Omega^n(U')$$

From 11.8 we see that the above definition does not depend on the choice of the representative from $[\Omega]$.

If M is orientable, we can find an atlas in which every chart has positive orientation by choosing an atlas of connected charts and, if a chart has negative orientation (see 11.7), composing it with a reflection. Thus, in 11.5 (*ii*), the atlas consists of positively oriented charts.

11.10. Definition. *Let* V *be a submanifold of an n-manifold* M. *We say* V *has* **codimension** k *iff* V, *considered as a manifold, has dimension* $n - k$.

Now since a curve in V is also a curve in M, we can say $T_vV \subset T_vM$, and it is clear from §5 that the submanifold V has codimension k iff T_vV has dimension $n - k$ for each $v \in V$ iff for each $v \in V$ there is a vector space W_v of dimension k so that $T_vM = T_vV \oplus W_v$ (direct sum).

11.11. Proposition. *Suppose M is an orientable n-manifold and V is a submanifold of codimension k with trivial normal bundle. That is, there are C^∞ maps N_i: $V \to TM$, $i = 1, \ldots, k$ such that $N_i(v) \in T_v(M)$, and $N_i(v)$ span a subspace W_v such that $T_vM = T_vV \oplus W_v$ for all $v \in V$. Then V is orientable.*

Proof. Let Ω be a volume on M. Form $\Omega|V$: $V \to \Omega^n(M)$. Let us first note that $\Omega|V$ is a smooth mapping of manifolds. (This was obvious earlier when we considered open submanifolds.) This follows at once by using charts with the submanifold property, where the local representative is a restriction to a subspace (3.5). Now define $\Omega_0 : V \to \Omega^{n-k}(V)$ as follows: for

$$X_1, \ldots, X_{n-k} \in \mathscr{X}(V)$$

put

$$\Omega_0(v)(X_1(v), \ldots, X_{n-k}(v)) = \Omega(v)(N_1(v), \ldots, N_k(v), X_1(v), \ldots, X_{n-k}(v))$$

(analogous to an inner product; however N_i are not vectorfields on M). It is clear that $\Omega_0(v) \neq 0$ for all v. It remains only to show that Ω_0 is smooth, but this follows from the fact that $\Omega|V$ is smooth. ∎

For some proofs it will be convenient to use a Riemannian metric, although this is not essential in the development of mechanics in Chapter III.

11.12. Definition. *A* **Riemannian metric** *on a manifold M is a tensor $G \in \mathscr{T}^0_2(M)$ such that for all $m \in M$, $G(m)$ is symmetric and positive-definite.*

11.13. Proposition. *On any manifold there exists a Riemannian metric.*

Proof. Let $\{(U_i, \varphi_i, g_i)\}$ be a partition of unity on M, with $U_i' = \varphi_i(U_i) \subset \mathbf{R}^n$. If H_i is the standard Riemannian metric on U_i',

$$H_i(u)(v, w) = \sum v^i w^i$$

let $G_i \in \mathscr{T}^0_2(m)$ be defined by

$$G_i(m) = \begin{cases} g_i(m)(\varphi_i^{-1})^* H_i(m) & \text{if} \quad m \in U_i \\ 0 & \text{if} \quad m \notin U_i \end{cases}$$

Then $G = \Sigma_i G_i$ is a Riemannian metric on M. ∎

Note that if $G \in \mathscr{T}^0_2(M)$, we may identify G with an $\mathscr{F}$ linear mapping $G_\flat \in L(\mathscr{X}, \mathscr{X}^*)$ and if G is a Riemannian metric, obviously $G_\flat$ is an isomorphism. In this case we write $G_\sharp = (G_\flat)^{-1}$, and the maps $G_\sharp$ and $G_\flat$ are called raising and lowering indices, respectively. (For smoothness, see 13.7.)

11.14. Definition. *Let M be a manifold with a Riemannian metric G. For $f \in \mathscr{F}(M)$, $\operatorname{grad} f = G_\sharp(df)$ is called the* **gradient** *of f.*

Thus, $\operatorname{grad} f \in \mathscr{X}(M)$. The above machinery allows us to obtain the following consequence of 11.11.

11.15. Theorem. *Suppose M is an orientable manifold, $H \in \mathscr{F}(M)$ and $c \in \mathbf{R}$ is a regular value of H (5.17). Then $V = H^{-1}(c)$ is an orientable submanifold of M of codimension one, if it is non-empty.*

Proof. Suppose c is a regular value of H and $H^{-1}(c) = V \neq \phi$. Then V is a submanifold of codimension one. Let G be a Riemannian metric of M and $N = grad(H)|V$. Then $N(v) \notin T_v V$ for $v \in V$, because $T_v V$ is the kernel of $dH(v)$, and $dH(v)[N(v)] = G(N, N)(v) > 0$ as $dH(v) \neq 0$ by hypothesis. Then 11.11 applies, and V is orientable. ∎

Thus if we interpret V as the "energy surface," we see that it is an oriented submanifold for "almost all" energy values (Sard's theorem, 5.19).

Let us now examine the effect of volumes under maps more closely.

11.16. Definition. *Let M and N be two orientable n-manifolds with volumes Ω_M and Ω_N respectively. Then we call a C^∞ map $f: M \to N$* **volume preserving** *(with respect to Ω_M and Ω_N) iff $f_*\Omega_N = \Omega_M$, and we call f* **orientation preserving** *iff $f_*(\Omega_N) \in [\Omega_M]$, and* **orientation reversing** *iff $f_*(\Omega_N) \in [-\Omega_M]$.*

From 11.8, $[f_*\Omega_N]$ depends only on $[\Omega_N]$. Thus the first part of the definition depends explicitly on Ω_M and Ω_N while the last two parts depend only on the orientations $[\Omega_M]$ and $[\Omega_N]$. Furthermore, we see from 11.8 that if f is volume preserving with respect to Ω_M, Ω_N, then f is volume preserving with respect to $h\Omega_M$, $g\Omega_N$ iff $h = g \circ f$. It is also clear that if f is volume preserving with respect to Ω_M, Ω_N, then f is orientation preserving with respect to $[\Omega_M]$, $[\Omega_N]$.

11.17. Proposition. *Let M and N be n-manifolds with volumes Ω_M and Ω_N, respectively. Suppose $f: M \to N$ is of class C^∞. Then (i) $f_*(\Omega_N)$ is a volume iff f is a local diffeomorphism; that is, for each $m \in M$, there is a neighborhood V of m such that $f|V: V \to f(V)$ is a diffeomorphism. (ii) If M is connected, then f is a local diffeomorphism iff f is orientation preserving or orientation reversing.*

Proof. If f is a local diffeomorphism, then clearly $f_*(\Omega_N)(m) \neq 0$, by 10.9 (*ii*). Conversely, if $f_*(\Omega_N)$ is a volume, then as in 11.2, the determinant of the derivative of the local representative is not zero, and hence by 9.11 the derivative is an isomorphism. The result then follows by 2.10. Finally, (*ii*) follows at once from (*i*) and 11.7. ∎

Next we consider the global analogue of the determinant (§9).

11.18. Definition. *Suppose M and N are orientable n-manifolds with volumes Ω_M and Ω_N, respectively. If $f: M \to N$ is of class C^∞, the unique C^∞ function $det_{(\Omega_M,\Omega_N)} f \in \mathscr{F}(M)$ such that $f_*\Omega_N = (det_{(\Omega_M,\Omega_N)} f)\Omega_M$ (see 11.5 (i)) is called the* **determinant** *of f (with respect to Ω_M and Ω_N). If $f: M \to M$ we write $det_{\Omega_M} f = det_{(\Omega_M,\Omega_M)} f$.*

The basic properties of determinants given in §9 also hold in the global case, as follows.

11.19. Proposition. *In the notation of* 11.18, *f is a local diffeomorphism iff $det_{(\Omega_M,\Omega_N)}f(m) \neq 0$ for all $m \in M$.*

This follows at once from 11.17.

11.20. Proposition. *Let M be an orientable manifold with volume Ω. Then*

(*i*) *if $f\colon M \to M$, $g\colon M \to M$ are of class C^∞, then $det_\Omega(f \circ g) = [(det_\Omega f) \circ g][det_\Omega g)$;*

(*ii*) *If $h\colon M \to M$ is the identity, then $det_\Omega h = 1$;*

(*iii*) *If $f\colon M \to M$ is a diffeomorphism, then*

$$det_\Omega(f^{-1}) = 1/[(det_\Omega f) \circ f^{-1}]$$

Proof. For (*i*),

$$\begin{aligned} det_\Omega(f \circ g)\Omega &= (f \circ g)_*\Omega = g_* \circ f_*\Omega & \text{(by 10.8)} \\ &= g_*(det_\Omega f)\Omega = ((det_\Omega f) \circ g)g_*\Omega & (10.9) \\ &= (det_\Omega f) \circ g(det_\Omega g)\Omega \end{aligned}$$

Part (*ii*) follows since, by 10.8 (*iii*), h_* is the identity. For (*iii*) we have

$$det_\Omega(f \circ f^{-1}) = 1 = ((det_\Omega f) \circ f^{-1})(det_\Omega f^{-1}) \quad \blacksquare$$

If $f\colon U \subset \mathbf{E} \to \mathbf{E}$, then $det\, f$ is the Jacobian determinant of f which reduces to the determinant of f if f is linear (since $Df(u) = f$ if f is linear). Then in this case, (*i*) above is the usual "chain rule" for Jacobian determinants. (See the proof of 11.5.)

11.21. Proposition. *Let $(M, [\Omega_M])$ and $(N, [\Omega_N])$ be oriented manifolds and $f\colon M \to N$ be of class C^∞. Then f is orientation preserving iff $det_{(\Omega_M,\Omega_N)}f(m) > 0$ for all $m \in M$, and orientation reversing iff $det_{(\Omega_M,\Omega_N)}f(m) < 0$ for all $m \in M$. Also, f is volume preserving with respect to Ω_M, Ω_N iff $det_{(\Omega_M,\Omega_N)}f = 1$.*

This proposition follows at once from the definitions. Note that the first two assertions depend only on the orientations $[\Omega_M]$ and $[\Omega_N]$ since

$$det_{(h\Omega_M,g\Omega_N)}f = \left(\frac{g \circ f}{h}\right) det_{(\Omega_M,\Omega_N)}f$$

which the reader can easily check. Here $g \in \mathcal{F}(N)$, $h \in \mathcal{F}(M)$, $g(n) \neq 0$, $h(m) \neq 0$ for all $n \in N$, $m \in M$. However, this depends on Ω_M and Ω_N.

Suppose that X is a vectorfield on $\mathbf{R}^n$ and $\Omega_0 = dx^1 \wedge \cdots \wedge dx^n$ is the standard volume on $\mathbf{R}^n$. Then $\mathbf{L}_X\Omega_0 = \mathbf{L}_X dx^1 \wedge dx^2 \wedge \cdots \wedge dx^n + \cdots + dx^1 \wedge \cdots \wedge \mathbf{L}_X dx^n$ (since $\mathbf{L}_X$ is a derivation §10). But $\mathbf{L}_X dx^i = d\mathbf{L}_X x^i$ (10.11), and $\mathbf{L}_X x^i = dx^i(X) = X^i$, the components of X. Hence

$$\mathbf{L}_X dx^i = dX^i = \left(\frac{\partial X^i}{\partial x^j}\right) dx^j \quad \text{and} \quad \mathbf{L}_X\Omega_0 = \left(\frac{\partial X^i}{\partial x^i}\right)\Omega_0$$

since $dx^i \wedge dx^i = 0$. That is, $\mathbf{L}_X\Omega_0 = (div\ X)\Omega_0$ where $div\ X$ is the usual divergence of a vectorfield on $\mathbf{R}^n$. The generalization of this is as follows.

11.22. Definition. *Let M be an orientable manifold with volume Ω, and X a vectorfield on M. Then the unique function $div_\Omega X \in \mathscr{F}(M)$, such that $\mathbf{L}_X\Omega = (div_\Omega X)\Omega$ is called the* **divergence** *of X. (See* 11.5(*i*) *and* 11.18.) *We say X is* **incompressible** *(with respect to Ω) iff $div_\Omega X = 0$.*

11.23. Proposition. *Let M be an orientable manifold with volume Ω, and X a vectorfield on M. Then*

(*i*) *If $f \in \mathscr{F}(M)$ and $f(m) \neq 0$ for all $m \in M$, then*

$$div_{f\Omega} X = div_\Omega X + \frac{\mathbf{L}_X f}{f}$$

(*ii*) *For $g \in \mathscr{F}(M)$, $div_\Omega gX = g\ div_\Omega X + \mathbf{L}_X g$.*

Proof. Since $\mathbf{L}_X$ is a derivation, we have

$$\mathbf{L}_X(f\Omega) = (\mathbf{L}_X f)\Omega + f\mathbf{L}_X\Omega$$

Thus, by 11.22, since $f\Omega$ is a volume, $(div_{f\Omega}X)(f\Omega) = (\mathbf{L}_X f)\Omega + f(div_\Omega X)\Omega$. Then (*i*) follows. For (*ii*), we have, by 10.13, $\mathbf{L}_{gX}\Omega = g\mathbf{L}_X\Omega + dg \wedge \mathbf{i}_X\Omega$. Now from the antiderivation property of $\mathbf{i}_X$, $\mathbf{d}g \wedge \mathbf{i}_X\Omega = \mathbf{i}_X(\mathbf{d}g \wedge \Omega) + \mathbf{i}_X\mathbf{d}g \wedge \Omega$. But $\mathbf{d}g \wedge \Omega \in \Omega^{n+1}(M)$, and hence $\mathbf{d}g \wedge \Omega = 0$. Also, $\mathbf{i}_X\mathbf{d}g = \mathbf{L}_X g$ (see 10.13) and so $\mathbf{L}_{gX}\Omega = g\mathbf{L}_X\Omega + (\mathbf{L}_X g)\Omega$. The result follows at once from this. ∎

11.24. Proposition. *Let M be a manifold with volume Ω and X a vectorfield on M. Then X is incompressible (with respect to Ω) iff every flow box of X is volume preserving; that is, for the diffeomorphism $F_\lambda: U \to V$, F_λ is volume preserving with respect to $\Omega|U$ and $\Omega|V$.*

Proof. If X is incompressible, $\mathbf{L}_X\Omega = 0$, and, by 8.21, Ω is constant along integral curves of X; $\Omega(m) = (F_\lambda)_*\Omega(m)$. Hence F_λ is volume preserving. Conversely, if $(F_\lambda)_*\Omega(m) = \Omega(m)$, then from 8.20, $\mathbf{L}_X\Omega = 0$. ∎

11.25. Corollary. *Let M be an orientable manifold with volume Ω, and X a complete vectorfield with flow F on M (see 7.13). Then X is incompressible iff $det_\Omega F_\lambda = 1$ for all $\lambda \in \mathbf{R}$.*

Since all flow boxes are restrictions of F, this corollary follows at once from 11.24 and 11.21.

Exercises

11A. Notice that the definition of divergence does not depend on a metric, but rather on a volume element. Compare with the divergence used in Riemannian geometry. Compare the coordinate proof of 11.23 with that given here.

11B. Complete the proof of 11.21, and examine its geometrical meaning in the case $f: \mathbf{R}^n \to \mathbf{R}^n$.

§12. INTEGRATION ON MANIFOLDS

The aim of this section is to define integrals of n forms with compact support on an n-manifold M. We begin with a summary of the basic results on $\mathbf{R}^n$.

Suppose $f\colon \mathbf{R}^n \to \mathbf{R}$ is continuous and has compact support. Then $\int f\,dx^1 \cdots dx^n$ is defined as the Riemann integral over any rectangle containing the support of f (see Apostol [1, Chapter 10]). Recall that such a rectangle always exists (§A4), f is necessarily bounded, and the integral is independent of the rectangle chosen.

12.1. *Definition.* *Let $U \subset \mathbf{R}^n$ be open, and $\omega \in \Omega^n(U)$ have compact support. (Compactness in U is the same as compactness in $\mathbf{R}^n$; see §A4.) If, relative to the standard basis of $\mathbf{R}^n$,*

$$\omega(u) = \omega_{i_1\cdots i_n}(u)dx^{i_1} \wedge \cdots \wedge dx^{i_n} = n!\,\omega_{1\cdots n}(u)\,dx^1 \wedge \cdots \wedge dx^n$$

where

$$\omega_{i_1\cdots i_n}(u) = \omega(u)(\mathbf{e}_{i_1}, \ldots, \mathbf{e}_{i_n})$$

we define

$$\int \omega = \int n!\,\omega_{1\cdots n}(u)\,dx^1 \cdots dx^n$$

Clearly, if we regard $\omega \in \Omega^n(\mathbf{R}^n)$, the integral is unchanged.

The change of variables rule takes the following form.

12.2. *Theorem.* *Let U, V be open subsets of $\mathbf{R}^n$ and suppose $f\colon U \to V$ is an orientation preserving diffeomorphism. Then if $\omega \in \Omega^n(V)$ has compact support, $f_*\omega \in \Omega^n(U)$ has compact support and $\int f_*\omega = \int \omega$, or the following diagram commutes:*

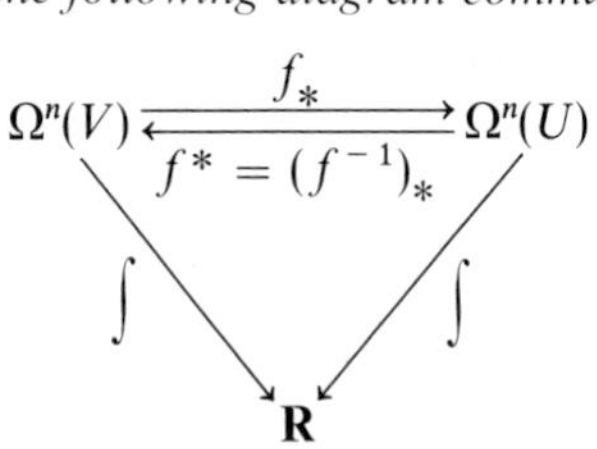

Proof. If $\omega = n!\,\omega_{1\cdots n}\,dx^1 \wedge \cdots \wedge dx^n$, then from 11.18, $f_*\omega = n!(\omega_{1\cdots n} \circ f) \times (det_{\Omega_0} f)\Omega_0$, where $\Omega_0 = dx^1 \wedge \cdots \wedge dx^n$ is the standard volume on $\mathbf{R}^n$. Since f is a diffeomorphism, the support of $f_*\omega$ is compact (§A4). Then

$$\int f_*\omega = \int n!(\omega_{1\cdots n} \circ f)(det_{\Omega_0} f)\,dx^1 \cdots dx^n$$

As was discussed in §11, $det_{\Omega_0} f > 0$ is the Jacobian determinant of f. Now by covering the support of ω by a finite number of disks, we see that the usual change of variables formula applies in this case (Apostol [1, p. 271]);

namely,

$$\int \omega_{1\cdots n}\, dx^1 \cdots dx^n = \int (\omega_{1\cdots n} \circ f)(det_\Omega f)\, dx^1 \cdots dx^n$$

which implies $\int f_* \omega = \int \omega$. ∎

Suppose that (U, φ) is a chart on a manifold M, and $\omega \in \Omega^n(M)$. Then if $supp\ \omega \subset U$, we may form $\omega | U$, which has the same support. Then $\varphi^*(\omega|U)$ has compact support, as we may state the following.

12.3. *Definition.* *Let M be an orientable n-manifold with orientation Ω. Suppose $\omega \in \Omega^n(M)$ has compact support $C \subset U$ where (U, φ) is a positively oriented chart. Then we define $\int_{(\varphi)} \omega = \int \varphi^*(\omega|U)$.*

12.4. *Proposition.* *Suppose $\omega \in \Omega^n(M)$ has compact support $C \subset U, \cap V$, where (U, φ), (V, ψ) are two positively oriented charts on the oriented manifold M. Then*

$$\int_{(\varphi)} \omega = \int_{(\psi)} \omega$$

Proof. By 12.2 $\int \varphi^*(\omega|U) = \int (\psi \circ \varphi^{-1})^* \varphi^*(\omega|U)$. Hence $\int \varphi^*(\omega|U) = \int \psi^*(\omega|U)$. (Recall that for diffeomorphisms $f^* = (f^{-1})_*$ and $(f \circ g)^* = f^* \circ g^*$.) ∎

Thus we merely define $\int \omega = \int_{(\varphi)} \omega$ where (U, φ) is any positively oriented chart containing the compact support of ω (if one exists).

More generally, we can define $\int \omega$ where ω has compact support as follows.

12.5. *Definition.* *Let M be an oriented manifold and $\mathscr{A}$ an atlas of positively oriented charts. Let $P = \{(U_\alpha, \varphi_\alpha, g_\alpha)\}$ be a partition of unity subordinate to $\mathscr{A}$ (§11). Define $\omega_\alpha = g_\alpha \omega$ (so ω_α has compact support in some U_i). Then define*

$$\int_P \omega = \sum_\alpha \int \omega_\alpha$$

(This is an infinite sum of real numbers.)

12.6. *Proposition.* *(i) The above sum contains only a finite number of nonzero terms, and hence $\int_P \omega \in \mathbf{R}$.*

(ii) For any other atlas of positively oriented charts and subordinate partition of unity Q we have $\int_P \omega = \int_Q \omega$.

The common value is denoted $\int \omega$, the **integral** of $\omega \in \Omega^n(M)$.

Proof. For any $m \in M$, there is a neighborhood U such that only a finite number of g_α are nonzero on U. By compactness of $supp\ \omega$, a finite number of such neighborhoods cover $supp\ \omega$. Hence only a finite number of g_α are nonzero on the union of these U. For (ii), let $P = \{(U_\alpha, \varphi_\alpha, g_\alpha)\}$ and $Q = \{(V_\beta, \psi_\beta, h_\beta)\}$ be two partitions of unity with positively oriented charts. Then the functions $\{g_\alpha h_\beta\}$ have $g_\alpha h_\beta(m) = 0$ except for a finite number of indices (α, β), and $\Sigma_\alpha \Sigma_\beta g_\alpha h_\beta(m) = 1$, for all $m \in M$. Hence, since $\Sigma_\beta h_\beta = 1$,

$$\int_P \omega = \sum_\alpha \int g_\alpha \omega$$

$$= \sum_\beta \sum_\alpha \int h_\beta g_\alpha \omega$$

$$= \sum_\alpha \sum_\beta \int g_\alpha h_\beta \omega = \int_Q \omega \quad \blacksquare$$

The globalization of the change of variables formula is as follows.

12.7. Theorem. *Suppose M and N are oriented n-manifolds and $f\colon M \to N$ is an orientation preserving diffeomorphism. Then if $\omega \in \Omega^n(N)$ has compact support, $f_*\omega$ has compact support, and $\int \omega = \int f_*\omega$.*

Proof. First, *supp* $f_*\omega = f^{-1}$(*supp* ω), which is compact. For the second part, let $\{U_i, \varphi_i\}$ be an atlas of positively oriented charts of M and let $P = \{g_i\}$ be a subordinate partition of unity. Then $\{f(U_i), \varphi_i \circ f^{-1}\}$ is an atlas of positively oriented charts of N and $Q = \{g_i \circ f^{-1}\}$ is a partition of unity subordinate to the covering $\{f(U_i)\}$. Then

$$\int f_*\omega = \sum_\alpha \int g_\alpha f_*\omega = \sum_\alpha \int \varphi^*(g_\alpha f_*\omega)$$

$$= \sum_\alpha \int \varphi^* \cdot (f^{-1})^*(g_\alpha \circ f^{-1})\omega \qquad \text{(see 10.9)}$$

$$= \sum_\alpha \int (\varphi \circ f^{-1})^*(g_\alpha \circ f^{-1})\omega$$

$$= \int \omega \qquad \text{(by 12.6)} \quad \blacksquare$$

As in 12.2, we have the following commutative diagram:

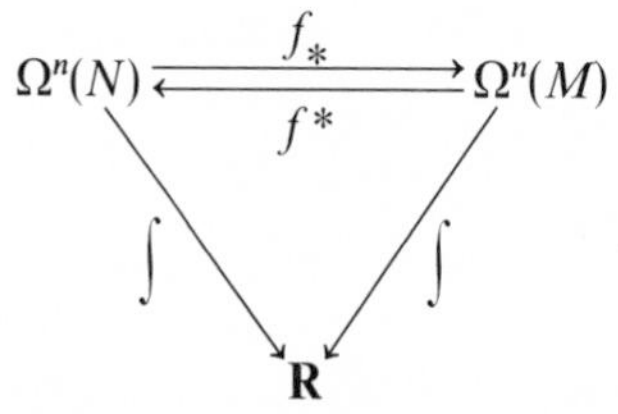

We also can integrate functions of compact support as follows.

12.8. Definition. *Let M be an orientable manifold with volume Ω. Suppose $f \in \mathscr{F}(M)$ and f has compact support. Then we define $\int_\Omega f = \int f\Omega$, the* **integral** *of f with respect to Ω.*

The reader can easily check that since the Riemann integral is **R** linear, so is the integral above.

The next theorem will show that the foregoing integral can be obtained in a unique way from a measure on M. (The reader unfamiliar with measure theory can find the necessary background in Royden [1]. However, this will not be essential for future sections.) The integral we have described can clearly be extended to all continuous functions with compact support. Then we have the following.

12.9. Theorem (Riesz representation theorem). *Let M be an orientable manifold with volume Ω. Let $\mathscr{B}$ denote the Borel sets of M, the σ algebra generated by the open (or closed, or compact) subsets of M. Then there is a unique measure μ_Ω on $\mathscr{B}$ (and hence a completion $\bar{\mu}_\Omega$) such that for every continuous function of compact support, $\int f\, d\mu_\Omega = \int_\Omega f$.*

Proof. Existence of such a μ_Ω is proved in Royden [1, p. 251]. Here A4.4 is used. For uniqueness, it is enough to consider bounded open sets (by the Hahn extension theorem). Thus, let U be open in M, and let C_U be its characteristic function. From 8.7 we can construct a sequence of C^∞ functions of compact support, φ_n such that $\varphi_n \downarrow C_U$, pointwise. Hence from the monotone convergence theorem $\int_\Omega \varphi_n = \int \varphi_n\, d\mu_\Omega \to \int C_U\, d\mu_\Omega = \mu_\Omega(U)$. Thus, μ_Ω is unique. ∎

Then one can define the space $L^p(M, \Omega)$, $p \in \mathbf{R}$, consisting of all measurable functions f such that $|f|^p$ is integrable. For $p \geq 1$, the norm $\|f\|_p = (\int |f|^p\, d\mu_\Omega)^{1/p}$ makes $L^p(M, \Omega)$ into a Banach space (that is, a complete, normed vector space; see §1).

The behavior of these spaces under mappings can give information about the manifold. In particular, the effect under flows is of importance in statistical mechanics. In this connection we have the following.

12.10. Proposition. *Let M be an orientable manifold with volume Ω. Suppose X is a complete vectorfield on M with flow F (see 7.13). Then X is incompressible iff μ_Ω is F invariant, that is, $\int f\, d\mu_\Omega = \int f \circ F_\lambda\, d\mu_\Omega$ for all λ, and $f \in L^1(M, \Omega)$.*

Proof. If X is incompressible, and f is continuous with compact support, then $\int f \circ F_\lambda \Omega = \int f \circ F_\lambda (F_\lambda)_* \Omega = \int (F_\lambda)_* f\Omega = \int f\Omega$, by §11 and 12.7. Hence, by uniqueness in 12.9, we have $\int f\, d\mu_\Omega = \int (f \circ F_\lambda)\, d\mu_\Omega$ for all integrable f. Conversely, if $\int (f \circ F_\lambda)\, d\mu_\Omega = \int f\, d\mu_\Omega$, then taking f continuous with compact support, we see

$$\int (f \circ F_\lambda)\, \Omega = \int (f \circ F_\lambda)\, F_{\lambda *}\Omega \qquad \text{(by 12.7)}$$

$$= \int (f \circ F_\lambda)(det_\Omega F_\lambda)\, \Omega$$

Thus, for every integrable f, $\int f\, d\mu_\Omega = \int (f\, det_\Omega F_\lambda)\, d\mu_\Omega$, by 12.9. Hence, $det_\Omega F_\lambda = 1$, which implies X is incompressible. ∎

Finally, we consider manifolds with boundary and state a general form of Stokes' theorem.

12.11. Definition. *A* **compact manifold with boundary** *is a triple* $(V, V_0, bd V_0)$ *where* V *is an n-manifold,* V_0 *is an open submanifold of* V, *and* $bd V_0$ *is the (topological) boundary of* V_0 (§A1), *such that*

(MB 1) V_0^c *is compact in* V;

(MB 2) $bd V_0$ *is a submanifold of* V *of codimension* 1 ($bd V_0$ *has dimension* $n - 1$).

An **oriented compact manifold with boundary** *is a compact manifold with boundary* $(V, V_0, bd V_0)$ *in which* V *is an oriented manifold and for each* $v \in bd V_0$ *there is a positively oriented chart having the following property.*

(MB 3) *For each* $v \in bd V_0$ *there is a submanifold chart of* $bd V_0$ *such that*

(*i*) $\varphi(U) \subset U' \times I \subset \mathbf{R}^{n-1} \times \mathbf{R}$, $\varphi(v) = (\mathbf{0}, 0)$,
(*ii*) $\varphi(U \cap bd V_0) = U' \times \{0\}$, *and*
(*iii*) $\varphi(U \cap V_0) \subset U' \times (\mathbf{0}, \lambda)$ *where* $\lambda > 0$.

Roughly speaking, (MB 3) guarantees that V_0 always lies on one side of the boundary (see Figure 12-1).

Also note that (MB 3) is essential. For example, on the circle $S^1 = V$, $p \in S^1$, $V_0 = V \setminus \{p\}$ satisfies (MB 1) and (MB 2) but not (MB 3).

If $(V, V_0, bd V_0)$ is an oriented compact manifold with boundary, then V_0 and $bd V_0$ are oriented by (11.11). Also note that $bd V_0$ is compact and, as a subset of V, has measure zero.

12.2. Theorem (Stokes). *Let* M *be a manifold and* $\alpha \in \Omega^{k-1}(M)$. *Suppose* $(V, V_0, bd V_0)$ *is an oriented compact k-manifold with boundary,*

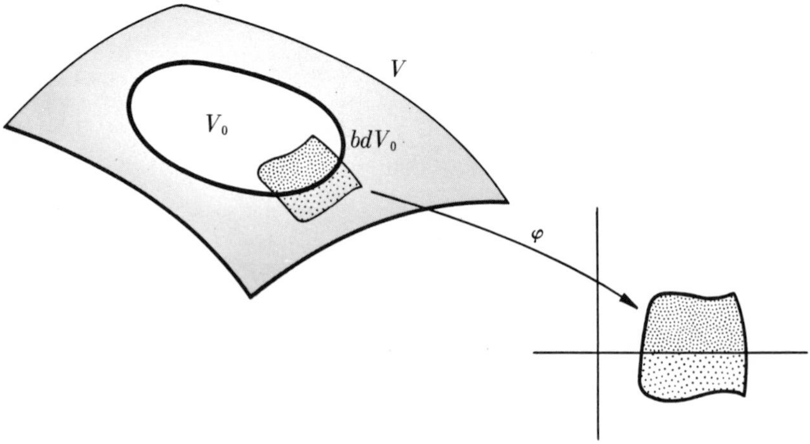

Figure 12-1

and $\varphi: V \to M$ is a C^∞ mapping. Let $i: bdV_0 \to V$ be the inclusion map, so that $\varphi_*\alpha \in \Omega^{k-1}(V)$ and $i_*\varphi_*\alpha \in \Omega^{k-1}bdV_0$. Then,

$$\int_{bdV_0} i_*\varphi_*\alpha = \int_{V_0} \varphi_*\mathbf{d}\alpha$$

This fundamental theorem reduces to the usual theorems of Stokes and Gauss in $\mathbf{R}^n$. For a proof, see Fleming [1, p. 275].

Exercises

12A. Give the details for the construction of the sequence described in the proof of 12.10. Give the version of 12.11 that applies to vectorfields that are not necessarily complete.

12B. Suppose M is an orientable manifold and $X \in \mathscr{X}(M)$ is incompressible. Let $A \subset M$ be a measurable set and $A_\lambda = F_\lambda(A)$, where F is the (local) flow of X. Then $\mu_\Omega(A) = \mu_\Omega(A_\lambda)$. Interpret physically. (*Hint:* Use 12.10.)

Notes

Our treatment of differential calculus (§§7–10) follows Lang [1] closely, with the exception of the definition of the Lie derivative. This is made in a more conceptual manner, following Willmore, which works only in the finite-dimensional case.

Our treatment of integral calculus assumes classical integration theory (for example, Royden [1]) as a prerequisite. This is the easiest transition to integration on manifolds for those having this background, which seems to be fairly common among physicists. Integration is used only peripherally in the sequel, and can be omitted if desired For self-contained explications of this subject, see Fleming [1], Spivak [1], or Sternberg [1].

CHAPTER III

CONSERVATIVE MECHANICS

By conservative mechanics we mean classical Hamiltonian systems that are autonomous, or time independent. In this chapter we systematically translate the basic structure of this classical theory into the language of calculus on manifolds. Possibly this will seem severely unmotivated without some background in classical mechanics, and for this any standard text in the subject is sufficient. The treatment may also seem unnecessarily abstract, but we have included only the minimum that is needed for a rigorous analysis of the applications in the later chapters.

§13. SYMPLECTIC ALGEBRA

Symplectic manifolds are the setting for Hamiltonian mechanics. In this section we will consider the linear case as well as some other prerequisites for the next section.

13.1. Definition. *Let* **E** *be a finite-dimensional real vector space and* $\boldsymbol{\omega} \in T_2^0(\mathbf{E}) = L^2(\mathbf{E}, \mathbf{R})$ (6.1). *Then* $\boldsymbol{\omega}$ *is* **nondegenerate** *iff* $\boldsymbol{\omega}(\mathbf{e}_1, \mathbf{e}_2) = 0$ *for all* $\mathbf{e}_2 \in \mathbf{E}$ *implies* $\mathbf{e}_1 = 0$. *The matrix* $[\boldsymbol{\omega}]_{\hat{\mathbf{e}}}$ *of* $\boldsymbol{\omega}$ *relative to an ordered basis* $\hat{\mathbf{e}} = (\mathbf{e}_i)$ *of* **E** *is the matrix of components* $\boldsymbol{\omega}_{ij} = \boldsymbol{\omega}(\mathbf{e}_i, \mathbf{e}_j)$.

Thus $\boldsymbol{\omega} = \omega_{ij}\boldsymbol{\alpha}^i \otimes \boldsymbol{\alpha}^j$, where $(\boldsymbol{\alpha}^i)$ is the dual ordered basis. Then $\boldsymbol{\omega}$ is nondegenerate iff $\boldsymbol{\omega}^t$, defined by $\boldsymbol{\omega}^t(\mathbf{e}, \mathbf{e}') = \boldsymbol{\omega}(\mathbf{e}', \mathbf{e})$, is nondegenerate, or equivalently, the matrix of $\boldsymbol{\omega}$ relative to any basis is a nonsingular matrix, or the map $\boldsymbol{\omega}_\flat : \mathbf{E} \to \mathbf{E}^*$ defined by $\boldsymbol{\omega}_\flat(\mathbf{e}) \cdot \mathbf{e}' = \boldsymbol{\omega}(\mathbf{e}, \mathbf{e}')$ is an isomorphism.

If $\hat{\mathbf{e}} = (\mathbf{e}_i)$ and $\hat{\mathbf{e}}' = (\mathbf{e}_i')$ are two ordered bases of **E**, with $\mathbf{e}_i' = A_i^j \mathbf{e}_j$, then the matrices of $\boldsymbol{\omega} \in T_2^0(\mathbf{E})$ are related by congruence: $[\boldsymbol{\omega}]_{\hat{\mathbf{e}}'} = A^t[\boldsymbol{\omega}]_{\hat{\mathbf{e}}}A$. We have the following canonical form for symmetric and skew symmetric bilinear forms.

13.2. Proposition. *Let* **E** *be an n-dimensional real vector space. Then*

(*i*) *If* $\boldsymbol{\omega} \in L_s^2(\mathbf{E}, \mathbf{R})$ (1.6), *there is an ordered basis* $\hat{\mathbf{e}} = (\mathbf{e}_i)$ *of* **E**, *with dual ordered basis* $(\boldsymbol{\alpha}^i)$ *such that*

$$\boldsymbol{\omega} = \sum_{i=1}^{s} \eta_i \boldsymbol{\alpha}^i \otimes \boldsymbol{\alpha}^i \quad \textit{where} \quad \eta_i = \pm 1, s \leq n$$

(*ii*) *If* $\boldsymbol{\omega} \in \Omega^2(\mathbf{E}) = L_a^2(\mathbf{E}, \mathbf{R})$ (9.1), *there is an ordered basis* $\hat{\mathbf{e}} = (\mathbf{e}_i)$ *of* **E** *with dual ordered basis* $(\boldsymbol{\alpha}^i)$ *such that*

$$\omega = \sum_{i=1}^{r} \alpha^i \wedge \alpha^{i+r} \quad \textit{where} \quad 2r \leq n$$

The **rank** of ω is the integer s in case (*i*), or $2r$ in case (*ii*), or equivalently, the rank of the linear map $\omega_\flat$; or the dimension of $\omega_\flat(\mathbf{E})$. We leave the proof as an exercise. In 3.2 (*ii*) note that the matrix of ω is

$$\begin{bmatrix} 0 & I & 0 \\ -I & 0 & 0 \\ 0 & 0 & 0 \end{bmatrix}$$

where I is the $r \times r$ identity matrix.

If

$$\omega = \sum_{i=1}^{r} \alpha^i \wedge \alpha^{i+r}$$

as in 13.2 (*ii*), note that

$$\omega_\flat(\mathbf{e}_i) = \sum_{j=1}^{n} \omega_\flat(\mathbf{e}_i)(\mathbf{e}_j)\alpha^j$$

But

$$\omega_\flat(\mathbf{e}_i)(\mathbf{e}_j) = \omega(\mathbf{e}_i, \mathbf{e}_j) = \sum_{k=1}^{r} \alpha^k \wedge \alpha^{k+r}(\mathbf{e}_i, \mathbf{e}_j)$$

$$= \sum_{k=1}^{r} \tfrac{1}{2}(\delta_i^k \delta_j^{k+r} - \delta_i^{k+r}\delta_j^k) = \tfrac{1}{2}(\delta_j^{i+r} - \delta_i^{j+r})$$

if $i, j \leq 2r$ (§9). Thus

$$\omega_\flat(\mathbf{e}_i) = \begin{cases} \tfrac{1}{2}\alpha^{i+r} & \text{if } i \leq r \\ -\tfrac{1}{2}\alpha^{i-r} & \text{if } r < i \leq 2r \\ \mathbf{0} & \text{if } 2r < i \end{cases}$$

It will also be useful to consider the map $\mathbf{e} \rightsquigarrow \mathbf{e}^\flat = \mathbf{i}_\mathbf{e}\omega \in \mathbf{E}^*$, where $\mathbf{i}_\mathbf{e}\omega(\mathbf{e}') = 2\omega(\mathbf{e}, \mathbf{e}')$ (see 10.12). Thus, in the above basis

$$\mathbf{e}_i^\flat = \begin{cases} \alpha^{i+r} & \text{if } i \leq r \\ -\alpha^{i-r} & \text{if } r < i \leq 2r \\ \mathbf{0} & \text{if } 2r < i \end{cases}$$

A useful criterion for nondegeneracy is the following.

13.3. Proposition. *Let* $\mathbf{E}$ *be a finite-dimensional real vector space, and* $\omega \in \Omega^2(\mathbf{E})$. *Then* ω *is nondegenerate iff* $\mathbf{E}$ *has even dimension, say* $2n$, *and* $\omega^n = \omega \wedge \cdots \wedge \omega$ *is a volume on* $\mathbf{E}$.

Proof. Suppose $\boldsymbol{\omega}$ is nondegenerate. Choose a basis of $\mathbf{E}$ such that $\boldsymbol{\omega} = \Sigma_{i=1}^{r} \boldsymbol{\alpha}^i \wedge \boldsymbol{\alpha}^{i+r}$. Since the rank of $\boldsymbol{\omega}$ is the dimension of $\mathbf{E}$, we have *dim* $\mathbf{E} = 2r$. Then, by induction we easily verify that

$$\boldsymbol{\omega}^k = \sum_{j_1, \cdots, j_k = 1}^{r} \boldsymbol{\alpha}^{j_1} \wedge \boldsymbol{\alpha}^{j_1+r} \wedge \cdots \wedge \boldsymbol{\alpha}^{j_k} \wedge \boldsymbol{\alpha}^{j_k+r}$$

so

$$\boldsymbol{\omega}^r = r!(-1)^{(r/2)} \boldsymbol{\alpha}^1 \wedge \cdots \wedge \boldsymbol{\alpha}^{2r}$$

which is a volume (9.8). Conversely, if $\boldsymbol{\omega}^n$ is a volume, the rank of $\boldsymbol{\omega}$ is $2n$. ∎

13.4. Definition. *Let M be a manifold, and $\omega \in \mathscr{T}_2^0(M)$. Then ω is* **nondegenerate** *iff $\omega(m)$ is nondegenerate for each $m \in M$.*

Thus, from 13.3 we obtain the following.

13.5. Proposition. *Let M be a manifold and $\omega \in \Omega^2(M)$. Then ω is nondegenerate iff M is even-dimensional, say $2n$, and $\omega^n = \omega \wedge \cdots \wedge \omega$ is a volume on M.*

Then, if $\omega \in \Omega^2(M)$ is nondegenerate, M is orientable. We shall use the standard volume

$$\Omega_\omega = \frac{(-1)^{(n/2)}}{n!} \omega^n$$

(see the proof of 13.3).

The globalization of the map $\boldsymbol{\omega}_\flat$ (13.1) is given as follows.

13.6. Definition. *Let M be a manifold and $\omega \in \mathscr{T}_2^0(M)$. Define $\omega_\flat \colon TM \to T^*M$ by $\omega_\flat(m) = \omega(m)_\flat$; that is, $\omega(m)_\flat(\mathbf{e}) \cdot \mathbf{e}' = \omega(m)(\mathbf{e}, \mathbf{e}')$, where $\mathbf{e}, \mathbf{e}' \in T_mM$. Also, for $X \in \mathscr{X}(M)$, define $\omega_\flat X \colon M \to T^*M$ by $\omega_\flat X(m) = \omega_\flat(m) \cdot X(m)$.*

Note that the following proposition applies to Riemannian metrics (11.12), pseudo-Riemannian metrics (that is, in 11.12, positive definite is replaced by the weaker condition of nondegeneracy), and nondegenerate two forms.

13.7. Proposition. *Let M be a manifold and $\omega \in \mathscr{T}_2^0(M)$. Then*

(i) $\omega_\flat \colon TM \to T^*M$ is a vector bundle mapping;

(ii) If $X \in \mathscr{X}(M)$, then $\omega_\flat X \in \mathscr{X}^*(M)$ and $\omega_\flat$ is $\mathscr{F}(M)$ linear as a mapping $\mathscr{X}(M) \to \mathscr{X}^*(M)$;

(iii) If ω is nondegenerate, then $\omega_\flat \colon TM \to T^*M$ is a vector bundle isomorphism (in particular, a diffeomorphism). In this case we write $\omega_\sharp = \omega_\flat^{-1}$.

Proof. Let (U, φ) be a chart of M with $\varphi(U) = U' \subset \mathbf{E}$. The local representative of $\omega_\flat$ with respect to the natural charts is then

$$(T\varphi)_1^0 \circ \omega_\flat \circ (T\varphi^{-1}) \colon U' \times \mathbf{E} \to U' \times \mathbf{E}^* \colon (u', \mathbf{e}) \rightsquigarrow (u', \omega_\flat^2(u) \cdot \mathbf{e})$$

where ω^2 is the second factor in the local representative of ω, so that

$\omega_\flat^2(u)\cdot\mathbf{e}(\mathbf{e}') = \omega^2(u)(\mathbf{e},\mathbf{e}')$. To prove (*i*) then we must show that $\omega_\flat^2 : U' \to L(\mathbf{E},\mathbf{E}^*)$ is smooth. According to 1.3 we may use any convenient norm on the vector space $L(\mathbf{E},\mathbf{E}^*)$. In fact, use $\|\omega_\flat^2(u)\| = \max\{\|\omega_\flat^2(u)\cdot\mathbf{e}\| : \mathbf{e}\in\mathbf{E}, \|\mathbf{e}\| = 1\}$ for some norms on $\mathbf{E}$ and $\mathbf{E}^*$. Now we can use the norm $\|\omega^2(u)\| = \|\omega_\flat^2(u)\|$ on $T_2^0(\mathbf{E})$. Since $\omega^2(u)$ is of class C^∞, we then find that $\omega_\flat^2(u)$ is also. Indeed, the derivative of $\omega_\flat^2$ is the following linear map (at $u'\in U'$): $\mathbf{e}\rightsquigarrow L(\mathbf{e})$, where $L(\mathbf{e})\in L(\mathbf{E},\mathbf{E}^*)$ is defined by $L(\mathbf{e})\cdot\mathbf{e}_1(\mathbf{e}_2) = D\omega^2(u')(\mathbf{e})\cdot(\mathbf{e}_1,\mathbf{e}_2)$. This can be readily checked using the above norms. To prove (*ii*), note that $\mathscr{F}(M)$ linearity is clear from linearity of $\omega_\flat$ on each fiber, and $\omega_\flat X$ is of class C^∞ by (*i*) and 2.11 in local representation. Finally, for (*iii*), if ω is nondegenerate, $\omega_\flat$ is clearly a bijection and an isomorphism on each fiber (13.1). We must show that $\omega_\sharp$ is smooth. The local representative of $\omega_\sharp$ is $(u',\boldsymbol{\alpha})\rightsquigarrow(u',\omega_\flat^2(u)^{-1}\cdot\boldsymbol{\alpha})$. From the proof of 6.8, however, $\omega_\flat^2(u)^{-1}$ is of class C^∞. ∎

In component notation, $\omega_\flat$ lowers indices and $\omega_\sharp$ raises indices. More generally, if $t\in\mathscr{T}_s^r(M)$, we can define $\omega_\flat t\in\mathscr{T}_{s+1}^{r-1}(M)$ by

$$\omega_\flat t(\alpha',\ldots,\alpha^{r-1},X_1,\ldots,X_{s+1}) = t(\alpha',\ldots,\alpha^{r-1},\omega_\flat X_{s+1},X_1,\ldots,X_s)$$

to lower the last contravariant index.

13.8. Definition. *A* **symplectic form** *on a vector space* $\mathbf{E}$ *is a nondegenerate 2-form* $\boldsymbol{\omega}\in\Omega^2(\mathbf{E})$. *The pair* $(\mathbf{E},\boldsymbol{\omega})$ *is called a* **symplectic vector space**. *If* $(\mathbf{E},\boldsymbol{\omega})$ *and* $(\mathbf{F},\boldsymbol{\rho})$ *are symplectic vector spaces, a linear map* $f:\mathbf{E}\to\mathbf{F}$ *is* **symplectic** *iff* $f_*\boldsymbol{\rho} = \boldsymbol{\omega}$ (*see* 9.14).

If $(\mathbf{E},\boldsymbol{\omega})$ *is a symplectic vector space we have an orientation defined on* $\mathbf{E}$, *by*

$$\boldsymbol{\Omega}_{\boldsymbol{\omega}} = \frac{(-1)^{(n/2)}}{n!}\boldsymbol{\omega}^n$$

where $\mathbf{E}$ *has dimension* $2n$ (*see* 13.3).

13.9. Proposition. *Let* $(\mathbf{E},\boldsymbol{\omega})$ *and* $(\mathbf{F},\boldsymbol{\rho})$ *be symplectic vector spaces of dimension* $2n$, *and* $f:\mathbf{E}\to\mathbf{F}$ *be a symplectic mapping. Then* f *is volume preserving, and hence* f *is orientation preserving, and* $\det_{(\boldsymbol{\Omega}_\omega,\boldsymbol{\Omega}_\rho)}f = 1$ (*see* 11.18). *In particular,* f *is an isomorphism.*

Proof. By 9.15 (vi), we have

$$f_*\boldsymbol{\Omega}_\rho = f_*\left[\frac{(-1)^{(n/2)}}{n!}\boldsymbol{\rho}\wedge\cdots\wedge\boldsymbol{\rho}\right] = \frac{(-1)^{(n/2)}}{n!}f_*\boldsymbol{\rho}\wedge\cdots\wedge f_*\boldsymbol{\rho} = \boldsymbol{\Omega}_\omega$$

Hence f is volume preserving. The last statements follow at once (§9). ∎

13.10. Example. A volume preserving map need not be symplectic, for consider $\mathbf{R}^4$ with vectors denoted (x^1,x^2,y^1,y^2) and $\boldsymbol{\omega} = \boldsymbol{\alpha}^1\wedge\boldsymbol{\beta}^1 + \boldsymbol{\alpha}^2\wedge\boldsymbol{\beta}^2$ where $(\boldsymbol{\alpha}^1,\boldsymbol{\alpha}^2,\boldsymbol{\beta}^1,\boldsymbol{\beta}^2)$ is a basis dual to the standard basis $(\mathbf{e}_1,\mathbf{e}_2,\mathbf{f}_1,\mathbf{f}_2)$. Consider the map $(x^1,x^2,y^1,y^2)\rightsquigarrow(-x^1,-x^2,y^1,y^2)$. This preserves the volume $\boldsymbol{\Omega}_\omega = \boldsymbol{\alpha}^1\wedge\boldsymbol{\alpha}^2\wedge\boldsymbol{\beta}^1\wedge\boldsymbol{\beta}^2$ but maps $\boldsymbol{\omega}\rightsquigarrow-\boldsymbol{\omega}$. On $\mathbf{R}^2$, however, every area preserving map is symplectic.

13.11. Proposition. *Let* $(\mathbf{E}, \boldsymbol{\omega})$ *be a symplectic vector space. Then the set of all symplectic mappings* $f: \mathbf{E} \to \mathbf{E}$ *forms a group with composition, called the* **symplectic group,** *denoted by* $Sp(\mathbf{E}, \boldsymbol{\omega})$.

Proof. Since $L_{\text{iso}}(\mathbf{E}, \mathbf{E})$ forms a group, we need only show that if $f, g \in Sp(\mathbf{E}, \boldsymbol{\omega})$, then $f \circ g$ and $f^{-1} \in Sp(\mathbf{E}, \boldsymbol{\omega})$. But $(f \circ g)_* \boldsymbol{\omega} = g_* \circ f_* \boldsymbol{\omega} = g_* \boldsymbol{\omega} = \boldsymbol{\omega}$, and $(f^{-1})_* \boldsymbol{\omega} = (f_*)^{-1} f_* \boldsymbol{\omega} = \boldsymbol{\omega}$. ∎

Next we examine the condition that $f \in Sp(\mathbf{E}, \boldsymbol{\omega})$ in matrix notation. As we saw in 13.2, there is an ordered basis of $\mathbf{E}$ such that the matrix of $\boldsymbol{\omega}$ is

$$J = \begin{bmatrix} 0 & I \\ -I & 0 \end{bmatrix}$$

Hence, for $f \in L(\mathbf{E}, \mathbf{E})$ with matrix $A = (A^i_j)$ relative to the above basis, the condition $f_* \boldsymbol{\omega} = \boldsymbol{\omega}$, or $\boldsymbol{\omega}(f(\mathbf{e}), f(\mathbf{e}')) = \boldsymbol{\omega}(\mathbf{e}, \mathbf{e}')$ becomes

$$A^t J A = J$$

We saw in 13.9 that $det\, A = 1$. The reader may wish to provide the algebraic proof in this case. Also, if $A = \begin{pmatrix} a & b \\ c & d \end{pmatrix}$ where a, b, c, d are $n \times n$ matrices, $f \in Sp(\mathbf{E}, \boldsymbol{\omega})$ iff ac^t, bd^t are symmetric and $a^t d - bc^t = I$.

A condition on the eigenvalues of $f \in Sp(\mathbf{E}, \boldsymbol{\omega})$ is given by the following.

13.12. Proposition. *Suppose* $(\mathbf{E}, \boldsymbol{\omega})$ *is a symplectic vector space,* $f \in Sp(\mathbf{E}, \boldsymbol{\omega})$ *and* $\lambda \in \mathbf{C}$ *is an eigenvalue of* f. *Then* $1/\lambda$, $\bar{\lambda}$, *and* $1/\bar{\lambda}$ *are eigenvalues of* f *(*$\bar{\lambda}$ *denotes the complex conjugate of* λ*).*

Proof 1. Let $\tilde{\mathbf{E}}$ denote the complexification of $\mathbf{E}$, $\tilde{\mathbf{E}} = \mathbf{E} \oplus i\mathbf{E}$, and extend $f, \boldsymbol{\omega}$ linearly to $\tilde{\mathbf{E}}$. If $f(\mathbf{e}) = \lambda \mathbf{e}$ ($\mathbf{e} \neq \mathbf{0}$), then $\boldsymbol{\omega}(f(\mathbf{e}), f(\mathbf{e}')) = \boldsymbol{\omega}(\mathbf{e}, \mathbf{e}')$, or $\boldsymbol{\omega}(\mathbf{e}, f(\mathbf{e}') - \mathbf{e}'/\lambda) = 0$ for all $\mathbf{e}'$. Thus, as $\boldsymbol{\omega}$ is nondegenerate, the mapping $f - I/\lambda$ is not an isomorphism, or $1/\lambda$ is an eigenvalue of f. Since f is real, $f(\mathbf{e}) = \lambda \mathbf{e}$ iff $f(\bar{\mathbf{e}}) = \bar{\lambda} \bar{\mathbf{e}}$. Note that 0 is not an eigenvalue of f, from 13.9. ∎

For the reader more familiar with real matrices than complex linear algebra, we offer an alternate proof.

Proof 2. Let $\hat{\mathbf{e}}$ be an ordered basis of $\mathbf{E}$ such that $[\boldsymbol{\omega}]_{\hat{\mathbf{e}}} = J$ and $[f]_{\hat{\mathbf{e}}} = A$. Then $A^t J A = J$, or $J A J^{-1} = B$, where $B = (A^t)^{-1} = (A^{-1})^t$. Let $P(\lambda) = det(A - \lambda I)$, considered as a polynomial in the complex variable λ, with real coefficients. Then as $J^{-1} = J$, if $\lambda \neq 0$,

$$\begin{aligned} P(\lambda) &= det(A - \lambda I) = det[J(A - \lambda I)J] = det(B - \lambda I) = det(A^{-1} - \lambda I) \\ &= det[A^{-1}(I - \lambda A)] = det(I - \lambda A) = det\left[\lambda\left(\frac{1}{\lambda} I - A\right)\right] \\ &= \lambda^n\, det\left(\frac{1}{\lambda} I - A\right) = (-\lambda)^n P\left(\frac{1}{\lambda}\right) \end{aligned}$$

if $n = dim(\mathbf{E})$. As 0 is not an eigenvalue of A, $P(\lambda) = 0$ iff $P(1/\lambda) = 0$. As P has real coefficients, $P(\lambda) = 0$ iff $P(\bar{\lambda}) = 0$. ∎

As a matter of fact, $Sp(\mathbf{E}, \boldsymbol{\omega}) \subset L_{\text{iso}}(\mathbf{E}, \mathbf{E}) = GL(\mathbf{E})$ is a submanifold, and composition is C^∞, so $sp(\mathbf{E}, \boldsymbol{\omega})$ is a *Lie group* (§22). We resist the temptation to go into the details, and refer the reader instead to Helgason [1, Chapters II and IX]. Nevertheless, it underlies the final exposition of this section, which is in fact a description of the Lie algebra of $Sp(\mathbf{E}, \boldsymbol{\omega})$, denoted by $sp(\mathbf{E}, \boldsymbol{\omega}) \subset L(\mathbf{E}, \mathbf{E})$.

Note that $L(\mathbf{E}, \mathbf{E})$ is a Lie algebra with the composition $[u, v] = u \circ v - v \circ u$. This algebra is associated to the group $GL(\mathbf{E})$ as follows. First $T_f GL(\mathbf{E}) = \{f\} \times L(\mathbf{E}, \mathbf{E})$. We identify $T_I GL(\mathbf{E})$ and $L(\mathbf{E}, \mathbf{E})$. Second, if $f(t)$ and $g(t)$ are C^2 curves at the identity $I \in GL(\mathbf{E})$, with $u = f'(0)$, $v = g'(0)$, then the curve $[fg](t) = f^{-1}(t) \circ g^{-1}(t) \circ f(t) \circ g(t)$ is C^2 and $[fg]''(0) = [u, v)$ (see 2.11 and 6.8, or Helgason [1, p. 96]).

13.13. Definition. *A linear mapping $u \in L(\mathbf{E}, \mathbf{E})$ is* **infinitesimally symplectic** *with respect to a symplectic form $\boldsymbol{\omega}$ iff $\boldsymbol{\omega}(u\mathbf{e}, \mathbf{e}') + \boldsymbol{\omega}(\mathbf{e}, u\mathbf{e}') = 0$ for all $\mathbf{e}, \mathbf{e}' \in \mathbf{E}$. Let $sp(\mathbf{E}, \boldsymbol{\omega})$ denote the set of all linear mappings in $L(\mathbf{E}, \mathbf{E})$ that are infinitesimally symplectic with respect to ω.*

13.14. Proposition. *The set $sp(\mathbf{E}, \boldsymbol{\omega}) \subset L(\mathbf{E}, \mathbf{E})$ is a Lie subalgebra.*

We leave the proof to the reader.

13.15. Proposition. *If $u \in sp(\mathbf{E}, \boldsymbol{\omega})$ and λ is an eigenvalue of u, so are $-\lambda$, $\bar{\lambda}$, and $-\bar{\lambda}$.*

Proof. We proceed exactly as in 13.12, noting that $u\mathbf{e} = \lambda\mathbf{e}$ implies $\boldsymbol{\omega}(\mathbf{e}, \lambda\mathbf{e}' + u\mathbf{e}') = 0$. ∎

The eigenvalue properties of 13.12 and 13.15 can be strengthened as follows.

13.16. Proposition (Symplectic eigenvalue theorem). *Suppose $(\mathbf{E}, \boldsymbol{\omega})$ is a symplectic vector space, $f \in Sp(\mathbf{E}, \boldsymbol{\omega})$ and λ is an eigenvalue of f of multiplicity k. Then $1/\lambda$ is an eigenvalue of f of multiplicity k. Moreover, the multiplicities of the eigenvalues $+1$ and -1, if they occur, are even.*

Proof. We saw that if P is the characteristic polynomial of f, then $P(\lambda) = \lambda^{2n} P(1/\lambda)$ where $dim\, \mathbf{E} = 2n$ (13.12). Suppose λ_0 occurs with multiplicity k. Then $P(\lambda) = (\lambda - \lambda_0)^k Q(\lambda)$, so that

$$P\left(\frac{1}{\lambda}\right)\lambda^{2n} = (\lambda - \lambda_0)^k Q(\lambda) = (\lambda\lambda_0)^k \left(\frac{1}{\lambda} - \frac{1}{\lambda_0}\right)^k Q(\lambda)$$

Now $(\lambda_0^k/\lambda^{2n-k})Q(\lambda)$ is a polynomial in $1/\lambda$, as Q is of degree $2n - k$ and $k \leq 2n$. Hence $1/\lambda_0$ occurs with multiplicity $l \geq k$. Reversing the roles of λ_0, $1/\lambda_0$, we see $k \leq l$, so $k = l$.

Note that $\lambda_0 = 1/\lambda_0$ iff λ_0 is $+1$ or -1. Thus, from the above, the multiplicity of the eigenvalues $+1$ and -1 is even. But, as $det\, f = 1$ (the product of the eigenvalues) the number of each must be even. ■

In a similar way we can prove the following. Note that if u is infinitesimally symplectic with characteristic polynomial P, then $P(\lambda) = P(-\lambda)$, so $tr(u) = 0$ (sum of eigenvalues).

13.17. Proposition (Infinitesimally symplectic eigenvalue theorem). *Let* $(\mathbf{E}, \boldsymbol{\omega})$ *be a symplectic vector space and* $u \in sp(\mathbf{E}, \boldsymbol{\omega})$. *Then if* λ *is an eigenvalue of multiplicity* k, $-\lambda$ *is an eigenvalue of multiplicity* k. *Moreover*, 0, *if it occurs, has even multiplicity.*

We leave this easier proof for the reader.

The possible eigenvalue configurations for a symplectic linear mapping $A \in Sp(\mathbf{R}^4, \boldsymbol{\omega}_0)$, graphed with relation to the unit circle in the complex plane, are illustrated in Figure 13-1.

The corresponding configurations for an infinitesimally symplectic mapping $u \in sp(\mathbf{R}^4, \boldsymbol{\omega}_0)$ are illustrated in Figure 13-2.

The eigenvalue properties 13.12–13.17 are basic to the qualitative theory

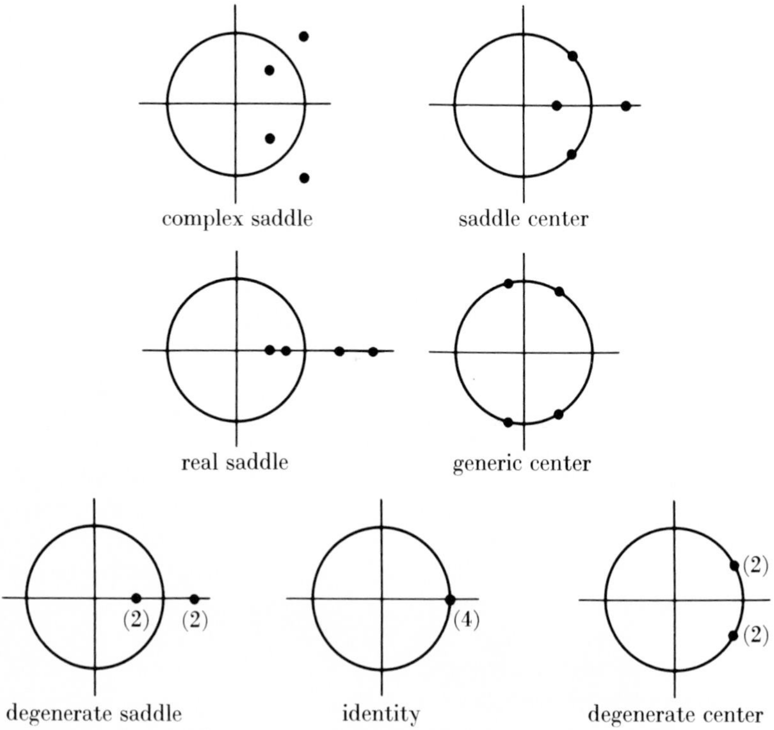

Figure 13-1

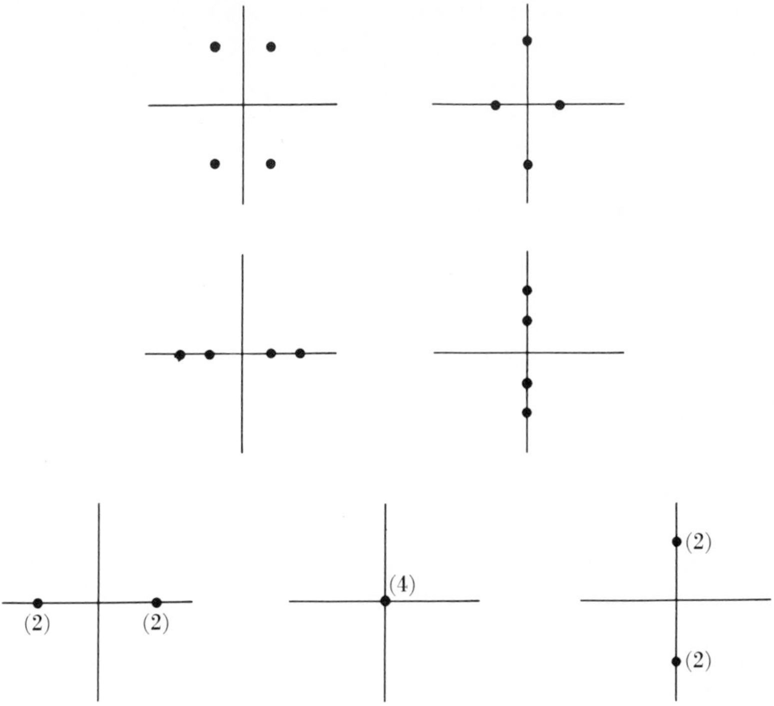

Figure 13-2

of Hamiltonian systems. Although $Sp(\mathbf{R}^{2n}, \omega_0)$ is the fundamental group underlying classical mechanics, very little application of its structure seems to have been made beyond these elementary eigenvalue properties. For additional properties of the symplectic group, see Helgason [1] and Artin [1].

Exercises

13A. (i) In 13.1 show that $\boldsymbol{\omega}$ is nondegenerate iff $\boldsymbol{\omega}_\flat$ is an isomorphism. Deduce that $\boldsymbol{\omega}$ is nondegenerate iff $\boldsymbol{\omega}^t$ is nondegenerate.

(ii) Prove 13.2 (a standard exercise in linear algebra). In 13.2 (i) show that the number of -1's and 1's is independent of the diagonalization procedure by supplying intrinsic definitions.

13B. (i) Verify the remarks following 13.11 on the matrix representation of $Sp(\mathbf{E}, \boldsymbol{\omega})$. Show that the eigenvalue configurations shown for $A \in Sp(\mathbf{R}^4, \boldsymbol{\omega}_0)$ are the only ones possible (Figure 13-1).

(ii) Supply the proofs for 13.14 and 13.15. Show that, in general, $sp(\mathbf{E}, \boldsymbol{\omega})$ is not a group under composition.

13C. Repeat the computation of the $\flat$ and $\sharp$ actions using the properties of the inner product (10.13).

§14. SYMPLECTIC GEOMETRY

The globalization of the symplectic algebra of §13 is symplectic geometry. Our first goal will be Darboux's theorem (1876), which states that for a nondegenerate, closed 2-form ω on a manifold M (ω is called a *symplectic form*), the canonical form of 13.2 (*ii*) can be extended to some chart about each $m \in M$. (For a full treatment of the general case, we refer the reader to Sternberg [2, p. 140].)

14.1. Definition. *Let M be a manifold and $\omega \in \Omega^2(M)$ be nondegenerate. Then we define the map $\flat$: $\mathscr{X}(M) \to \mathscr{X}^*(M)$: $X \rightsquigarrow X^\flat = i_X\omega$ (see 10.12). (Hence $X^\flat = 2\omega_\flat(X)$) and the map $\sharp$: $\mathscr{X}^*(M) \to \mathscr{X}(M)$: $\alpha \rightsquigarrow \alpha^\sharp = \frac{1}{2}\omega_\sharp(\alpha)$.*

Thus we see that $(X^\flat)^\sharp = X$ and $(\alpha^\sharp)^\flat = \alpha$. Note that this vector bundle isomorphism differs from $\omega_\flat$ by a factor of 2. (See §13.)

For Darboux's theorem we shall need several technical lemmas.

14.2. Lemma. *Let θ be a 1-form on a $2n$ manifold M such that $\theta(m) \neq 0$ for some $m \in M$ and $\mathbf{d}\theta$ is nondegenerate in some neighborhood of m. Then there is a chart (U, φ) with $\varphi(U) = U' \subset \mathbf{R}^{2n}$, $\varphi(m) = 0$ and $\varphi(u) = (x^1(u), \ldots, x^{2n-1}(u), t(u))$ such that $\theta|U = (t+1)\theta^0$, where θ^0 has the form*

$$\theta^0 = \sum_{i=1}^{2n-1} \theta_i^0\, dx^i \quad \theta_i^0 \in \mathscr{F}(U) \quad \textit{and} \quad \frac{\partial \theta_i^0}{\partial t} = 0 \qquad (\textit{see } 10.4)$$

Proof. Let $\omega = \mathbf{d}\theta$ so that, from 13.7, $\theta^\sharp = \frac{1}{2}\omega_\sharp(\theta) = \xi \in \mathscr{X}(U'')$ on some neighborhood U'' of m. Now $\mathbf{i}_\xi\omega = \theta$, and $\mathbf{i}_\xi\theta = 0$, so by 10.13 (*iv*), $\mathbf{L}_\xi\theta = \mathbf{i}_\xi\,\mathbf{d}\theta = \mathbf{i}_\xi\omega = \theta$. Since $\xi(m) \neq 0$, there is a chart (U, φ) at m, $U \subset U''$ such that $\varphi(U) = U' \subset \mathbf{R}^{2n}$, $\varphi(m) = 0$, $\varphi(u) = (x^1(u), \ldots, x^{2n-1}(u), s(u))$ and $\xi|U = \underset{\sim}{e}_{2n}$ using notation of 10.4. The existence of such a chart was proven in 7.9. If

$$\theta = \sum_{i=1}^{2n-1} \theta_i dx^i + \theta_{2n}\, ds$$

then

$$\theta_{2n} = \theta(\underset{\sim}{e}_{2n}) = \theta(\xi) = \mathbf{i}_\xi\omega(\xi) = \omega(\xi, \xi) = 0$$

Hence

$$\theta = \sum_{i=1}^{2n-1} \theta_i\, dx^i$$

so

$$\mathbf{L}_\xi\theta = (\mathbf{L}_\xi\theta_i)\, dx^i = \theta_i\, dx^i$$

or

$$\frac{\partial \theta_{i\varphi}}{\partial s} \circ \varphi^{-1} = \theta_i$$

(see 10.4), and so

$$\theta_{i\varphi} = e^s\theta_{i\varphi}^0 \quad \text{where} \quad \frac{\partial \theta_{i\varphi}^0}{\partial s} = 0$$

Let $t = e^s - 1$. Then the map $(x^1, \ldots, x^{2n-1}, s) \rightsquigarrow (x^1, \ldots, x^{2n-1}, t)$ is a diffeomorphism in some neighborhood of the origin by 2.10, so that in the new chart

$$\theta = \sum_{i=1}^{2n-1} (t+1)\theta_i^0 \, dx^i$$

as required. ■

14.3. Lemma. *Let $\pi: E \to B$, $\rho: F \to C$ be vector bundles with fibers of dimension n. Let $\varphi: E \to F$ be a vector bundle mapping of rank r in some neighborhood $E|U$ of $b \in B$ (that is, φ restricted to each fiber is of rank r). Then there are $n - r$ (pointwise) linearly independent C^∞ sections of E, say $X_1, \ldots, X_{n-r}$, defined in some neighborhood of b such that $\varphi(X_i) = 0$ (that is, $\varphi(X_i) \in C$) $i = 1, \ldots, n - r$ (see §4, and 4.7 in particular).*

Proof. Using local bundle charts, we see that it is sufficient to consider the case $\varphi: U \times \mathbf{E} \to V \times \mathbf{F}$. Let φ_u denote the restriction of φ to the fiber over u, so that $\varphi_u \in L(\mathbf{E}, \mathbf{F})$ and has rank r. For $b \in U$, suppose $\mathbf{e}_1, \ldots, \mathbf{e}_n$ is a basis of $\mathbf{E}$ such that $\varphi_b(\mathbf{e}_1), \ldots, \varphi_b(\mathbf{e}_r)$ are linearly independent. Let $\varphi_b(\mathbf{e}_1), \ldots, \varphi_b(\mathbf{e}_r), f_{r+1}, \ldots, f_n$ be a basis of $\mathbf{F}$. Using continuity of φ and 6.7, we have that for some neighborhood of b, $\varphi_u(\mathbf{e}_1), \ldots, \varphi_u(\mathbf{e}_r)$ are linearly independent and $\varphi(\mathbf{e}_1), \ldots, \varphi_u(\mathbf{e}_r), \mathbf{f}_{r+1}, \ldots, \mathbf{f}_n$ form a basis of $\mathbf{F}$. Now define $\psi_u \in L_{\text{iso}}(\mathbf{E}, \mathbf{F})$ by $\mathbf{e}_1, \ldots, \mathbf{e}_n \rightsquigarrow \varphi_u(\mathbf{e}_1), \ldots, \varphi_u(\mathbf{e}_r), \mathbf{f}_{r+1}, \ldots, \mathbf{f}_n$. Then $u \rightsquigarrow \psi_u$ is smooth, and by the proof of 6.8, $u \rightsquigarrow \psi_u^{-1} \in L_{\text{iso}}(\mathbf{F}, \mathbf{E})$ is smooth. Now define $X_i(u) = \psi_u^{-1}(\varphi_u(\mathbf{e}_{r+i})) - \mathbf{e}_{r+i}$. Clearly $X_i(u)$ are linearly independent and smooth, and $\varphi_u(X_i(u)) = 0$, $i = 1, \ldots, n - r$. ■

14.4. Lemma. *Let M be a $(2n-1)$-manifold and $\theta \in \Omega^1(M)$, such that $\mathbf{d}\theta$ has rank $2n - 2$ in some neighborhood of $m \in M$. Then there is a chart (U, φ) at m with $\varphi(U) = U' \subset \mathbf{R}^{2n-1}$, $\varphi(u) = (x^1(u), \ldots, x^{2n-2}(u), t(u))$, such that $\theta|U = \mathbf{d}f + \theta^0$ for some $f \in \mathscr{F}(U)$,*

$$\theta^0 = \sum_{i=1}^{2n-2} \theta_i^0 \, dx^i \quad \text{and} \quad \frac{\partial \theta_i^0}{\partial t} = 0$$

Proof. By lemma 14.3 there is a vectorfield ξ defined in some neighborhood of m such that $\mathbf{i}_\xi(\mathbf{d}\theta) = 0$, and $\xi(u) \neq 0$. Namely, we consider the vector bundle map $2(\mathbf{d}\theta)_\flat: TM \to T^*M$ (see 13.7 (*i*)), which has rank $2n - 2$ and note that $2(\mathbf{d}\theta)_\flat(\xi) = \mathbf{i}_\xi(\mathbf{d}\theta)$ (see 13.6). As in lemma 14.2 we take (U, φ) to be a chart for ξ as given by 7.9. Then define θ_φ^0 by

$$\theta_\varphi^0(x, t) = \sum_{i=1}^{2n-2} \theta_{i\varphi}(x, 0) \, dx^i \quad \text{if} \quad \theta_\varphi = \sum_{i=1}^{2n-2} \theta_{i\varphi} \, dx^i + \theta_{(2n-1)\varphi} \, dt$$

(see 7.9(*i*)). As $\mathbf{i}_\xi \, \mathbf{d}\theta = 0$, $\mathbf{d}\theta$ contains no terms of the form $dx^i n \, dt$, hence

$$\mathbf{d}\theta_\varphi = \sum_{\substack{i=1 \\ j=1}}^{2n-2} \partial_j \theta_{i\varphi} \, dx^j \wedge dx^i$$

But $\mathbf{L}_\xi \mathbf{d}\theta = \mathbf{i}_\xi \mathbf{dd}\theta + \mathbf{d}\mathbf{i}_\xi \mathbf{d}\theta = 0$, so $\partial_j \theta_{i\varphi}$ is independent of t. Thus $\mathbf{d}\theta_\varphi = \mathbf{d}\theta^0_\varphi$. By Poincaré's lemma (10.17), there is a neighborhood about m so that $\theta_\varphi - \theta^0_\varphi = \mathbf{d}f$ for some f. ∎

14.5. Lemma. *Under the hypotheses of lemma* 14.1, *there is a chart* (U, φ) *at* m *with* $\varphi(U) = U' \subset \mathbf{R}^{2n}$, $\varphi(m) = \mathbf{0}$, *and* $\varphi(u) = (x^1(u), \ldots, x^{2n-2}(u), t(u), s(u))$ *such that* $\theta|U = (s+1)(dt + \theta^0)$ *where* θ^0 *has the form*

$$\theta^0 = \sum_{i=1}^{2n-2} \theta^0_i\, dx^i \quad \theta^0_i \in \mathscr{F}(U) \quad \textit{and} \quad \frac{\partial \theta^0_i}{\partial t} = 0 \quad \frac{\partial \theta^0_i}{\partial s} = 0$$

Proof. From lemma 14.1 we may write $\theta|U = (s+1)\theta^0$ where

$$\theta^0 = \sum_{i=1}^{2n-1} \theta^0_i\, dx^i \quad \text{and} \quad \frac{\partial \theta^0_i}{\partial s} = 0$$

Now $\mathbf{d}\theta^0$ has rank $2n-2$ since $\mathbf{d}\theta$ has rank $2n$. Since θ^0 is independent of s, we can consider θ^0_φ as a one form on the submanifold of $U' \cap \mathbf{R}^{2n-1}$ consisting of the intersection of U' with the subspace of the first $2n-1$ coordinates. Then we can find a coordinate system $(y', \ldots, y^{2n-2}, t')$ so that $\theta^0 = \mathbf{d}f + \theta^{00}$ where θ^{00} is independent of t', and of course s. Combining these gives a coordinate system in which $\theta = (s+1)(\mathbf{d}f + \theta^{00})$. Now $\mathbf{d}\theta(\underset{\sim}{e}_{2n-1}, \underset{\sim}{e}_{2n}) = ds \wedge \mathbf{d}f(\underset{\sim}{e}_{2n-1}, \underset{\sim}{e}_{2n}) = \partial f/\partial t' \neq 0$ (see 10.4, and note that $\mathbf{d}\theta$ is nondegenerate). Hence, by 2.10, $t' \rightsquigarrow t'' = f - f(m)$ is a diffeomorphism in some neighborhood of 0. Thus in the coordinate system so defined, θ has the required form. ∎

14.6. Lemma. *Let* M *be a* $2n$ *manifold and* $\theta \in \Omega^1(M)$ *such that* $\theta(m) \neq 0$, *and* $\mathbf{d}\theta$ *is nondegenerate. Then for each* $m \in M$ *there is a chart* (U, φ) *at* m *with* $\varphi(U) = U' \subset \mathbf{R}^{2n}$, $\varphi(m) = 0$, $\varphi(u) = (x^1(u), \ldots, x^n(u), y^1(u), \ldots, y^n(u))$ *and*

$$\theta|U = \sum_{i=1}^{n} (x^i + 1)\, dy^i$$

Proof. For $n = 1$, the result follows at once from 14.4. Proceeding by induction, we can find a coordinate system $(x^1, \ldots, x^{2n-2}, t, s)$ for which $\theta = (s+1)(dt + \theta^0)$. In local representation, θ^0 defines a 1-form on $\mathbf{R}^{2n-2}$, so we can find a coordinate system $(y^1, \ldots, y^{2n-2}, t, s)$ for which

$$\theta^0_\varphi = \sum_{i=1}^{n-1} (y^i + 1)\, dy^{i+(n-1)}$$

Consider the map $x^1, \ldots, x^{2n-2}, t, s \rightsquigarrow (s+1)(y^1+1) - 1, (s+1)(y^2+1) - 1, \ldots, (s+1)(y^{2n-2}+1) - 1, t, s$, which defines a new coordinate system with the desired properties. ∎

Finally we are ready to prove Darboux's theorem.

14.7. Theorem (Darboux). *Suppose ω is a nondegenerate two form on a 2n-manifold M (see 13.5). Then* $\mathbf{d}\omega = 0$ *iff there is a chart (U, φ) at each $m \in M$ such that $\varphi(m) = 0$ and with $\varphi(u) = (x^1(u), \ldots, x^n(u), y^1(u), \ldots, y^n(u))$ we have*

$$\omega|U = \sum_{i=1}^{n} dx^i \wedge dy^i$$

Proof. The *if* part is obvious. For the converse, we may write $\omega = \mathbf{d}\theta$ for some $\theta \in \Omega^1(U)$ and some neighborhood of m (10.17). We may assume $\theta(m) \neq 0$, by adding $\mathbf{d}f$ to θ for suitable $f \in \mathscr{F}(U)$. By 14.6 we may write

$$\theta = \sum_{i=1}^{n} (x^i + 1)\, dy^i$$

for some chart. Then

$$\mathbf{d}\theta = \sum_{i=1}^{n} dx^i \wedge dy^i \qquad \blacksquare$$

14.8. Definition. *A* **symplectic form** (*or a* **symplectic structure**) *on a manifold M is a nondegenerate, closed 2-form ω on M. A* **symplectic manifold** *(M, ω) is a manifold M together with a symplectic form ω on M. As in §13, we let Ω_ω denote the volume $[(-1)^{(n/2)}/n!]\omega^n$. The charts guaranteed by Darboux's theorem are called* **symplectic charts** *and the component functions x^i, y^i are called* **canonical coordinates**.

Thus, in a symplectic chart,

$$\omega = \sum_{i=1}^{n} dx^i \wedge dy^i \quad \text{and} \quad \Omega_\omega = dx^1 \wedge \cdots \wedge dx^n \wedge dy^1 \wedge \cdots \wedge dy^n$$

The global analogue of a symplectic linear map (13.8) is given as follows.

14.9. Definition. *Let (M, ω) and (N, ρ) be symplectic manifolds. A C^∞ mapping $F: M \to N$ is called* **symplectic** *iff $F_* \rho = \omega$* (10.7).

From 10.9 (*i*), 11.17, and 11.21 we obtain the following.

14.10. Proposition. *If (M, ω) and (N, ρ) are symplectic 2n-manifolds and $F: M \to N$ is symplectic, then F is volume preserving, $\det_{(\Omega_\omega, \Omega_\rho)} F = 1$, and F is a local diffeomorphism.*

As in §13, the converse of 14.10 is false in general (except of course for 2-manifolds).

It is clear that if (M, ω) is a symplectic manifold and $\varphi: M \to N$ is a diffeomorphism, then $(N, \varphi^*\omega)$ is a symplectic manifold and φ is a symplectic map. (See, for example, 10.9 (*ii*).)

14.11. Proposition. *Suppose (M, ω) and (N, ρ) are symplectic manifolds and $F: M \to N$ is of class C^∞. Suppose $\varphi: M \to M'$ and $\psi: N \to N'$ are diffeomorphisms. Then F is symplectic iff $\psi \circ F \circ \varphi^{-1}$ is a symplectic mapping of $(M', \varphi^*\omega)$ into $(N', \psi^*\rho)$. In particular, F is symplectic iff the local representatives of F are symplectic.*

Proof. If F is symplectic, then $(\psi \circ F \circ \varphi^{-1})_* \psi^* \rho = \varphi_*^{-1} \circ F_* \circ \psi_* \circ \psi^* \rho = \varphi_*^{-1} \circ F_* \rho = \varphi_*^{-1} \omega = \varphi^* \omega$. Conversely, if $\psi \circ F \circ \varphi^{-1}$ is symplectic, then $F_* \rho = \varphi_* \circ \varphi_*^{-1} \circ F_* \circ \psi_* \psi^* \rho = \varphi_* \circ (\psi \circ F \circ \varphi^{-1})_* \circ \psi^* \rho = \varphi_* \circ \varphi^* \omega = \omega$. ∎

14.12. Proposition. *Let (M, ω) and (N, ρ) be symplectic 2n-manifolds and $f: M \to N$ a symplectic mapping. Then for each $m \in M$ there are symplectic charts (U, φ) at m and (V, ψ) at $f(m)$ such that $f(U) = V$, $\varphi(U) = \psi(V)$, and the local representative $f_{\varphi\psi}$ of f is the identity.*

Proof. Since f is a local diffeomorphism (14.10), we can find neighborhoods U_1 of m and V_1 of $f(m)$ such that $f|U_1: U_1 \to V_1$ is a diffeomorphism. Let (V, ψ) be a symplectic chart at $f(m)$ with $V \subset V_1$ (Darboux's theorem). Then let $U = (f|U_1)^{-1}(V)$ and $\varphi = \psi \circ f|U$. Clearly $f_{\varphi\psi}$ is the identity. Also, (U, φ) is a symplectic chart, for $\varphi^* \omega = \omega_\varphi = (\psi \circ f)^* \omega = \psi^* \circ f^* \omega = \psi^* \omega = \omega_\psi$ on $\varphi(U) = \psi(V)$. (Note that if $t \in \mathscr{T}^r_s(M)$, the local representative of t in the natural charts is $\varphi^* t$.) ∎

The connection with §13 is given by the following.

14.13. Proposition. *Let $(\mathbf{E}, \boldsymbol{\omega})$ and $(\mathbf{F}, \boldsymbol{\rho})$ be symplectic vector spaces, which also may be regarded as symplectic manifolds ($\boldsymbol{\omega}, \boldsymbol{\rho}$ being constant sections). Then a C^∞ map $F: U \subset \mathbf{E} \to \mathbf{F}$ is symplectic iff $DF(u) \in L(\mathbf{E}, \mathbf{F})$ is symplectic for each $u \in U$ (§13).*

Proof. This follows at once from the definition $F_* \boldsymbol{\rho} = (TF)_* \circ \boldsymbol{\rho} \circ F$ applied to the second factors (2.4). ∎

In most mechanical problems, the basic symplectic manifold is the phase space of a configuration space. In fact, if the configuration space is a manifold V, the momentum phase space is its cotangent bundle T^*V, which has a standard symplectic form as follows.

14.14. Theorem. *Let V be an n-manifold and $M = T^*V$. Consider $\tau_V^*: M \to V$ (6.14) and $T\tau_V^*: TM \to TV$. Let $\alpha_v \in M$ $(v \in V)$ denote points of M and ω_{α_v} points of TM in the fiber over α_v. Define*

$$\theta_{\alpha_v}: T_{\alpha_v} M \to \mathbf{R}: \omega_{\alpha_v} \rightsquigarrow \alpha_v \circ T\tau_V^*(\omega_{\alpha_v}) \quad \text{and} \quad \theta_0: \alpha_v \rightsquigarrow \theta_{\alpha_v}$$

Then $\theta_0 \in \mathscr{X}^*(M)$, and $\omega_0 = -d\theta_0$ is a symplectic form on M; $-\theta_0$ and ω_0 are called the **canonical forms** *on M.*

Proof. Let (U, φ) be a chart on V with $\varphi(U) = U' \subset \mathbf{R}^n$ and $\varphi(u) = (q^1(u), \ldots, q^n(u))$; $q^i \in \mathscr{F}(U)$. Then a chart on M is $(T^*U, (T\varphi)^0_1)$, $(T\varphi)^0_1: T^*U \to U' \times (\mathbf{R}^n)^*$.

If $(\mathbf{e}_1, \ldots, \mathbf{e}_n)$ is the standard ordered basis of $\mathbf{R}^n$, $(\boldsymbol{\alpha}^1, \ldots, \boldsymbol{\alpha}^n)$ the dual basis, and if $\alpha \in T^*U$, then

$$(T\varphi)^0_1 \alpha = (q^1(\alpha), \ldots, q^n(\alpha), p_1(\alpha), \ldots, p_n(\alpha)) \in U' \times (\mathbf{R}^n)^*$$

where $q^i(\alpha) = q^i(\boldsymbol{\tau}_V^* \alpha)$ and $p_i(\alpha) = \alpha(\underline{e}_i)$ (see 10.4). Thus, $q^i, p_i \in \mathscr{F}(T^*U)$.

Hence, elements of TM have the form

$$\omega = \sum_{i=1}^{n} (\beta^i \underline{e}_i + \gamma_i \underline{\alpha}^i)$$

in the chart $(T^*U, (T\varphi)_1^0)$. Note that, in this chart, $\underline{e}_i, \ldots, \underline{e}_n, \underline{\alpha}^1, \ldots, \underline{\alpha}^n$ is the basis dual to $(dq^1, \ldots, dq^n, dp_1, \ldots, dp_n)$ (see 10.4). Now in local representation,

$$\boldsymbol{\tau}^*_{V\varphi}(q^1(\alpha), \ldots, q^n(\alpha), p_1(\alpha), \ldots, p_n(\alpha)) = (q^1(\alpha), \ldots, q^n(\alpha), 0, 0, \ldots, 0)$$

and so

$$T\boldsymbol{\tau}^*_V(\omega) = \sum_{i=1}^{n} \beta^i \underline{e}_i \in TV$$

Thus,

$$\theta_\alpha(\omega) = \sum_{i=1}^{n} p_i(\alpha)\, dq^i(\alpha) \cdot \left(\sum_{j=1}^{n} \beta^j(\alpha) \underline{e}_i(\alpha) \right) = \sum_{i=1}^{n} p_i(\alpha) \beta^i(\alpha)$$

where $\boldsymbol{\tau}_M(\omega) = \alpha$. Hence we see that

$$\theta_0 | T^*U = \sum_{i=1}^{n} p_i dq^i$$

Thus $\theta_0 \in \mathscr{X}^*(M)$. Also

$$\mathbf{d}\theta_0 = \sum_{i=1}^{n} dp_i \wedge dq^i = -\sum_{i=1}^{n} dq^i \wedge dp_i \qquad ■$$

Not only does this show that $\mathbf{d}\theta_0$ has maximum rank, but also that *the natural charts are symplectic charts for* $-\mathbf{d}\theta_0$.

14.15. Corollary. *The cotangent bundle of any manifold is orientable.*

This follows at once from 14.14 and the fact that any symplectic manifold is orientable (see 13.5).

A basic method for generating symplectic mappings on T^*M from mappings on M is given by the following.

14.16. Theorem. *Let M be a manifold and $\varphi: M \to M$ a diffeomorphism. Then $\varphi^*: T^*M \to T^*M$ is a symplectic diffeomorphism on T^*M. (We use the natural symplectic structure on T^*M, as given in* 14.14.)

Proof. It is sufficient to show that $(\varphi^*)_*\theta_0 = \theta_0$, where θ_0 is the canonical 1-form on T^*M. If

$$w_{\alpha_m} \in T_{\alpha_m}(T^*M)$$

then

$$\begin{aligned}(\varphi^*)_*\theta_0(\alpha_m)(w_{\alpha_m}) &= \theta_0(\varphi^*\alpha_m) \cdot T\varphi^* \circ w_{\alpha_m} \\ &= \varphi^*\alpha_m \cdot (T\boldsymbol{\tau}^*_M \circ T\varphi^* \cdot w_{\alpha_m}) \\ &= \alpha_m \cdot (T\varphi^{-1} \circ T\boldsymbol{\tau}^*_M \circ T\varphi^* \cdot w_{\alpha_m}) \\ &= \alpha_m \cdot (T(\varphi^{-1} \circ \boldsymbol{\tau}^*_M \circ \varphi^*) \cdot w_{\alpha_m})\end{aligned}$$

However, $\varphi^{-1} \circ \tau_M^* \circ \varphi^*(\beta_m) = \varphi^{-1} \circ \varphi(m) = \tau_M^* \beta_m$. Hence the result follows. (See also 10.8 (*iv*).) ∎

A similar statement holds for $\varphi: M \to N$.

For mechanics, one of the most important operations given by the symplectic structure of the phase space is that of the Poisson bracket. In fact, Jost [1] has shown that a symplectic structure can be derived from the Poisson brackets.

14.17. Definition. *Suppose* (M, ω) *is a symplectic manifold and* $\alpha, \beta \in \mathscr{X}^*(M)$. *The* **Poisson bracket** *of* α *and* β *is the* 1-*form* $\{\alpha, \beta\} = -[\alpha^\sharp, \beta^\sharp]^\flat$ *(see* 14.1).

Note that we have the following commutative diagram:

$$\begin{array}{ccc} \mathscr{X} \times \mathscr{X} & \xrightarrow{-[\;]} & \mathscr{X} \\ {\scriptstyle \flat \times \flat}\downarrow & & \downarrow{\scriptstyle \flat} \\ \mathscr{X}^* \times \mathscr{X}^* & \xrightarrow[\{\;\}]{} & \mathscr{X}^* \end{array}$$

Thus 8.13, together with linearity of $\flat$, yields the following.

14.18. Proposition. $\mathscr{X}^*(M)$ *as a real vector space, together with the composition* $\{\;\}$, *is a Lie algebra.*

14.19. Proposition. *Let* (M, ω) *be a symplectic manifold and* $\alpha, \beta \in \mathscr{X}^*(M)$. *Then* $\{\alpha, \beta\} = -\mathbf{L}_{\alpha^\sharp}\beta + \mathbf{L}_{\beta^\sharp}\alpha + \mathbf{d}(\mathbf{i}_{\alpha^\sharp}\mathbf{i}_{\beta^\sharp}\omega)$.

Proof. From 10.15 (*ii*) we have the following formula for 2-forms,

$$(\mathbf{d}\omega)(X, Y, Z) = \tfrac{1}{3}\{\mathbf{L}_X(\omega(Y, Z)) + \mathbf{L}_Y(\omega(Z, X)) + \mathbf{L}_Z(\omega(X, Y)) - \omega[X, Y], Z) - \omega([Y, Z], X) - \omega([Z, X], Y)\}$$

Setting $X = \alpha^\sharp$, $Y = \beta^\sharp$ and observing that $\omega(\alpha^\sharp, Z) = \frac{1}{2}\alpha(Z)$ yields

$$0 = \tfrac{1}{2}\{\mathbf{L}_{\alpha^\sharp}(\beta(Z)) - \mathbf{L}_{\beta^\sharp}(\alpha(Z)) - \mathbf{L}_Z(\mathbf{i}_{\alpha^\sharp}\mathbf{i}_{\beta^\sharp}\omega) + \{\alpha, \beta\}(Z) + \alpha(\mathbf{L}_{\beta^\sharp}Z) - \beta(\mathbf{L}_{\alpha^\sharp}Z)\}$$

Then, using 10.15 (*i*),

$$0 = (\mathbf{L}_{\alpha^\sharp}\beta)(Z) - (\mathbf{L}_{\beta^\sharp}\alpha)(Z) - \mathbf{d}(\mathbf{i}_{\alpha^\sharp}\mathbf{i}_{\beta^\sharp}\omega)(Z) + \{\alpha, \beta\}(Z)$$

as required. ∎

14.20. Proposition. *If* $\alpha, \beta \in \mathscr{X}^*(M)$ *are closed, then* $\{\alpha, \beta\}$ *is exact.*

Proof. If ρ is closed, then $\mathbf{L}_X\rho = \mathbf{i}_X\mathbf{d}\rho + \mathbf{d}\mathbf{i}_X\rho = \mathbf{d}\mathbf{i}_X\rho$. Thus the result follows at once from 14.19. ∎

14.21. Definition. *Let* $\mathscr{X}^*_{\mathscr{C}}(M)$ *denote the set of closed* 1-*forms, and* $\mathscr{X}^*_{\mathscr{E}}(M)$ *the exact* 1-*forms on a manifold* M.

14.22. Proposition. $\mathscr{X}^*_{\mathscr{C}}(M)$ *and* $\mathscr{X}^*_{\mathscr{E}}(M)$ *form Lie subalgebras of* $\mathscr{X}^*(M)$.

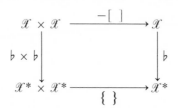

Proof. Since $\mathbf{d}$ is $\mathbf{R}$ linear, it is clear that $\mathscr{X}^*_{\mathscr{C}}(M)$ and $\mathscr{X}^*_{\mathscr{E}}(M)$ are subspaces of $\mathscr{X}^*(M)$ as real vector spaces. Also, if $\alpha, \beta \in \mathscr{X}^*_{\mathscr{C}}(M)$, then $\{\alpha, \beta\} \in \mathscr{X}^*_{\mathscr{E}}(M) \subset \mathscr{X}^*_{\mathscr{C}}(M)$ by 14.20. It is also clear that if $\alpha, \beta \in \mathscr{X}^*_{\mathscr{E}}(M)$, then $\{\alpha, \beta\} \in \mathscr{X}^*_{\mathscr{E}}(M)$. ∎

14.23. Definition. *Let (M, ω) be a symplectic manifold and $f, g \in \mathscr{F}(M)$. Then we define $X_f = (\mathbf{d}f)^\# \in \mathscr{X}(M)$, and the* **Poisson bracket** *of f and g is the function*

$$\{f,g\} = -\mathbf{i}_{X_f}\mathbf{i}_{X_g}\omega$$

14.24. Proposition. *Let (M, ω) be a symplectic manifold and $f, g \in \mathscr{F}(M)$. Then*

$$\{f, g\} = -\mathbf{i}_{X_f}\mathbf{i}_{X_g}\omega = -\mathbf{L}_{X_f}g = +\mathbf{L}_{X_g}f$$

Proof. By 10.13 (*iii*), $\mathbf{L}_{X_f}g = \mathbf{i}_{X_f}\mathbf{d}g$. However

$$\mathbf{d}g = \mathbf{i}_{X_g}\omega \qquad \text{for} \qquad \mathbf{i}_{X_g}\omega(Y) = 2\omega(X_g, Y) = 2\omega((\mathbf{d}g)^\#, Y)$$
$$= \omega(\omega_\#(\mathbf{d}g), Y) = \mathbf{d}g(Y)$$

Since $\mathbf{i}_X\mathbf{i}_Y\omega = -\mathbf{i}_Y\mathbf{i}_X\omega = 2\omega(Y, X)$, the last formula follows at once. ∎

14.25. Corollary. *For $f_0 \in \mathscr{F}(M)$, the map $g \rightsquigarrow \{f_0, g\}$ is a derivation on $\mathscr{F}(M)$.*

This follows at once from 14.24 and 8.4.

14.26. Proposition. *Let (M, ω) be a symplectic manifold and $f, g \in \mathscr{F}(M)$. Then $\mathbf{d}\{f, g\} = \{\mathbf{d}f, \mathbf{d}g\}$.*

Proof. By 14.19

$$\{\mathbf{d}f, \mathbf{d}g\} = -\mathbf{L}_{X_f}\mathbf{d}g + \mathbf{L}_{X_g}\mathbf{d}f + \mathbf{d}(\mathbf{i}_{X_f}\mathbf{i}_{X_g}\omega) = -\mathbf{d}(\mathbf{L}_{X_f}g + \mathbf{L}_{X_g}f + \mathbf{i}_{X_f}\mathbf{i}_{X_g}\omega)$$
$$= \mathbf{d}\{f, g\} + \mathbf{d}\{f, g\} - \mathbf{d}\{f, g\} = \mathbf{d}\{f, g\} \quad ∎$$

14.27. Proposition. *The real vector space $\mathscr{F}(M)$, together with the composition $\{\ \}$ of 14.23, forms a Lie algebra (8.13).*

Proof. Since $\mathbf{d}$ and $\omega_\#$ are $\mathbf{R}$ linear, the map $X: f \rightsquigarrow X_f$ is $\mathbf{R}$ linear. Hence $\{f, g\} = -\mathbf{i}_{X_f}\mathbf{i}_{X_g}\omega$ is $\mathbf{R}$ bilinear. It is also clear that $\{f, f\} = 0$. For Jacobi's identity (8.13 (*iii*)) we have

$$\{f, \{g, h\}\} = -\mathbf{L}_{X_f}\{g, h\} = -\mathbf{L}_{X_f}(\mathbf{L}_{X_g}h)$$
$$\{g, \{h, f\}\} = -\mathbf{L}_{X_g}(\mathbf{L}_{X_h}f) = +\mathbf{L}_{X_g}(\mathbf{L}_{X_f}h)$$
$$\{h, \{f, g\}\} = +\mathbf{L}_{X_{\{f,g\}}}h$$

However, $\mathbf{X}_{\{f,g\}} = (\mathbf{d}\{f, g\})^\# = \{\mathbf{d}f, \mathbf{d}g\}^\# = -[(\mathbf{d}f)^\#, (\mathbf{d}g)^\#]$ by 14.17 and 14.26. Hence $X_{\{f,g\}} = -[X_f, X_g]$ and the result follows by 8.12. ∎

Thus, Jacobi's identity, restated, gives this corollary.

14.28. Corollary. $X_{\{f,g\}} = -[X_f, X_g]$.

A convenient criterion for symplectic diffeomorphisms is given by the following.

14.29. Theorem. *Let (M, ω) and (N, ρ) be symplectic manifolds and $f\colon M \to N$ be a diffeomorphism. Then f is symplectic iff for all $h \in \mathscr{F}(N)$, $f_* X_h = X_{h \circ f}$* (14.23).

Proof. If f is symplectic, then $f_*(\mathbf{d}h)^\# = (f_*\mathbf{d}h)^\# = \mathbf{d}(h \circ f)^\# = X_{h \circ f}$. (Exercise 14C). Conversely, if $f_* X_h = X_{h \circ f}$, then

$$\mathbf{d}(h \circ f) = \mathbf{i}_{X_{h \circ f}}\omega$$

On the other hand,

$$\begin{aligned}\mathbf{d}(h \circ f) = f_*\mathbf{d}h &= f_*\mathbf{i}_{X_h}\rho \\ &= \mathbf{i}_{f_* X_h} f_*\rho \qquad (10.14)\end{aligned}$$

Therefore

$$\mathbf{i}_{X_{h \circ f}}\omega = \mathbf{i}_{X_{h \circ f}} f_*\rho \qquad \text{for all} \qquad h \in \mathscr{F}(N)$$

But from 8.6 we see that every vector in $T_m M$ has the form $X_{h \circ f}(m)$ for some h. Thus $\omega = f_*\rho$ and f is symplectic. ∎

Preserving Poisson brackets also characterizes symplectic mappings as follows.

14.30. Proposition. *Let (M, ω) and (N, ρ) be symplectic manifolds and $F\colon M \to N$ a diffeomorphism. Then F is symplectic iff F preserves Poisson brackets of functions (resp. 1-forms); that is, for all $f, g \in \mathscr{F}(M)$, $\{F^*f, F^*g\} = F^*\{f, g\}$ (resp. for all $\alpha, \beta \in \Omega^1(M)$, $\{F^*\alpha, F^*\beta\} = F^*\{\alpha, \beta\}$); or F^* is a Lie algebra isomorphism on $\mathscr{F}$ (resp. Ω^1).*

Proof. By 8.3,

$$F^*\{f, g\} = F^*\mathbf{L}_{X_g} f = \mathbf{L}_{F^*X_g} F^*f$$

Hence F preserves Poisson brackets iff

$$\mathbf{L}_{F^*X_g} F^*f = \mathbf{L}_{X_{F^*g}} F^*f$$

iff $F^*X_g = X_{F^*g}$ iff F is symplectic (14.29). We leave the second part as an exercise. ∎

Symplectic diffeomorphisms are known classically as **homogeneous canonical** (or **contact**) **transformations**. In §21 we shall see that they are exactly the time independent canonical transformations.

The connection with the coordinate definition of Poisson brackets is given by the following.

14.31. Proposition. *Let (M, ω) be a symplectic 2n-manifold and $f, g \in \mathscr{F}(M)$. Let (U, φ) be a symplectic chart* (14.7). *Then, using the notation of* 10.4 *and* 14.7,

$$\{f, g\} = \sum_{i=1}^{n} \left(\frac{\partial f}{\partial x^i}\frac{\partial g}{\partial y^i} - \frac{\partial f}{\partial y^i}\frac{\partial g}{\partial x^i} \right)$$

Proof. By the computation done in §13, we see $(dx^i)^\sharp = -e_{i+n}$, $(\mathbf{d}y^i)^\sharp = e_1$ $i = 1, \ldots, n$. Hence, since $\sharp$ is $\mathscr{F}$-linear,

$$X_f = (\mathbf{d}f)^\sharp = + \sum_{i=1}^{n} \left(-\frac{\partial f}{\partial x^i} e_{i+n} + \frac{\partial f}{\partial y^i} e_i \right)$$

Hence

$$\begin{aligned}
\{f, g\} &= -\mathbf{i}_{X_f}\mathbf{i}_{X_g}\omega = -2\omega(X_g, X_f) \\
&= -2 \sum_{i=1}^{n} (dx^i \wedge dy^i)(X_g, X_f) \\
&= -\sum_{i=1}^{n} (dx^i \otimes dy^i - dy^i \otimes dx^i)(X_g, X_f) \qquad \text{(see 9.2 and 9.4)} \\
&= + \sum_{i=1}^{n} \left(\frac{\partial f}{\partial x^i}\frac{\partial g}{\partial y^i} - \frac{\partial f}{\partial y^i}\frac{\partial g}{\partial x^i} \right) \qquad \blacksquare
\end{aligned}$$

Exercises

14A. Give the details of 14.13. What are the canonical forms on a local manifold (intrinsically)? Prove that the tangent bundle of any manifold is orientable (13.7, 11.13).

14B. Let (M, ω) be a symplectic manifold. Show that the collection of symplectic diffeomorphisms $\varphi: M \to M$ form a group under composition.

14C. Show that a diffeomorphism F between symplectic manifolds is symplectic iff $(F^*\alpha)^\sharp = F^*(\alpha^\sharp)$ for all 1-forms α. Hence complete the proofs of 14.29 and 14.30 using 8.14. Draw the appropriate commutative diagrams.

14D. Let (M, ω) be a symplectic manifold and $X, Y \in \mathscr{X}(M)$. Define the **Lagrange brackets** of X and Y by $(X, Y) = \omega(X, Y) \in \mathscr{F}(M)$. Then show:

(i) $(X_f, X_g) = \{f, g\}$;

(ii) a diffeomorphism $F: M \to N$ is symplectic iff it preserves Lagrange brackets;

(iii) use a symplectic chart to establish the connection with the usual coordinate definition.

14E. Let (M, ω) be a symplectic manifold and (U, φ) a chart on M such that if $\varphi(u) = (x^1(u), x^2(u), y_1(u), y_2(u))$, then

$$\omega | U = dx^1 \wedge dy_1 + dx^2 \wedge dy_2 + f\, dx^1 \wedge dy_2$$

for some $f \in \mathscr{F}(U)$ (so that (U, φ) is not a symplectic chart). Then show, by determining the $\flat$ and $\sharp$ actions,

(i) $f = \{y^1, x_2\}$

(ii) If $H \in \mathscr{F}(M)$, then in local representation,

$$\begin{aligned} X_H = & -\frac{\partial H}{\partial x^1}\underset{\sim}{e}_3 - \frac{\partial H}{\partial x^2}\underset{\sim}{e}_4 \\ & + \frac{\partial H}{\partial y_1}\underset{\sim}{e}_1 + \frac{\partial H}{\partial y_2}\underset{\sim}{e}_2 \\ & + \left(\frac{\partial H}{\partial x^2}\right) f\underset{\sim}{e}_3 - \frac{\partial H}{\partial y_1} f\underset{\sim}{e}_2 \end{aligned}$$

where $(\mathbf{e}_1, \mathbf{e}_2, \mathbf{e}_3, \mathbf{e}_4)$ is the standard basis;

(iii) A curve $c: I \to M$ is an integral curve of X_H iff, in local representation,

$$\begin{aligned} \frac{dx^1}{dt}(c(t)) &= \frac{\partial H}{\partial y_1}(c(t)) \\ \frac{dx^2}{dt}(c(t)) &= \left(\frac{\partial H}{\partial y_2} - f\frac{\partial H}{\partial y_1}\right)(c(t)) \\ \frac{dy_1}{dt}(c(t)) &= \left(-\frac{\partial H}{\partial x^1} + f\frac{\partial H}{\partial x^2}\right)(c(t)) \\ \frac{dy_2}{dt}(c(t)) &= -\frac{\partial H}{\partial x_2}(c(t)) \end{aligned}$$

Compare with the Hamiltonian equations if the chart is symplectic ($f = 0$). Note, however, that the integral curves are the same, irrespective of the chart used. That is, *the above equations are canonical even if they do not look it.*

14F. Consider the polar coordinate diffeomorphism ρ from the upper half of the cylinder $\mathbf{R} \times S^1$ onto $\mathbf{R}^2 \backslash \{0\}$, defined by $(r, \theta) \rightsquigarrow (r\cos\theta, r\sin\theta)$ (note that θ is not defined globally on S^1, but $\mathbf{d}\theta$ is). Show that $\mathbf{d}(r^2/2) \wedge \mathbf{d}\theta$ is a volume on $S^1 \times \mathbf{R}$ and, relative to this volume and the standard one on $\mathbf{R}^2$, ρ is symplectic. Compare with the statement: $dx\,dy = r\,dr\,d\theta$.

14G. If $X \in \mathscr{X}(M)$, define $f_X: T^*M \to \mathbf{R}$ by $f_X(\alpha_m) = \alpha_m(X(m))$. Show $f_X \in \mathscr{F}(T^*M)$, and if $X, Y \in \mathscr{X}(M)$, then $\{f_X, f_Y\} = f_{[X,Y]}$ in the natural symplectic structure.

§15. INTEGRAL INVARIANTS

In the next few sections we develop some of the basic topics of classical mechanics. In this section we transcribe to the context of symplectic geometry the integral invariants of Poincaré. These are mainly of historical interest, as in the past they were thought to be a general method for solving problems of mechanics. The reader may wish to compare the methods used here with those of Whittaker [1], Goldstein [1], or Cartan [1].

15.1. Definition. *Let M be a manifold and X a vectorfield on M. Let $\alpha \in \Omega^k(M)$. We call α an* **invariant k form of X** *iff $\mathbf{L}_X\alpha = 0$.*

From 8.21 we obtain the following.

15.2. Proposition. *Let M be a manifold and $X \in \mathscr{X}(M)$, $\alpha \in \Omega^k(M)$. Then α is an invariant k form of X iff α is constant along the integral curves of X, that is, $(F_\lambda)_*\alpha$ is independent of λ, for any flow box (U, a, F) of X.*

Thus, if we think of the integral curves of X as the motion of a system, α is a *constant of the motion*. The term *integral k* form arises because of the following.

15.3. Theorem (Poincaré–Cartan). *Let X be a complete vectorfield on a manifold M, with flow F (7.13), and let $\alpha \in \Omega^k(M)$. Then α is an invariant k-form of X iff for all oriented compact k-manifolds with boundary (V, V_0, bdV_0) and C^∞ mappings $\varphi\colon V \to M$, we have $\int_{V_0} (F_\lambda \circ \varphi)_*\alpha = \int_{V_0} \varphi_*\alpha$, independent of λ.*

Proof. If α is invariant (Poincaré), then by 15.2 $(F_\lambda)^*\alpha = \alpha$, $(F_\lambda)_*\alpha = \alpha$. Hence $\int_{V_0} (F_\lambda \circ \varphi)_*\alpha = \int_{V_0} \varphi_* \circ (F_\lambda)_*\alpha = \int_{V_0} \varphi_*\alpha$ (10.8). Note that, since V is compact and orientable, the integral is well defined according to §12. Conversely (Cartan), if the integral is invariant under the flow, then for any local k disc $(D, D_0, S = bdD_0)$ in V (a solid sphere in local representation in $\mathbf{R}^k$) we have $\int_D (F_\lambda \circ \varphi)_*\alpha = \int_D \varphi_*\alpha$, since D is compact. But the Lebesgue integral of 12.10 is a (signed) measure, and the discs above generate the Borel sets on V_0. Hence, over any measurable set A we have, by the Hahn extension theorem, $\int_A (F_\lambda \circ \varphi)_*\alpha = \int_A \varphi_*\alpha$. Thus $(F_\lambda \circ \varphi)_*\alpha = \varphi_*\alpha$. Then, by choosing V to be a portion of various subspaces in local representation, we see that $(F_\lambda \circ \varphi)_*\alpha = \varphi_* \circ F_{\lambda *}\alpha = \varphi_*\alpha$ for all such φ implies $F_{\lambda *}\alpha = \alpha$, or, by 15.2, α is an invariant k-form of X. ∎

Note that X need not be complete for 15.3, the statement of the theorem merely requiring independence for all local flow boxes such that the integrals are defined; that is, the domain of F_λ should contain $\varphi(V)$.

15.4. Proposition. *Let X be a vectorfield on a manifold M and α, β invariant forms of X. Then*

(*i*) $\mathbf{i}_X\alpha$ *is an invariant form of X* (10.12);
(*ii*) $\mathbf{d}\alpha$ *is an invariant form of X* (10.6);
(*iii*) $\mathbf{L}_X\gamma$ *is closed iff* $\mathbf{d}\gamma$ *is an invariant form, for any $\gamma \in \Omega^k(M)$;*
(*iv*) $\alpha \wedge \beta$ *is an invariant form of X.*

Proof. Note that $\mathbf{L}_X\mathbf{i}_X = \mathbf{i}_X\mathbf{L}_X$; since $\mathbf{L}_X\mathbf{i}_X = \mathbf{d}\mathbf{i}_X\mathbf{i}_X + \mathbf{i}_X\mathbf{d}\mathbf{i}_X = \mathbf{i}_X\mathbf{d}\mathbf{i}_X$ and $\mathbf{i}_X\mathbf{L}_X = \mathbf{i}_X\mathbf{d}\mathbf{i}_X + \mathbf{i}_X\mathbf{i}_X\mathbf{d} = \mathbf{i}_X\mathbf{d}\mathbf{i}_X$ (see 10.13). This also follows from the relation $\mathbf{i}_{[X,Y]} = \mathbf{L}_X\mathbf{i}_Y - \mathbf{i}_Y\mathbf{L}_X$ mentioned in 10C. Thus $\mathbf{L}_X\mathbf{i}_X\alpha = \mathbf{i}_X\mathbf{L}_X\alpha = 0$ and (*i*) holds. For (*ii*), $\mathbf{L}_X\mathbf{d}\alpha = \mathbf{d}\mathbf{L}_X\alpha = 0$ by 10.11. This same relation $\mathbf{L}_X\mathbf{d} = \mathbf{d}\mathbf{L}_X$ proves (*iii*). Finally, (*iv*) follows since $\mathbf{L}_X$ is a tensor, and hence a $\wedge$ derivation; $\mathbf{L}(\alpha \wedge \beta) = (\mathbf{L}\alpha) \wedge \beta + \alpha \wedge \mathbf{L}\beta$. ∎

Since $\mathbf{L}_X$ is $\mathbf{R}$ linear, we obtain the following.

15.5. Corollary. *Let $X \in \mathscr{X}(M)$, and let $\mathscr{A}_X$ denote the invariant forms of X. Then $\mathscr{A}_X$ is a $\wedge$ subalgebra of $\Omega(M)$, which is closed under* $\mathbf{d}$ *and* $\mathbf{i}_X$.

15.6. Definition. *Let X be a vectorfield on a manifold M and $\alpha \in \Omega^k(M)$. Then α is called a* **relatively invariant** k-**form of** X *iff* $\mathbf{L}_X\alpha$ *is closed.*

Thus α is a relatively invariant k-form of X iff $\mathbf{d}\alpha$ is an invariant $(k + 1)$-form of X (15.1).

For the integral properties of relatively invariant forms (Whittaker [1, p. 271]) we employ Stokes' theorem, 12.12.

15.7. Theorem (Poincaré–Cartan). *Let X be a complete vectorfield with flow F on a manifold M. Let $\alpha \in \Omega^{k-1}(M)$. Then α is a relatively invariant $(k - 1)$-form of X iff for all oriented compact k manifolds with boundary (V, V_0, bdV_0) and C^∞ maps $\varphi: V \to M$ we have*

$$\int_{bdV_0} (F_\lambda \circ \varphi \circ i)_*\alpha = \int_{bdV_0} (\varphi \circ i)_*\alpha$$

that is, is independent of $\lambda \in \mathbf{R}$ ($i: bdV_0 \to V$ is the inclusion map).

Proof. The form α is relatively invariant iff $\mathbf{d}\alpha$ is an invariant form of X. But then, by Stokes' theorem and 15.3, we have

$$\int_{bdV_0} (F_\lambda \circ \varphi \circ i)_*\alpha = \int_{V_0} (F_\lambda \circ \varphi)_*\mathbf{d}\alpha = \int_{V_0} \varphi_*\mathbf{d}\alpha = \int_{bdV_0} i_* \circ \varphi_*\alpha$$

The converse may be proven, as in 15.3. ∎

We may now summarize the algebraic relationships between the invariant forms of a fixed vectorfield.

15.8. Definition. *If $X \in \mathscr{X}(M)$, let $\mathscr{A}_X$ be the set of all invariant forms of X, $\mathscr{R}_X$ the set of all relatively invariant forms of X, $\mathscr{C}$ the set of all closed forms in $\Omega(M)$, and $\mathscr{E}$ the set of all exact forms in $\Omega(M)$.*

Note that $\mathscr{A}_X \subset \mathscr{R}_X$, and $\mathscr{E} \subset \mathscr{C} \subset \mathscr{R}_X$. By 15.5, $\mathscr{A}_X$ is a differential subalgebra of $\Omega(M)$, but $\mathscr{R}_X$ is not. However, it is obviously an $\mathbf{R}$ subspace. Further relationships as $\mathbf{R}$ subspaces may be expressed in the convenient language of exact sequences of $\mathbf{R}$ linear mappings.

15.9. Definition. *Let* $\mathbf{E}_i$ *be a real vector space, and* $\alpha_i\colon \mathbf{E}_i \to \mathbf{E}_{i+1}$ *a linear mapping,* $i \in \mathbf{Z}$, *the integers. Then the diagram*

$$\cdots \xrightarrow{\alpha_{i-1}} \mathbf{E}_i \xrightarrow{\alpha_i} \mathbf{E}_{i+1} \xrightarrow{\alpha_{i+1}} \mathbf{E}_{i+2} \xrightarrow{\alpha_{i+2}} \cdots$$

is an **exact sequence** *iff for all i,* $Im(\alpha_{i-1}) = Ker(\alpha_i)$.

Especially, we write $\mathbf{E} \xrightarrow{\alpha} \mathbf{F} \longrightarrow \mathbf{0}$ **exact** *iff* α *is surjective, and*

$\mathbf{0} \longrightarrow \mathbf{E} \xrightarrow{\alpha} \mathbf{F}$ **exact** *iff* α *is injective.*

Note that for any linear mapping $\alpha\colon \mathbf{E} \longrightarrow \mathbf{F}$, we have the exact sequence

$$\mathbf{0} \longrightarrow Ker(\alpha) \xrightarrow{i} \mathbf{E} \xrightarrow{\alpha} \mathbf{F} \xrightarrow{\pi} F/\mathrm{Im}(\alpha) \longrightarrow \mathbf{0}$$

where i is the inclusion map, and π the projection onto the quotient space.

With these notations the following is a trivial restatement of definitions and elementary properties.

15.10. Proposition. *If* $X \in \mathscr{X}(M)$, *the following sequences are exact.*

(i) $\mathbf{0} \longrightarrow \mathscr{A}_X \xrightarrow{i} \mathscr{R}_X \xrightarrow{\mathbf{L}_X} \Omega(M) \xrightarrow{\mathbf{d}} \Omega(M) \xrightarrow{\pi} \Omega(M)/\mathscr{E} \longrightarrow \mathbf{0}$

(ii) $\mathbf{0} \longrightarrow \mathscr{A}_X \xrightarrow{i} \Omega(M) \xrightarrow{\mathbf{L}_X} \Omega(M) \xrightarrow{\pi} \Omega(M)/Im(L_X) \longrightarrow \mathbf{0}$

(iii) $\mathbf{0} \longrightarrow \mathscr{C} \xrightarrow{i} \mathscr{R}_X \xrightarrow{\mathbf{d}} \mathscr{A}_X \xrightarrow{\pi} \mathscr{A}_X/\mathscr{E} \cap \mathscr{A}_X \longrightarrow \mathbf{0}$

In addition,

(iv) $\mathscr{C} \wedge \mathscr{R}_X \subset \mathscr{R}_X$.

Finally, we consider the problem of finding invariant volumes on submanifolds. Recall that if M is orientable and $V \subset M$ is a submanifold with trivial normal bundle, then V is orientable (11.11). We ask, if Ω_M is a volume on M invariant under $X \in \mathscr{X}(M)$, $\mathbf{L}_X\Omega_M = 0$, can we find a volume Ω_V on V that is also invariant under X? The first requirement, of course, must be that V itself is invariant under X.

15.11. Definition. *If* $V \subset M$ *is a submanifold and* $X \in \mathscr{X}(M)$, *then* V *is an* **invariant manifold** *of* X *iff for all* $v \in V$, $X(v) \in T_vV \subset T_vM$.

From this infinitesimal characterization of invariance follows immediately an integral characterization. For if V is invariant under X, then $X|V \in \mathscr{X}(V)$. Thus, by the uniqueness of integral curves, we have the following.

15.12. Proposition. *If* $V \subset M$ *is an invariant manifold of* $X \in \mathscr{X}(M)$, $v \in V$, *and* $c\colon I \to M$ *is an integral curve at* v, *then there is a neighborhood* J *of* $0 \in I$ *such that* $c(J) \subset V$, *and conversely.*

For the question of invariant volumes on V, we consider only an invariant manifold V defined by the vanishing of invariant 1-forms of X.

15.13. Theorem (Hamilton–Jacobi). *Let* $\varphi_1, \ldots, \varphi_k \in \mathscr{X}^*(M)$ *be invariant forms of* $X \in \mathscr{X}(M)$, *and* $V \subset M$ *an invariant manifold of* X *such that for all* $v \in V$, $T_vV = \{w_v \in T_vM \mid \varphi_i(v)w_v = 0,\ i = 1, \ldots, k\}$

and $\varphi_i(v)$ are linearly independent. Then if there is an invariant volume of X on M, there is an invariant volume of $X|V$ on V.

Proof. Let g be a Riemannian metric of M (11.12), $Y_i = g_\sharp(\varphi_i)$, and $N_i = Y_i|V$. Then the mappings $N_1, \ldots, N_k$ give a trivialization of the normal bundle of V (11.11). For if $v \in V$, $\{\varphi_i(v)\}$ is linearly independent, and $g_\sharp(v)$ is an isomorphism, so $\{N_i(v)\}$ is linearly independent. Also, $N_i(v) \notin T_vV$. For $T_vV \subset Ker(\varphi_i(v))$, and if $w_v \in T_vV$, $g(N_i(v), w_v) = \varphi_i(v)(w_v) = 0$, so in fact, $\{N_i(v)\}$ spans the orthogonal complement to $T_vV \subset T_vM$. Now let Ω be an invariant volume of X, and

$$\Omega_0 = \mathbf{i}_{Y_1} \cdots \mathbf{i}_{Y_k}\Omega$$

Then if $v: V \to M$ is the inclusion map, $v_*\Omega_0$ is a volume on V (11.11). We seek a function $f \in \mathscr{F}(V)$ such that $\Omega_V = fv_*\Omega_0$ is invariant under X. But there is a unique function $g_0 \in \mathscr{F}(M)$ such that

$$\Omega_1 = \varphi_1 \wedge \cdots \wedge \varphi_k \wedge \Omega_0 = g_0\Omega$$

and φ_i is invariant. Also, $\Omega_1(v)$ is nonzero for $v \in V$, and thus by continuity, $\Omega_1|U$ is a volume, for some open set $U \subset M$ containing V. Thus on U, we have g_0 nonvanishing. Let $f \in \mathscr{F}(U)$ be the reciprocal of g_0, so if $\Omega_2 = f\Omega_0$, then on U

$$\varphi_1 \wedge \cdots \wedge \varphi_k \wedge \Omega_2 = \Omega$$

Now φ_i is invariant, and $\mathbf{L}_X$ is a $\wedge$ derivation, so we have

$$\varphi_1 \wedge \cdots \wedge \varphi_k \wedge \mathbf{L}_X\Omega_2 = 0$$

Let $\Omega_V = v_*\Omega_2$. Then as V is invariant under X

$$\mathbf{L}_{X|V}\Omega_V = v_*(\mathbf{L}_X\Omega_2)$$

But if $w_1, \ldots, w_{n-k} \in T_vV$, then

$$\begin{aligned} 0 &= \varphi_1 \wedge \cdots \wedge \mathbf{L}_X\Omega_2(N_1, \ldots, N_k, w_1, \ldots, w_{n-k}) \\ &= \frac{(n-k)!}{n!} det[\varphi_i(N_j)]\mathbf{L}_X\Omega_2(w_1, \ldots, w_{n-k}) \\ &= \frac{(n-k)!}{n!} det[g(N_i, N_j)]\mathbf{L}_X\Omega_2(w_1, \ldots, w_{n-k}) \end{aligned}$$

As $\{N_i(v)\}$ linearly independent, $det[g(N_i, N_j)] \neq 0$, so $\mathbf{L}_X\Omega_2(w_1,\ldots,w_{n-k}) = 0$ for all $w_i \in T_vV$, or $v_*(\mathbf{L}_X\Omega_2) = 0$, or $\mathbf{L}_{X|V}\Omega_V = 0$, so Ω_V is invariant under $X|V$. ∎

Exercises

15A. Complete the proof of 15.7 and examine the corresponding version in $\mathbf{R}^n$.

15B. Prove 15.10, and write out the explicit meanings of these statements.

§16. HAMILTONIAN SYSTEMS

We saw in §14 how a symplectic manifold has a distinguished 2 form that gives rise to coordinate charts in which the Poisson bracket takes on its familiar form. In this section we show that for a vectorfield preserving the symplectic structure, the equations for its integral curves become the usual Hamiltonian canonical equations in a symplectic chart. Note that no Riemannian metric is required for this theory.

16.1. Definition. *Let (M, ω) be a symplectic manifold, and X a vectorfield on M. We say that X is* **locally Hamiltonian** *iff ω is an invariant 2-form of X; that is, $\mathbf{L}_X\omega = 0$. The set of locally Hamiltonian vectorfields on M is denoted by $\mathscr{X}_{\mathscr{L}\mathscr{H}}(M)$.*

Thus, as in 15.2, ω is constant along the integral curves of X. We also have the following integral invariants of Poincaré.

16.2. Proposition. *Let X be a locally Hamiltonian vectorfield on a symplectic 2n-manifold (M, ω). Then $\omega, \omega^2, \ldots, \omega^n$ are invariant forms of X.*

This proposition follows at once from the fact that $\mathbf{L}_X$ is a $\wedge$ derivation. Note that this provides a necessary and sufficient condition for X to be locally Hamiltonian (see 15.3).

16.3. Proposition. *$\mathscr{X}_{\mathscr{L}\mathscr{H}}(M)$ is a Lie subalgebra of $\mathscr{X}(M)$* (8.13).

Proof. First, $\mathscr{X}_{\mathscr{L}\mathscr{H}}$ is a vector subspace since the map $X \rightsquigarrow \mathbf{L}_X$ is $\mathbf{R}$ linear (8.9). Second, if $X_1, X_2 \in \mathscr{X}_{\mathscr{L}\mathscr{H}}$, then

$$\mathbf{L}_{[X_1, X_2]}\omega = \mathbf{L}_{X_1}\mathbf{L}_{X_2}\omega - \mathbf{L}_{X_2}\mathbf{L}_{X_1}\omega = 0$$

and $[X_1, X_2] \in \mathscr{X}_{\mathscr{L}\mathscr{H}}$. ∎

Some basic properties of $\mathscr{X}_{\mathscr{L}\mathscr{H}}(M)$, sometimes taken as definitions, are the following.

16.4. Proposition. *Let (M, ω) be a symplectic manifold and $X \in \mathscr{X}(M)$. Then the following are equivalent:*

(*i*) *X is locally Hamiltonian;*
(*ii*) *$X^\flat = \mathbf{i}_X\omega$ is closed;*
(*iii*) *For each $m \in M$, there is a neighborhood U of m and $H \in \mathscr{F}(U)$ such that $X|U = X_H = (dH)^\sharp$ (see* 14.1*);*
(*iv*) *For every flow box of X, F_λ is a symplectic diffeomorphism.*

Proof. Since ω is closed, $\mathbf{L}_X\omega = \mathbf{d}\mathbf{i}_X\omega$. Thus (*i*) is equivalent to (*ii*). Also, as we noted in 15.2, (*i*) and (*iv*) are equivalent. Now $X^\flat$ is closed iff there is a neighborhood U and an $H \in \mathscr{F}(U)$ so that $X^\flat = \mathbf{d}H$ iff $X = (X^\flat)^\sharp = (\mathbf{d}H)^\sharp$ (10.17). Thus (*ii*) and (*iii*) are equivalent. ∎

16.5. Definition. *Let $X \in \mathscr{X}_{\mathscr{L}\mathscr{H}}(M)$. Then a function H, as in* 16.4 (*iii*), *is called a* **local Hamiltonian** *for X.*

16.6. Corollary (Liouville). *Let* $X \in \mathscr{X}_{\mathscr{L}\mathscr{H}}(M)$ *and* (U, a, F) *be a flow box for* X. *Then*

(*i*) *X is incompressible;*
(*ii*) *F_λ is volume and measure preserving, and det* $F_\lambda = 1 \in \mathscr{F}(U)$.

Proof. From 16.2, $\mathbf{L}_X \omega^n = 0$. Hence $div_\Omega X = 0$. For (*ii*) we have $F_{\lambda *}\Omega_\omega = \Omega_\omega$ since $F_{\lambda *}$ is a homomorphism of $\wedge$ algebras (10.9). Then by definition, *det* $F_\lambda = 1$. That F_λ is measure preserving follows from 12.10 applied to U. ∎

16.7. Proposition. *Let* (M, ω) *be a symplectic manifold,* $X \in \mathscr{X}_{\mathscr{L}\mathscr{H}}(M)$, *and* $H \in \mathscr{F}(U)$ *a local Hamiltonian for* X. *Then* H *is constant along the integral curves of* X *in* U.

Proof. $\mathbf{L}_X H = dH(X) = dH(dH^\sharp) = \frac{1}{2}\omega((dH)^\sharp, (dH)^\sharp) = 0$. The result follows by 8.21. Alternatively, $\mathbf{L}_X H = \mathbf{L}_{X_H} H = \{H, H\} = 0$ (14.27). ∎

This proposition says that H is a constant of the motion, or *energy is conserved.*

16.8. Proposition. *Let* X *be a locally Hamiltonian, complete vectorfield with flow* F *on a symplectic manifold* (M, ω). *Then, for* $\alpha, \beta \in \Omega^1(M)$ *and* $f, g \in \mathscr{F}(M)$ *we have* $\{F_{\lambda *}\alpha, F_{\lambda *}\beta\} = F_{\lambda *}\{\alpha, \beta\}$ *and* $\{F_{\lambda *}f, F_{\lambda *}g\} = F_{\lambda *}\{f, g\}$.

This follows at once from 16.4 (*iv*) and 14.30.

Hence we obtain at once (see also 15.5; *invariant form* may be read *constant of the motion*) the following.

16.9. Corollary (Poisson). *Let* $X \in \mathscr{X}_{\mathscr{L}\mathscr{H}}(M)$ *where* (M, ω) *is a symplectic manifold. Then the invariant* 1*-forms of* X *form a Lie subalgebra of* $\mathscr{X}^*(M)$ (14.18), *and the invariant functions form a Lie subalgebra of* $\mathscr{F}(M)$ (14.27).

That is, if $\alpha, \beta \in \Omega^1(M)$ are constants of the motion, then so is $\{\alpha, \beta\} \in \Omega^1(M)$; if $f, g \in \mathscr{F}(M)$ are constants of the motion, then so is $\{f, g\} \in \mathscr{F}(M)$ (Whittaker [1, p. 320].)

16.10. Proposition. *Let* (M, ω) *be a symplectic* $2n$ *manifold and* X *a locally Hamiltonian vectorfield on* M. *Suppose* $\Lambda \in \Omega^{2n}(M)$ *and* $\Lambda = \rho\Omega_\omega$ (11.5). *Then* Λ *is an invariant form of* X *iff* ρ *is an invariant form (function).*

Proof. This follows at once from $\mathbf{L}_X(\rho\Omega) = (\mathbf{L}_X\rho)\Omega + (\mathbf{L}_X\Omega)\rho$ and the fact that $\mathbf{L}_X\Omega = 0$ (16.6 (*ii*)). ∎

An application from §15 is the following.

16.11. Proposition. *Consider the symplectic manifold of* 14.14, $(M, \omega) = (T^*V, -d\theta_0)$, *where* $-\theta_0$ *is the canonical* 1*-form. Then* $X \in \mathscr{X}(M)$ *is locally Hamiltonian iff* θ_0 *is a relatively invariant* 1*-form of* X (*see* 15.6 *and* 15.7).

Proof. Obviously θ_0 is relatively invariant iff $\mathbf{dL}_X\theta_0 = 0$. But $\mathbf{dL}_X\theta_0 = \mathbf{L}_X\mathbf{d}\theta_0 = -\mathbf{L}_X\omega_0 = 0$ iff X is locally Hamiltonian. ∎

Before proceeding with the theory, it should be helpful to make the connection with the usual canonical equations of Hamilton (Whittaker [1, Chapter X]).

16.12. Proposition. *Let X be a locally Hamiltonian vectorfield on a symplectic manifold (M, ω) with a local Hamiltonian function $H \in \mathscr{F}(U)$. Let (V, φ), $V \subset U$, be a symplectic chart with $\varphi(V) \subset \mathbf{R}^{2n}$ and $\varphi(v) = (q^1(v), \ldots, q^n(v), p_1(v), \ldots, p_n(v))$. Then a curve $c(t)$ on V is an integral curve of X iff*

$$\frac{dq^i}{dt}(c(t)) = \frac{\partial H}{\partial p^i}(c(t)) \qquad i = 1, \ldots, n$$

and

$$\frac{dp_i}{dt}(c(t)) = -\frac{\partial H}{\partial q^i}(c(t)) \qquad i = 1, \ldots, n$$

where $q^i(t) = q^i(c(t))$ and $p_i(t) = p_i(c(t))$, and notation as in 10.4.

Proof. Now

$$dH = \sum_{i=1}^{n} \left(\frac{\partial H}{\partial q^i} dq^i + \frac{\partial H}{\partial p^i} dp^i \right)$$

and so

$$X = X_H = \sum_{i=1}^{n} \left(\frac{\partial H}{\partial p_i} \underset{\sim}{e}_i - \frac{\partial H}{\partial q^i} \underset{\sim}{e}_{i+n} \right)$$

on U (notation as in 10.4). Thus, by the computation at the beginning of §7, we have the result. ∎

The following is often referred to as *the equations of motion in Poisson bracket notation.*

16.13. Proposition. *Let X be a locally Hamiltonian vectorfield on a symplectic manifold (M, ω) with a local Hamiltonian $H \in \mathscr{F}(U)$. Then for $f \in \mathscr{F}(U)$ we have $\mathbf{L}_X f = \{f, H\}$ on U.*

This of course follows at once from 14.24. The reader may wish to use this to verify 16.12. Note that 16.7 also follows from this.

To free the Hamiltonian of its local nature, we globalize it as follows.

16.14. Definition. *Let (M, ω) be a symplectic manifold, and $X \in \mathscr{X}(M)$. Then X is* **globally Hamiltonian** *iff there is an $H \in \mathscr{F}(M)$ such that $X = X_H = (\mathbf{d}H)^\sharp$. We call H a* **Hamiltonian function** *for X. The set of all Hamiltonian vectorfields on M is denoted by $\mathscr{X}_{\mathscr{H}}(M)$.*

16.15. Proposition. *Let (M, ω) be a symplectic manifold. Then $\mathscr{X}_{\mathscr{H}}(M)$ is a Lie subalgebra of $\mathscr{X}_{\mathscr{L}\mathscr{H}}(M)$, and of $\mathscr{X}(M)$.*

Proof. Clearly $\mathscr{X}_{\mathscr{L}\mathscr{H}} \supset \mathscr{X}_{\mathscr{H}}$, from 16.4 (*ii*). Also, $\mathscr{X}_{\mathscr{H}}$ is a vector subspace, since $H \rightsquigarrow X_H$ is $\mathbf{R}$ linear. Finally, if $X = X_H$, $Y = X_K$, then $[X, Y] = -X_{\{H,K\}}$ by 14.28, which completes the proof. ∎

In particular, note that all the results obtained so far for locally Hamiltonian vectorfields also hold for globally Hamiltonian vectorfields.

16.16. Proposition. *Let X be a vectorfield on a symplectic manifold (M, ω). Then $X \in \mathscr{X}_{\mathscr{H}}(M)$ iff $X^\flat \in \mathscr{X}^*_{\mathscr{E}}(M)$. (Compare 16.4 (ii).)*

Proof. If $X = X_H = (\mathbf{d}H)^\sharp$ then $X^\flat = ((\mathbf{d}H)^\sharp)^\flat = \mathbf{d}H$. Conversely, if $X^\flat = \mathbf{d}f$, then $X = (\mathbf{d}f)^\sharp$. ∎

For uniqueness of the Hamiltonian we need the following.

16.17. Proposition. *Let M be a manifold. Then M is connected iff, for each $f \in \mathscr{F}(M)$, $\mathbf{d}f = 0$ implies f is constant.*

Proof. If M is not connected, let $U \subset M$, $U \neq \phi$, $U \neq M$ be both open and closed (§A7). Consider

$$f(m) = \begin{cases} 1 & \text{if} \quad m \in U \\ 0 & \text{if} \quad m \notin U \end{cases}$$

Thus in some neighborhood of every point f is constant. Hence $\mathbf{d}f = 0$. Conversely, if M is connected, $\mathbf{d}f = 0$, and f is not constant, then there is a point $m_0 \in M$ such that f is not constant in any neighborhood of m_0. For if every point has a neighborhood on which f is constant, we see that $V = f^{-1}(f(m))$ is both open and closed. Now $\mathbf{d}f(X) = \mathbf{L}_X f = 0$ for any vectorfield X. Hence f is constant along the integral curves of X. In local representation we see that this implies f is constant in some neighborhood of m_0. This is a contradiction, and hence f is constant. ∎

16.18. Corollary. *Let M be a connected symplectic manifold and $X \in \mathscr{X}_{\mathscr{H}}(M)$. Then any two Hamiltonians for X differ by a constant function.*

Proof. Suppose $X = X_H = X_{H'}$. Then $X_{H-H'} = 0$. Thus $\mathbf{d}(H - H')^\sharp = 0$ and $\mathbf{d}(H - H') = 0$. Thus by 16.17, $H - H'$ is constant. ∎

This corollary corresponds to the arbitrariness in the *zero level of the energy* of a system.

Sometimes the spaces $\mathscr{X}_{\mathscr{H}}$ and $\mathscr{F}(M)$ are identified. Indeed, if we consider the equivalence relation: $f_1 \sim f_2$ iff $f_1 - f_2 =$ constant on M, then the space of equivalence classes becomes a vector space denoted by $\mathscr{F}(M)/\sim$. Then, from 16.18 we obtain this.

16.19. Proposition. *The map $H \rightsquigarrow X_H$ induces an isomorphism between the vector spaces $F(M)/\sim$ and $\mathscr{X}_{\mathscr{H}}$, if M is connected.*

A more refined statement about the conservation laws is the following.

16.20. Proposition. *Let (M, ω) be a connected symplectic manifold and $H, K \in \mathscr{F}(M)$. Then*

(i) $\{H, K\}$ is constant iff X_H is constant along integral curves of X_K iff X_K is constant along integral curves of X_H;

(ii) $\{H, K\} = 0$ iff H is constant along the integral curves of X_K iff K is constant along the integral curves of X_H.

Proof. Part (*i*) follows at once from $X_{\{H,K\}} = -[X_H, X_K]$ (14.28), and 8.21. Also, (*ii*) is a consequence of

$$\{H, K\} = -L_{X_H}K = L_{X_K}H \qquad (14.24)\ \blacksquare$$

Note that if X_H is complete, the statements about conservation may be applied globally. That is, the flow boxes and local integral curves may be replaced by the flow. In practice, however, they are usually not complete; in fact, this is one of the basic difficulties in the n-body problem (collisions).

16.21. Proposition. *Let X be a globally Hamiltonian vectorfield with Hamiltonian H. Suppose X is complete, with flow F. Then for $K \in \mathscr{F}(M)$, $\{H, K\} = 0$ iff $F_\lambda(K^{-1}(c)) \subset K^{-1}(c)$ for each $c \in \mathbf{R}$ and $\lambda \in \mathbf{R}$.*

This is a special case of 16.20.

Next we extend the concept of energy surface slightly and prove the Hamilton–Jacobi theorem (15.13) in this case. We require a good part of §A7 for this discussion.

16.22. Definition. *Let M be a manifold, $H \in \mathscr{F}(M)$ and $e \in \mathbf{R}$. Then a component Σ_e of $H^{-1}(e)$ is called a* **regular energy surface** *of H iff each point of Σ_e is a regular point; that is, for $m \in \Sigma_e$, $\mathbf{d}H(m) \neq 0$ (see 5.17).*

16.23. Proposition. *Let Σ_e be a regular energy surface of $H \in \mathscr{F}(M)$. Then there exists an open subset $\mathcal{O} \subset M$ such that $\Sigma_e \subset \mathcal{O}$ and $\mathcal{O} \cap H^{-1}(e) = \Sigma_e$.*

Proof. As H is continuous, $H^{-1}(e)$ is closed, and thus also Σ_e and $H^{-1}(e) \setminus \Sigma_e$, for $\Sigma_e \subset H^{-1}(e)$ is both open and closed, being open by 5.16 together with A7.4 (ii), and being closed by A7.5. As M is normal (A5.4), there exists an open subset $\mathcal{O}$ in M such that $\Sigma_e \subset \mathcal{O}$ and $\mathcal{O} \cap (H^{-1}(e) \setminus \Sigma_e) = \phi$, so $\mathcal{O} \cap H^{-1}(e) = \Sigma_e$. $\blacksquare$

Applying 5.18 to $H|\mathcal{O}$, we obtain the following.

16.24. Corollary. *If Σ_e is a regular energy surface of $H \in \mathscr{F}(M)$, then $\Sigma_e \subset M$ is a connected submanifold of codimension one.*

We saw in 11.15 that if e is a regular value of H, $H^{-1}(e)$ is an orientable submanifold, if M is orientable. This also holds for regular energy surfaces, applying 11.15 to $H|\mathcal{O}$.

16.25. Proposition. *Let M be an orientable manifold and Σ_e a regular energy surface of $H \in \mathscr{F}(M)$. Then Σ_e is orientable.*

Also, 15.12 holds globally as follows.

16.26. Proposition. *Let Σ_e be a regular energy surface of $H \in \mathscr{F}(M)$, where (M, ω) is a symplectic manifold. Then every integral curve of X_H that meets Σ_e lies wholly in Σ_e.*

Proof. Let $c: I \to H^{-1}(e)$ be a curve such that $c(I) \cap \Sigma_e \neq \phi$. Since $c(I)$ is connected, $c(I) \subset \Sigma_e$, as Σ_e is a component of $H^{-1}(e)$. (See A7.4.) $\blacksquare$

Then the Hamilton–Jacobi theorem is expressed as follows.

16.27. Theorem. *Let (M, ω) be a symplectic manifold, $H \in \mathscr{F}(M)$, and Σ_e a regular energy surface of H. Then there is a volume on Σ_e which is invariant under $X_H|\Sigma_e$.*

Proof. First note that the integral curves of X_H lie in Σ_e if they intersect it, so that $X_H|\Sigma_e$ defines a vectorfield on Σ_e (§5, 16.7). Now $\mathbf{d}H$ is an invariant form of X_H since

$$\mathbf{L}_{X_H}\mathbf{d}H = \mathbf{dL}_{X_H}H = 0 \qquad (10.11, 16.7)$$

But Σ_e is an invariant manifold of X_H (15.11), so the result follows from 15.13. ∎

As we have seen, H is always a constant of the motion for X_H. Thus, for any $c \in \mathbf{R}$, any integral curve that meets the set $H^{-1}(c)$ lies entirely within it. Also, we saw in §5 that for almost all c, $H^{-1}(c)$ is a submanifold of M (5.19). Hence if this is the case, we have reduced the problem to a manifold of one lower dimension. If, further, K can be found such that $\{H, K\} = 0$ and $\mathbf{d}H$, $\mathbf{d}K$ linearly independent, then this process may be repeated. The resultant invariant submanifold has an invariant volume by the Hamilton–Jacobi theorem (15.13). This reduces the dimension of the problem, and in some cases (called *completely integrable*) effects a complete solution. In practice, one can look for symmetries of the Hamiltonian to get conservation of linear and angular momentum or other invariant functions (see §22). In general, the cases in which this can be done globally are rare. In fact, it seems very plausible that almost all Hamiltonian vectorfields X_H have only the invariants generated by H and ω. Nevertheless, in exceptional cases, the *integrals in involution* play an important part in the solution.

16.28. Definition. *Let M be a symplectic manifold and $f_1, \ldots, f_k \in \mathscr{F}(M)$. Then we say $\{f_1, \ldots, f_k\}$ is in* **involution** *iff*

(*i*) *$\{df_i(m)\}$ are linearly independent in T_m^*M for each $m \in M$, and*
(*ii*) *$\{f_i, f_j\} = 0$ for $i, j = 1, \ldots, k$ (see* 16.20).

16.29. Theorem. *Let (M, ω) be a symplectic 2n-manifold.*

(*i*) *If $\{f_1, \ldots, f_k\}$ are in involution, then $k \le n$.*
(*ii*) **(Carathéodory–Jacobi)**. *If $\{f_1, \ldots, f_k\}$ is in involution and $k < n$, there is a neighborhood U about each point of M and functions $f_{k+1}, \ldots, f_n$ on U so that $\{f_1, \ldots, f_n\}$ is in involution on U.*

Note that (*i*) is clear since T_m^*M is $2n$ dimensional and ω nondegenerate. For (*ii*) see Carathéodory [1, p. 55]. The method of (*ii*) is sometimes called Jacobi's integration method. See, for example, Duff [1, p. 66].

Finally, we mention some results from differential topology in support of the view that global involution systems are rare.

16.30. Theorem (Arnold [3]). *Let M be a symplectic 2-manifold, and suppose that there are n functions $f_1, \ldots, f_n \in \mathscr{F}(M)$ in* *involution, with X_{f_i} complete. If $\mathbf{a} \in \mathbf{R}^n$ and $V_{\mathbf{a}} = \{m \in M | (f_1(m), \ldots, f_n(m)) = \mathbf{a}\} \neq \phi$, then $V_{\mathbf{a}} \subset M$ is a submanifold of dimension n, is invariant under X_{f_i}, and is diffeomorphic to a union of cylinders $\mathbf{R}^k \times \mathbf{T}^{n-k}$. ($\mathbf{T}^r$ is the r-dimensional torus, the quotient group of $\mathbf{R}^r$ by the group of points of $\mathbf{R}^r$ with integer coordinates, §A9.)*

Proof. The proof is a little beyond our scope, so we give only an outline; for details, see Arnold–Avez [1]. We consider the mapping $F: M \to \mathbf{R}^n: M \rightsquigarrow (f_1(m), \ldots, f_n(m))$. As $\{\mathbf{d}f_i(m)\}$ is linearly independent, F is a submersion, that is, has no critical values. Then $V_{\mathbf{a}} = F^{-1}(\mathbf{a})$, if nonempty, is a submanifold of dimension n by the implicit mapping theorem, and is invariant under X_{f_i} (see 15.11). Let $X_i = X_{f_i}|V_{\mathbf{a}}$. Then $\{X_i(v)\}$ is linearly independent, and $[X_i, X_j] = 0$. As X_i is complete, $\{X_1, \ldots, X_n\}$ is the infinitesimal generator of an action of $\mathbf{R}^n$ on $V_{\mathbf{a}}$, that is, an n parameter group of diffeomorphisms. As this action has no singularity, it acts transitively, and each component of $V_{\mathbf{a}}$ is diffeomorphic to a quotient group of $\mathbf{R}^n$, by the isotopy subgroup, which is discrete. Thus $V_{\mathbf{a}}$ is diffeomorphic to a disjoint union of cylinders. ∎

The proof shows in addition that the flow of X_i on a cylindrical component of $V_{\mathbf{a}}$ is a translation flow. Also, we see that M is foliated by cylinders. In fact, the mapping F is a locally trivial fibration by the Thom isotopy theorem (Abraham–Robbin [1]), and if $A = F(M) \subset \mathbf{R}^n$ is contractible, F is a trivial fibration. If the fibers $V_{\mathbf{a}}$ are compact and connected, then M is necessarily diffeomorphic to $\mathbf{T}^n \times A$, an open subset of $T^*(\mathbf{T}^n)$. Thus the existence of a system in involution puts strong restrictions on the topology of M. For more results in this direction, see Arnold [3].

It is a standard result of the classical theory (Liouville's theorem) that if a Hamiltonian vectorfield X_{f_i} has integral functions $f_2, \ldots, f_n$ such that $\{f_1, \ldots, f_n\}$ is in involution (*dim* $M = 2n$), then the system is completely integrable (Whittaker [1, p. 323]). As a possible global generalization of this, we might suggest the following.

16.31. Conjecture (Avez). *If $\varphi_1, \ldots, \varphi_n \in \Omega^1(M)$, dim$(M) = 2n$, are*

(i) closed;
(ii) linearly independent at each point $m \in M$;
(iii) $\{\varphi_i, \varphi_j\} = 0$;

then there exist $\psi_1, \ldots, \psi_n \in \Omega^1(M)$ such that (i), (ii), and (iii) hold for $\{\psi_i\}$; and also,

(iv) $\{\varphi_1, \ldots, \varphi_n, \psi_1, \ldots, \psi_n\}$ linearly independent at each point $m \in M$, and
(v) $\{\varphi_i, \psi_j\} = 0$ if $i \neq j$, $\{\varphi_i, \psi_j\}$ nowhere zero if $i = j$.

Exercises

16A. Let (M, ω) be a symplectic manifold. Show $\mathscr{X}_{LH}(M) = \mathscr{X}_H(M)$ iff M is simply connected (§A10).

16B. Let (M, ω) and (N, ρ) be symplectic manifolds and $F: M \to N$ a symplectic diffeomorphism. Then if K is a constant of the motion for X_H $(H \in \mathscr{F}(M))$, then $K \circ F^{-1}$ is a constant of the motion for $X_{H \circ F^{-1}}$.

16C. Use 16.4 to make precise the statement: The evolution of a Hamiltonian system may be thought of as a succession of infinitesimal canonical transformations (here, meaning symplectic diffeomorphisms).

§17. LAGRANGIAN SYSTEMS

We saw in 14.14 how T^*M has a natural symplectic structure. Therefore it is possible to study Hamiltonian vectorfields on the *momentum phase space*, T^*M. This section is concerned with an alternative description on the *velocity phase space*, TM.

Roughly, the idea is as follows. We consider a function L on TM and solutions to a certain second-order equation. From L we can derive an energy function E on TM which, when translated to T^*M by means of the "fiber derivative" $FL: TM \to T^*M$ (the derivative of L in each fiber of TM), yields a suitable Hamiltonian. Then the solution curves in T^*M (Hamiltonian equations) and in TM (Lagrangian equations) will coincide when projected to M. The following diagram may help to keep the locations in mind.

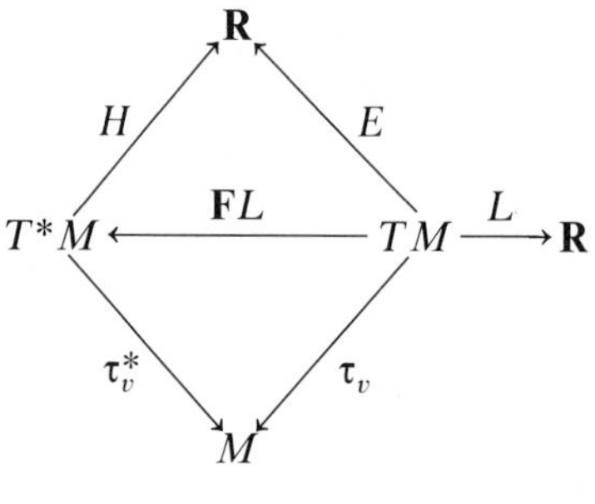

We shall also see, in the next section, how the process may be reversed to allow passage from the Hamiltonian formulation to the Lagrangian. In any case, the key mapping is $\mathbf{F}L$, the *Legendre transformation*.

Notice that the two formulations take place on different spaces, which in general cannot be canonically identified. Thus, the relation between H and L is not merely a change of variables.

We begin, then, with the fiber derivative in a slightly more general context.

17.1. Definition. *Let $\pi: E \to M$ and $\rho: F \to M$ be vector bundles over the common base space M, and let $f: E \to F$ be a C^∞ mapping (not necessarily a vector bundle mapping) that is fiber* *preserving and such that f_0 is the identity (see 4.6 for notations); that is, the following diagram commutes:*

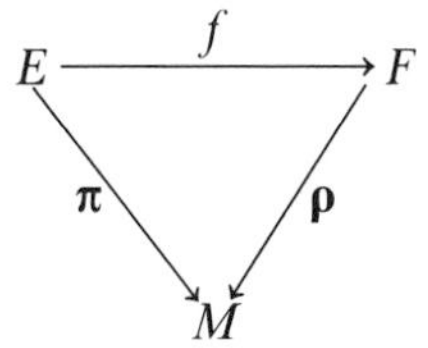

Let f_v denote $f|E_v$ where $E_v = \pi^{-1}(v)$ is the fiber over $v \in M$. Then the map

$$\mathbf{F}f : E \to \bigcup_{v \in M} L(E_v, F_v) : e_v \rightsquigarrow Df_v(e_v) \in L(E_v, F_v)$$

is called the **fiber derivative** *of f.*

It may be easily shown, as in §6, that

$$L(E, F) = \bigcup_{v \in M} L(E_v, F_v)$$

becomes a vector bundle over M, with charts induced in a natural way from those of E and F. Then it is easy to see that $\mathbf{F}f$: $E \to L(E, F)$ is smooth and fiber preserving. The situation that concerns us is f: $TM \to \mathbf{R}$, so we will be content with the proofs in this case.

17.2. Definition. *Let M be a manifold and $L \in \mathscr{F}(TM)$. Then the map $\mathbf{F}L$: $TM \to T^*M$: $w_m \rightsquigarrow DL_m(w_m) \in L(T_mM, \mathbf{R}) = T_m^*M$ is called the* **fiber derivative** *of L. Again L_m denotes the restriction of L to the fiber over $m \in M$ (see 2.3).*

We leave it to the reader to show that $\mathbf{F}L = \mathbf{F}\tilde{L}$ according to 17.1, where $\tilde{L}$: $TM \to M \times \mathbf{R}$: $w_m \rightsquigarrow (m, L(w_m))$ and $\tau_M(w_m) = m$ (5.3).

17.3. Proposition. *Let M be a manifold and $L \in \mathscr{F}(TM)$. Then $\mathbf{F}L$: $TM \to T^*M$ is a fiber preserving smooth mapping.*

Note that $\mathbf{F}L$ is not necessarily a vector bundle mapping.

Proof. Suppose f: $U \times V \to \mathbf{F}$ is C^∞, where $U \subset \mathbf{E}_1$, $V \subset \mathbf{E}_2$. Then Df: $U \times V \to L(\mathbf{E}_1 \times \mathbf{E}_2, \mathbf{F})$ (§2). If $D_2 f$: $U \times V \to L(\mathbf{E}_2, \mathbf{F})$ denotes the restriction of Df (at each (u, v)) to $\{\mathbf{0}\} \times \mathbf{E}_2$, then clearly $D_2 f$ (the *partial derivative*, see 2.12) is smooth since it is Df composed with a restriction. For the proposition, let (U, φ) be a chart of M with $\varphi(U) = U' \subset \mathbf{E}$. Then $(TU, T\varphi)$ and $(T^*U, (T\varphi)_1^0)$ are charts of TM and T^*M respectively. Then the local representative of $\mathbf{F}L$ is

$$(\mathbf{F}L)_\varphi = (T\varphi)_1^0 \circ \mathbf{F}L \circ T\varphi^{-1} : U' \times \mathbf{E} \to U' \times \mathbf{E}^*$$

Because $T\varphi$ is linear on the fibers, we see that if $L_\varphi = L \circ T\varphi^{-1}$ is the local representative of L, then $(\mathbf{F}L)_\varphi$: $(u', \mathbf{e}) \rightsquigarrow (u', D_2 L_\varphi(u', \mathbf{e}))$ where $D_2 L_\varphi(u', \mathbf{e}) \in L(\mathbf{E}, \mathbf{R}) = \mathbf{E}^*$. Thus, by our above remarks it is clear that $(\mathbf{F}L)_\varphi$ is smooth. ∎

Moreover, we have the following.

17.4. Corollary. *If $L: TM \to \mathbf{R}$ is smooth and φ is a chart on M, then $(\mathbf{F}L)_\varphi = \mathbf{F}(L_\varphi)$.*

17.5. Notation. *Let M be a manifold and (U, φ) a chart on M with $\varphi(u) = (q^1(u), \ldots, q^n(u)) \in \mathbf{R}^n$. Then we write*

$$T\varphi(v) = (q^1(v), \ldots, q^n(v), \dot{q}^1(v), \ldots, \dot{q}^n(v)) \in \mathbf{R}^{2n}$$

(As we saw in §4, $q^i(v) = q^i(\tau_M v)$, which justifies the same q^i for φ and $T\varphi$.) Then if $L \in \mathscr{F}(TM)$, we write $L_{\dot{q}} = D_2 L_\varphi$ and $L_q = D_1 L_\varphi$, with similar notation for higher derivatives. The components in the standard basis are denoted $L_{\dot{q}^i}$, and L_{q^i}. Thus $L_{\dot{q}^i}$, L_{q^i} represent the usual partial derivatives of L_φ.

A simple property of the fiber derivative is that it is a homomorphism. This property may be more precisely expressed as follows.

17.6. Proposition. *Let M be a manifold, and let $\mathscr{B}$ denote the collection of fiber preserving smooth maps: $TM \to T^*M$. Then $\mathscr{B}$ is a real vector space, and $\mathbf{F}: \mathscr{F}(TV) \to \mathscr{B}; L \rightsquigarrow \mathbf{F}L$ is a linear map.*

Proof. $\mathscr{B}$ forms a vector space in the obvious way; $(L_1 + L_2)(w_m) = L_1 w_m + L_2 w_m$, addition in the fiber over m. Also, $\mathbf{F}(L_1 + L_2)(w_m) = DL_{1m}(w_m) + DL_{2m}(w_m) = FL_1(w_m) + FL_2(w_m) = (FL_1 + FL_2)(w_m)$, since D is $\mathbf{R}$ linear. ∎

17.7. Definition. *Let M be a manifold and $L \in \mathscr{F}(TM)$. We call L a* **regular Lagrangian** *iff* $\mathbf{F}L$ *is regular (at all points) in the sense of* 5.17.

17.8. Proposition. *Let $L \in \mathscr{F}(TM)$ for a manifold M. Then L is a regular Lagrangian iff $\mathbf{F}L$ is a local diffeomorphism, iff $\omega_L = \mathbf{F}L_*(\omega_0)$ is a symplectic form on TM. (ω_0 is the canonical symplectic form on T^*M; see* 14.14.)

Proof. From 14.10 it is sufficient to prove the first assertion. However L is a regular Lagrangian iff $T_{\omega_m}\mathbf{F}L$ is onto. Since the dimensions of TM and T^*M are the same, $T_{\omega_m}\mathbf{F}L$ is onto iff $T_{\omega_m}\mathbf{F}L$ is an isomorphism. Thus the result follows at once from the inverse mapping theorem (5.15). ∎

Thus we have the following.

17.9. Corollary. *If L is a regular Lagrangian on M, then $\mathbf{F}L: TM \to T^*M$ is a symplectic mapping of the symplectic manifolds (TM, ω_L), (T^*M, ω_0).*

Now $\mathbf{F}L: TM \to T^*M$, and according to 17.1, $\mathbf{F}(\mathbf{F}L): TM \to L(TM, T^*M) \approx T_2^0(M)$ (see §6).

17.10. Proposition. *Let L be a smooth function on the tangent bundle of a manifold M. Then $\mathbf{F}^2L: TM \to T_2^0(M)$ is smooth and symmetric. Moreover, L is a regular Lagrangian iff $\mathbf{F}^2L$ is non-*

degenerate; that is, for each $w_m \in TM$, $\mathbf{F}^2L(w_m) \in L_s^2(T_mM, \mathbf{R})$ *is nondegenerate* (13.1).

Proof. From 17.4, we see that it is sufficient to consider local vector bundles. Thus, assume $L: U \times \mathbf{E} \to \mathbf{R}$ so that $\mathbf{F}L: U \times \mathbf{E} \to U \times \mathbf{E}^*: (u, \mathbf{e}) \rightsquigarrow (u, D_2L(u, \mathbf{e}))$ (see the proof of 17.3). Now L is a regular Lagrangian iff $T\mathbf{F}L$ is an isomorphism (in the fiber) at each point. This will be true iff $D\mathbf{F}L$ is an isomorphism at each point. (See 2.4, 5.17, and note that a linear map between vector spaces of the same dimension is an isomorphism iff it is onto.) However $D\mathbf{F}L(u, \mathbf{e}): \mathbf{E} \times \mathbf{E} \to \mathbf{E} \times \mathbf{E}^*$ for each $(u, \mathbf{e}) \in U \times \mathbf{E}$, is given by $(\mathbf{e}_1, \mathbf{e}_2) \rightsquigarrow (\mathbf{e}_1, DD_2L(u, \mathbf{e}) \cdot (\mathbf{e}_1, \mathbf{e}_2))$. (See 2.12.) Now as in 17.3,

$$DD_2L(u, \mathbf{e}) \cdot (\mathbf{e}_1, \mathbf{e}_2) = D_1D_2L(u, \mathbf{e}) \cdot \mathbf{e}_1 + D_2D_2L(u, \mathbf{e}) \cdot \mathbf{e}_2$$

where we identify $(\mathbf{e}_1, \mathbf{0})$ with $\mathbf{e}_1$. (From the definition of derivative, it is easy to see that the partial derivative may be obtained by restricting either the function or the resulting derivative, as in 17.3.)

Now it is clear that $D\mathbf{F}L(u, \mathbf{e})$ is onto iff $D_2D_2L(u, \mathbf{e})$ is onto (for example, take $\mathbf{e}_1 = \mathbf{0}$, etc.). However,

$$\mathbf{F}^2L(u, \mathbf{e}): U \times \mathbf{E} \to U \times \mathbf{E}^*: (u, \mathbf{e}) \rightsquigarrow (u, D_2D_2L(u, \mathbf{e}) \cdot \mathbf{e}_2)$$

and $\mathbf{F}^2L$ is nondegenerate iff $D_2D_2(u, \mathbf{e})$ is an isomorphism for each $(u, \mathbf{e})$. (The reader may wish to carry out this proof in the more familiar notation of partial derivatives, 17.5.) ∎

We now express ω_L in terms of a natural chart on TM. Let (U, φ) be a chart on M, with $\varphi(U) = U' \subset \mathbf{R}^n$. Then we have natural charts $T\varphi: TU \to U' \times \mathbf{R}^n \subset \mathbf{R}^n \times \mathbf{R}^n$ and $T^*\varphi: T^*U \to U' \times \mathbf{R}^{n^*} \subset \mathbf{R}^n \times \mathbf{R}^{n^*}$. Let the component functions of these two natural charts be $(q^1, \ldots, q^n, \dot{q}^1, \ldots, \dot{q}^n)$ and $(q^1, \ldots, q^n, p_1, \ldots, p_n)$ respectively. Then $\omega_L|TU$ is a linear combination of terms $dq^i \wedge d\dot{q}^j$, etc. In the notations of 17.5, we have $\mathbf{F}L: TU \to T^*U: (u, \mathbf{e}) \rightsquigarrow L_{\dot{q}}(u, \mathbf{e})$; if we write $\mathbf{e} = \dot{q}^j \underline{e}_j$, then $L_{\dot{q}}(u, \mathbf{e})$ is defined by $L_{\dot{q}}(u, \dot{q}^j \underline{e}_j) = L_{\dot{q}^j}(u)\dot{q}^j$ (both sides summed on j). Also, let

$$L_{\dot{q}^i\dot{q}^j} = \frac{\partial^2 L}{\partial \dot{q}^i \partial \dot{q}^j} \qquad \text{etc.}$$

Thus in U,

$$dL_{\dot{q}^j} = L_{q^i\dot{q}^j}\, dq^i + L_{\dot{q}^i\dot{q}^j}\, d\dot{q}^i$$

17.11. Proposition. *If* $L \in \mathscr{F}(TM)$ *and* (U, φ) *is a chart on* M, *then with the notations above*

$$\omega_L|TU = L_{\dot{q}^i q^j}\, dq^i \wedge dq^j + L_{\dot{q}^i\dot{q}^j}\, dq^i \wedge d\dot{q}^j$$

(*summed on* $i, j = 1, \ldots, n$).

Proof. In terms of these coordinate functions, we have $\omega_0|T^*U = dq^i \wedge dp_i$.

Thus

$$\begin{aligned}\omega_L|TU &= (FL_*\omega_0)|TU = FL_*(\omega_0|U)\\ &= FL_*(\mathbf{d}q^i \wedge \mathbf{d}p_i) = (FL_*\mathbf{d}q^i)\wedge(FL_*\mathbf{d}p_i)\\ &= \mathbf{d}(FL_*q^i)\wedge \mathbf{d}(FL_*p_i)\\ &= \mathbf{d}(q^i \circ FL)\wedge \mathbf{d}(p_i \circ FL)\\ &= \mathbf{d}q^i \wedge \mathbf{d}L_{\dot q^i}\end{aligned}$$

from which the result follows at once. ■

The index lowering action of ω_L may be expressed in terms of dq^i, $\underset{\sim}{e}_i$, etc., as follows. In the notation above, we have

$$\begin{aligned}\underset{\sim}{e}_i^\flat &= \underset{\sim}{e}_i^\flat(\underset{\sim}{e}_j)dq^j + \underset{\sim}{e}_i^\flat(\underset{\sim}{f}_j)d\dot q^j\\ &= 2\omega_L(\underset{\sim}{e}_i, \underset{\sim}{e}_j)dq^j + 2\omega_L(\underset{\sim}{e}_i, \underset{\sim}{f}_j)d\dot q^j\end{aligned}$$

Using the expression of ω_L of 17.11, we get

$$\underset{\sim}{e}_i^\flat = (L_{\dot q^i q^j} - L_{\dot q^j q^i})dq^j + L_{\dot q^i \dot q^j}dq^j$$

Similarly, we find

$$\underset{\sim}{f}_i^\flat = -L_{\dot q^i q^j}dq^j$$

The index raising action of ω_L is obtained by inverting these expressions. We suppose then that L is a regular Lagrangian. Thus $L_{\dot q \dot q}$ is invertible. Let M denote its inverse, with components M^{ij}. Then applying $\sharp$ to $\underset{\sim}{f}_i^\flat$, we obtain

$$\underset{\sim}{f}_i = -L_{\dot q^i q^j}(dq^j)^\sharp$$

or applying M,

$$(dq^j)^\sharp = -M^{ji}\underset{\sim}{f}_i$$

Treating $\underset{\sim}{e}_i^\flat$ similarly, we find

$$(d\dot q^j)^\sharp = M^{ji}\underset{\sim}{e}_i + M^{jk}(L_{\dot q^k q^l} - L_{\dot q^l q^k})M^{li}\underset{\sim}{f}_i$$

Using these expressions, we may compute $X_E = (\mathbf{d}E)^\sharp$ (with respect to ω_L) in U, where $E \in \mathscr{F}(TM)$. As $\sharp$ is $\mathscr{F}$ linear, we have

$$(\mathbf{d}E)^\sharp = E_{q^j}(dq^j)^\sharp + E_{\dot q^j}(d\dot q^j)^\sharp$$

and by substituting the above, we find

$$\mathbf{d}E^\sharp = E_{q^j}(-M^{ji}\underset{\sim}{f}_i) + E_{\dot q^j}(M^{ji}\underset{\sim}{e}_i + N^{ji}\underset{\sim}{f}_i)$$

where $N^{ji} = M^{jk}(L_{\dot q^k q^l} - L_{\dot q^l q^k})M^{li}$, so

$$\mathbf{d}E^\sharp = M^{ji}E_{\dot q^j}\underset{\sim}{e}_i + (N^{ji}E_{\dot q^j} - M^{ji}E_{q^j})\underset{\sim}{f}_i$$

In summary, we have proved the following.

17.12. Proposition. *Let M be a manifold, and $L \in \mathscr{F}(TM)$ a regular Lagrangian. If (U, φ) is a chart on M with $\varphi(U) = U' \subset \mathbf{R}^n$, let the component functions of $T\varphi\colon TU \to U' \times \mathbf{R}^n \subset \mathbf{R}^n \times \mathbf{R}^n$ be denoted by $(q^1, \ldots, q^n, \dot{q}^1, \ldots, \dot{q}^n)$, and the standard basis in $\mathbf{R}^n \times \mathbf{R}^n$ by $(\mathbf{e}_1, \ldots, \mathbf{e}_n, \mathbf{f}_1, \ldots, \mathbf{f}_n)$. Then, if $E \in \mathscr{F}(TM)$, the Hamiltonian vectorfield X_E of the symplectic form ω_L satisfies:*

$$X_E|U = M^{ji}E_{\dot{q}^j}\underline{e}_i + (N^{ji}E_{\dot{q}^i} - M^{ji}E_{q^j})\underline{f}_i$$

where $M = (L_{\dot{q}\dot{q}})^{-1}$, and $N^{ji} = M^{jk}(L_{q^k q^l} - L_{q^l q^k})M^{li}$.

For $E \in \mathscr{F}(TM)$, $X_E = (\mathbf{d}E)^\sharp$ forms a globally Hamiltonian vectorfield on the symplectic manifold (TM, ω_L) (where L is a regular Lagrangian).

We now examine the conditions under which the equations defining the integral curves of X_E become the usual Lagrangian equations, and their relationship to the Hamiltonian equations of $H = E \circ \mathbf{F}L^{-1}$, on T^*M.

One of the main differences between the Hamiltonian and Lagrangian formulations is that *second-order equations* are possible on TM, but not on T^*M.

17.13. Definition. *A* **second-order equation** *on a manifold M is a vectorfield X on TM such that $T\tau_M \circ X$ is the identity on TM.*

Thus, if X is a second-order equation on M we have the following commutative diagram (except for cycles involving only two arrows).

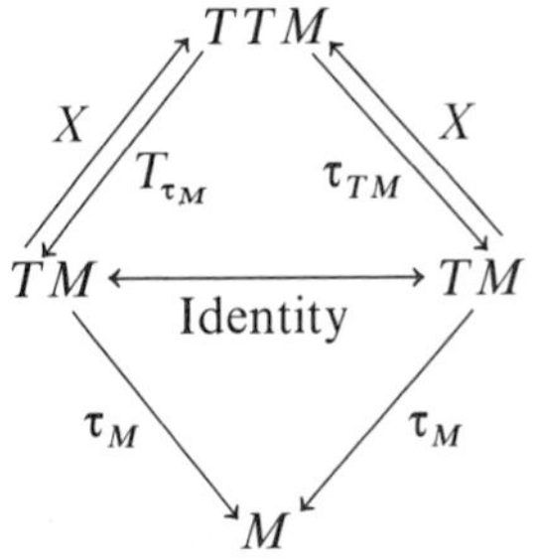

Second-order equations may be characterized in terms of their integral curves as follows.

17.14. Proposition. *Let X be a vectorfield on TM. Then X is a second-order equation on M iff for all integral curves $c\colon I \to TM$ of X, $(\tau_M \circ c)' = c$.*

Proof. From §7, for each $w_m \in TM$ there is a curve c at w_m so $Tc(t, 1) = c'(t) = X(c(t))$ for $t \in I$. Then $T\tau_M \circ X$ is the identity iff $T\tau_M \circ c'(t) = c(t)$. But $T\tau_M \circ c'(t) = T\tau_M \circ Tc(t, 1) = T(\tau_M \circ c)(t, 1) = (\tau_M \circ c)'(t)$. ∎

17.15. Definition. *If $c\colon I \to TM$ is an integral curve of a vectorfield X on TM, we call $\tau_M \circ c\colon I \to M$ a* **base integral curve** *of*

X. Similarly, if X is a vectorfield on T^*M and $c: I \to T^*M$ is an integral curve of X, $\tau_M^* \circ c: I \to M$ is called a **base integral curve** *of X.*

Thus, from 17.14, X is a second-order equation on TM iff for every integral curve c of X, c equals the derivative of its base integral curve.

There is also a simple criterion for second-order equations in terms of local coordinates.

17.16. Proposition. *Let $X \in \mathscr{X}(TM)$ and (U, φ) be a chart on M with $\varphi(U) = U' \subset \mathbf{E}$. Suppose that the local representative of X has the form*

$$X_\varphi: U' \times \mathbf{E} \to U' \times \mathbf{E} \times \mathbf{E} \times \mathbf{E};\ (u', \mathbf{e}) \rightsquigarrow (u', \mathbf{e}, X_1(u, \mathbf{e}), X_2(u, \mathbf{e}))$$

Then X is a second-order equation iff, for every chart, $X_1(u, \mathbf{e}) = \mathbf{e}$ for all $\mathbf{e} \in \mathbf{E}$.

Proof. Since $\tau_{M\varphi}: U' \times \mathbf{E} \to U', (u, \mathbf{e}) \rightsquigarrow u'$, and

$$T(\tau_{M\varphi}) = (T\tau_M)_\varphi: U' \times \mathbf{E} \times \mathbf{E} \times \mathbf{E} \to U' \times \mathbf{E};\ (u', \mathbf{e}, \mathbf{e}_1, \mathbf{e}_2) \rightsquigarrow (u', \mathbf{e}_1)$$

we see that $(T\tau_M)_\varphi \circ X_\varphi = identity$ iff $T\tau_M \circ X = identity$ iff $X_1(u, \mathbf{e}) = \mathbf{e}$. ∎

The usual notion of second-order equation is related to ours in the following way.

17.17. Proposition. *Let X be a second-order equation on M. Suppose (U, φ) is a chart on M with $\varphi(u) = (q^1(u), \ldots, q^n(u)) \in U' \subset \mathbf{R}^n$ and $T\varphi(v) = (q^1(v), \ldots, q^n(v), \dot{q}^1(v), \ldots, \dot{q}^n(v)) \in U' \times \mathbf{R}^n \subset \mathbf{R}^n \times \mathbf{R}^n$. Suppose the local representative of X has the form $X_\varphi: U' \times \mathbf{R}^n \to U' \times \mathbf{R}^n \times \mathbf{R}^n \times \mathbf{R}^n;\ (u', \mathbf{e}) \rightsquigarrow (u', \mathbf{e}, \mathbf{e}, X_2(u', \mathbf{e}))$. Then $c: I \to M$ is a base integral curve of X iff*

$$\frac{d^2}{dt^2} q^i(c(t)) = X_2^i(q(c(t)), \dot{q}(c'(t)))$$

where X_2^i denotes the components of X_2, $i = 1, \ldots, n$, and $(q(c(t)), \dot{q}(c'(t)))$ stands for $T\varphi(c'(t))$.

The proposition follows at once from 17.16 and the discussion at the beginning of §7.

Let us now return to the Lagrangian equations.

17.18. Definition. *Let L be a regular Lagrangian on M and* $\mathbf{F}L$*: $TM \to T^*M$ its fiber derivative. Then define $A: TM \to \mathbf{R}$; $w_m \rightsquigarrow \mathbf{F}L(w_m) \cdot w_m \in \mathbf{R}$. (Recall that $\mathbf{F}L(w_m) \in T_m^*M$.) We call A the* **action** *of L, and $E = A - L$ the* **energy** *of L.*

17.19. Proposition. *If L is a regular Lagrangian on M, then A and E are smooth, and $X_E = (\mathbf{d}E)^\#$ (on the symplectic manifold (TM, ω_L)) is a second-order equation on M.*

Proof. It is sufficient to consider the local case, $L\colon U \times \mathbf{R}^n \to \mathbf{R}$, and

$$FL\colon U \times \mathbf{R}^n \to U \times \mathbf{R}^{n*}\colon (u, \mathbf{e}) \rightsquigarrow (u, D_2L(u, \mathbf{e}))$$

Now $A\colon U \times \mathbf{R}^n \to \mathbf{R}$, $(u, \mathbf{e}) \rightsquigarrow D_2L(u, \mathbf{e}) \cdot \mathbf{e}$. Clearly, A (and hence E) is smooth, by Leibnitz' rule, 2.11. Now $\mathbf{d}E = \mathbf{d}A - \mathbf{d}L$ and, from 8.1, $\mathbf{d}A = DA$. Then by 2.11

$$DA(u, \mathbf{e})\colon \mathbf{R}^n \times \mathbf{R}^n \to \mathbf{R}\colon (\mathbf{e}_1, \mathbf{e}_2) \rightsquigarrow D_2L(u, \mathbf{e}) \cdot \mathbf{e}_2 + DD_2L(u, \mathbf{e}) \cdot (\mathbf{e}_1, \mathbf{e}_2) \cdot \mathbf{e}$$

Hence

$$\begin{aligned}\mathbf{d}E(u, \mathbf{e})(\mathbf{e}_1, \mathbf{e}_2) &= D_2L(u, \mathbf{e}) \cdot \mathbf{e}_2 + DD_2L(u, \mathbf{e}) \cdot (\mathbf{e}_1, \mathbf{e}_2) \cdot \mathbf{e} - DL(u, \mathbf{e}) \cdot (\mathbf{e}_1, \mathbf{e}_2) \\ &= D_1D_2L(u, \mathbf{e}) \cdot (\mathbf{e}_1) \cdot \mathbf{e} + D_2D_2L(u, \mathbf{e}) \cdot (\mathbf{e}_2) \cdot \mathbf{e} - D_1L(u, \mathbf{e}) \cdot \mathbf{e}_1\end{aligned}$$

Thus in the component notations of 17.12, we have

$$E_{\dot{q}^i} = \dot{q}^k L_{\dot{q}^k \dot{q}^j}$$

From 17.12, the first component of $X_E = (\mathbf{d}E)^\sharp$ is $M^{ji}E_{\dot{q}^j}\underline{e}_i$, where M^{ji} is the inverse of $L_{\dot{q}^k\dot{q}^j}$. Substituting the value of $E_{\dot{q}^j}$ above, the first component becomes $\dot{q}^i\underline{e}_i = \mathbf{e}$. Thus X_E is a second-order equation. ∎

With the notations above, we may consider the second component of X_E, and obtain a more familiar expression of the Lagrangian equations. As $E = \dot{q}^k L_{\dot{q}^k} - L$, we have

$$E_{q^j} = \dot{q}^k L_{\dot{q}^k q^j} - L_{q^j}$$

and substituting into the second component Y of X_E in 17.12, we find

$$Y(\mathbf{q}, \dot{\mathbf{q}}) = [N^{ji}\dot{q}^k L_{\dot{q}^k\dot{q}^j} - M^{ji}(\dot{q}^k L_{\dot{q}^k q^j} - L_{q^j})]\underline{f}_i$$

But

$$N^{ji} = M^{jr}(L_{\dot{q}^r q^s} - L_{\dot{q}^s q^r})M^{si}$$

so the first term above is $\dot{q}^r M^{si}(L_{\dot{q}^s q^s} - L_{\dot{q}^s q^r})$ or, changing indices,

$$\dot{q}^k M^{ji}(L_{\dot{q}^k q^j} - L_{\dot{q}^j q^k})$$

Substituting above and canceling, we have

$$Y(\mathbf{q}, \dot{\mathbf{q}}) = -M^{ji}(\dot{q}^k L_{\dot{q}^j q^k} - L_{q^j})\underline{f}_i$$

Thus the second order equation defined by X_E is, according to 17.17,

$$\frac{d^2q^i}{dt^2} = M^{ji}\left(L_{q^j} - \frac{dq^k}{dt} L_{\dot{q}^j q^k}\right)$$

Applying $L_{\dot{q}^i\dot{q}^k}$, the inverse of M^{ji}, to both sides, this becomes

$$\frac{d}{dt}\{L_{\dot{q}^i}(\mathbf{q}(t), \dot{\mathbf{q}}(t))\} - L_{q^i} = 0$$

the familiar classical form of the Lagrangian equations. We summarize this computation as follows.

17.20. Proposition. *Let M be a manifold, $L \in \mathscr{F}(TM)$ a regular Lagrangian, E its energy, and ω_L the induced symplectic form. If (U, φ) is a chart on M with $\varphi(U) = U' \subset \mathbf{R}^n$, let the component functions of $T\varphi: TU \to U' \times \mathbf{R}^n \subset \mathbf{R}^n \times \mathbf{R}^n$ be denoted by $(q^1, \ldots, q^n, \dot{q}^1, \ldots, \dot{q}^n)$. Then a curve $c: I \to U$ is a base integral curve of the Lagrangian vectorfield X_E iff its local representative $\mathbf{b} = \varphi \circ c: I \to U': t \mapsto (b^1(t), \ldots, b^n(t))$ satisfies*

$$\frac{d}{dt}\{L_{\dot{q}^i}(\mathbf{b}(t), \mathbf{b}'(t))\} - L_{q^i}(\mathbf{b}(t), \mathbf{b}'(t)) = 0$$

for all $t \in I$.

Exercises

17A. Complete the general discussion of fiber derivatives and the connection with 17.2.

17B. Show that *regular Lagrangian* does not mean regular in the sense of 5.17. Hint: Use $L: \mathbf{R} \times \mathbf{R} \to \mathbf{R}$; $L(x, y) = x$ or $L(x, y) = x + y^2$.

17C. On $T\mathbf{R}^n = \mathbf{R}^n \times \mathbf{R}^n$ suppose

$$L(q^1, \ldots, \dot{q}^n) = \sum_{i=1}^{n} m_i \frac{(\dot{q}^i)^2}{2} - V(q^1, \ldots, q^n)$$

where $m_i \in \mathbf{R}$, $V \in \mathscr{F}(\mathbf{R}^n)$. Show L is regular iff $m_i \neq 0$ for all i, compute the action and energy of L, and write down Lagrange's equations.

§18. THE LEGENDRE TRANSFORMATION

Let us now give the precise relationship between the Lagrangian formulation on TM and the Hamiltonian formulation on T^*M. In fact, they are equivalent in the *hyperregular* case, and are transformed one into the other by the Legendre transformation.

18.1. Definition. *Let M be a manifold and $L \in \mathscr{F}(TM)$. Then L is called a* **hyperregular Lagrangian** *iff $\mathbf{F}L: TM \to T^*M$ is a diffeomorphism. In this case, $\mathbf{F}L$ is called a* **Legendre transformation**.

Recall that we define $\omega_L = (\mathbf{F}L)_* \omega_0$, where ω_0 is the canonical two form on T^*M (14.14). Hence $\mathbf{F}L$ becomes a symplectic diffeomorphism, and thus preserves Poisson brackets (14.30). It is also clear that a hyperregular Lagrangian is regular.

The transition from the Lagrangian formulation to the Hamiltonian is given by the following.

18.2. Theorem. *Let L be a hyperregular Lagrangian on M, and let $H: T^*M \to \mathbf{R}$ be defined by $H = E \circ \mathbf{F}L^{-1}$ where E is the energy of L. Then the base integral curves of X_E coincide with the base integral curves of X_H.*

Proof. Let $c: I \to TM$ be an integral curve of X_E. Now $X_H = (\mathbf{d}H)^\#$. However, $\mathbf{d}H = \mathbf{d}(\mathbf{F}L^{-1}{}_* E) = \mathbf{F}L^{-1}{}_* \mathbf{d}E = \mathbf{F}L^* \mathbf{d}E$ (10.9). Now since $\mathbf{F}L$ is a symplectic diffeomorphism, we see easily that $(\mathbf{d}H)^\# = \mathbf{F}L^*(\mathbf{d}E)^\#$ (see §14). Thus $X_H = \mathbf{F}L^* X_E$. Then if $c'(t) = X_E(c(t))$, we have that $FL \circ c$ is an integral curve of X_H for

$$X_H(\mathbf{F}L \circ c(t)) = \mathbf{F}L^* X_E(FL \circ c(t)) = T\mathbf{F}L \circ X_E(c(t)) \qquad \text{(see 6.16)}$$

$$= T\mathbf{F}L \circ Tc(t, 1) = T(\mathbf{F}L \circ c)(t, 1) = (\mathbf{F}L \circ c)'(t)$$

The result follows at once from the following commutative diagram (see 17.1 and 17.2):

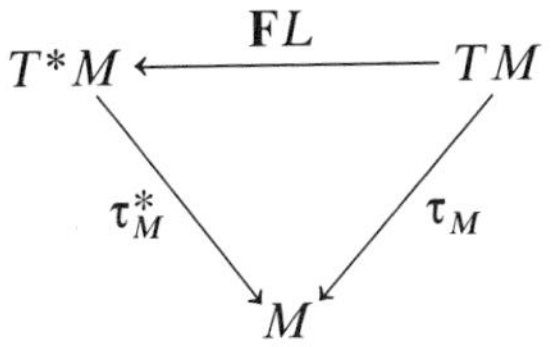

∎

Thus the diffeomorphism $\mathbf{F}L$ relates in a natural way the (globally) Hamiltonian vectorfield X_E (which gives rise to the Lagrangian equations), and the (globally) Hamiltonian vectorfield X_H.

For the reverse construction we need the following.

18.3. Proposition. *Let L be a hyperregular Lagrangian on M and $H = E \circ (\mathbf{F}L)^{-1}$, where E is the energy of L. Then $-\theta_0(X_H) = A \circ (\mathbf{F}L)^{-1}$, where A is the action of L.*

Proof. We must show $-\theta_0(X_H) \circ \mathbf{F}L = A$. Let $w_m \in TM$ and $\alpha_m = \mathbf{F}L(w_m)$. Then

$$\begin{aligned}
-\theta_0(X_H) \circ \mathbf{F}L(w_m) &= -\theta_0(X_H)(\alpha_m) \\
&= \alpha_m \cdot T\tau_M^* X_H(\alpha_m) && (14.14) \\
&= \alpha_m \circ T\tau_M^* \mathbf{F}L^* X_E(\alpha_m) && (18.2) \\
&= \alpha_m \circ T\tau_M^* \circ T\mathbf{F}L \circ X_E(w_m) && (6.16) \\
&= \alpha_m \circ T(\tau_M^* \circ \mathbf{F}L) \circ X_E(w_m) && (5.7) \\
&= \alpha_m \circ T(\tau_M) \circ X_E(w_m) && (18.2) \\
&= \alpha_m \cdot w_m
\end{aligned}$$

since X_E is a second-order equation (17.13). But $\alpha_m \cdot w_m = \mathbf{F}L(w_m) \cdot w_m = A(w_m)$ by definition. ∎

This proposition may also be proven using natural coordinates, in which the action takes the more familiar form

$$-\theta_0(X_H) = \sum_{i=1}^{n} p_i \frac{\partial H}{\partial p_i}$$

18.4. Corollary. *Let L be a hyperregular Lagrangian on M and $\theta_L = \mathbf{F}L_*\theta_0$ (so that $\omega_L = -\mathbf{d}\theta_L$). Then $-A = \theta_L(X_E)$, where E is the energy, and A the action of L.*

Proof. $A = -\theta_0(X_H) \circ \mathbf{F}L$. Let $w_m \in TM$ and $\alpha_m = \mathbf{F}L(w_m)$; then

$$\begin{aligned} A(w_m) &= -\theta_0(X_H)(\alpha_m) = -\theta_0(\alpha_m)(X_H(\alpha_m)) = -\theta_0(\alpha_m)(\mathbf{F}L^* X_E(\alpha_m)) \\ &= -\theta_0(\alpha_m)(T\mathbf{F}L \circ X_E(w_m)) = -\theta_L(w_m)(X_E(w_m)) = -\theta_L(X_E)(w_m) \quad \blacksquare \end{aligned}$$

This proposition then tells us that we can recover L if we know $\mathbf{F}L$ and E.

If $H \in \mathscr{F}(T^*M)$, note that $\mathbf{F}H$: $T^*M \to T^{**}M \approx TM$. Then, as for L, we have the following.

18.5. Proposition. *Let M be a manifold and $H \in \mathscr{F}(T^*M)$. Then $\mathbf{F}H$: $T^*M \to TM$ is smooth and fiber preserving; that is, the following diagram commutes:*

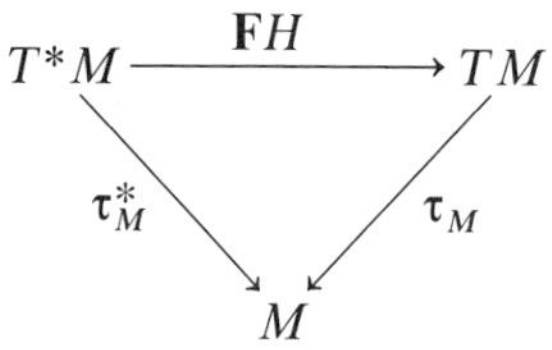

The proof is similar to that of 17.3.

The following proposition is proven in the same way as the corresponding statement for L.

18.6. Proposition. *Let $H \in \mathscr{F}(T^*M)$. Then $\mathbf{F}H$ is a local diffeomorphism iff $\mathbf{F}^2H$ is nondegenerate. If this is the case, we call H a* **regular Hamiltonian**

As was the case for L, we need the stronger condition of hyperregularity for transition to the Lagrangian formulation.

18.7. Definition. *If $H \in \mathscr{F}(T^*M)$, we call $G = -\theta_0(X_H)$ the* **action** *of H. Also, H is called a* **hyperregular Hamiltonian** *iff $\mathbf{F}H$: $T^*M \to TM$ is a diffeomorphism.*

18.8. Proposition. *Let H be a hyperregular Hamiltonian on T^*M. Then define $E = H \circ (\mathbf{F}H)^{-1}$, $A = G \circ (\mathbf{F}H)^{-1}$, and $L = A - E$. Then L is a hyperregular Lagrangian on TM, and in fact $\mathbf{F}L = (\mathbf{F}H)^{-1}$.*

Proof. It is sufficient to consider the local case, H: $\mathbf{R}^n \times \mathbf{R}^{n*} \to \mathbf{R}$, and $\mathbf{F}H$: $\mathbf{R}^n \times \mathbf{R}^{n*} \to \mathbf{R}^n \times \mathbf{R}^{n**}$. We denote coordinates on $\mathbf{R}^n \times \mathbf{R}^{n*}$ by $(q^1, \ldots, q^n, p_1, \ldots, p_n)$; that is, coordinates relative to the standard basis $\mathbf{e}_1, \ldots, \mathbf{e}_n, \boldsymbol{\alpha}^1, \ldots, \boldsymbol{\alpha}^n$. Then $\mathbf{F}H$ is given by $(\mathbf{e}, \boldsymbol{\alpha}) \rightsquigarrow (\mathbf{e}, D_2H(\mathbf{e}, \boldsymbol{\alpha}))$, where, as in

§17, D_2 denotes the partial derivative with respect to the second factor. From 14.14, we see

$$-\theta_0 = \sum_1^n p_i dq^i$$

so that

$$G = -\theta_0(X_H) = -\theta_0 \sum_1^n \left(\frac{\partial H}{\partial p_i} \mathbf{e}_i - \frac{\partial H}{\partial q^i} \boldsymbol{\alpha}^i \right) = \sum_{i=1}^n p_i \frac{\partial H}{\partial p_i}$$

Thus $G(\mathbf{e}, \boldsymbol{\alpha}) = \boldsymbol{\alpha} \cdot D_2 H(\mathbf{e}, \boldsymbol{\alpha})$. Now by definition, $L \circ \mathbf{F}H = G - H$, so that $L \circ \mathbf{F}H(\mathbf{e}, \boldsymbol{\alpha}) = L(\mathbf{e}, D_2 H(\mathbf{e}, \boldsymbol{\alpha})) = \boldsymbol{\alpha} \cdot D_2 H(\mathbf{e}, \boldsymbol{\alpha}) - H(\mathbf{e}, \boldsymbol{\alpha})$. Hence

$$\begin{aligned} D_2 L(\mathbf{e}, D_2 H(\mathbf{e}, \boldsymbol{\alpha})) \cdot D_2 D_2 H(\mathbf{e}, \boldsymbol{\alpha}) &= \boldsymbol{\alpha} \cdot D_2 D_2 H(\mathbf{e}, \boldsymbol{\alpha}) + D_2 H(\mathbf{e}, \boldsymbol{\alpha}) - D_2 H(\mathbf{e}, \boldsymbol{\alpha}) \\ &= \boldsymbol{\alpha} \cdot D_2 D_2 H(\mathbf{e}, \boldsymbol{\alpha}) \end{aligned}$$

Since $D_2 D_2 H(\mathbf{e}, \boldsymbol{\alpha})$ is nonsingular (17.6), $D_2 L(\mathbf{e}, D_2 H(\mathbf{e}, \boldsymbol{\alpha})) = \boldsymbol{\alpha}$. Thus the mappings $\mathbf{F}L$: $(\mathbf{e}, \mathbf{f}) \rightsquigarrow (\mathbf{e}, D_2 L(\mathbf{e}, \mathbf{f}))$ and $\mathbf{F}H$: $(\mathbf{e}, \boldsymbol{\alpha}) \rightsquigarrow (\mathbf{e}, D_2 H(\mathbf{e}, \boldsymbol{\alpha}))$ are inverses, which proves the result. ∎

Thus, we may state the following as the transition from the Hamiltonian formulation to the Lagrangian.

18.9. Theorem. *Let H be a hyperregular Hamiltonian on T^*M, with G, A, E, and L defined as in* 18.8. *Then the base integral curves of X_H coincide with the base integral curves of X_E. Moreover, the Hamiltonian derived from L (which is a hyperregular Lagrangian), according to* 18.2, *is H.*

This follows at once from 18.8 and 18.2. Note also that if L is a hyperregular Lagrangian on TM, then $H = E \circ \mathbf{F}L^{-1}$ is a hyperregular Hamiltonian on T^*M.

Thus the Legendre transformation provides a bijection between the Hamiltonian and Lagrangian formulations in the hyperregular case. We also saw in 18.2 that the Legendre transformation relates X_H and X_E together with their integral curves in a natural way.

Hence, in summary, we have the following commutative diagrams:

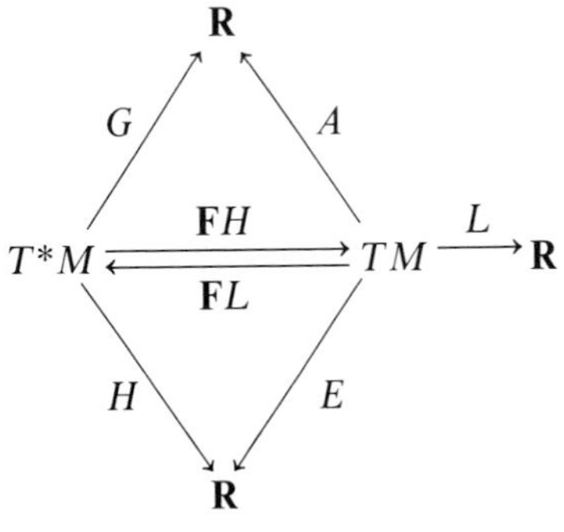

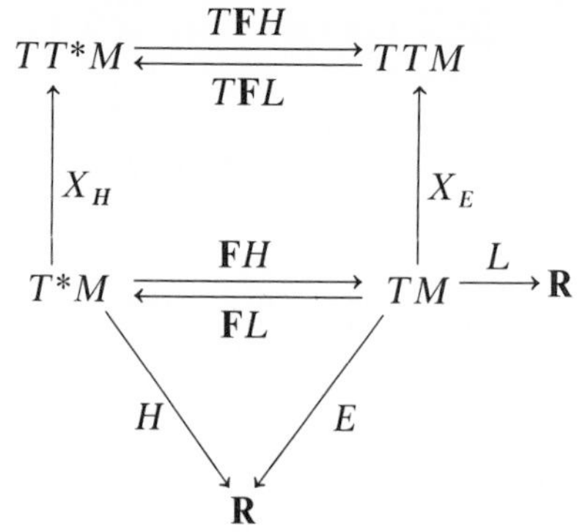

We turn now to some examples.

18.10. Example. Let M be a manifold and $\mathbf{m} \in \mathcal{T}^0_2(M)$ a Riemannian metric on M (11.12). Define $L = T\colon TM \to \mathbf{R}$; $w_m \rightsquigarrow \frac{1}{2}m(w_m, w_m)$. Then $\mathbf{F}L = \mathbf{m}_\flat\colon TM \to T^*M$ (see 13.1), for $T_mM \to T_{m_M} \times T_mM : w_m \to (w_m, w_m)$ is a linear map, and $\mathbf{m}\colon T_mM \times T_mM \to \mathbf{R}$ is bilinear. The result then follows from Leibnitz' rule, 2.11. Thus, from 13.7, L is a hyperregular Lagrangian. Moreover, $\mathbf{F}L$ is a vector bundle isomorphism, not merely a diffeomorphism. The action of L is $A\colon TM \to \mathbf{R}$, $A(w_m) = \mathbf{m}_\flat(w_m) \cdot w_m = \mathbf{m}(w_m, w_m) = 2T = 2L$. Thus the energy of L is $E = A - L = 2L - L = L$. Also, the corresponding $H\colon T^*M \to \mathbf{R}$ is defined by $H = E \circ \mathbf{F}L^{-1}$, so $H(\boldsymbol{\alpha}_m) = \frac{1}{2}\mathbf{m}(w_m, w_m)$ where w_m is the unique vector such that $\alpha_m(v_m) = \mathbf{m}(w_m, v_m)$.

In summary, we have proved the following.

18.11. Proposition. *Let M be a manifold and suppose $\mathbf{m} \in \mathcal{X}^0_2(M)$ is symmetric and nondegenerate (a* **pseudo-Riemannian metric**). *Then $H \in \mathcal{F}(T^*M)\colon \alpha_m \rightsquigarrow \frac{1}{2}\mathbf{m}(\mathbf{m}_\flat\alpha_m, \mathbf{m}_\flat\alpha_m)$ is derivable from the Lagrangian $L \in \mathcal{F}(TM)\colon w_m \rightsquigarrow \frac{1}{2}\mathbf{m}(w_m, w_m)$.*

The base integral curves of X_H and X_E coincide as we saw in 18.2. In physical terminology, these base integral curves are called *the orbits of a free particle.* They coincide with the motion of a free particle in general relativity, for example. Formally, we make the following.

18.12. Definition. *Let M be a manifold and $\mathbf{m} \in \mathcal{T}^0_2(M)$ be nondegenerate and symmetric (that is, a* **pseudo-Riemannian metric**). *Let E be the energy of the Lagrangian $L\colon w_m \rightsquigarrow \frac{1}{2}\mathbf{m}(w_m, w_m)$. Then X_E is called the* **geodesic spray** *of* $\mathbf{m}$ *and a base integral curve of X_E is called a* **geodesic** *of* $\mathbf{m}$; *M is called* **geodesically complete** *iff X_E is complete.*

For a general discussion of sprays, see Lang [1, pp. 67, 109].

We have the following, which connects the preceding definition with the usual geodesic equations.

18.13. Proposition. *Let M be a manifold and $\mathbf{m} \in \mathcal{T}^0_2(M)$ be a pseudo-Riemannian metric. Then a curve $c\colon I \to M$ is a geodesic of*

M iff, in the notation of 17.17,

$$\frac{d^2}{dt^2}q^i + \Gamma^i_{jk}\frac{dq^j}{dt}\frac{dq^k}{dt} = 0$$

where

$$\Gamma^i_{jk} = \tfrac{1}{2}\mathbf{m}^{li}\left(\frac{\partial \mathbf{m}_{lk}}{\partial q^j} + \frac{\partial \mathbf{m}_{lj}}{\partial q^k} - \frac{\partial \mathbf{m}_{jk}}{\partial q^l}\right)$$

$\mathbf{m}_{ij}$ *represents the components of* $\mathbf{m}_\flat$, *and* $\mathbf{m}^{ij}$ *those of* $\mathbf{m}^\sharp$, *relative to the standard basis.*

This is a straightforward computation using the Lagrangian equations, 17.20. Of course, the *Christoffel symbols* Γ^i_{jk} are not the components of a tensor.

Suppose E is as defined in 18.12, and $e \in \mathbf{R}$ is a regular value of E. Then $\Sigma_e = \{w_m | E(w_m) = e\}$ (if nonempty) is a submanifold of TM of codimension one. In the case of a Riemannian metric we have the following criterion of critical points.

18.14. Proposition. *Let M be a manifold with Riemannian metric* $\mathbf{m}$, *and $L = E \in \mathscr{F}(TM)$ defined as in* 18.12. *Then $w_m \in TM$ is a critical point of E iff $w_m = 0$ iff $E(w_m) = 0$.*

Proof. In local representation, if

$$E: U \times \mathbf{E} \to \mathbf{R}: (u, \mathbf{e}) \rightsquigarrow \tfrac{1}{2}\mathbf{m}(u)\cdot(\mathbf{e}, \mathbf{e})$$

then

$$DE(u, \mathbf{e}): \mathbf{E} \times \mathbf{E} \to \mathbf{R}: (\mathbf{e}_1, \mathbf{e}_2) \rightsquigarrow \tfrac{1}{2}D\mathbf{m}(u)(\mathbf{e})\cdot(\mathbf{e}_1, \mathbf{e}_2) + \tfrac{1}{2}\mathbf{m}(u)\cdot(\mathbf{e}, \mathbf{e}_2) + \tfrac{1}{2}\mathbf{m}(u)\cdot(\mathbf{e}_1, \mathbf{e})$$

where $D\mathbf{m}(u): \mathbf{E} \to T^0_2(\mathbf{E})$. Hence, $DE(u, \mathbf{e}) = 0$ iff $\mathbf{e} = \mathbf{0}$, as $D\mathbf{m}(u)(\mathbf{e})\cdot(\mathbf{e}_1, \mathbf{e}_2) \geq 0$. ∎

Notice that, even for a pseudo-Riemannian metric, w_m is a critical point of E iff $w_m = 0$; however, there are w_m so $E(w_m) = 0$ and $w_m \neq 0$ (vectors on the light cone).

18.15. Definition. *Let M be a manifold with pseudo-Riemannian metric* $\mathbf{m}$. *For any $e \in \mathbf{R}$, $e > 0$ let $\Sigma_e = \{w_m | \tfrac{1}{2}m(w_m, w_m) = e\}$. Then Σ_e is called the* **pseudosphere bundle of** *M* **of energy** *e, also denoted $T_{(2e)^{1/2}}M$.*

By 18.14, Σ_e is a submanifold of TM of codimension one. If $\mathbf{m}$ is Riemannian, then Σ_e is actually a sphere bundle.

Thus if $c: I \to M$ is a geodesic (base integral curve of $X_{\dot{E}}$), then c' is an integral curve of X_E by 17.14. Thus, $\|c'(t)\|^2 = \mathbf{m}(c'(t), c'(t)) = 2e$, a constant. This is a well known property of geodesics. Clearly, base integral curves are not unique, and may be obtained from one another by changing e, which corresponds to changing t by a multiplicative constant. The parameter determined by the choice $e = \frac{1}{2}$ (that is, the base integral curve of the curve in Σ_e) is called the *arc length parameter* for obvious reasons. If X_E is complete, the flow induced on $T_1 V$ is called the *geodesic flow.*

The example 18.10 may be easily generalized to include potentials (particle moving under the influence of conservative forces) as follows.

18.16. Example. Let $\mathbf{m}$ be a pseudo-Riemannian metric on M and let $V_0 \in \mathscr{F}(M)$ and $V = V_0 \circ \tau_M$. Then consider the Lagrangian $L = T - V$ where T is as defined in 18.10. Clearly, $FL = FT$ since V is constant on the fibers. Thus, L is hyperregular. The corresponding action is $2T$, as before, and $E = A - L = T + V$ is the energy. The corresponding hyperregular Hamiltonian function on T^*M is $H_0 + V_0 \circ \tau_M^*$ where H_0 is H as defined in 18.10. Then in this case the equations for base integral curves of X_E differ from those of the geodesic equation by *forcing terms* $\partial V/\partial q^i$. Suppose that V_0 is bounded and $e > V_0(m)$ for all m. Then $\tilde{\mathbf{m}}_e = (e - V)\mathbf{m}$ is clearly a pseudo-Riemannian metric on M called the **Jacobi metric** for energy e. Then X_E and $\tilde{\mathbf{m}}_e$ are related by the following, sometimes called the *principle of Maupertuis.*

18.17. Theorem (Jacobi). *Let* $\mathbf{m}$ *be a pseudo-Riemannian metric on* M *and* $V_0 \in \mathscr{F}(M)$, $L = T - V$ *as defined above. Then* $e \in \mathbf{R}$ *is a regular value of* E *if* $e > V_0(m)$ *for all* $m \in M$. *Moreover,* $c: I \to M$ *is a base integral curve of* X_E *iff* $b: J \to M$ *is a geodesic of* $\tilde{\mathbf{m}}_e$ *(parameterized by arc length), where* $b = c \circ \tau^{-1}$ *and* $\tau: I \to J$ *is given by* $\tau(t) = \int_0^t \|c'(s)\|_{\tilde{\mathbf{m}}_e}\, ds$.

Proof. Consider an integral curve c_1 of X_E of energy e, which satisfies

$$\frac{d}{dt}\left(\frac{\partial T}{\partial \dot{q}^i}\right) - \frac{\partial T}{\partial q^i} + \frac{\partial V}{\partial q^i} = 0$$

or

$$\frac{d}{dt}\left(\frac{\partial T}{\partial \dot{q}^i}\right) - 2\frac{\partial T}{\partial q^i} = 0$$

since $T + V = e$. On the other hand, a geodesic of $\tilde{\mathbf{m}}_e$ satisfies the equation

$$\frac{d}{dt}\left(\frac{\partial}{\partial \dot{q}^i}[(e - V)T]\right) - \frac{\partial}{\partial q^i}((e - V)T) = 0$$

or

$$\frac{d}{dt}\frac{\partial}{\partial \dot{q}^i}(T^2) - \frac{\partial}{\partial q^i}(T^2) = 0$$

If we project from $\tilde{\mathbf{m}}_e = 1$, whereon $\|c'\|_{m_e} = 1$, or $\|c'\|_{\tilde{\mathbf{m}}_e} = (2T)^{-1/2}$ to the surface $T + V = e$ on which $\|c'\|_{\mathbf{m}} = (2(e - V))^{1/2}$. The change in t-parameter is then $t \rightsquigarrow \tau = 2Tt$ as we pass from one surface to the other (see discussion following 18.15). Then

$$\frac{d}{dt}\frac{\partial}{\partial \dot{q}^i}(T^2) - \frac{\partial}{\partial q^i}(T^2) = 0$$

becomes, in terms of τ,

$$2T\frac{d}{d\tau}\frac{\partial}{\partial \dot{q}^i}T - 2T\frac{\partial}{\partial q^i}T = 0$$

where $\dot{q}^i = (d/d\tau)q^i$. ∎

This geodesic characterization may also be useful for generalizing qualitative results of differential geometry to dynamical systems, for example, the theorem of Anosov on the ergodicity of geodesic flows for compact Riemannian manifolds of negative sectional curvature (see Anosov [1]).

Exercises

18A. Prove 18.5 and 18.6.

18B. Prove 18.3 in component notation. Also, prove 18.13.

18C. Let M be a manifold and $\mathbf{m}$ a pseudo-Riemannian metric on M. Define $H \in T^*M$ by $H = T + F + V$ where T is the kinetic energy (18.11), V a potential (18.16), and F has the form $F(\alpha_m) = \alpha_m(Y(m))$ for some $Y \in \mathscr{X}(M)$ (*friction*). Show that H is hyperregular. What are the Hamiltonian equations in local representation?

§19. SUMMARY OF VARIATIONAL PRINCIPLES

Historically, variational principles have played a fundamental role in the evolution of mathematical models in mechanics, but in the last few sections we have obtained the bulk of classical mechanics without a single reference to the calculus of variations. In principle, we may envision two equivalent models for mechanics. In the first, we may take the Hamiltonian or Lagrangian equations as an axiom and, if we wish, obtain variational principles as theorems. In the second, we may assume variational principles and derive the Hamiltonian and Lagrangian equations as theorems. We prefer the first because it is quite difficult to be rigorous in the calculus of variations, and in practice the variational principles are not necessary to the predictions of the model. In fact, in the model-theoretic view, we consider the variational principles important primarily to the inductive formation of the theory. After this most basic function, they do not have a crucial role within the theory.

Others may prefer the second model, especially those metaphysicians who hold, with Maupertuis, that *nature always acts in the simplest way*.

In this section we summarize these principles and sketch, without mathematical justification, how they may be obtained as theorems in our model.

For the details on the calculus of variations in the large that are needed to actually carry out the proofs in our context, see Smale [3]. For the corresponding local theory, Gelfand-Fomin [1] is adequate.

The basic idea of a variational principle is the following. Let M be a manifold and $L: TM \to \mathbf{R}$ a regular Lagrangian. Consider a fixed interval $[a, b]$ and two points $m_1, m_2 \in M$. Let Ω_{m_1,m_2} denote all the curves $c: I \to M$ with $c(a) = m_1$, $c(b) = m_2$ where $I \supset [a, b]$. (I is open, so that our previous definitions of smoothness make sense; $[a, b]$ is not a manifold but may be regarded as a manifold with boundary; see §12.) Now define a map J: $\Omega_{m_1,m_2} \to \mathbf{R}$ by $J(c) = \int_a^b L \circ c'(t)\, dt$. It can be shown that Ω_{m_1,m_2} can be made into a Banach manifold; that is, a manifold locally homeomorphic to an open subset of a Banach space (a complete normed vector space) rather than a finite-dimensional vector space. Moreover, in this case an exterior derivative may be defined with the usual properties. The appropriate definition is actually 10.15 (ii); and of course the simple version of 10.5 will not be valid in the infinite-dimensional case. For further details, see Lang [1, Chapter V]. Then we say that a curve $c_0 \in \Omega_{m_1,m_2}$ is a critical point of J iff $\mathbf{d}J(c_0) = 0$. This of course coincides with the definition 5.17. The above condition $\mathbf{d}J(c_0) = 0$ is often denoted $\delta \int_a^b L(c_0(t))\, dt = 0$ in the classical theory. Then the basic result is that c_0 is a critical value of J iff c_0 is a base integral curve of X_E, that is, satisfies the Lagrangian equations. (E denotes the energy of L, as in §17.) This is the **variational principle of Hamilton**. We have seen that the energy is necessarily constant along c_0'. Suppose that e is a regular value of E so that $\Sigma_e = E^{-1}(e)$ is a submanifold of TM. Then on Σ_e, L differs from the action A by a constant. Hence, if we consider only elements of $c \in \Omega_{m_1,m_2}$ such that c' lies in Σ_e; again these form a Banach manifold; let $\mathbf{d}_e$ denote the exterior derivative on it. Then $\mathbf{d}_e K(c_0) = 0$ iff $\mathbf{d}_e J(c_0) = 0$ if $\mathbf{d}J(c_0) = 0$, where $K(c) = \int_a^b A \circ c'(t)\, dt \in \mathbf{R}$. This is the **principle of least action of Maupertuis**.

The important special case of $L = T$ for a pseudo-Riemannian metric m was briefly discussed in §18. Recall that $T: w_m \rightsquigarrow \frac{1}{2}\mathbf{m}(w_m, w_m) \in \mathbf{R}$. Here, T is also the total energy, and we see that $A = 2T$, so the principles of Hamilton and Maupertuis are essentially the same in this case. Also, base integral curves of X_E are called geodesics. By conservation of energy, $\|c'(t)\|^2 =$ constant $= 2e$, so that a parameterization freedom exists in the base integral curve (but of course the integral curves, that is, maps $c: I \to TM$, are uniquely determined), namely, any linear transformation of arc length. More specifically, in the case of a *Riemannian metric* we can consider the map $T^{1/2}$, which will be smooth if we remove the zero section (the critical values of T). Then we can again consider the variational problem for $T^{1/2}$. This time we are extremizing arc length. Then the critical values of $\int_a^b T^{1/2} \circ c(t)\, dt$ and $\int_{a'}^{b'} T^{1/2} \circ c(t)\, dt$ coincide, except possibly for a parameter change. Indeed, the latter integral is easily seen to be independent of parameterization.

In §17 we also discussed a more general situation, where L has the form $L = T - V$, where T is as above (the ordinary *kinetic energy* in the Euclidean metric), and $V = V_0 \circ \tau_M$, $V_0 \in \mathscr{F}(M)$ (that is, V is not *velocity dependent*). The action is $2T$, so the principle of least action extremizes T on Σ_e. We also saw that the base integral curves are geodesics of the Jacobi metric $\tilde{\mathbf{m}}_e = (e - V)m$ when $e > V_0(m)$ for all $m \in M$. So in this case, the variational principle of Hamilton, with the energy constrained, is equivalent to

$$\delta \int_a^b \sqrt{2T}\, dt = 0$$

which is **Jacobi's form of the principle of least action**. Because geodesics extremize curvature as well as arc length, this is related also to the *geometrical principles of Gauss and Hertz.* (See Whittaker [1, Chapter IX].)

Notes.

In this chapter I have borrowed freely from the classical texts, especially Whittaker [1] and Pars [1]. Of the elementary books, Corbin–Stehle [1] is the most modern in spirit.

The attributions to some of the old masters are not to be taken too seriously, as I am not a historian. For the early history, see Dugas [1] and Brunet [1].

This version of mechanics has been slowly evolving since Cartan [1]. The first modern exposition of Hamiltonian systems on symplectic manifolds seems to be due to Reeb [6] in 1952. An early version of Lagrangian systems in this context appears in Mackey [1]. This formulation of mechanics was widely known in mathematical circles by 1962, and is explained in a letter by Richard Palais that circulated privately at about that time. This and other material from §14 and §15 can also be found in Sternberg [2], Jost [1], and Hermann [1].

Proof 2 of the eigenvalue theorem (13.12) is due to Jurgen Moser; the proof of Darboux's theorem (14.7) is adapted from the original proof of Darboux (1878); and the treatment of the Legendre transformation in §17 is due to Stephen Smale.

It is a pleasure to thank Shlomo Sternberg and Joel Westman for suggesting improvements in this chapter, and Noel Hicks, Stephen Smale, Jurgen Moser, and Manfred Breuer for helpful discussions in the past.

CHAPTER IV

TIME DEPENDENT MECHANICS

The nonconservative or time dependent mechanics can also be generalized to manifolds. Contact manifolds rather than symplectic manifolds are basic. A full translation of the classical theory would take a great deal of space, and the applications we wish to consider are conservative. Therefore we develop in this chapter only the basic facts of the time dependent case that are important tools in the time independent applications.

§20. CONTACT MANIFOLDS AND TIME DEPENDENT SYSTEMS

Section 16 was concerned with Hamiltonian vectorfields on a symplectic manifold (M, ω). If, instead, we are given a mapping $X: \mathbf{R} \times M \to TM$, (a *time dependent vectorfield*), then the analysis of §16 is no longer appropriate. In fact, $\mathbf{R} \times M$ cannot be a symplectic manifold, as it has odd dimension; but it does have a *contact structure*. Contact manifolds will also be of importance for canonical transformations, which we study in the next section. (Historically, the terms *contact* and *canonical* have been used in a variety of ways; see Whittaker [1, p. 290].)

20.1. Definition. *A* **contact manifold** *is a pair (M, ω) consisting of an odd-dimensional manifold M and a closed 2-form ω of maximal rank on M* (§13). *An* **exact contact manifold** (M, θ) *consists of a $(2n + 1)$-dimensional manifold M and a 1-form θ on M such that $\theta \wedge (\mathbf{d}\theta)^n$ is a volume on M* (11.4).

From Darboux's theorem (14.7) and lemma 14.4 we obtain the following.

20.2. Theorem. *Let (M, ω) be a contact manifold. Then for each $m \in M$ there is a chart (U, φ) at m with $\varphi(u) = (t(u), q^1(u), \ldots, q^n(u), p_1(u), \ldots, p_n(u))$ such that*

$$\omega|U = \sum_{i=1}^{n} dq^i \wedge dp_i$$

Similarly, if (M, θ) is an exact contact manifold, there is a chart (U, φ) at m so

$$\theta|U = dt + \sum_{i=1}^{n} p_i dq^i$$

For the last part of this theorem note that $\theta(m) \neq 0$. We also need the fact that if (M, θ) is an exact contact manifold, then $(M, \mathbf{d}\theta)$ is a contact manifold, which follows at once from this proposition.

20.3. Proposition (Gray [1]). *Let M be a $(2n+1)$-manifold and $\theta \in \Omega^1(M)$. Then (M, θ) is an exact contact manifold iff $\mathbf{d}\theta(m)$ restricted to $R_m = \{v_m \in T_mM | \theta(m) \cdot v_m = 0\}$ is nondegenerate for each $m \in M$.*

Proof. Let ρ denote $\mathbf{d}\theta(m)$ restricted to R_m. By 13.3 ρ is nondegenerate iff R_m is even dimensional and $\rho^n \neq 0$. But R_m is $2n$ dimensional iff $\theta(m) \neq 0$, and $(\theta(m) \wedge \rho^n)(v_1, \ldots, v_{2n+1}) = \theta(m) \cdot v_1 \wedge \rho^n(v_2, \ldots, v_{2n+1})/(2n+1)!$ if $v_2, \ldots, v_{2n+1} \in R_m$. This proves the assertion. ∎

From 20.2 then, we see that a contact manifold is *locally* an exact contact manifold.

From the proof as 20.3 we obtain these corollaries.

20.4. Corollary. *Let M be a $(2n+1)$-manifold and ω a closed 2 form on M. Then (M, ω) is a contact manifold iff for each $m \in M$, $\exists \alpha_m \in T_m^*M$ so $\alpha_m \wedge \omega(m)^n \neq 0$.*

20.5. Corollary. *Suppose (M, ω) is a contact manifold, $\omega = \mathbf{d}\theta$, and $\theta(m) \neq 0$ for all $m \in M$. Then (M, θ) is an exact contact manifold. In particular M is orientable.*

20.6. Definition. *Let M be a manifold and $\omega \in \mathcal{T}_2^0(M)$, of constant rank. Then $R_\omega = \{v_m \in TM | m \in M, \mathbf{i}_{v_m}\omega(m) = 0\}$ is called the* **characteristic bundle** *of ω. Also, $X \in \mathcal{X}(M)$ is called a* **characteristic vectorfield** *of ω iff $\mathbf{i}_X\omega = 0$; that is, $X(m) \in R_\omega$ for all $m \in M$.*

Then applying lemma 14.3 to $\omega_\flat: TM \to T^*M$ we obtain the following.

20.7. Proposition. *Let M be an n-manifold and $\omega \in \mathcal{T}_2^0(M)$. Suppose ω has rank $r < n$. Then for each $m \in M$ there is a neighborhood U of m and linearly independent characteristic vectorfields $X_1, \ldots, X_{n-r}$ of ω defined on U and which span $R_\omega \cap T_mM$ at each point of U.*

Thus R_ω becomes a vector bundle with base space M in a natural way. Namely, if (U, φ); $\varphi(U) = U' \subset \mathbf{R}^n$ is a chart of M, and $X_1, \ldots, X_{n-r}$ are defined on U as above, we can write for each

$$v_u \in R_\omega \qquad v_u = \sum_{i=1}^{n-r} v_u^i X_i(u)$$

Then consider the map

$$v_u \rightsquigarrow (\varphi(u), v_u^1, \ldots, v_u^{n-r}) \in U' \times \mathbf{R}^{n-r}$$

which will be a vector bundle chart of R_ω (§4).

In particular, if (M, ω) is a contact manifold, R_ω becomes a vector bundle with one-dimensional fibers. An example of a contact manifold is the energy surface of a Hamiltonian H on a symplectic manifold (M, ω).

20.8. Proposition. *Let* (M, ω) *be a symplectic manifold,* $H \in \mathscr{F}(M)$, *and* Σ_e *a regular energy surface of* H (16.22). *Then if* $i\colon \Sigma_e \to M$ *denotes the inclusion map,* $(\Sigma_e, i_*\omega)$ *is a contact manifold* (20.1).

Proof. First, $\mathbf{d}i_*\omega = i_*\mathbf{d}\omega = 0$ (10.9). It is also clear that $i_*\omega$ has maximal rank since ω is nondegenerate on M. (See 13.2.) ∎

20.9. Proposition. *Under the hypotheses of the preceding proposition,* $X_H|\Sigma_e$ *is a characteristic vectorfield of* $i_*\omega$ *on* Σ_e.

Proof. $\mathbf{i}_{X_H}\omega(Y) = \omega(dH)^\sharp, (Y) = dH(Y)$. But on Σ_e, H is constant, so

$$\mathbf{i}_{X_H|\Sigma_e} i_*\omega = 0$$

In addition, $dH(m) \neq 0$, $m \in \Sigma_e$, so $X_H|\Sigma_e$ generates the characteristic line bundle of $i_*\omega$. ∎

For the case of exact contact manifolds we have this analogue.

20.10. Proposition. *Let* Σ_e *be a regular energy surface of* $H \in \mathscr{F}(T^*V)$ *where* V *is an* n *manifold. Suppose* $\theta_0(X_H)$ *is never zero on* Σ_e, *where* $-\theta_0$ *is the canonical 1-form on* T^*V. *Then if* $i\colon \Sigma_e \to T^*V$ *denotes the inclusion mapping,* $(\Sigma_e, i_*\theta_0)$ *is an exact contact manifold.*

Proof. From 20.8, $(\Sigma_e, i_*\mathbf{d}\theta_0)$ is a contact manifold. But $i_*\theta_0$ is nonzero on Σ_e. The result then follows from 20.5. ∎

An application of this is the following.

20.11. Corollary. *Let* M *be a manifold with Riemannian metric* $\mathbf{m}$. *For* $V_0 \in \mathscr{F}(M)$ *define* $V = V_0 \circ \tau_M^* \in \mathscr{F}(T^*M)$ *and* $T\colon T^*M \to \mathbf{R}\colon \alpha_{m_0} \rightsquigarrow \frac{1}{2}\mathbf{m}(\mathbf{m}_\flat(\alpha_{m_0}), \mathbf{m}_\flat(\alpha_{m_0}))$. *Let* $H = T + V$ *and* Σ_e *be a regular energy surface of* H *such that* $\Sigma_e \cap T^*M_0 = \phi$. *Then* $(\Sigma_e, i_*\theta_0)$ *is an exact contact manifold.*

Note that $-\theta_0(X_H)$, the action of H, is merely $2T$, as we saw earlier.

We now turn to the second example of a contact structure and the basic properties of time dependent Hamiltonians. We stress the Hamiltonian formulation, although the time dependent Lagrangian formulation (§17 and §18) could similarly be described.

20.12. Proposition. *Let* (M, ω) *be a symplectic manifold. Let* $\mathbf{R} \times M$ *be the product manifold of* $\mathbf{R}$ *and* M (3.4), *and* $\pi^2\colon \mathbf{R} \times M \to M\colon (t, m) \rightsquigarrow m$. *Then* $(\mathbf{R} \times M, \tilde{\omega}) = (\mathbf{R} \times M, \pi_*^2\omega)$ *is a contact manifold. If* $\omega = \mathbf{d}\theta$, *let* $\tilde{\theta} \in \Omega^1(\mathbf{R} \times M)$ *be given by* $\tilde{\theta} = \mathbf{d}t + \pi_*^2\theta$, *where* $t\colon \mathbf{R} \times M \to \mathbf{R}$; $(s, m) \rightsquigarrow s$. *Then* $(\mathbf{R} \times M, \tilde{\theta})$ *is an exact contact manifold.*

The first part follows as in 20.8 and the second follows from 20.5. Here we use the identifications of 5.8.

20.13. Proposition. *Under the hypotheses of* 20.12, $\underline{t}$ *is a characteristic vectorfield of* $\tilde{\omega} = \pi_*^2\omega$, *where* $\underline{t}(s, m) = (s, 1; 0_m) \in T\mathbf{R} \times TM \approx T(\mathbf{R} \times M)$.

Proof. $\mathbf{i}_t\tilde{\omega}(X) = 2\tilde{\omega}(\underline{t}, X) = 2\pi^2_*\omega(\underline{t}, X) = 2\omega(T\pi^2 \circ \underline{t}, T\pi^2 \circ X) = 0$ since $T\pi^2 \circ \underline{t} = 0$ (see 10.7). ∎

Thus $\underline{t}$ generates the characteristic line bundle of $\tilde{\omega}$.

To obtain the Hamiltonian equations for a time dependent Hamiltonian $H \in \mathscr{F}(\mathbf{R} \times M)$ we study first the general time dependent equation.

20.14. Definition. *Let M be a manifold and $X: \mathbf{R} \times M \to TM$ be smooth. We call X a* **time dependent** *(or* **nonautonomous***)* **vectorfield** *on M iff for each $t \in \mathbf{R}$, $\tau_M \circ X(t, m) = m$. In this case we define $\tilde{X}: \mathbf{R} \times M \to T(\mathbf{R} \times M) \approx T\mathbf{R} \times TM: (t, m) \rightsquigarrow ((t, 1), X(t, m))$. If X is a time dependent vectorfield on M, a curve $b: I \to M$ is an* **integral curve** *of X at m iff $b'(t) = X(t, b(t))$ for all $t \in I$, and $b(0) = m$.*

20.15. Proposition. *The map $\tilde{X}$ defined in 20.14 is a vectorfield on $\mathbf{R} \times M$. Moreover, $c: I \to M$ is an integral curve of $\tilde{X}$ at $(0, m)$ iff $c(t) = (t, b(t))$, where $b: I \to M$ is an integral curve of X at m (20.14).*

Proof. In local representation, $\tilde{X}$ is the Cartesian product of smooth maps and hence is smooth (2.12). For the second part, $c(t) = (a(t), b(t))$ is an integral curve of $\tilde{X}$ if $c'(t) = (a'(t), b'(t)) = \tilde{X}(c(t))$ (5.8) iff $Ta(t, 1) = (a(t), 1)$ and $b'(t) = X(t, b(t))$. But $Ta(t, 1) = (a(t), Da(t) \cdot 1)$ and $Ta(t, 1) = (a(t), 1)$ iff $Da(t) \cdot 1 = 1$ iff $D(a(t) - t) = 0$. As I is connected, $D(a(t) - t) = 0$ iff $a(t) - t =$ constant (16.17). However, $a(0) = 0$ since c is a curve at $(0, m)$. ∎

Thus, changing X to $\tilde{X}$ *suspends* the integral curves of X (see Figure 20-1).

We now construct the time dependent Hamiltonian equations as follows.

20.16. Definition. *Let (M, ω) be a symplectic manifold and $H \in \mathscr{F}(\mathbf{R} \times M)$. For each $t \in \mathbf{R}$ define $H_t: M \to \mathbf{R}$ by $H_t(m) = H(t, m)$. (Clearly $H_t \in \mathscr{F}(M)$ and $X_{H_t} = (\mathbf{d}H_t)^\# \in \mathscr{X}(M)$ (14.1).) Then put $X_H: \mathbf{R} \times M \to TM: (t, m) \rightsquigarrow X_{H_t}(m)$ and define $\tilde{X}_H$ as in 20.14.*

20.17. Proposition. *Let (U, φ) be a symplectic chart of M with $\varphi(u) = (q^1(u), \ldots, q^n(u), p_1(u), \ldots, p_n(u))$, so $(\mathbf{R} \times U, t \times \varphi)$ is a*

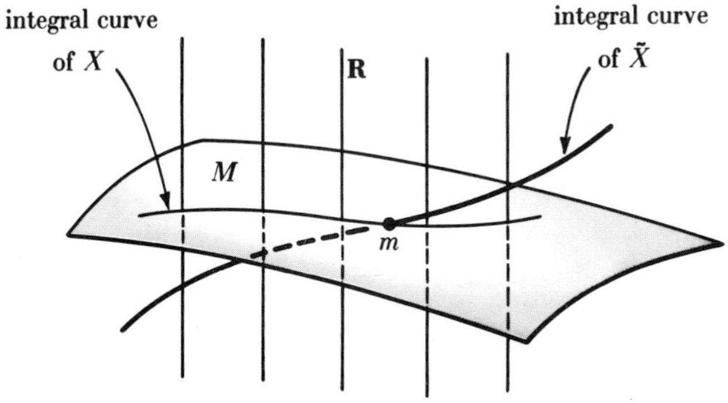

Figure 20-1

chart of $\mathbf{R} \times M$, *where* $t\colon \mathbf{R} \times M \to \mathbf{R}$ *is the projection onto the first factor. Then* $c\colon I \to \mathbf{R} \times U\colon t \rightsquigarrow (t, b(t))$ *is an integral curve of* $\tilde{X}_H$ *or, equivalently,* $b\colon I \to U$ *is an integral curve of* X_H, *iff*

$$\frac{d}{dt}[q^i(b(t))] = \frac{\partial H}{\partial p_i}(t, b(t)) \qquad i = 1, \ldots, n$$

$$\frac{d}{dt}[p_i(b(t))] = -\frac{\partial H}{\partial q^i}(t, b(t)) \qquad i = 1, \ldots, n$$

This shows that $\tilde{X}_H$ is really the global form of the traditional time dependent Hamiltonian equations. It follows at once from 16.12 and 20.15.

In the time independent case we saw that $\mathbf{L}_{X_H} H = 0$, or H is constant along the integral curves of X_H. For the time dependent case the Hamiltonian is not an integral invariant.

20.18. Proposition. *If* $\tilde{X}_H$ *is defined as in* 20.16

$$\mathbf{L}_{\tilde{X}_H} H = \frac{\partial H}{\partial t} \equiv \mathbf{d}H(\underline{t})$$

where $\underline{t} \in \mathscr{X}(\mathbf{R} \times M)$ *is defined by* $\underline{t}(t, m) = (t, 1; 0_m) \in \mathbf{R} \times \mathbf{R} \times TM \approx T(\mathbf{R} \times M)$.

Proof. As $\tilde{X}_H = \underline{t} + X_H \in T\mathbf{R} \times TM \approx T(\mathbf{R} \times M)$, we have

$$\mathbf{L}_{\tilde{X}_H} H = \mathbf{d}H \cdot (\underline{t} + X_H) = \mathbf{d}H(\underline{t}) = \frac{\partial H}{\partial t}$$

because $\mathbf{d}H(X_H) = 0$, as in the autonomous case. ∎

20.19. Proposition. *Let* (M, ω) *be a symplectic manifold,* $H \in \mathscr{F}(\mathbf{R} \times M)$, *and* $\omega_H = \tilde{\omega} + \mathbf{d}H \wedge \mathbf{d}t \in \Omega^2(\mathbf{R} \times M)$. *Then* $(\mathbf{R} \times M, \omega_H)$ *is a contact manifold. If* $\omega = d\theta$ *and* $\theta_H = i_*\theta + H\mathbf{d}t$, *then* $(\mathbf{R} \times M, \theta_H)$ *is an exact contact manifold, if* $H(t, m) \neq 0$, *for all* $(t, m) \in \mathbf{R} \times M$.

Proof. By 20.4 it is sufficient to verify that $\mathbf{d}t \wedge \omega_H^n$ is a volume. But $\omega_H^n = \tilde{\omega}^n + \tilde{\omega}^{n-1} \wedge \mathbf{d}H \wedge \mathbf{d}t$, so $\mathbf{d}t \wedge \omega_H^n = \mathbf{d}t \wedge \tilde{\omega}^n$, which is a volume (see proof of 20.3). The second part follows from 20.5. ∎

20.20. Proposition (Cartan). *Let* (M, ω) *be a symplectic manifold with* $H \in \mathscr{F}(\mathbf{R} \times M)$ *and* $\tilde{X}_H, \omega_H$ *defined as above. Then* $\tilde{X}_H$ *is the unique vectorfield that is a characteristic vectorfield of* ω_H *and satisfies* $\mathbf{i}_{\tilde{X}_H}\mathbf{d}t = 1$.

Proof. $\mathbf{i}_{\tilde{X}_H}\omega_H = \mathbf{i}_{\tilde{X}_H}\tilde{\omega} + (\mathbf{i}_{\tilde{X}_H}\mathbf{d}H)\mathbf{d}t - (\mathbf{i}_{\tilde{X}_H}\mathbf{d}t)\mathbf{d}H$. Now $\tilde{X}_H = X_H + \underline{t}$, where $X_H = (\mathbf{d}_M H)^\sharp$ (taken at fixed t; $\mathbf{d}_M$ denotes $\mathbf{d}$ on M). Then $\mathbf{i}_{\tilde{X}_H}\tilde{\omega}(Y) = 2\tilde{\omega}(X_H + \underline{t}, Y) = 2\omega(X_H, Y) = \mathbf{d}_M H(Y)$. Also, $\mathbf{i}_{\tilde{X}_H}\mathbf{d}H = \mathbf{d}H(\underline{t})$ and $\mathbf{i}_{\tilde{X}_H}\mathbf{d}t = 1$. For uniqueness, since the characteristic line bundle is one-dimensional, any characteristic vectorfield Y of ω_H is of the form $Y = f\tilde{X}_H; f \in \mathscr{F}(\mathbf{R} \times M)$. But, from $\mathbf{i}_Y\mathbf{d}t = 1$, we find $f = 1$. ∎

The time dependent analogue of 16.2 is the following.

20.21. Proposition (Cartan). *If* (M, ω) *is a symplectic manifold,* $H \in \mathscr{F}(\mathbf{R} \times M)$, *and* ω_H, θ_H *are as in* 20.19, *then* $\omega_H, \omega_H^2, \ldots, \omega_H^n$ *are invariant forms of* $\tilde{X}_H$ *and* θ_H *is a relatively invariant form of* $\tilde{X}_H$ (§15).

Proof. $\mathbf{L}_{\tilde{X}_H}\omega_H = \mathbf{i}_{\tilde{X}_H}\mathbf{d}\omega_H + \mathbf{d}\mathbf{i}_{\tilde{X}_H}\omega_H = 0$ since ω_H is closed and $\tilde{X}_H$ is a characteristic vectorfield of ω_H. The statements for ω_H^k follow at once, for $\mathbf{L}_{\tilde{X}_H}$ is a $\wedge$ derivation. Finally

$$\mathbf{dL}_{\tilde{X}_H}\theta_H = \mathbf{L}_{\tilde{X}_H}\mathbf{d}\theta_H = \mathbf{L}_{\tilde{X}_H}\omega_H = 0 \qquad (10.11) \quad \blacksquare$$

Finally, the time dependent case of Liouville's theorem (16.6) takes the following form.

20.22. Proposition. *Under the hypotheses of the previous proposition,* $div_\Omega \tilde{X}_H = 0$, *where* $\Omega = \mathbf{d}t \wedge \tilde{\omega}_H^n = \mathbf{d}t \wedge \tilde{\omega}^n$ (20.19).

Proof. $\mathbf{L}_{\tilde{X}_H}\Omega = \mathbf{L}_{\tilde{X}_H}\mathbf{d}t \wedge \tilde{\omega}^n_H$, from 20.21. But

$$\mathbf{L}_{\tilde{X}_H}\mathbf{d}t = \mathbf{d}(\mathbf{L}_{X_H + \underline{t}}t) = \mathbf{d}(\mathbf{d}t(X_H + \underline{t})) = \mathbf{d}(1) = 0 \quad \blacksquare$$

This shows that, in addition to the invariant forms of Cartan, we have also $\mathbf{d}t$, $\mathbf{d}t \wedge \omega_H$, $\mathbf{d}t \wedge \omega_H^2$, and so on.

Exercises

20A. Adapt the Lagrangian formulation to the time dependent case.

20B. Show that the theory of time dependent vectorfields carries through using an open subset of $\mathbf{R} \times M$. That is, translate the proof of 20.15 to classical notations.

20C. (*Reduction to the autonomous case.*) Let (M, ω) be a symplectic manifold, and $H \in \mathscr{F}(\mathbf{R} \times M)$. Show that, on $\mathbf{R} \times (\mathbf{R} \times M)$ with first and second factor projections s and t, $\mathbf{d}s \wedge \mathbf{d}t + \tilde{\omega}$ is a symplectic form, as is $\mathbf{d}s \wedge \mathbf{d}t + \tilde{\omega}_H$ ($\tilde{\omega} = \pi^3_* \omega$, where $\pi^3 : (s, t, m) \rightsquigarrow m$, etc.). Also, define $\tilde{H}(s, t, m) = H(t, m)$. Using either symplectic form, show that the integral curves of $X_{\tilde{H}}$ are related to those of $\tilde{X}_H$ by projection. Moreover, show that, if F is the flow of $X_{\tilde{H}}$, then $s(F_t(m)) = H(t, m)$. Hint: Recall that $L_{\tilde{X}_H}H = \partial H/\partial t$.

20D. Let (M, ω) be a symplectic manifold and $\Omega = dt \wedge \tilde{\omega}^n$, the volume on $\mathbf{R} \times M$. For $X \in \mathscr{X}(\mathbf{R} \times M)$, write $X(t, m) = X_m(t) + X_t(m)$ as the vertical and horizontal components (see 5.8). Then show

$$div_\Omega X(t, m) = \frac{dX_m}{dt}(t) + div_{\omega^n} X_t(m)$$

§21. CANONICAL TRANSFORMATIONS

In this section we study mappings that preserve the form of the time dependent Hamiltonian equations or, more precisely, that transform one Hamiltonian vectorfield into another.

As an example, consider a complete Hamiltonian vectorfield X_H on a symplectic manifold (M, ω) (§16). Suppose X_H has flow $F: \mathbf{R} \times M \to M$ (§7). Then define

$$\tilde{F}: \mathbf{R} \times M \to \mathbf{R} \times M: (\lambda, m) \rightsquigarrow (\lambda, F(\lambda, m))$$

which becomes a diffeomorphism. In fact, $\tilde{F}^{-1}$ maps the integral curves of $\tilde{X}_H$ (20.16) into integral curves of $\underline{t}$, that is, fibers of the line bundle π^2: $\mathbf{R} \times M \to M$. We say that $\tilde{F}$ *transforms H to equilibrium.* (See Figure 21-1.)

We shall see shortly that $\tilde{F}$ is an example of a canonical transformation.

21.1. Definition. *Let (M, ω) and (N, ω_0) be symplectic manifolds and $(\mathbf{R} \times M, \tilde{\omega})$ the corresponding contact manifold* (20.12). *A smooth mapping $F: \mathbf{R} \times M \to \mathbf{R} \times N$ is called a* **canonical transformation** *iff each of the following holds:*

(C1) *F is a diffeomorphism;*

(C2) *F preserves time; that is, $F_* t = t$, or the following diagram commutes:*

$$\begin{array}{ccc} \mathbf{R} \times M & \xrightarrow{F} & \mathbf{R} \times N \\ & {\scriptstyle t}\searrow \quad \swarrow{\scriptstyle t} & \\ & \mathbf{R} & \end{array}$$

(C3) *There is a function $K_F \in \mathscr{F}(\mathbf{R} \times M)$ such that*

$$F_* \tilde{\omega}_0 = \omega_{K_F}$$

where $\omega_{K_F} = \tilde{\omega} + \mathbf{d}K_F \wedge dt$ (20.10).

In the following, we will also allow the domain and range of F to be open subsets of $\mathbf{R} \times M$ (or N).

The function K_F is sometimes called the **generating function** of F, although

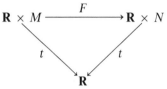

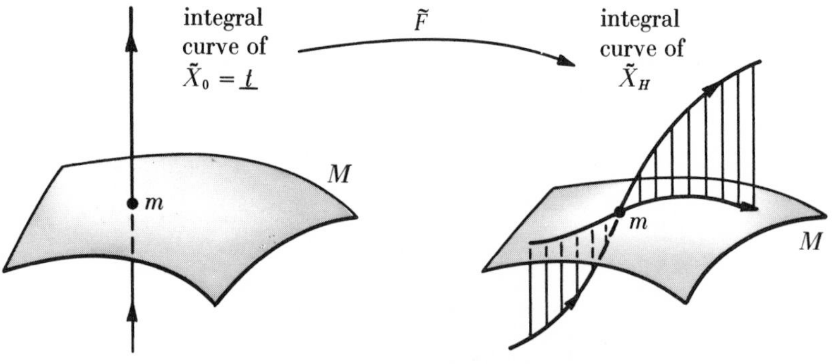

Figure 21-1

in this general context it does not generate F in any sense. We shall soon derive several more familiar conditions, equivalent to (C3). First, let us note the following.

21.2. Proposition. *The set of all canonical transformations on $(\mathbf{R} \times M, \tilde{\omega})$ forms a group under composition.*

Proof. Let F and G be canonical transformations on $(\mathbf{R} \times M, \tilde{\omega})$; that is, from $\mathbf{R} \times M$ onto $\mathbf{R} \times M$. We must show that $F \circ G^{-1}$ satisfies (C1), (C2), and (C3). However, (C1) and (C2) are clear, and for (C3), by 10.8

$$(F \circ G^{-1})_* \tilde{\omega} = G_*^{-1} \circ F_* \tilde{\omega} = G_*^{-1}(\tilde{\omega} + \mathbf{d}K_F \wedge \mathbf{d}t)$$

But $G_* \tilde{\omega} = \tilde{\omega} + \mathbf{d}K_G \wedge \mathbf{d}t$, so, by 10.9

$$\begin{aligned}(F \circ G^{-1})_* \tilde{\omega} &= \tilde{\omega} - G_*^{-1}(\mathbf{d}K_G \wedge \mathbf{d}t) + G_*^{-1}(\mathbf{d}K_F \wedge \mathbf{d}t) \\ &= \tilde{\omega} - \mathbf{d}(K_G \circ G^{-1}) \wedge \mathbf{d}(t \circ G^{-1}) + \mathbf{d}(K_F \circ G^{-1}) \wedge \mathbf{d}(t \circ G^{-1}) \\ &= \tilde{\omega} + \mathbf{d}(K_F \circ G^{-1} - K_G \circ G^{-1}) \wedge \mathbf{d}t \qquad \blacksquare\end{aligned}$$

As a corollary, we have

$$K_{F \circ G^{-1}} = K_F \circ G^{-1} - K_G \circ G^{-1}$$

It will now be convenient to give several definitions we will be using throughout this section.

21.3. Notations. *Let (M, ω) be a symplectic manifold and $(\mathbf{R} \times M, \tilde{\omega}) = (\mathbf{R} \times M, \pi_*^2 \omega)$ the corresponding contact manifold, where $\pi^2 : \mathbf{R} \times M \to M; (s, m) \rightsquigarrow m$. Let $j^t : M \to \mathbf{R} \times M; m \rightsquigarrow (t, m)$, so that $\pi^2 \circ j^t$ is the identity on M and $t \circ j^s = s$. For $F: \mathbf{R} \times M \to \mathbf{R} \times M$ we put $F_t = \pi^2 \circ F \circ j^t : M \to M$, as before. Also, if $X : \mathbf{R} \times M \to TM$ is a time dependent vectorfield, let $\tilde{X} = X + \underline{t} \in T(\mathbf{R} \times M) \approx T\mathbf{R} \times TM$ (20.14), so that $T\pi^2 \circ \tilde{X} = X$.*

21.4. Definition. *Let $F: \mathbf{R} \times M \to \mathbf{R} \times N$ be a smooth mapping satisfying* (C1) (21.1). *Then F is said to have* **property** (*S*) *iff $F_t: M \to N$ is symplectic for each $t \in \mathbf{R}$.*

21.5. Proposition. *A mapping $F: \mathbf{R} \times M \to \mathbf{R} \times N$ has property (S) iff there is a 1 form α on $\mathbf{R} \times M$ so that $F_* \tilde{\omega} = \tilde{\omega} + \alpha \wedge \mathbf{d}t$.*

Proof. If $F_* \tilde{\omega} = \tilde{\omega} + \alpha \wedge \mathbf{d}t$, then

$$\begin{aligned}F_{t*} \omega &= j_*^t \circ F_* \circ \pi_*^2 \omega = j_*^t \circ F_* \tilde{\omega} \\ &= j_*^t(\tilde{\omega} + \alpha \wedge \mathbf{d}t) = (\pi^2 \circ j^t)_* \omega + j_*^t \alpha \wedge \mathbf{d}_{j*}^t t \\ &= \omega \qquad \text{as} \qquad \mathbf{d}j_*^t t = \mathbf{d}(t \circ j^t) = 0\end{aligned}$$

For the converse, suppose F_t is symplectic and let $\beta = F_* \tilde{\omega} - \tilde{\omega}$. Then, as above, $j_*^t \beta = 0$. But, since $T(\mathbf{R} \times M) \approx T\mathbf{R} \times TM$, we easily see that any

2 form λ on $\mathbf{R} \times M$ has the form $\lambda = \gamma + \alpha \wedge \mathbf{d}t$ where, for each t, γ is a 2 form on $M \times \{t\}$, so $j^t_* \lambda = \gamma$. Then for $\lambda = \beta$, F_t symplectic implies $j^t_* \beta = 0$, or $\gamma = 0$. ■

Taking $\alpha = \mathbf{d}K_F$, we get the following.

21.6. Corollary. *If F satisfies* (C3) *of* 21.1, *then F satisfies* (S).

Of course, the symplectic manifold of greatest importance is the momentum phase $(T^*V, -\mathbf{d}\theta_0)$ (14.14). In this case, (C3) is clearly equivalent to the following.

(C4) There is a K_F such that $F_*\tilde{\theta}_0 - \theta_{K_F}$ is closed, where $\theta_{K_F} = \tilde{\theta}_0 - K_F\mathbf{d}t$.

However, for the general theory, only the situation described in 21.1 is required.

21.7. Proposition. *Suppose* $F: \mathbf{R} \times M \to \mathbf{R} \times N$ *satisfies* (C2) *of* 21.1. *Then* (C3) *is equivalent to the following.*

(C5) *For all* $H \in \mathscr{F}(\mathbf{R} \times N)$, *there is a* $K \in \mathscr{F}(\mathbf{R} \times M)$ *such that*

$$F_*\omega_H = \omega_K$$

Proof. If (C3) holds, let

$$K = H \circ F + K_F$$

Then

$$\begin{aligned} F_*\omega_H &= F_*(\tilde{\omega}_0 + \mathbf{d}H \wedge \mathbf{d}t) \\ &= F_*\tilde{\omega}_0 + \mathbf{d}(H \circ F) \wedge \mathbf{d}(t \circ F) \\ &= F_*\tilde{\omega}_0 + \mathbf{d}(H \circ F) \wedge \mathbf{d}t \\ &= \tilde{\omega} + \mathbf{d}K_F \wedge \mathbf{d}t + \mathbf{d}(H \circ F) \wedge \mathbf{d}t \\ &= \tilde{\omega} + \mathbf{d}K \wedge \mathbf{d}t \end{aligned}$$

by 10.9 and (C2).

Conversely, let K_F denote the K determined by $H = 0$. Then $F_*\omega_H = \omega_K$ reduces to (C3). ■

21.8. Proposition. *Let* $F: \mathbf{R} \times M \to \mathbf{R} \times N$ *satisfy* (C1) *and* (C2) *of* 21.1. *Then* (C3) *is equivalent to each of the following.*

(C6) (S) *holds and, for all* $H \in \mathscr{F}(\mathbf{R} \times N)$, *there is a* $K \in \mathscr{F}(\mathbf{R} \times M)$ *such that* $F_*\tilde{X}_H = \tilde{X}_K$.

(C7) (S) *holds, and there is a function* $K_F \in \mathscr{F}(\mathbf{R} \times M)$ *such that* $F_*\underline{t} = \tilde{X}_{K_F}$.

Proof. Assume (C3) holds. Then by 21.6, (S) holds. Let K be given by $K = H \circ F + K_F$. From (C5), $F_*\omega_H = \omega_K$. Thus to prove (C6) it suffices to show

$$\mathbf{i}_{F_*\tilde{X}_H}\omega_K = 0 \quad \text{and} \quad \mathbf{i}_{F_*\tilde{X}_H}\mathbf{d}t = 1$$

from 20.20. But using 10.14

$$\begin{aligned} \mathbf{i}_{F_*\tilde{X}_H}\omega_K &= \mathbf{i}_{F_*\tilde{X}_H}F_*\omega_H \\ &= F_*\mathbf{i}_{\tilde{X}_H}\omega_H = 0 \end{aligned}$$

Similarly

$$\begin{aligned}\mathbf{i}_{F_*\tilde{X}_H}\mathbf{d}t &= \mathbf{i}_{F_*\tilde{X}_H}F_*\mathbf{d}t\\ &= F_*\mathbf{i}_{\tilde{X}_H}\mathbf{d}t\\ &= F_*\cdot 1 = 1\end{aligned}$$

Second, (C6) implies (C7) by taking $H = 0$.

Finally, we must show (C7) implies (C3). From 21.5, $F_*\tilde{\omega} = \tilde{\omega} + \alpha\wedge\mathbf{d}t$. Hence

$$\mathbf{i}_{\tilde{X}_{K_F}}F_*\tilde{\omega} = \mathbf{i}_{\tilde{X}_{K_F}}\tilde{\omega} + (\mathbf{i}_{\tilde{X}_{K_F}}\alpha)\wedge\mathbf{d}t - \alpha\wedge\mathbf{i}_{\tilde{X}_{K_F}}\mathbf{d}t$$

On the other hand,

$$\tilde{X}_{K_F} = F_*\underline{t} \qquad \text{by (C7) so} \qquad \mathbf{i}_{\tilde{X}_{K_F}}F_*\tilde{\omega} = F_*\mathbf{i}_{\underline{t}}\tilde{\omega} = 0$$

from 20.13, and

$$\mathbf{i}_{\tilde{X}_{K_F}}\mathbf{d}t = 1$$

since $F_*t = t$ by (C2). Comparing the two expressions, and using

$$\mathbf{i}_{\tilde{X}_{K_F}}\mathbf{d}t = 1$$

we have $\alpha = \mathbf{i}_{F_*\underline{t}}\tilde{\omega} + (\mathbf{i}_{F_*\underline{t}}\alpha)\,\mathbf{d}t$. Thus $F_*\tilde{\omega} = \tilde{\omega} + (\mathbf{i}_{F_*\underline{t}}\tilde{\omega})\wedge dt$, and as

$$\mathbf{i}_{F_*\underline{t}}\tilde{\omega} = \mathbf{i}_{\tilde{X}_{K_F}}\tilde{\omega} = dK_F - \frac{\partial K_F}{\partial t}\,dt \qquad (20.20)$$

we have $F_*\tilde{\omega} = \tilde{\omega} + dK_F\wedge dt$ (C3). ∎

The statement $F_*\tilde{X}_H = \tilde{X}_K$ of (C6) is the precise meaning of the assertion: *F preserves the form of all time dependent Hamiltonian equations.*

The classical form for a canonical transformation is essentially (C6) without the condition (S), as follows.

21.9. Theorem (Jacobi). *If* $F: \mathbf{R}\times M\to\mathbf{R}\times N$ *satisfies* (C1) *and* (C2) *of* 21.1, *then* (C3) *is equivalent to the following.*

(C8) *There is a function* $K_F\in\mathscr{F}(\mathbf{R}\times M)$ *such that for all* $H\in\mathscr{F}(\mathbf{R}\times N)$, $F_*\tilde{X}_H = \tilde{X}_K$ *where* $K = H\circ F + K_F$.

Proof. That (C3) implies (C8) was shown in 21.8. For the converse, taking $H = 0$, we have $F_*\underline{t} = \tilde{X}_{K_F}$ and so for an arbitrary H we have

$$F_*\tilde{X}_H = F_*X_H + \tilde{X}_{K_F} \qquad (21.3)$$

By (C8)

$$\tilde{X}_K = X_K + \underline{t} = X_{H\circ F} + X_{K_F} + \underline{t} \qquad \text{and} \qquad \tilde{X}_K = F_*\tilde{X}_H$$

so combining the two expressions

$$F_*X_H = X_{H\circ F}$$

Therefore

$$j^t_* F_* \pi^2_* X_{H_t}(m) = X_{H_t \circ F_t} \qquad \text{where} \qquad H_t = H \circ j^t = j^t_* H$$

or

$$F_{t*} X_{H_t} = X_{H_t \circ F_t}$$

As this follows from (C8) for all $H \in \mathscr{F}(\mathbf{R} \times N)$, F_t is symplectic by 14.29. Consequently, (C8) implies (C6) and hence (C3), by 21.8. ∎

We now wish to give an important application of the above theory. Suppose X_H is a Hamiltonian vectorfield. Then the integral curves lie in an energy surface and, by 7.9, the curve parameter t can be taken as a local coordinate. We now wish to prove that, in fact, *the time t and energy H are canonically conjugate coordinates.*

21.10. Theorem (Hamiltonian flow box). *Let (M, ω) be a symplectic manifold, $H \in \mathscr{F}(M)$, and suppose $\mathbf{d}H(m) \neq 0$ for some $m \in M$. Then there is a symplectic chart (U, φ) at m with $\varphi(U) = I \times W \subset \mathbf{R} \times \mathbf{R}^{2n-1}$, $I = (-a, a)$, $\varphi(u) = (q^1(u), \ldots, q^n(u), p_1(u), \ldots, p_n(u))$ and $\varphi(m) = (0, \mathbf{0})$ such that $\varphi^{-1}|I \times \{w\}$ is an integral curve of X_H for all $w \in W$ (with parameter q^1) and $p_1(u) = e - H(u)$, where $e = H(m)$.*

Proof. First, we may assume that X_H is complete. For, choosing neighborhoods U_1, U_2 of m with $U_1 \subset U_2$ and U_2 compact, let $h \in \mathscr{F}(M)$ be a bump function with $h|U_1 = 1$ and $h|U_2 = 0$ in 8.7. Then by 7.15, hX_H is complete and coincides with X_H on U_1.

Thus suppose X_H complete, with flow F. Define $\tilde{F}\colon \mathbf{R} \times M \to \mathbf{R} \times M$ by $(\lambda, m) \rightsquigarrow (\lambda, F(\lambda, m))$. Clearly $\tilde{F}$ is a diffeomorphism and preserves time. Also, F_t is symplectic and $\tilde{F}^{-1}_* \underline{t} = \tilde{X}_H$, by 16.4 and 7.3. Thus by (C7), $\tilde{F}$ is a canonical transformation with $K_{F^{-1}} = H$, and $K_F = -H \circ F$ (21.2).

Next, let (U_0, ψ) be a symplectic chart at m such that $\mathbf{d}H(u) \neq 0$ in U. Also, we may assume that at m, $X_H(m) = T\varphi^{-1}(\mathbf{e}_1)$; that is, X_H points in the direction of the first coordinate axis. This is possible because, in the proof of Darboux's theorem, the initial vector is arbitrary (see 14.2). If $\psi(u) = (q^1(u), \ldots, q^n(u), p_1(u), \ldots, p_n(u))$, let V_0 be the submanifold defined by $q^1 = 0$. From the proof of 7.9 there is an $\varepsilon > 0$ and $V \subset V_0$ such that F maps $V_1 = (-\varepsilon, \varepsilon) \times V$ diffeomorphically into U_0 (see Figure 21-2.)

Let $U = F(V_1)$ and F also stand for F restricted to V_1. On U we have defined, by means of the chart (U_0, ψ), $q^1, \ldots, q^n, p_1, \ldots, p_n \in \mathscr{F}(U)$ and, in addition, $t = \pi^1 \circ F^{-1}$ where π^1 is the projection onto the first factor. Define a mapping

$$\alpha\colon (-\varepsilon, \tau) \times V \to \mathbf{R}^{2n}\colon \quad v \rightsquigarrow (\pi^1(v), q^2 \circ F(v), \ldots, q^n \circ F(v),$$
$$e - H \circ F(v), p_2 \circ F(v), \ldots, p_n \circ F(v))$$

and a mapping

$$\varphi\colon U \to \mathbf{R}^{2n};\, u \rightsquigarrow (t(u), q^2(u), \ldots, q^n(u), e - H(u), p_2(u), \ldots, p_n(u))$$

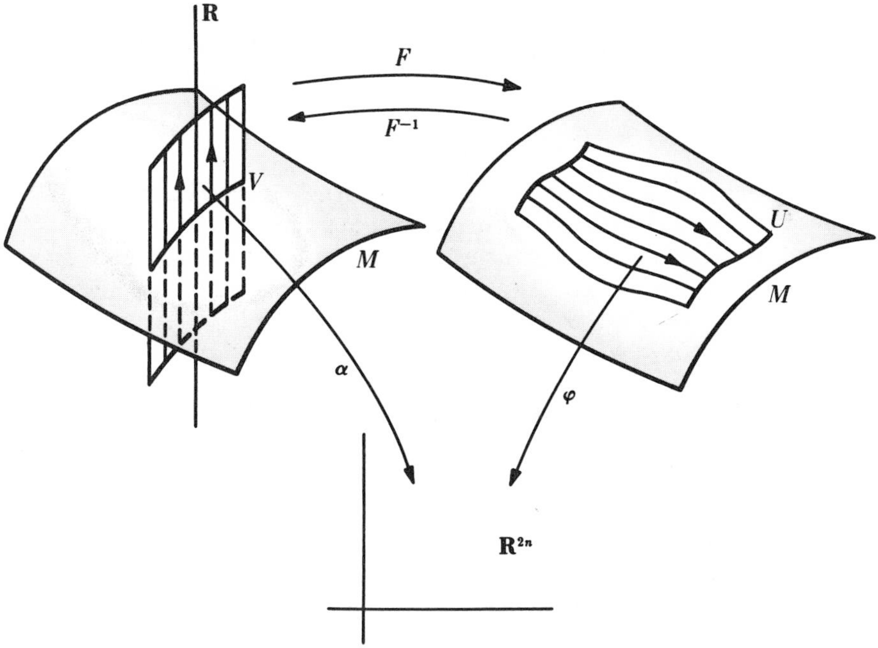

Figure 21-2

so the above diagram commutes. If ω_0 denotes the canonical two form on $\mathbf{R}^{2n}$, we must show that $\varphi_*(\omega_0) = \omega$, the result then following by 14.10. But, by 10.9, we have

$$\alpha_*(\omega_0) = -\mathbf{d}\pi^{-1} \wedge \mathbf{d}(H \circ F) + \sum_{i=2}^{n} \mathbf{d}(q^i \circ F) \wedge \mathbf{d}(p_i \circ F)$$

Also, $\tilde{F}_*\tilde{\omega} = \tilde{\omega} - \mathbf{d}(H \circ F) \wedge \mathbf{d}(t \circ F)$ since $K_F = -H \circ F$, as was shown earlier. Hence, restricting F to V_1, $(q^1 = 0)$,

$$F_*\omega = \sum_{i=2}^{n} \mathbf{d}q^i \wedge \mathbf{d}p_i - \mathbf{d}(H \circ F) \wedge \mathbf{d}(t \circ F) = \alpha_*(\omega_0)$$

Hence,

$$\begin{aligned} \varphi_*(\omega_0) &= (\alpha \circ F^{-1})_*(\omega_0) \\ &= F^* \circ \alpha_*(\omega_0) = \omega \qquad \blacksquare \end{aligned}$$

This theorem is often used classically to reduce the number of degrees of freedom locally, (see Whittaker [1, p. 313]).

We now consider a special type of canonical transformation, which is actually "generated" by its generation function. This is the context of the classical Hamilton–Jacobi theory, which is restricted to the local case. We consider only the case of a manifold V which is actually Euclidean space, $V = \mathbf{R}^n$, although the case of an arbitrary local manifold $V \subset \mathbf{R}^n$ (open set) could be developed similarly.

21.11. Definition. *Let* $F: \mathbf{R} \times M \to \mathbf{R} \times M$ *be a canonical transformation, and* $H \in \mathscr{F}(\mathbf{R} \times M)$. *We say that* F **transforms** H **to equilibrium** *iff* $K = H \circ F + K_F = 0$ *(see* (C8) *in* 21.9).

21.12. Definition. *Let* $\mathbf{E}$ *be a finite-dimensional real vector space and* $S: \mathbf{R} \times \mathbf{E} \times \mathbf{E} \to \mathbf{R}$ *be a smooth mapping. Define* S_t: $\mathbf{E} \times \mathbf{E} \to \mathbf{R}$ *by* $(e_1, e_2) \rightsquigarrow S(t, e_1, e_2)$ *and*

$$\mathbf{F}_1 S: \mathbf{R} \times \mathbf{E} \times \mathbf{E} \to \mathbf{R} \times T^*\mathbf{E} = \mathbf{R} \times \mathbf{E} \times \mathbf{E}^*$$

$$: (t, \mathbf{e}_1, \mathbf{e}_2) \rightsquigarrow (t, \mathbf{e}_1, D_1 S_t(\mathbf{e}_1, \mathbf{e}_2))$$

where $D_1 S_t$ *denotes the partial derivative of* S_t *with respect to the first factor. Similarly, define*

$$\mathbf{F}_2 S: \mathbf{R} \times \mathbf{E} \times \mathbf{E} \to \mathbf{R} \times T^*\mathbf{E} = \mathbf{R} \times \mathbf{E} \times \mathbf{E}^*$$

$$: (t, \mathbf{e}_1, \mathbf{e}_2) \rightsquigarrow (t, \mathbf{e}_2, D_2 S_t(\mathbf{e}_1, \mathbf{e}_2))$$

(Note the order.) Then S *is called a* **principal function** *iff* $\mathbf{F}_1 S$ *and* $\mathbf{F}_2 S$ *are diffeomorphisms.*

Then we have the following.

21.13. Proposition. *Let* $S: \mathbf{R} \times \mathbf{E} \times \mathbf{E} \to \mathbf{R}$ *be a principal function. Then* $G = -\mathbf{F}_1 S \circ (\mathbf{F}_2 S)^{-1}: \mathbf{R} \times T^*\mathbf{E} \to \mathbf{R} \times T^*\mathbf{E}$ *is a canonical transformation, with*

$$K_G = -\frac{\partial S}{\partial t} \circ (\mathbf{F}_2 S)^{-1}$$

Proof. Clearly, G satisfies (C1) and (C2) of 21.1. To prove the proposition we establish (C4); that is,

$$G_* \tilde{\theta} - \tilde{\theta} + K_G \mathbf{d}t = -\mathbf{F}_2 S_*^{-1} \circ \mathbf{F}_1 S_* \tilde{\theta} - \tilde{\theta} - \frac{\partial S}{\partial t} \circ \mathbf{F}_2 S^{-1} \mathbf{d}t$$

is closed. Equivalently, by 10.9, we show

$$\mathbf{F}_1 S_* \tilde{\theta} + \mathbf{F}_2 S_* \tilde{\theta} + \frac{\partial S}{\partial t} \mathbf{d}t$$

is closed, as

$$\mathbf{F}_2 S_*^{-1} \left(\frac{\partial S}{\partial t} \circ \mathbf{F}_2 S^{-1} \wedge \mathbf{d}t \right) = \mathbf{F}_2 S_*^{-1} \frac{\partial S}{\partial t} \circ \mathbf{F}_2 S^{-1} \wedge \mathbf{F}_2 S_*^{-1} \mathbf{d}t$$

$$= \frac{\partial S}{\partial t} \wedge \mathbf{d}(t \circ \mathbf{F}_2 S^{-1}) = \frac{\partial S}{\partial t} \mathbf{d}t$$

In fact, we will prove that

$$\mathbf{F}_1 S_* \tilde{\theta} + \mathbf{F}_2 S_* \tilde{\theta} + \frac{\partial S}{\partial t}\mathbf{d}t = \mathbf{d}S$$

For this it is sufficient to prove that $\mathbf{F}_1 S_{t*}\theta_0 + \mathbf{F}_2 S_{t*}\theta_0 = \mathbf{d}S_t$ for all $t \in \mathbf{R}$.

Recall from 14.14 that the canonical 1-form θ_0 is given as follows:

$$\theta_0 : \mathbf{E} \times \mathbf{E}^* \times \mathbf{E} \times \mathbf{E}^* \to \mathbf{R} : (\mathbf{e}_1, \alpha_1, \mathbf{e}_2, \alpha_2) \rightsquigarrow \alpha_1(\mathbf{e}_2)$$

On the other hand

$$\mathbf{F}_1 S_t : \mathbf{E} \times \mathbf{E} \to \mathbf{E} \times \mathbf{E}^* : (\mathbf{e}_1, \mathbf{e}_2) \rightsquigarrow (\mathbf{e}_1, D_1 S_t(\mathbf{e}_1, \mathbf{e}_2))$$

and

$$\mathbf{F}_2 S_t : \mathbf{E} \times \mathbf{E} \to \mathbf{E} \times \mathbf{E}^* : (\mathbf{e}_1, \mathbf{e}_2) \rightsquigarrow (\mathbf{e}_2, D_2 S_t(\mathbf{e}_1, \mathbf{e}_2))$$

so that

$$T\mathbf{F}_1 S_t : \mathbf{E} \times \mathbf{E} \times \mathbf{E} \times \mathbf{E} \to \mathbf{E} \times \mathbf{E}^* \times \mathbf{E} \times \mathbf{E}^* :$$
$$(\mathbf{e}_1, \mathbf{e}_2, \mathbf{e}_3, \mathbf{e}_4) \rightsquigarrow (\mathbf{e}_1, D_1 S_t(\mathbf{e}_1, \mathbf{e}_2), \mathbf{e}_3, DD_1 S_t(\mathbf{e}_1, \mathbf{e}_2)(\mathbf{e}_3, \mathbf{e}_4))$$

and

$$T\mathbf{F}_2 S_t : \mathbf{E} \times \mathbf{E} \times \mathbf{E} \times \mathbf{E} \to \mathbf{E} \times \mathbf{E}^* \times \mathbf{E} \times \mathbf{E}^* :$$
$$(\mathbf{e}_1, \mathbf{e}_2, \mathbf{e}_3, \mathbf{e}_4) \rightsquigarrow (\mathbf{e}_2, D_2 S_t(\mathbf{e}_1, \mathbf{e}_2), \mathbf{e}_4, DD_2 S_t(\mathbf{e}_1, \mathbf{e}_2)(\mathbf{e}_3, \mathbf{e}_4))$$

Therefore

$$\begin{aligned}
&(\mathbf{F}_1 S_{t*}\theta_0 + \mathbf{F}_2 S_{t*}\theta_0)(\mathbf{e}_1, \mathbf{e}_2)(\mathbf{e}_3, \mathbf{e}_4) \\
&\quad = (\theta_0)(T\mathbf{F}_1 S_t + T\mathbf{F}_2 S_t)(\mathbf{e}_1, \mathbf{e}_2, \mathbf{e}_3, \mathbf{e}_4) \\
&\quad = (\theta_0)\{(\mathbf{e}_1, D_1 S_t(\mathbf{e}_1, \mathbf{e}_2), \mathbf{e}_3, DD_1 S_t(\mathbf{e}_1, \mathbf{e}_2)(\mathbf{e}_3, \mathbf{e}_4)) \\
&\qquad + (\mathbf{e}_2, D_2 S_t(\mathbf{e}_1, \mathbf{e}_2), \mathbf{e}_4, DD_2 S_t(\mathbf{e}_1, \mathbf{e}_2)(\mathbf{e}_3, \mathbf{e}_4))\} \\
&\quad = D_1 S_t(\mathbf{e}_1, \mathbf{e}_2) \cdot \mathbf{e}_3 + D_2 S_t(\mathbf{e}_1, \mathbf{e}_2) \cdot \mathbf{e}_4 \\
&\quad = DS_t(\mathbf{e}_1, \mathbf{e}_2)(\mathbf{e}_3, \mathbf{e}_4)
\end{aligned}$$

which proves the assertion. ∎

We say that S **transforms** H **to equilibrium** iff $G = -\mathbf{F}_1 S \circ \mathbf{F}_2 S^{-1}$ transforms H to equilibrium. Of course, if this is the case, the integral curves of H are known; they are $G(\mathbf{R} \times \{(\mathbf{e}_1, \mathbf{e}_2)\})$, as we have seen earlier. Thus we have the following.

21.14. Theorem (Hamilton–Jacobi). *Let* $S: \mathbf{R} \times \mathbf{E} \times \mathbf{E} \to \mathbf{R}$ *be a principal function and* $H \in \mathscr{F}(\mathbf{R} \times T^*\mathbf{E})$*. Then* S *transforms* H *to equilibrium iff*

$$H \circ \mathbf{F}_1 S + \frac{\partial S}{\partial t} = 0$$

or, in coordinate notation

$$H\left(t, q^i, \frac{\partial S}{\partial q^j}\right) + \frac{\partial S}{\partial t} = 0$$

Proof. From 21.13, S transforms H to equilibrium iff $H \circ G + K_G = 0$. But $G = -\mathbf{F}_1 S \circ \mathbf{F}_2 S^{-1}$ and

$$K_G = -\frac{\partial S}{\partial t} \circ \mathbf{F}_2 S^{-1} \qquad \blacksquare$$

Exercises

21A. Suppose $\varphi: M \to N$ is a symplectic diffeomorphism. Let $U \subset \mathbf{R}$ be open and define $\bar{\varphi}: U \times M \to U \times N: (t, m) \rightsquigarrow (t, \varphi(m))$. Show that $\bar{\varphi}$ is a canonical transformation with $K_{\bar{\varphi}} = 0$.

21B. A mapping $J: \mathbf{R} \times M \to \mathbf{R} \times N$ is a *locally canonical transformation* iff it satisfies (C1), (C2), and (S) (21.4). Show that:

(i) For each $m \in M$ there is a neighborhood U of m such that $J|\mathbf{R} \times U$ is canonical. Hint: Use the relative Poincaré lemma, 10.19.

(ii) If M is simply connected, then a locally canonical transformation is canonical (see §A10).

(iii) Let $M = T^*S^1$. Then define $J: \mathbf{R} \times M \to \mathbf{R} \times M$ by $J(t, m) = (t, \varphi_t(m))$ where φ_t is the symplectic diffeomorphism induced by a rotation on S^1 by an angle t (see 14.16). Show that J is locally canonical, but not canonical.

21C. Adapt the classical calculations to 21.13. See, for example, Flanders [1, §10.5].

§22. GROUPS OF SYMMETRIES AND INTEGRAL INVARIANTS

It is well known that a Hamiltonian in Euclidean space that is invariant under translations (or rotations) admits constants of the motion, the linear (or angular) momentum. More generally, if the Hamiltonian is invariant under a *p parameter group*, then there should be *p conservation laws*. In this section this idea is made precise. We begin by reviewing the basic definitions of Lie groups.

22.1. Definition. *A* **Lie group** *G is a manifold together with a group operation, $G \times G \to G: (g_1, g_2) \rightsquigarrow g_1 g_2$, which is a smooth mapping of manifolds. The identity element of G is denoted by e.*

A **left translation** *by $g \in G$ is the mapping $L_g: G \to G; g' \rightsquigarrow gg'$. A vectorfield X on G is called* **left invariant** *iff $L_g^* X = X$ for all $g \in G$.*

One can similarly define right translations and invariant tensors.

22.2. Proposition. *Let G be a Lie group. For each $g \in G$, $L_g: G \to G$ is a diffeomorphism. Also, the set of left invariant vector-*

fields on G forms a Lie subalgebra of $\mathscr{X}(G)$ (8.13), called the **Lie algebra** *of G and denoted by $\mathscr{L}_G$.*

Proof. Clearly L_g is smooth, as it is the composition $g' \rightsquigarrow (g, g') \rightsquigarrow gg'$. Also, it is a bijection with inverse $L_{g^{-1}}$. Note that $\{L_g | g \in G\}$ forms a group isomorphic to G, the isomorphism being $g \rightsquigarrow L_g$. As L_g^* is $\mathbf{R}$ linear (6.17), $\mathscr{L}_G$ is a subspace of $\mathscr{X}(G)$. That it is a subalgebra follows at once from 8.14, as $X_1, X_2 \in \mathscr{L}_G$ implies $L_g^*[X_1, X_2] = [L_g^* X_1, L_g^* X_2] = [X_1, X_2]$. ∎

22.3. *Proposition.* *Let G be a Lie group and $X_0 \in T_{g_0}G$. Then there is a unique element of $\mathscr{L}_G$ such that $X(g_0) = X_0$.*

Proof. Clearly, the unique X is given by

$$X(g) = L_{gg_0^{-1}}^* X_0$$

We leave to the reader the proof that X is smooth. ∎

Thus, $\mathscr{L}_G$, as a vector space, is isomorphic to T_gG, for any $g \in G$. The Lie algebra consisting of T_eG with the Lie bracket operation induced by this isomorphism is denoted by ℓ_G.

22.4. *Proposition.* *Let G be a Lie group and $X \in \mathscr{L}_G$. Then X is complete.*

22.5. *Definition.* *If F_X denotes the flow of $X \in \mathscr{L}_G$, the map $X \rightsquigarrow \exp tX = F_X(e, t)$ is called the* **exponential mapping**, *and $\exp(X) = F_X(e, 1)$ is sometimes denoted by e^X, or e^A if $A = X(e) \in \ell_G$.*

For the proof of 22.4 we use the following characterization of invariance of a vectorfield under a diffeomorphism.

22.6. Lemma. *Let M be a manifold, $\varphi: M \to M$ a diffeomorphism and $X \in \mathscr{X}(M)$. Then if (U, a, F) is a flow box of X (7.3) at $m_0 \in M$, $(\varphi(U), a, \varphi^* F)$ is a flow box of $\varphi^* X$ at $\varphi(m_0)$, where*

$$\varphi^* F(m, t) = \varphi \circ F(\varphi^{-1} m, t)$$

Proof. If I is the identity mapping of $(-a, a)$, then $\varphi^* F = \varphi \circ F \circ (\varphi^{-1} \times I)$. As (U, a, F) is a flow box of X, we have

$$TF(m, t)(\mathbf{0}, 1) = X \circ F(m, t)$$

for all $(m, t) \in U \times (-a, a)$. Thus by the composite mapping theorem (5.7)

$$\begin{aligned} T(\varphi^* F)(m, t)(\mathbf{0}, 1) &= T\varphi[F(\varphi^{-1} m, t)] \circ TF[\varphi^{-1} m, t)] \cdot (\mathbf{0}, 1) \\ &= T\varphi[F(\varphi^{-1} m, t)] \cdot X[F(\varphi^{-1} m, t)] \\ &= T\varphi(\varphi^{-1} n) \cdot X(\varphi^{-1} n) = \varphi^* X(n) \end{aligned}$$

where $n = \varphi^* F(m, t)$. Thus $(\varphi(U), a, \varphi^* F)$ is a flow box of $\varphi^* X$ at $\varphi(m_0)$. ∎

22.7. *Corollary.* *If $\varphi: M \to M$ is a diffeomorphism and $X \in \mathscr{X}(M)$, then $\varphi^* X = X$ iff φ, suitably restricted, commutes with F_t for every flow box (U, F, a) of X.*

This follows immediately from 22.5 because of the local uniqueness of flow boxes (7.7). We now use this consequence of invariance to prove 22.4.

Proof of 22.4. Let (U, F, a) be a flow box of $X \in \mathscr{L}_G$ at the identity $e \in G$. Then if $g \in G$, X is invariant under L_g, that is, $L_g^* X = X$, so by 22.7, $(L_g U, a, L_g^* F)$ is a flow box at $L_g e = g_0$. As then every point $g \in G$ admits a flow box with the same time interval $(-a, a)$, X is complete. (See the proof of 7.14.) ∎

Perhaps the most widely used Lie group is $G = GL(n, \mathbf{R})$, the group of linear isomorphisms of $\mathbf{R}^n$ with composition. This has the manifold structure of an open subset of $\mathbf{R}^{n^2}$ (9.13). Then $\ell_G = T_e G = gl(n, \mathbf{R}) = L(\mathbf{R}^n, \mathbf{R}^n)$, and the bracket operation in ℓ_G is given by $[T, S] = T \circ S - S \circ T$. This was indicated briefly in §13. Also, in this case, the exponential mapping is the usual one ($\exp T = \Sigma_0^\infty T^k/k!$), as is easily seen from the differential equations. For details see Chevalley [1, p. 106].

Rather than the structure of Lie groups themselves, their action on a manifold is of interest in mechanics. The definitions seem more natural if we pretend that the group $D(M)$ of C^∞ diffeomorphisms of M with composition is a Lie group with Lie algebra $\ell_{D(M)} = \mathscr{X}(M)$. In fact this can be made rigorous.

22.8. Definition. *Let G be a Lie group and M a manifold. An* **action of** *G* **on** *M is a group homomorphism* $\Phi: G \to D(M)$ *such that the mapping*

$$ev_\Phi : G \times M \to M : (g, m) \rightsquigarrow \Phi(g)(m)$$

is C^∞.

The action is **essential** *iff* Φ *is a monomorphism (injection).*

If in fact $D(M)$ were a Lie group in the ordinary sense, we would define an action of G on M as a (smooth) Lie group homomorphism $\Phi: G \to D(M)$. Then the tangent at the identity

$$T_e\Phi : \ell_G \to \ell_{D(M)} = \mathscr{X}(M)$$

would be a Lie algebra monomorphism, and according to a standard theorem, $T_e\Phi'$ would completely determine Φ if G is simply connected (see, for example, Chevalley [1, p. 113]). It is not hard to see that $T_e\Phi$ would be exactly the mapping Φ', defined as follows.

Let $\Phi: G \to D(M)$ be an action of G on M, $\mathbf{x} \in \ell_G$, and $X \in \mathscr{L}_G$ the unique left invariant vectorfield such that $X(e) = \mathbf{x}$ (22.3).

As X is complete (22.4), we have a global flow $F_\mathbf{x}: G \times \mathbf{R} \to G$ generated by X. Obviously the mapping

$$H_\mathbf{x}: M \times \mathbf{R} \to M : (m, t) \rightsquigarrow \Phi F_\mathbf{x}(e, t)m = \Phi e^{t\mathbf{x}}(m)$$

is a flow also, as $H_\mathbf{x}$ is the composite

$$M \times \{e\} \times \mathbf{R} \xrightarrow{i} M \times G \times \mathbf{R} \xrightarrow{I_M \times F_\mathbf{x}} M \times G \xrightarrow{ev_\Phi} M$$

where i is the obvious injection. Thus $H_{\mathbf{x}}$ is generated by a unique vectorfield $Y_{\mathbf{x}} \in \mathscr{X}(M)$. Also, $Y_{[\mathbf{x},\mathbf{y}]} = [Y_{\mathbf{x}}, Y_{\mathbf{y}}]$.

22.9. Definition. *If* $\Phi: G \to D(M)$ *is an action of* G *on* M, *the* **infinitesimal generator of** Φ *is the Lie algebra homomorphism*

$$\Phi': \ell_G \to \mathscr{X}(M): \mathbf{x} \rightsquigarrow Y_{\mathbf{x}}$$

and $Y_{\mathbf{x}}$ *is the* **infinitesimal transformation** *of* $\mathbf{x}$.

The name generator and the heuristic argument above based on the fictitious identification $\Phi' = T_e\Phi$ is justified by the following, at least if M is compact. Recall that a manifold is *simply connected* iff every closed 1-form is exact. See §A10.

22.10. Theorem (Palais). *Let* G *be a simply connected Lie group,* M *a compact manifold, and* $\varphi: \ell_G \to \mathscr{X}(M)$ *a Lie algebra homomorphism. Then there exists a unique action* $\Phi: G \to D(M)$ *such that* $\Phi' = \varphi$.

For the proof, see Palais [1, Chapters II and III]. The technique relies on the integration of φ to define Φ. The hypothesis of simple connectivity of G is essential, but the compactness of M can be replaced by additional hypotheses on φ, as Palais has shown.

It follows that in the context of this theorem, the actions of G on M are in bijection with the potential infinitesimal generators, or homomorphisms of ℓ_G into $\mathscr{X}(M)$. In our analogy $\Phi' = T_e\Phi$ above, it is clear that Φ should be essential iff Φ' is a monomorphism, and this is in fact made rigorous by the proof of 22.10 (omitted). Thus the essential actions of G on M are parameterized by isomorphisms of ℓ_G onto subalgebras of $\mathscr{X}(M)$. These in turn may be parameterized as follows. Choose an ordered basis $(\mathbf{x}_1, \ldots, \mathbf{x}_k)$ for the real vector space ℓ_G. The **constants of structure** $\{c^{\gamma}_{\alpha\beta}\}$ are defined by the **commutation relations**

$$[\mathbf{x}_\alpha, \mathbf{x}_\beta] = c^{\gamma}_{\alpha\beta}\mathbf{x}_\gamma$$

(summed on $\gamma = 1, \ldots, k$). Then a monomorphism $\varphi: \ell_G \to \mathscr{X}(M)$ is uniquely determined for any ordered linearly independent set $(Y_1, \ldots, Y_k) \subset \mathscr{X}(M)$ satisfying the same commutation relations

$$[Y_\alpha, Y_\beta] = c^{\gamma}_{\alpha\beta} Y_\gamma$$

by the condition $\varphi(\mathbf{x}_\alpha) = Y_\alpha$, and linear extension over ℓ_G.

In this way we obtain a bijection between essential actions of G on M and k-tuples of vectorfields on M that are linearly independent and satisfy a fixed system of commutation relations. In case G is not simply connected or M is not compact, the parameterization of essential actions is considerably more complicated. This aspect of the theory is not explicitly needed in the usual examples of actions in mechanics, but is useful for the intuition it provides. For more details, see Palais [1] and Hermann [3].

We consider now actions of a group on a symplectic manifold, and their effects on Hamiltonian systems.

22.11. Proposition. *If $\Phi\colon G \to D(M)$ is an action of a Lie group G on a symplectic manifold (M, ω), then $\Phi(g)$ is symplectic for all $g \in G$ iff $\Phi'(\ell_G) \subset \mathscr{X}_{\mathscr{L}\mathscr{H}}(M)$; that is, every infinitesimal transformation of Φ is locally Hamiltonian.*

The proof follows at once from the definition, 22.8.

22.12. Definition. *Let Φ be an action of a Lie group on a symplectic manifold M. Then Φ is* **symplectic** *iff $\Phi'(\ell_G) \subset \mathscr{X}_{\mathscr{L}\mathscr{H}}(M)$, and Φ is* **Hamiltonian** *iff $\Phi'(\ell_G) \subset \mathscr{X}_{\mathscr{H}}(M)$; that is, each infinitesimal transformation of Φ is globally Hamiltonian. If $H \in \mathscr{F}(M)$, Φ* **is an action of symmetries that conserves** *H (or G is a* **symmetry group** *of H under the action Φ) iff Φ is a Hamiltonian action and $\Phi(g)$ leaves H invariant; that is, $\Phi(g)_* H = H \circ \Phi(g) = H$ for all $g \in G$.*

For example, consider the group of rotations acting on $\mathbf{R}^3$. These induce symplectic diffeomorphisms on the phase space $T^*\mathbf{R} \approx \mathbf{R}^6$ by "rotating" the momenta as well as the coordinates. On $\mathbf{R}^6$, a locally Hamiltonian vectorfield is globally Hamiltonian (see Poincaré's lemma (10.17)), so that if H is invariant under such double rotations, the action conserves H. More generally, symplectic actions may be obtained from 14.16.

22.13. Theorem. *If $\Phi\colon G \to D(M)$ is a Hamiltonian action on a symplectic manifold M and $H \in \mathscr{F}(M)$, then Φ conserves H iff $\mathbf{L}_Y H = 0$ for all infinitesimal transformations $Y \in \Phi'(\ell_G)$, and in this case if $K \in \mathscr{F}(M)$ is a Hamiltonian for Y, or $Y = X_K$, then K is a constant of the motion (§16).*

The proof is immediate from definition 22.9 and propositions 16.13 and 16.20.

In the usual applications we consider an essential action $\Phi\colon G \to D(M)$ conserving H. Choosing a basis $\{\mathbf{x}_1, \ldots, \mathbf{x}_k\}$ for the vector space ℓ_G, the action determines a basis $\{Y_1, \ldots, Y_k\}$ for $\Phi'(\ell_G) \subset \mathscr{X}_H(M)$, which is a subalgebra, by $Y_\alpha = \Phi'(\mathbf{x}_\alpha)$. This basis uniquely characterizes the action Φ. We suppose for simplicity that M is connected. Let $\mathscr{C}(M) \subset \mathscr{F}(M)$ denote the constant functions and $\mathscr{F}_0(M)$ the quotient vector space $\mathscr{F}(M)/\mathscr{C}(M)$, with projection $\pi\colon \mathscr{F}(M) \to \mathscr{F}_0(M)$. Then each of the basis infinitesimal transformations Y_α corresponds to a unique $\tilde{K}_\alpha \in \mathscr{F}_0(M)$ such that $Y_\alpha = X_{K_\alpha}$ for any $K_\alpha \in \pi^{-1}(\tilde{K}_\alpha)$ (16.19). In addition $\{Y_1, \ldots, Y_k\}$ is linearly independent in $\mathscr{X}(M)$ so $\{\mathbf{d}K_1, \ldots, \mathbf{d}K_k\}$ is linearly independent in $\mathscr{X}^*(M)$, and $\{\tilde{K}_1, \ldots, \tilde{K}_k\}$ is linearly independent in $\mathscr{F}_0(M)$. Furthermore, we may give $\mathscr{F}_0(M)$ a Lie algebra structure by means of the Poisson bracket (14.26), as $\{f, g\} = 0$ if $f, g \in \mathscr{C}(M)$. Thus if $\{c^\gamma_{\alpha\beta}\}$ are the constants of structure of ℓ_G with respect to $(\mathbf{x}_1, \ldots, \mathbf{x}_k)$, we have $[\mathbf{x}_\alpha, \mathbf{x}_\beta] = c^\gamma_{\alpha\beta}\mathbf{x}_\gamma$, so also $[Y_\alpha, Y_\beta] = c^\gamma_{\alpha\beta} Y_\gamma$, or $\{dK_\alpha, dK_\beta\} = -c^\gamma_{\alpha\beta} dK_\gamma$ (14.16), or $d(\{K_\alpha, K_\beta\} + c^\gamma_{\alpha\beta}K_\gamma) = 0$ (14.23), or $\{\tilde{K}_\alpha, \tilde{K}_\beta\} = -c^\gamma_{\alpha\beta}\tilde{K}_\gamma$.

We see then that up to sign and constants, the Hamiltonian functions $\{K_1, \ldots, K_k\}$ are linearly independent and satisfy the commutation relations of G. They form a basis for the k dimensional vector space of constants of motion induced by the symmetry group G. Also, if a subset $\{\mathbf{x}_1, \ldots, \mathbf{x}_j\} \subset \{\mathbf{x}_1, \ldots, \mathbf{x}_k\}$ generates the Lie algebra ℓ_G, then $K_{j+1}, \ldots, K_k$ may be obtained from $K_1, \ldots, K_j$ by successive Poisson bracket operations (up to constants).

In the example above of the rotation action of the rotation group $SO(3)$ on $T^*\mathbf{R}^3$, this observation yields the well-known result that if the angular momenta about the x and y axes are conserved, then so also is the angular momentum about the z axis.

This concludes the classical theory of symmetry conservation laws in the autonomous case. In the time dependent case only the simplest case seems to have been considered in the literature, that of a time independent action conserving a time dependent Hamiltonian. To formulate this we extend the Poisson brackets to the contact manifold $\mathbf{R} \times M$, and then outline the results. As the proofs and remarks above generalize very easily to this case, the details will be left to the reader.

22.14. Definition. *If $H, K \in \mathscr{F}(\mathbf{R} \times M)$, let $\{H, K\}: \mathbf{R} \times M \to \mathbf{R}$ be defined by $\{H, K\}_t = \{H_t, K_t\}$ for all $t \in \mathbf{R}$, where $H_t = H|\{t\} \times M$, etc.*

22.15. Proposition. *If $H, K \in \mathscr{F}(\mathbf{R} \times M)$, then $\{H, K\} \in \mathscr{F}(\mathbf{R} \times M)$ and*

$$\mathbf{L}_{\tilde{X}_H} K = \frac{\partial K}{\partial t} + \{K, H\}$$

22.16. Theorem. *Let $\Phi: G \to D(M)$ be a Hamiltonian action, and $\Psi: G \to D(\mathbf{R} \times M)$ be defined by $\Psi(g)(t, m) = (t, \Phi(g)(m))$. If $H \in \mathscr{F}(\mathbf{R} \times M)$, then Ψ conserves H, that is $\Psi(g)^*H = H$ for all $g \in G$, iff $\mathbf{L}_Y H = 0$ for all infinitesimal transformations $Y \in \Psi'(\ell_G) \subset \mathscr{X}(\mathbf{R} \times M)$. In this case $Y = X_K$ for some $K \in \mathscr{F}(\mathbf{R} \times M)$ with $\partial K/\partial t = 0$, and K is a constant of the motion, $\mathbf{L}_{\tilde{X}_H} K = 0$.*

We conclude this section with a brief outline of a more general conservation theorem, which may not be very useful in applications.

If $Y \in \mathscr{X}(\mathbf{R} \times M)$ is complete with flow $F: (\mathbf{R} \times M) \times \mathbf{R} \to \mathbf{R} \times M$, then the mapping F_t is a canonical transformation for all $t \in \mathbf{R}$ iff (by 21.1):

(IC 1) $\mathbf{L}_Y t = 0$, or Y "preserves time," and

(IC 2) $\mathbf{L}_Y \tilde{\omega} = \mathbf{d}S \wedge \mathbf{d}t$ for some $S \in \mathscr{F}(\mathbf{R} \times M)$.

In this case we call Y an **infinitesimal canonical transformation**. An action $\Psi: G \to D(\mathbf{R} \times M)$ is called a **canonical action** iff $\Psi(g)$ is a canonical transformation for all $g \in G$, and this is the case iff Y is an infinitesimal canonical transformation for all infinitesimal transformations $Y \in \Psi'(\ell_G)$. We say Ψ is a (time dependent) **Hamiltonian action** iff for every $Y \in \Psi'(\ell_G)$ there is a

$K \in \mathscr{F}(\mathbf{R} \times M)$ such that $Y = X_K$ (not $\tilde{X}_K$). Naturally we wish to know, then, for a function $H \in \mathscr{F}(\mathbf{R} \times M)$, when $\mathbf{L}_{\tilde{X}_H} K$ must vanish. This will not occur in general if the action Ψ leaves H invariant. Instead we have the following. Note that

$$\mathbf{L}_{X_K}\tilde{\omega} = \mathbf{d}S \wedge \mathbf{d}t \qquad \text{with} \qquad S = -\frac{\partial K}{\partial t}$$

for any $K \in \mathscr{F}(\mathbf{R} \times M)$, so a Hamiltonian action is always canonical. Then

$$\mathbf{L}_{\tilde{X}_H} K = \frac{\partial K}{\partial t} + \{K, H\} = 0 \quad \text{iff} \quad \mathbf{L}_{X_K} H = \frac{\partial K}{\partial t}$$

Thus K is a constant of the motion iff

$$\mathbf{L}_{X_K} H = \frac{\partial K}{\partial t}$$

so Ψ produces integrals only if it fails to conserve H itself in exactly this relation. Of course this relation coincides with conservation if $\partial K/\partial t = 0$, and this is exactly the situation in 22.15.

Finally, we note that an analogous theory can be developed in the Lagrangian formalism; this in fact occurs in the standard treatments of central field problems. Also, actions that are symplectic but not Hamiltonian are locally Hamiltonian and therefore provide local conservation laws.

Exercises

22A. Supply the proofs for 22.15 and 22.16, as well as for the remarks at the end of this section.

22B. Complete the proof of 22.3.

22C. If (M, ω) is a simply connected symplectic manifold, then every symplectic action is Hamiltonian (see Exercise 16A).

22D. Let SO(3) be the rotation group. Define its action on $\mathbf{R}^3$ and show it is essential. Construct the corresponding action on $T^*\mathbf{R}^3$. Find the constants of structure and the commutation relations, using as a basis infinitesimal rotations about the coordinate axes.

22E. Same question for the Lorentz group.

22F. (i) Let M be a manifold and $X, Y \in \mathscr{X}(M)$. Show that

$$\mathbf{L}_X \mathbf{i}_Y - \mathbf{i}_X \mathbf{L}_Y = \mathbf{i}_Y \mathbf{i}_X \circ \mathbf{d} - \mathbf{d} \circ \mathbf{i}_X \mathbf{i}_Y$$

(ii) Suppose $H \in \mathscr{F}(\mathbf{R} \times T^*M)$ and $\mathbf{L}_Y \theta_H = \mathbf{d}f$ where $\theta_H = \tilde{\theta}_0 + H\,\mathbf{d}t$ (20.27). Then show $g = \theta_H(Y) - f$ is a constant of the motion (i.e., $\mathbf{L}_{\tilde{X}_H} g = 0$). Show that $\mathbf{d}g = -\mathbf{i}_Y \omega_H$, and hence that, in the circumstances of 22.11 (22.14), we recover the same constant of the motion. (Under the weaker conditions here, g may depend on time.)

Notes

This material has been discussed very little in the recent literature, although some special cases are found in Flanders [1], Hermann [1], and unpublished notes of George Mackay on Hamilton–Jacobi theory.

The remark in §22 on the manifold structure of the group of diffeomorphisms is based on some of my unpublished work; see also Leslie [1].

CHAPTER V

QUALITATIVE THEORY OF VECTORFIELDS

The study of qualitative properties of the integral of a vectorfield has evolved into a vast subject since the early work of POINCARÉ, LIAPOUNOV, and HADAMARD in the 1880's. In this chapter we give a brief survey of the fundamentals. The definitions and basic properties will be used in the sequel, but the more important recent theorems are not applicable to the Hamiltonian case. We include them to indicate the scope and methods of current research in this area, which was revived by PEIXOTO, REEB, SMALE, and THOM in the 1950's. Hopefully they may be extended to Hamiltonian systems in the future.

At the end of the chapter we encounter the first examples of precise definitions of the notion of stability of a mathematical model discussed in the introduction.

§23. PHASE PORTRAITS AND CRITICAL ELEMENTS

In this section we survey some of the basic features of the general qualitative theory for the orbits of a vectorfield without special restrictions. Our main goal is to give the definitions needed later for the Hamiltonian case, but these are interspersed with a selection of difficult theorems that are offered without complete proofs to convey the flavor of the subject. As the general case is very difficult, most of these results are recent, and apply only to manifolds of dimension two. The statements require most of the ideas reviewed in Appendix A.

Perhaps the most ambitious objective of this program is the classification of all phase portraits on a given manifold, initiated by Poincaré in 1880.

23.1. Definition. *If X is a vectorfield on a manifold M, an* **orbit** *of X is the image $c(I)$ of a maximal integral curve $c: I \to M$ of X; that is, if $c_1: I_1 \to M$ is another integral curve with $c_1(0) = c(0)$, then $I_1 \subset I$. The set $\mathscr{P}(X)$ of all orbits of X is called the* **phase portrait** *of X.*

Roughly speaking, the phase portrait of X is the manifold M decomposed into nonparameterized maximal integral curves.

23.2. Definition. *Let M be a manifold and $X, Y \in \mathscr{X}(M)$. We say that $\mathscr{P}(X)$ and $\mathscr{P}(Y)$ are* **equivalent phase portraits** *iff there is a homeomorphism $h: M \to M$ such that $\gamma \in \mathscr{P}(X)$ iff $h(\gamma) \in \mathscr{P}(Y)$.*

The above relation is clearly an equivalence relation.

Intuitively, phase portraits are equivalent if their qualitative behavior appears the same to a topologist.

Phase portraits on a given manifold are so numerous and complex that a complete classification is very difficult. Yet for the simplest manifolds some progress has been made, which we now describe very briefly.

The first classification was given by Kneser in 1924, for regular (that is, nonvanishing) vectorfields on the torus and the Klein bottle (see §A9). He showed that these are the only compact, connected two-dimensional manifolds that admit a nonvanishing vectorfield, and moreover, of these only the torus admits vectorfields having no periodic (that is, noncompact) orbits. In the latter case the phase portrait is "represented" by curves $y = cx + d$ where c is irrational (see Figure 23-1). In the other cases on the torus there are regions (called *canonical regions*) separated by closed orbits (called *separatrices*). There can be a finite number of regions of the horseshoe type (see Figure 23-2), or a finite or countable number of spiraling regions

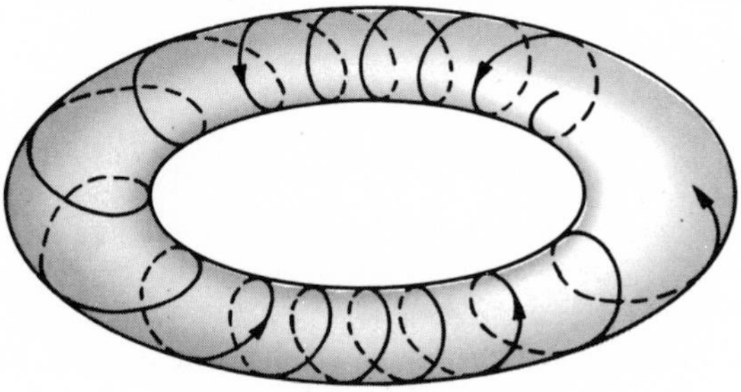

Figure 23-1

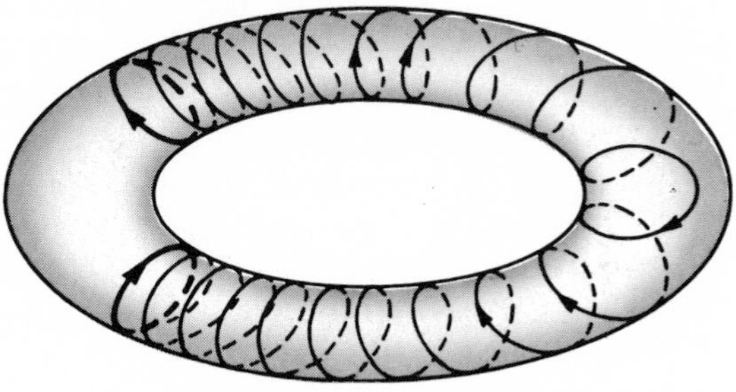

Figure 23-2

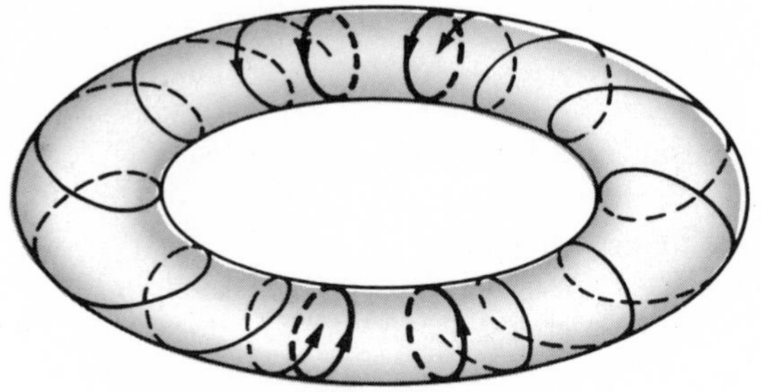

Figure 23-3

(see Figure 23-3), or finally, compatible combinations. For the details and proofs see Kneser [1].

The phase portrait classification problem for regular vectorfields on the plane $\mathbf{R}^2$ has been considered by Whitney (1933) and Kaplan (1940). Kaplan showed that the orbits are level surfaces of some function $h: \mathbf{R}^2 \to \mathbf{R}$ (not necessarily smooth), and thereby, using a *chordal system*, reduced the problem to an algebraic classification. Markus (1954) extended Kaplan's treatment to include isolated critical points. The idea of Markus' result is to locate special orbits, called *separatrices*, which in some sense divide the plane into *canonical regions* to which local theory applies.

Typical situations are illustrated in Figure 23-4.

For the details, see Markus [1].

These results give some idea of the complexity of general phase portraits. A more modest program, aimed at the location of critical elements within the phase portrait, was also initiated by Poincaré (1880). The remainder of this section is an introduction to this program.

23.3. Definition. *Let X be a vectorfield on a manifold M. A point $m \in M$ is called a* **critical point** *of X iff $X(m) = 0$. A* **closed orbit** *γ of X is an orbit on which X does not vanish and which is compact. A* **critical element** *of X is a set $\{m\}$ with m a critical point, or a closed orbit of X. We let Γ_X denote the union of critical elements of X.*

23.4. Proposition. *Let X be a vectorfield on a manifold M with integral $F: \mathscr{D}_X \subset M \times \mathbf{R} \to M$ (7.13). If $\gamma \subset M$ is a closed orbit of X, then $\gamma \times \mathbf{R} \subset \mathscr{D}_X$, $\gamma \subset M$ is a connected one-dimensional submanifold, and there exists a positive real number $\tau(\gamma)$ such that for any $m \in \gamma$, $F(m, t) = m$ iff $t = k\tau(\gamma)$ for some integer k.*

Proof. We show first that $\gamma \times \mathbf{R} \subset \mathscr{D}_X$. As M is normal (§A5), there exist for every point $m \in \gamma$ open neighborhoods $U(m)$, $V(m)$ such that $U(m)^c \subset V(m)$ and $V(m)^c$ is compact. As γ is compact there is a finite subset $\{m_1, \ldots, m_k\} \subset \gamma$ such that $\gamma \subset U = \bigcup_{i=1}^k U(m_i)$, $U^c \subset V = \bigcup_{i=1}^k V(m_i)$, and V^c compact. By 8.7, there is a bump function g with $g(m) = 1$ for $m \in U^c$, and $g(m) = 0$ for $m \in M \setminus V^c$. Now consider the modified vectorfield $Y = gX$. As g

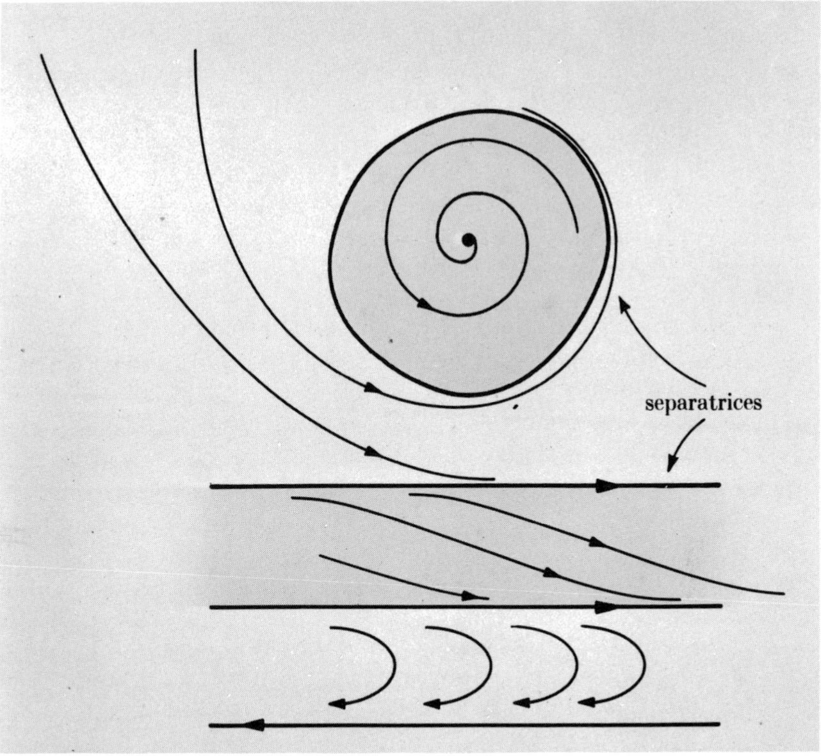

Figure 23-4

has compact support, Y is complete (7.15), with flow $G: \mathscr{D}_Y \to M$ where $\mathscr{D}_Y = M \times \mathbf{R}$. But $Y(m) = X(m)$ for $m \in U^c$, $\gamma \times \mathbf{R} \subset \mathscr{D}_Y$, $G(\gamma \times \mathbf{R}) = \gamma \subset U$, and $G|\{m_0\} \times \mathbf{R}$ is an integral curve of X at $m_0 \in \gamma$, so $\gamma \times \mathbf{R} \subset \mathscr{D}_X$.

We show next that γ is a submanifold of M. If $m_0 \in \gamma$, there exists a flow box chart $(U_2, 2a, \varphi)$ at m_0, with $\varphi(U_2) = V_2 \times (-2a, 2a) \subset \mathbf{R}^{n-1} \times \mathbf{R}$ and $\varphi^*(X(m)) = (\varphi(m), (\mathbf{0}, 1))$ for all $m \in U_2$ (7.9). Let $A_1 = \varphi^{-1}(\{\mathbf{0}\} \times (-a, a))$ and $A_2 = \varphi^{-1}(\{\mathbf{0}\} \times (-2a, 2a))$. Then in γ, A_1^c, and $\gamma \setminus A_2$ are closed subsets of γ, which is compact and therefore closed, so A_1^c and $\gamma \setminus A_2$ are disjoint closed subsets of M, and as M is normal (A5.4), there is an open neighborhood U_1' of $A_1^c \subset M$ such that $\gamma \setminus A_2 \cap U_1' = \phi$. As φ is a homeomorphism, there is an open neighborhood $V_1 \subset V_2$ of $\mathbf{0} \in \mathbf{R}^{n-1}$ such that $U_1 = \varphi^{-1}(V_1 \times (-a, a)) \subset U_1' \cap U_2$. Thus

$$U_1 \cap \gamma = \varphi^{-1}(\{\mathbf{0}\} \times (-a, a))$$

so $(U_1, 2a, \varphi_1)$, where $\varphi_1 = \varphi | U_1$, is a flow box chart at m_0 having the submanifold property ((SM) of 3.5) for γ. As $m_0 \in \gamma$ was an arbitrary point, γ is a one-dimensional submanifold of M. (Here we have not used the compactness of γ, only the fact that γ is closed. If γ were not closed, it might fail to be a submanifold.) As γ is the image of $\mathbf{R}$ under a continuous map, γ is connected (§A7).

Finally, we show that γ is a *periodic solution* of X. Choose a point $m_0 \in \gamma$, and let $c = F|\{m_0\} \times \mathbf{R}: \mathbf{R} \to \gamma$, where F is the integral of X.

Then $c'(t) = X(c(t)) \neq 0$, so c is a local diffeomorphism, by the inverse mapping theorem (2.10). Thus if c is injective, it is a homeomorphism, and $c^{-1}(\gamma) = \mathbf{R}$ is compact, a contradiction. Let $\pi(m_0) = \{t \in \mathbf{R} | c(t) = m_0\}$. This always contains zero, and in this case it contains another point as well, because c cannot be injective. Notice that $\pi(m_0) \subset \mathbf{R}$ is a subgroup of $(\mathbf{R}, +)$, and $t_1, t_2 \in \pi(m_0)$ imply $F_{t_1 - t_2}(m_0) = F_{t_1} \circ F_{t_2}^{-1}(m_0) = m_0$, or $t_1 - t_2 \in \pi(m_0)$. Also, $\pi(m_0) \subset \mathbf{R}$ is a discrete set (A1.5). For if $t_0 \in \pi(m_0)$ and $(U_1, 2a, \varphi_1)$ is a submanifold flow box chart at $m_0 \in \gamma$ as above, then $(F_{t_0}^{-1}(U_1), 2a, \varphi_1 \circ F_{t_0})$ is also a submanifold flow box chart at m_0, and thus

$$(t_0 - a, t_0 + a) \cap \pi(m_0) = \{t_0\}$$

Thus $\pi(m_0)$ is a discrete subgroup of $(\mathbf{R}, +)$, and is therefore an infinite cyclic group, generated by its smallest positive element, $\tau(m_0)$.

Finally, observe that if m_1 is another point of γ, then $\pi(m_0) = \pi(m_1)$. For if $t_0 \in \pi(m_0)$, then $F_{t_0}(m_0) = m_0$, $m_1 = F_{t_1}(m_0)$ for some $t_1 \in \mathbf{R}$, so

$$\begin{aligned} F_{t_0}(m_1) &= F_{t_0} \circ F_{t_1}(m_0) \\ &= F_{t_1} \circ F_{t_0}(m_0) \\ &= F_{t_1}(m_0) = m_1 \end{aligned}$$

which completes the proof. ∎

Note that the integral curve c defines a diffeomorphism $\mathbf{T}^1 \to \gamma$, where $\mathbf{T}^1$ is the quotient space $(\mathbf{R}, +)/\pi(m_0)$, and $\mathbf{T}^1$ is diffeomorphic to the circle S^1 (§A9). Thus every compact orbit is in fact a circle, and represents a periodic solution or "oscillation" in the classical theory of differential equations. Also, a (topologically) closed orbit is not necessarily a closed orbit.

23.5. Definition. *If γ is a closed orbit of X, the number $\tau(\gamma)$ defined in* 23.4 *is the* **period** *of γ. If m is a critical point of X, we define the* **period** *of m by $\tau(m) = 0$.*

The basic tool in the investigation of the qualitative behavior of orbits close to a closed orbit is the Poincaré map on a local transversal section, defined as follows.

23.6. Definition. *Let X be a vectorfield on M. A* **local transversal section of** X **at** $m \in M$ *is a submanifold $S \subset M$ of codimension one with $m \in S$ and for all $s \in S$, $X(s)$ is not contained in T_sS.*

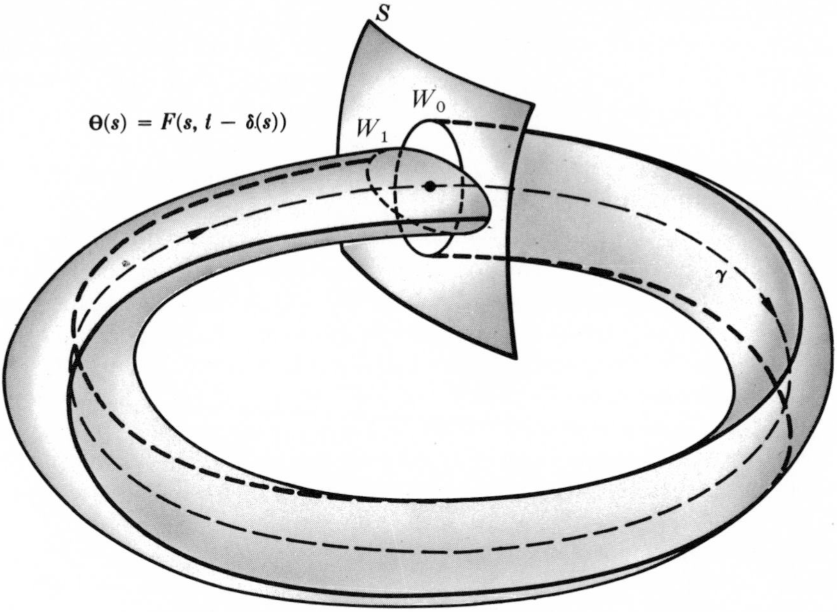

Figure 23-5

Let X be a vectorfield on a manifold M with integral $F: \mathscr{D}_X \subset M \times \mathbf{R} \to M$, γ a closed orbit of X with period τ, and S a local transversal section of X at $m \in \gamma$. A **Poincaré map** *of γ is a mapping $\Theta: W_0 \to W_1$ where:*

(PM 1) *$W_0, W_1 \subset S$ are open neighborhoods of $m \in S$, and Θ is a diffeomorphism;*

(PM 2) *there is a function $\delta: W_0 \to \mathbf{R}$ such that for all $s \in W_0$, $(s, \tau - \delta(s)) \in \mathscr{D}_X$, and $\Theta(s) = F(s, \tau - \delta(s))$; and finally,*

(PM 3) *if $t \in (0, \tau - \delta(s))$, then $F(s, t) \notin W_0$ (see Figure 23-5).*

23.7. Theorem (Existence and uniqueness of Poincaré maps).
(i) If X is a vectorfield on M, and γ is a closed orbit of X, then there exists a Poincaré map of γ.

(ii) If $\Theta: W_0 \to W_1$ is a Poincaré map of γ (in a local transversal section S at $m \in \gamma$) and Θ' also (in S' at $m' \in \gamma$), then Θ and Θ' are locally conjugate. That is, there are open neighborhoods W_2 of $m \in S$, W'_2 of $m' \in S'$, and a diffeomorphism $H: W_2 \to W'_2$, such that $W_2 \subset W_0 \cap W_1$, $W'_2 \subset W'_0$ and the diagram

$$\begin{array}{ccc} \Theta^{-1}(W_2)\cap W_2 & \xrightarrow{\ \Theta\ } & W_2\cap \boldsymbol{\Theta} W_2 \\ {\scriptstyle H}\big\downarrow & & \big\downarrow{\scriptstyle H} \\ W'_2 & \xrightarrow{\ \Theta'\ } & S' \end{array}$$

commutes.

Proof. (i) At any point $m \in \gamma$ we have $X(m) \neq 0$, so there exists a flow box chart (U, φ) at m with $\varphi(U) = V \times I \subset \mathbf{R}^{n-1} \times \mathbf{R}$ (7.9). Then $S = \varphi^{-1}(V \times \{0\})$ is a local transversal section at m. If $F : \mathscr{D}_X \subset M \times \mathbf{R} \to M$ is the integral of X, $\mathscr{D}_X$ is open, so we may suppose $U \times [-\tau, \tau] \subset \mathscr{D}_X$, where τ is the period of γ. As $F_\tau(m) = m \in U$ and F_τ is a homeomorphism, $U_0 = F_\tau^{-1} U \cap U$ is an open neighborhood of $m \in M$ with $F_\tau U_0 \subset U$. Let $W_0 = S \cap U_0$ and $W_2 = F_\tau W_0$. Then W_2 is a local transversal section at $m \in M$ and $F_\tau : W_0 \to W_2$ is a diffeomorphism (see Figure 23-6).

Now if $U_2 = F_\tau U_0$, then we may regard U_0, U_2 as open submanifolds of the vector bundle $V \times \mathbf{R}$ (by identification via φ) and then $F_\tau : U_0 \to U_2$ is a diffeomorphism mapping fibers into fibers, as φ identifies orbits with fibers, and F_τ preserves orbits. Thus W_2 is a section of an open subbundle. More precisely, if $\pi : V \times I \to V$ and $\rho : V \times I \to I$ are the projection maps, then the composite mapping

$$W_0 \xrightarrow{F_\tau} W_2 \xrightarrow{\varphi} V \times I \xrightarrow{\rho} V \xrightarrow{\varphi^{-1}} S$$

has a tangent that is an isomorphism at each point, and so by the inverse mapping theorem, it is a diffeomorphism onto an open submanifold. Let W_1 be its image, and Θ the composite mapping.

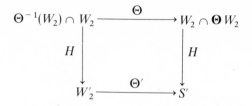

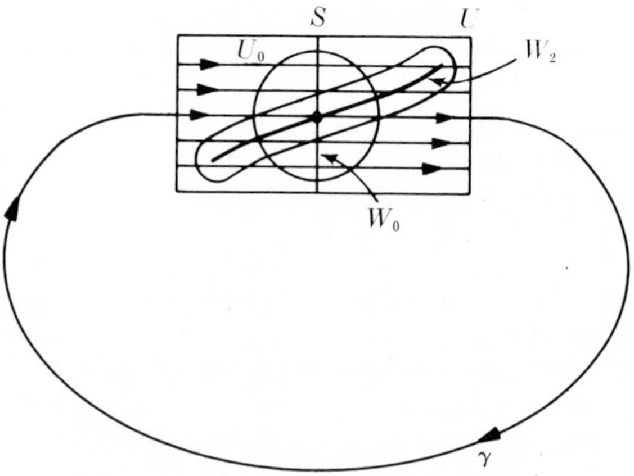

Figure 23-6

We now show that $\Theta: W_0 \to W_1$ is a Poincaré map (23.6). Obviously (PM 1) is satisfied. For (PM 2), we identify U and $V \times I$ by means of φ to simplify notations. Then $\pi: W_2 \to W_1$ is a diffeomorphism, and its inverse $(\pi|W_2)^{-1}: W_1 \to W_2 \subset W_1 \times \mathbf{R}$ is a section corresponding to a smooth function $\sigma: W_1 \to \mathbf{R}$. In fact σ is defined implicitly by

$$F_\tau(w_0) = (\pi F_\tau w_0, \rho F_\tau w_0) = (\pi F_\tau w_0, \sigma\pi F_\tau w_0)$$

or $\rho F_\tau w_0 = \sigma \pi F_\tau w_0$. Now let $\delta: W_0 \to \mathbf{R}: w_0 \rightsquigarrow \sigma\pi F_\tau w_0$. Then we have

$$\begin{aligned} F_{\tau - \delta(w_0)}(w_0) &= F_{-\delta(w_0)} \circ F_\tau(w_0) \\ &= (\pi F_\tau w_0, \rho F_\tau w_0 - \delta(w_0)) \\ &= (\pi F_\tau w_0, 0) \\ &= \Theta(w_0) \end{aligned}$$

Finally, (PM 3) is obvious as (U, φ) is a flow box.

(ii) The proof is burdensome because of the definition of local conjugacy, so we will be satisfied to prove this uniqueness under additional simplifying hypotheses that lead to global conjugacy (identified by italics). The general case will be left to the reader.

We consider first the special case $m = m'$. Then we choose a flow box chart (U, φ) at m, and *assume* $S \cup S' \subset U$, *and that* S *and* S' *intersect each fiber (orbit) in* U *at most once, and that they intersect exactly the same sets of orbits.* (These three conditions may always be obtained by shrinking S and S'.) Then let $W_2 = S$, $W'_2 = S'$, and $H: W_2 \to W'_2$ the bijection given by the orbits in U. As in (i), this is easily seen to be a diffeomorphism, and $H \circ \Theta = \Theta' \circ H$.

Finally, suppose $m \neq m'$. Then $F_a(m) = m'$ for some $a \in (0, \tau)$, and as $\mathscr{D}_X$ is open there is a neighborhood U of m such that $U \times \{a\} \subset \mathscr{D}_X$. Then $F_a(U \cap S) = S''$ is a local transversal section of X at $m' \in \gamma$, and $H = F_a$ effects a conjugacy between Θ and $\Theta'' = F_a \circ \Theta \circ F_a^{-1}$ on S''. By the preceding paragraph, Θ'' and Θ' are locally conjugate, but conjugacy is an equivalence relation. This completes the argument. ∎

Exercises

23A. Show that every (topologically) closed orbit is a one-dimensional submanifold. Find an example of an orbit that is not a submanifold. Hint: Consider a vectorfield on the torus with irrational slope.

23B. Let $m \in M$ be a critical point of a vectorfield $X \in \mathscr{X}(M)$. Then if $c: I \to M$ is an integral curve at m, $c(t) = m$ for all $t \in I$, so that $\{m\}$ is a (topologically) closed orbit.

23C. Complete the proof of 23.7.

§24. LIMIT AND MINIMAL SETS

The "final motion" or asymptotic behavior as time goes to $+\infty$ or $-\infty$ is described precisely in terms of the ω limit sets of the orbits of the phase portrait. Closely related to these are the minimal sets of the phase portrait, which are generalized critical elements. In this section we give the basic properties of limit and minimal sets, and illustrate their role in the qualitative theory by the Poincaré–Bendixon–Schwartz theorem for the two-dimensional case.

24.1. Definition. *Suppose X is a vectorfield on the manifold with integral $F: \mathscr{D}_X \subset M \times \mathbf{R} \to M$. Then the ω^σ* **limit set** *of m, $\sigma = +, -,$ or $\pm$, is defined by*

$$\omega^+(m) = \bigcap_{n \in \mathbf{Z}} \{F[(\{m\} \times (n, +\infty)) \cap \mathscr{D}_X]\}^c$$

$$\omega^-(m) = \bigcap_{n \in \mathbf{Z}} \{F[(\{m\} \times (-\infty, n)) \cap \mathscr{D}_X]\}^c$$

and

$$\omega^\pm(m) = \omega^+(m) \cup \omega^-(m)$$

where $\mathbf{Z}$ denotes the integers. Also, let $\Omega_X^\sigma = \bigcup \{\omega^\sigma(m) | m \in M\}$.

The ω^+ (resp. ω^-) limit set is sometimes called the ω (resp. α) limit set.

24.2. Proposition. *If m is σ complete, the limit set $\omega^\sigma(m)$ is the set of points $m_0 \in M$ for which there exists a sequence $\{t_n\}$ with $t_n \to \sigma\infty$ and $F(m, t_n) \to m_0$, for $\sigma = +$ or $\sigma = -$. If m is not σ complete, then $\omega^\sigma(m)$ is empty for $\sigma = +$ or $\sigma = -$.*

Proof. Let $A_n = F[\{m\} \times (n, \infty)]$. Then by definition, $m_0 \in \omega^+(m)$ iff $m_0 \in A_n^c$ for all $n \in \mathbf{Z}$. Let (U_n) be a sequence of open neighborhoods of m_0 such that $\bigcap_{n=1}^\infty U_n = \{m_0\}$. As $A_n \supset A_{n'}$ for $n < n'$, $m_0 \in A_n^c$ for all $n \in \mathbf{Z}$ iff $U_n \cap A_n = \phi$ for all $n \in \mathbf{Z}$. If $m_0 \in \omega^+(m)$, choose $t_n \in (n, \infty)$ such that $F(m, t_n) \in U_n$. Then $t_n > n$, so t_n tends to ∞ as n goes to ∞, and $F(m, t_n)$ converges to m_0. The converse and the case $\sigma = -$ are similar. The second assertion is obvious. ∎

For example, Figure 24-1 illustrates a possible situation on $\mathbf{R}^2$.

24.3. Definition. *Let X be a complete vectorfield on a manifold M, with flow F. A subset S of M is called* **positively invariant** *iff $F_t(S) \subset S$ for all $t \geq 0$ and* **negatively invariant** *iff $F_t(S) \subset S$ for all $t \leq 0$. S is called* **invariant** *if it is both positively and negatively invariant. (This is a generalization of 15.11.) A subset S of M is a* **minimal set** *iff S is closed, nonempty, invariant, and no proper subset of S has these properties.*

24.4. Proposition. *If $X \in \mathscr{X}(m)$ is complete and S is a minimal set of X, then S is connected. If S and T are minimal sets, then either $S = T$ or $S \cap T = \phi$.*

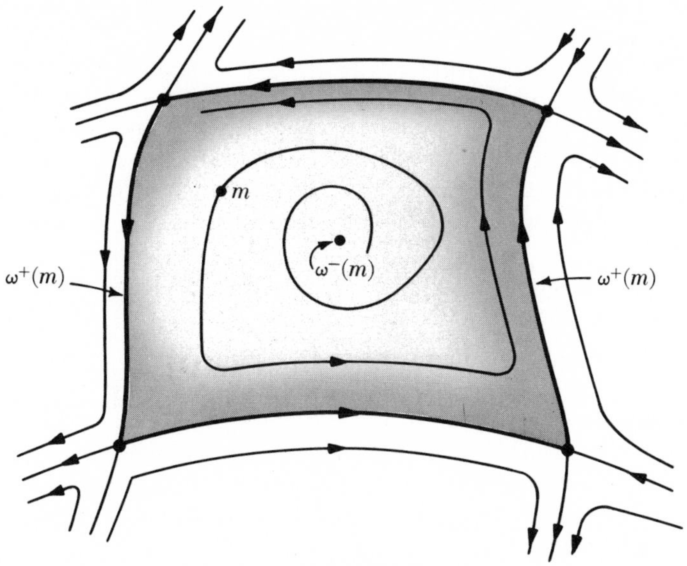

Figure 24-1

Proof. Suppose S is not connected. Then the components of S are closed, nonempty, and invariant, which contradicts minimality of S. If S and T are minimal sets and $S \cap T \neq \phi$, then $S \cap T$ is closed, nonempty, and invariant. By minimality, $S \cap T = S = T$. ∎

24.5. Proposition. *Let X be a vectorfield on a compact manifold M. Then $\omega^\sigma(m)$ is closed, nonempty, connected, and invariant ($\sigma = +$ or $\sigma = -$).*

Proof. It is clear that $\omega^\sigma(m)$ is closed. To show they are invariant, let $m_0 \in \omega^\sigma(m)$ and $m_t = F_t(m_0)$. Suppose $F_{t_j}(m) \to m_0$. Then $F_{t_j+t}(m) \to m_t$. Thus $m_t \in \omega^\sigma(m)$. Connectedness of $\omega^\sigma(m)$ follows at once from a basic lemma on compact Hausdorff spaces (A7.6) (that is, a nested sequence of closed connected sets has connected intersection). ∎

24.6. Proposition. *Suppose X is a vectorfield on a manifold M. If $\gamma \subset M$ is a critical element of X, then γ is a minimal set. Moreover, if M is compact, then $\omega^\sigma(m)$ contains a minimal set ($\sigma = +, -, \pm$).*

Proof. Obviously $\{m\}$ is minimal if m is a critical point. If γ is a closed orbit, then by 23.4 it is closed, invariant, and nonempty. In addition, γ is minimal, for if $m_1, m_2 \in \gamma$ there is a t so $F_t(m_1) = m_2$. Also if M is compact, $\omega^\sigma(m)$ is nonempty, closed, and invariant by 24.5, hence contains a minimal set. ∎

The main theorem on minimal sets for the two-dimensional case is the following.

24.7. Theorem (A. Schwartz). *Suppose M is a compact, two-dimensional manifold and $X \in \mathscr{X}(M)$. Let A be a minimal set of X*

which is nowhere dense. Then $A \in \Gamma_X$; that is, A is a critical point or a closed orbit.

For a proof see A. Schwartz [1] or Hartman [1, p. 185].

24.8. Corollary. *Let M be a compact, connected, two-dimensional manifold, $X \in \mathscr{X}(M)$ and A a minimal set of X. Then either*

(i) A is a critical point;

(ii) A is a closed orbit;

(iii) $A = M$ and $M = T^2 = S^1 \times S^1$.

Proof. Suppose (*i*) and (*ii*) do not hold. Then, by 24.7, $A^0 \neq \phi$, as A is closed. Also, A^0 is invariant, as F_t is a diffeomorphism. Thus, $bd(A)$ is closed and invariant. By minimality, $bd(A) = \phi$. Hence A is both open and closed and $A = M$ (§A7). As A is minimal, it contains no critical points or closed orbits (24.6) and, by a theorem of Kneser (§23), $M = T^2$. ∎

24.9. Definition. *Let X be a complete vectorfield on a manifold M and γ a closed orbit of X. An orbit $F_t(m_0)$ is said to* **wind toward** *γ iff for any transversal S to X at $m \in \gamma$, there is a t_0 so $F_{t_0}(m_0) \in S$ and successive applications of the Poincaré map yield a sequence of points that converges to m.*

To prove that an orbit winds toward a closed orbit it is sufficient to use any Poincaré map, by 23.7 (ii).

24.10. Theorem (Poincaré–Bendixon–Schwartz). *Let M be a compact, connected, orientable two manifold and $X \in \mathscr{X}(M)$. For $m \in M$ suppose $\omega^+(m)$ contains no critical points. Then either*

(i) $\omega^+(m) = M = T^2$; or

(ii) $\omega^+(m) = \gamma$ is a closed orbit and $F_t(m)$ winds toward γ.

The idea of the proof is as follows (see Schwartz [1]). By 24.6 $\omega^+(m)$ contains a minimal set, so by 24.8, either $\omega^+(m) = M = T^2$ or $\omega^+(m)$ contains a closed orbit. Then by a geometric argument special to the two-dimensional case, $F_t(m)$ winds toward γ, so in fact $\omega^+(m) = \gamma$.

For further details on Poincaré–Bendixon theory see Hartman [1].

Exercises

24A. Prove the converse in 24.2.

24B. Construct an example of a vectorfield on $\mathbf{R}^2$ in which only one point is contained in a minimal set, and another in which every limit set is empty.

24C. Discuss 24.7 in the case M is not orientable.

24D. Prove that for $X \in \mathscr{X}(M)$, $\Gamma_X \subset \Omega_X$ (23.3 and 24.1).

§25. GENERIC PROPERTIES

In this section we give a survey of the known generic properties of ordinary differential equations. Unfortunately none of these is directly relevant to the Hamiltonian case, but the insights and geometric methods are very useful in understanding mechanical systems. Undoubtedly the theory of generic Hamiltonian systems will develop along similar lines in the future, and we offer some (possibly very naive) conjectures in this direction in the next chapter.

One of the main ingredients of the generic qualitative theory is the location of critical elements in the phase portrait and the asymptotic behavior of nearby orbits. The latter is revealed by linear approximation of the flow, characterized by the *characteristic exponents* or *multipliers* of the critical element.

Recall that if $v \in T_mM$, then $T_v(TM)$ has a distinguished subspace $T_v(T_mM)$, the vertical tangent space, which can be identified naturally with T_mM itself. If v is in the zero section, $\mathbf{0} \subset TM$, then there is also a horizontal subspace $T_v\mathbf{0} \subset T_v(TM)$ that is complementary to $T_v(T_mM)$ and can also be naturally identified with T_mM, as $\mathbf{0} \approx M$. Thus we write $T_{0_m}(TM) = T_{0_m}\mathbf{0} \oplus T_{0_m}(T_mM) \approx T_mM \oplus T_mM$, and let $v_m\colon T_{0_m}(TM) \to T_mM$ denote the projection on the second (vertical) factor.

25.1. Definition. *If m is a critical point of $X \in \mathscr{X}(M)$, let $X'(m) = v_m \circ T_mX \in L(T_mM, T_mM)$. The* **characteristic exponents** *of X at m are the eigenvalues of $X'(m)$. The* **characteristic multipliers** *of X at m are the exponentials of the characteristic exponents.*

In local components, if $X(m) = (X^1(m), \ldots, X^n(m))$, then $X'(m)$ is the Jacobian matrix $A = (\partial X^i/\partial m^j)$ and the characteristic exponents are the eigenvalues of this matrix. As $X(m) = 0$, the Jacobian matrix defines a linear approximation to X near m, and the flow e^{tA}, which approximates the flow of X (for small t), is characterized by the characteristic exponents (via the real canonical form of A; see Coddington–Levinson [1, Chapter 15] for details).

If γ is a closed orbit of $X \in \mathscr{X}(M)$ and $m \in \gamma$, the behavior of nearby orbits is given by a Poincaré map Θ on a local transversal section S at m (23.6). Clearly $T_m\Theta \in L(T_mS, T_mS)$ is a linear approximation to Θ at m. By uniqueness of Θ up to local conjugacy (23.7 (ii)), $T_{m'}\Theta'$ is similar to $T_m\Theta$, for any other Poincaré map Θ' on a local transversal section at $m' \in \gamma$. Therefore the eigenvalues of $T_m\Theta$ are independent of $m \in \gamma$ and the particular section S at m.

25.2. Definition. *If γ is a closed orbit of $X \in \mathscr{X}(M)$, the* **characteristic multipliers** *of X at γ are the eigenvalues of $T_m\Theta$, for any Poincaré map Θ at any $m \in \gamma$.*

Another linear approximation to the flow near γ is given by $T_mF_\tau \in L(T_mM, T_mM)$ if $m \in \gamma$ and τ is the period of γ (23.5). Note that $F_\tau^*(X(m)) = X(m)$, so T_mF_τ always has an eigenvalue 1 corresponding to the eigenvector $X(m)$. The $(n - 1)$ remaining eigenvalues (if $dim(m) = n$) are in fact the characteristic multipliers of X at γ.

25.3. Proposition. *If γ is a closed orbit of $X \in \mathscr{X}(M)$ of period τ and c_γ is the set of characteristic multipliers of X at γ, then $c_\gamma \cup \{1\}$ is the set of eigenvalues of T_mF_τ, for any $m \in \gamma$.*

The proof follows easily from the construction of Θ in the proof of 23.7 (i). Alternatively, see Hartman [1, p. 253].

We now define the first of several properties that have recently been proven to be generic.

25.4. *Definition.* *If $X \in \mathscr{X}(M)$ and γ is a critical element of X, γ is an* **elementary critical element** *iff none of the characteristic multipliers of X at γ has modulus one. A vectorfield $X \in \mathscr{X}(M)$ has* **property (G2)** *iff every critical element is elementary.*

The property (G2) is important because the local qualitative behavior near an elementary critical element is especially simple. Also, elementary critical elements are isolated (see Abraham–Robbin [1, Chapter V]).

25.5. *Definition.* *If $X \in \mathscr{X}(M)$ and $A \subset M$ is a closed set, let*

$$S^\sigma(A) = \{m \in M | \omega^\sigma(m) = A\}$$

for $\sigma = +, -,$ or $\pm$, and $\omega^\sigma(m)$ is the ω^σ limit set of m (24.1). If γ is an elementary critical element, $S^+(\gamma)$ is called the **stable manifold** *of γ, and $S^-(\gamma)$ the* **unstable manifold** *of γ.*

Note that $S^+(\gamma)$ is the union of orbits that wind toward γ (with increasing time), and $S^-(\gamma)$ the union of orbits that wind away from γ (wind toward γ with decreasing time).

The following theorem, which is basic to the qualitative behavior near a critical element, has a long history, going back to Poincaré. We give here a generalized form due to Al Kelley. For the proof, see his appendix in Abraham–Robbin [1].

25.6. *Theorem (Local center-stable manifolds).* *If $\gamma \subset M$ is a critical element of $X \in \mathscr{X}(M)$, there exist submanifolds S^+, CS^+, C, CS^-, S^- of M such that*

(i) Each is invariant under X (15.11) and contains γ;

(ii) For $m \in \gamma$, $T_m(S^+)$ [resp. $T_m(CS^+)$, $T_m(C)$, $T_m(CS^-)$, $T(S^-)$] is the sum of the eigenspace in T_mM of characteristic multipliers of modulus <1 [resp. ≤ 1, $=1$, ≥ 1, >1], and the subspace $T_m\gamma$;

(iii) If $m \in S^\sigma$, then $\omega^\sigma(m) = \gamma$ ($\sigma = +$ or $-$);

(iv) S^+ and S^- are locally unique.

Note that the configuration of these manifolds is slightly different in the two cases covered: $\gamma = \{m\}$, a critical point, in which case $T_m\gamma = \{0\}$, or γ is a closed orbit, in which case $T_m\gamma$ is the subspace generated by $X(m)$. The two cases are illustrated in $\mathbf{R}^3$ in Figure 25-1. The theorem says, in addition, that if γ is elementary, then the nearby orbits behave qualitatively like the linear case. For details, see Coddington–Levinson [1, Chapter 13] and Coppel [1].

These manifolds are called respectively the *local stable* (S^+), *center-stable* (CS^+), *center* (C), *center-unstable* (CS^-), and *unstable* (S^-) *manifold of γ*.

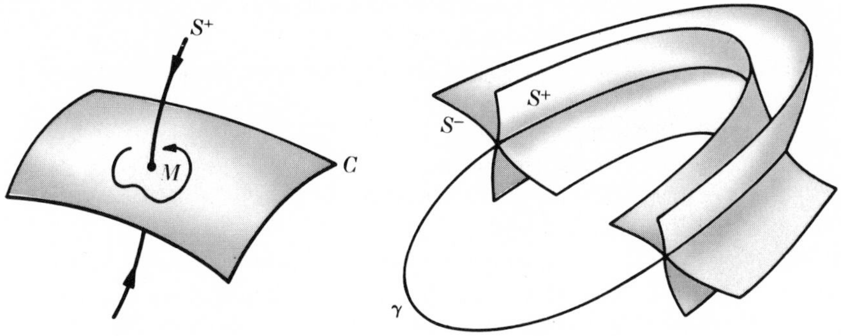

critical point with

$|\lambda_1| < 1,\ |\lambda_2| = |\lambda_3| = 1$

closed orbit with

$|\lambda_1| < 1,\ |\lambda_2| > 1$

Figure 25-1

In the case of an elementary critical element γ, we have only the locally unique manifolds $S^\sigma(\gamma)$, ($\sigma = +$ or $-$). These are easily extended to globally unique manifolds by expanding the local manifolds by means of the integral of X.

25.7. *Definition.* *A subset $S \subset M$ is an* **immersed submanifold** *iff it is the image of a mapping $f: V \to M$ that is injective and locally a diffeomorphism onto a submanifold of M.*

25.8. Corollary (Global stable manifold theorem of Smale). *If γ is an elementary critical element of $X \in \mathscr{X}(M)$, then $S^+(\gamma)$ and $S^-(\gamma)$ are immersed submanifolds. Also, $\gamma \subset S^+(\gamma) \cap S^-(\gamma)$, and for $m \in \gamma$, $T_m S^+(\gamma)$ and $T_m S^-(\gamma)$ generate $T_m M$. If n_+ is the number of characteristic multipliers of γ of modulus greater than one, and n_- the number of modulus less than one, then the dimension of $S^\sigma(\gamma)$ is $n_{-\sigma}$ (if γ is a critical point) or $n_{-\sigma} + 1$ (if γ is a closed orbit).*

Thus, for example, in the case of an elementary critical point on a two-dimensional manifold there are three possible local phase portraits (see Figure 25-2). For the proof, see Abraham–Robbin [1, Chapter VI].

The stable and unstable manifolds of all critical elements are special fixtures of the phase portrait that are second in importance only to the critical elements, as they are the higher-dimensional analogues of the separatrices of the two-dimensional case. Another generic property of vectorfields concerns the position of the intersections of these features.

25.9. *Definition.* *A vectorfield $X \in \mathscr{X}(M)$ has* **property (G3)** *iff X has property* (G2) *and if $m \in S^+(\gamma) \cap S^-(\delta)$ for any critical elements γ and δ, then $T_m S^+(\gamma)$ and $T_m S^-(\delta)$ generate $T_m M$.*

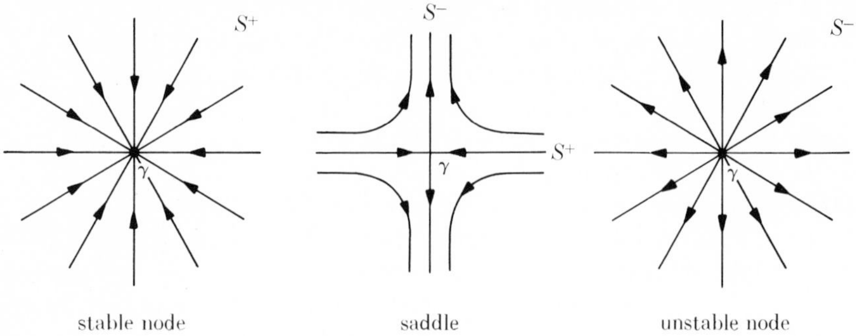

Figure 25-2

We wish next to express the fact that these properties are actually *generic*, and we begin by making this word precise. The main requirement is a topology on $\mathscr{X}(M)$. As the definition of the topology is somewhat involved, we give here just an outline. For details, see Abraham–Robbin [1, Chapter II].

If $U \subset \mathbf{E}$ is an open subset of a vector space and $\mathbf{F}$ is a vector space, we may put on the vector space $\mathscr{B}^r(U, \mathbf{F})$ of C^r mappings f from U to $\mathbf{F}$ ($r < \infty$) with $D^k f\colon U \to L_s^k(\mathbf{E}, \mathbf{F})$ bounded ($k = 0, \ldots, r$; $D^0 f = f$) a structure of Banach space by defining

$$\|f\|_r = \sup\left\{\sum_{k=0}^{r} \|D^k f(u)\| : u \in U\right\}$$

(see Abraham–Robbin [1, Chapter II]). Let $\mathscr{X}^r(M)$ be the set of C^r vectorfields on M, that is, mappings $X\colon M \to TM$ of class C^r such that $\tau_M \circ X$ is the identity. If (U, φ) is a chart on M, $\varphi(U) = U' \subset \mathbf{E}$, $(TU, T\varphi)$ is a natural chart on TM, and for $X \in \mathscr{B}^r(M)$ we have a local representative $X_\varphi \in C^\infty(U', \mathbf{E})$. If $(U')^c$ is contained in the image of a larger chart and is bounded in $\mathbf{E}$, then $X_\varphi \in \mathscr{B}^r(U'\mathbf{E})$. Thus there exists an atlas $\mathscr{A} = \{(U_i, \varphi_i)\}$ on M such that $X_{\varphi_i} \in \mathscr{B}^r(U'_i, \mathbf{E}_i)$ for every i, and the $\mathscr{A}^r$ *uniform topology* on $\mathscr{X}(M)$ is the smallest topology such that the mapping $X \rightsquigarrow X_{\varphi_i}$ is continuous for all i. If M is compact, it may be shown that this topology is independent of the atlas $\mathscr{A}$; it is then called the C^r *topology*. If M is not compact, we may take the union of $\mathscr{A}^r$ topologies for all admissible atlases $\mathscr{A}$ on M having the boundedness property above, which is the *Whitney* C^r *topology* on $\mathscr{X}^r(M)$.

We may now say precisely what we mean by a generic property of vectorfields.

25.10. Definition. *The space of C^r vectorfields on M with the Whitney C^r topology is denoted by $\mathscr{X}^r(M)$. A* **property of vectorfields** *in $\mathscr{X}^r(M)$ is a proposition $P(X)$ with a variable $X \in \mathscr{X}^r(M)$. A property*

$P(X)$ in $\mathscr{X}^r(M)$ is **generic** *iff the subspace $\{X \in \mathscr{X}^r(M) | P(X)\} \subset \mathscr{X}^r(M)$ contains a residual set* (§A11). *A property $P(X)$ in $\mathscr{X}(M)$ is* ***C^r generic*** *iff $\{X \in \mathscr{X}(M) | P(X)\}$ is the intersection of $\mathscr{X}(M)$ with a subspace of $\mathscr{X}^r(M)$ containing a residual set.*

Note that a property generic in $\mathscr{X}^r(M)$ is C^r generic in $\mathscr{X}(M)$ with the relative Whitney C^r topology. For it can be shown that the C^∞ vectorfields $\mathscr{X}(M) \subset \mathscr{X}^r(M)$ contain a residual set. Also, $\mathscr{X}^r(M)$ is a Banach space if M is compact, and is thus a Baire space (§A11). For noncompact M, $\mathscr{X}^r(M)$ is still a Baire space with the Whitney topology (see Morlet [1]). Thus in either case, residual sets are dense, so if $P(X)$ is a generic property, almost every vectorfield X has $P(X)$, or every vectorfield can be approximated as closely as we wish by one with the generic property.

We may now state very easily one of the main results of the qualitative theory.

25.11. Theorem (Kupka–Smale). *If M is compact and $r \geq 1$, the property* (G3) *on $\mathscr{X}(M)$ is C^r generic.*

This theorem was proved independently by Kupka [2] and Smale [4] (1963) in the case of a compact manifold M. The proof consists of a long sequence of careful approximations which, when written out in full detail, fill thirty pages (Abraham–Robbin [1]). The theorem has recently been extended to the noncompact case by Peixoto [3].

Two additional properties have recently been shown to be C^1 generic, called properties (G4) and (G5).

25.12. Definition. *If $X \in \mathscr{X}(M)$ with integral $F: \mathscr{D}_X \subset M \times$* **R** *$\to M$ and $m \in M$, then m is a* **nonwandering point** *of X iff $(m, t) \in \mathscr{D}_X$ for all $t > 0$, and for all neighborhoods U of $m \in M$ and all $t_0 \geq 0$ there is a $t > t_0$ such that $U \cap F(U \times \{t\})$ is nonempty. Let N_X denote the set of all nonwandering points of $X \in \mathscr{X}(M)$.*

25.13. Proposition. *If M is compact, and $X \in \mathscr{X}(M)$, then $N_X \subset M$ is compact, invariant, and $\Gamma_X^c \subset (\Omega_X^\pm)^c \subset N_X$* (23.3, 24.1).

The proof is left to the reader.

25.14. Definition. *A vectorfield $X \in \mathscr{X}(M)$ has* **property (G4)** *iff $N_X = \Gamma_X^c$.*

Note that (G4) implies $\Omega_X^\pm \subset \Gamma_X^c$ (see Exercise 25C).

25.15. Theorem (Pugh). *If M is compact, then* (G4) *is C^1 generic.*

The proof is a fairly easy corollary of Pugh's closing lemma (Pugh [2]). The genericity of (G5) also follows from this very difficult lemma.

25.16. Definition. *A* **regular first integral** *of a vectorfield $X \in \mathscr{X}(M)$ is a function $f: M \to$* **R** *of class C^r, where r is the dimension of M, such that f is not constant on any open subset of M and $\mathbf{L}_X f = 0$. A vectorfield $X \in \mathscr{X}(M)$ has* **property (G5)** *iff X has no regular first integral.*

25.17. Theorem (Thom). *If M is compact, then* (G5) *is* C^1 *generic.*

For a proof, see Peixoto [1]. It is not unreasonable to hope that (G4) and (G5) may be proved to be C^r generic for $r > 1$ in the future. Also, compactness may be unnecessary in the Pugh theorem (25.15), and in the Thom theorem if we add to 25.16 the condition that f be *proper*: inverse images of closed intervals are compact.

It is this theorem (25.17) which suggests that, generically, a Hamiltonian vectorfield X_H has no regular first integral other than H itself (see the remark preceding 16.28).

Exercises

25A. Let $X \in \mathscr{X}(M)$, $\varphi: M \to N$ be a diffeomorphism and $Y = \varphi^* X$. Then

(i) $m \in M$ is a critical point of X iff $\varphi(m)$ is a critical point of Y and the characteristic multipliers are the same for each.

(ii) $\gamma \subset M$ is a closed orbit of X iff $\varphi(\gamma)$ is a closed orbit of Y and the characteristic multipliers are the same.

25B. Prove 25.3.

25C. Prove that for $X \in \mathscr{X}(M)$, $\Gamma_X \subset \Omega_X^{\pm} \subset N_X$ (see Exercise 24D).

25D. Prove 25.13.

25E. Find an example of a vectorfield X on $\mathbf{R}^2$ and a point $m \in \mathbf{R}^2$ such that $m \in N_X$ (25.12) and $m \notin \Omega_X^{\pm}$ (24.1).

§26. STABILITY OF ORBITS

There are many different notions of stability of an orbit of a vectorfield. In this section we give a unified definition of several of these in terms of continuity of set valued mappings. This method is very convenient from the point of view of stability of models discussed in the Introduction and Conclusion, and is essential for the recent results.

Throughout this section we suppose that for a manifold M we have chosen a metric ρ, and let $\bar{\rho}$ denote the Hausdorff pseudometric on 2^M induced by ρ (see §A8).

As the topology on the subset of compact subsets in 2^M induced in this way is independent of ρ, the definitions that follow are indifferent to the choice of ρ, if M is compact.

26.1. Notation. *Let M be a manifold and X a vectorfield on M, with integral $F: \mathscr{D}_X \subset M \times \mathbf{R} \to M$* (7.10). *For $(m, t) \in \mathscr{D}_X$ let $m_t = F(m, t)$. Then for each $m \in M$, let*

$$m_+ = \cup\{m_t|(m, t) \in \mathscr{D}_X, t \geq 0\}$$

$$m_- = \cup\{m_t|(m, t) \in \mathscr{D}_X, t \leq 0\}$$

$$m_\pm = m_+ \cup m_-$$

These will be denoted m_σ, *where* σ *can be* $+$, $-$, *or* $\pm$.

In a similar way, if $\Theta: U \subset M \to M$ *is a diffeomorphism onto* $\Theta(U)$ *let* $\mathscr{D}_\Theta \subset U \times \mathbf{Z}$ *be the set of points* (u, n) *such that* $\Theta^n(u)$ *is defined, where* $\Theta^n(u) = \Theta \circ \cdots \circ \Theta(u)$ *(n factors) for* $n > 0$, Θ^0 *the identity, and* $\Theta^n = (\Theta^{-1})^{-n}$ *if* $n < 0$. *Let* $F_\Theta: \mathscr{D}_\Theta \to M: (u, n) \rightsquigarrow \Theta^n(u)$, *and* $u_n = F_\Theta(u, n)$ *for* $(u, n) \in \mathscr{D}_\Theta$. *Then define* u_σ *as above, and* $\omega^\sigma(u)$ *analogous to 24.1.*

In either case above, we define

$$S^\sigma(m) = \{m' \in M|\omega^\sigma(m') \subset m_\sigma^c\}$$

and

$$A^\sigma(m) = \{m' \in M|m' \text{ is } \sigma \text{ complete and } \lim_{t \to \sigma\infty} \rho(m_t, m'_t) = 0\}$$

if m is σ *complete, and* $A^\sigma(m) = \{m\}$ *otherwise.*

We also let 2_1^M *denote* 2^M *(the set of all subsets of M) with the Hausdorff topology, and* 2_0^M *denote* 2^M *with the discrete topology* (A1.8).

Then eighteen notions of stability of orbits may be defined as follows.

26.2. *Definition.* *Let M be a manifold with* $X \in \mathscr{X}(M)$, *or* $\Theta: U \subset M \to M$ *a diffeomorphism onto* $\Theta(U)$. *Then* $m \in M$ *is called* α^σ- **stable with respect to** X, *or* Θ, *where* $\alpha = o$, a, *or* L *and* $\sigma = +, -,$ *or* $\pm$, *iff*

(*i*) $\alpha = o$ **(orbital stability of Birkhoff)**
$\sigma: M \to 2_1^M; m' \rightsquigarrow m'_\sigma$ *is continuous at m;*

(*ii*) $\alpha = a$ **(asymptotic stability of Poisson)**
$S^\sigma: M \to 2_0^M; m' \rightsquigarrow S^\sigma(m')$ *is continuous at m;*

(*iii*) $\alpha = L$ **(Liapounov stability)**
$A^\sigma: M \to 2_0^M; m' \rightsquigarrow A^\sigma(m')$ *is continuous at m.*

If m is not α^σ*-stable with respect to X (or* Θ*) we say m is* α^σ-**unstable** *with respect to X (or* Θ*).*

Perhaps more familiar is the following equivalent form.

26.3. *Proposition.* *Let M be a manifold,* $X \in \mathscr{X}(M)$ *(or* $\Theta: U \subset M \to M$ *a diffeomorphism onto* $\Theta(U)$*) and* $m \in M$ *be* σ *complete. Then m is* α^σ*-stable iff for every* $\varepsilon > 0$ *there is a* $\delta > 0$ *so that* $\rho(m', m) < \delta$ *implies*

(*i*) $\alpha = o$; $\bar{\rho}(m_\sigma, m'_\sigma) < \varepsilon$ *(*$\bar{\rho}$ *is the Hausdorff metric);*

(*ii*) $\alpha = a$; $\lim_{t \to \sigma\infty} \rho(m_\sigma, m'_t) = 0$;

(*iii*) $\alpha = L$; $\lim_{t \to \sigma\infty} \rho(m_t, m'_t) = 0$.

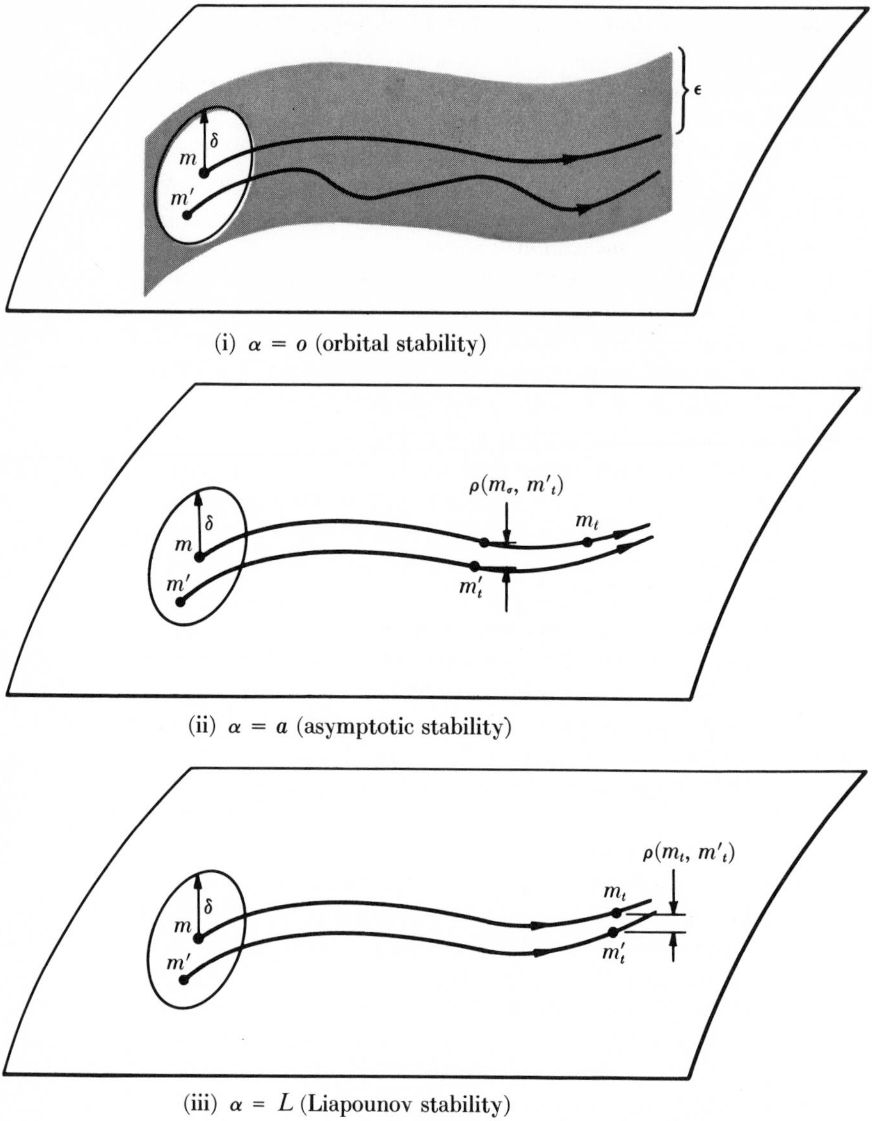

Figure 26-1

This follows easily from the definitions above and the definition of continuity (§A3). For other forms of these definitions and additional types of stability of orbits, see Coppel [1]. The three cases $\alpha = o, a, L$ for a vectorfield and $\sigma = t$ are illustrated in Figure 26-1.

26.4. Proposition. *Under the conditions of 26.3, if m is L^σ-stable, then m is a^σ-stable. If m is a^σ-stable, then m is o^σ-stable.*

The first part is clear and the second follows easily by continuity of the flow of X (or Θ).

These conditions simplify if m is a critical point, and in this case m is L^σ-stable iff m is a^σ-stable, but of course o^σ-stable remains weaker.

26.5. Proposition. *Let X be a vectorfield on a manifold M and γ a closed orbit of X. For $m, m' \in \gamma$, m is α^σ-stable iff m' is α^σ-stable (with respect to X) iff m is α^σ-stable with respect to any Poincaré map on a transversal section.*

The first part follows easily from the group property of the flow in the cases $\sigma = L$, $\alpha = a$ and continuity in the case $\alpha = o$. (See the discussion of closed orbits in §23.) The second part will be left to the reader.

26.6. Definition. *If γ is a closed orbit of $X \in \mathscr{X}(M)$, then γ is α^σ-***stable** *iff m is α^σ-stable for some $m \in \gamma$.*

A deeper stability theorem is the following.

26.7. Theorem (Pliss–Kelley). *Let X be a vectorfield on a manifold M and $\sigma = +$ or $-$. Let $\gamma \subset M$ be a critical element of X, and S^+, S^-, C the stable, unstable, and center manifolds of γ respectively (23.6). Then γ is α^σ-stable with respect to X on C iff m is α^σ-stable with respect to X on CS^σ.*

For the proof, see Appendix B by A. Kelley.

For example, if C and S^+ only occur, and o^+-stability on C is established, then it holds in a neighborhood of $m \in M$.

From the local center-stable manifold theorem (25.6), however, we obtain at once a condition for instability.

26.8. Proposition. *Let $X \in \mathscr{X}(M)$ and γ be a critical element of X. Then if γ has a characteristic multiplier of modulus greater than one, γ is α^+-unstable.*

A different type of stability has been introduced recently by Pugh.

26.9. Definition. *A vectorfield $X \in \mathscr{X}(M)$ is* **critically stable**, *or has* **property (G6)**, *iff the mapping $\Gamma^c: \mathscr{X}(M) \to 2_1^M: X \rightsquigarrow (\Gamma_X)^c$ is continuous at X.*

26.10. Theorem (Pugh). *If M is compact, then property* (G6) *is C^1 generic in $\mathscr{X}(M)$.*

This is in fact a fairly easy corollary of the Kupka–Smale (G3) density theorem (25.11). This was proved very ingeniously by Pugh [2], using properties of set valued mappings with the Hausdorff metric, and used by him with the closing lemma to prove the (G4) density theorem (25.15).

Exercises

26A. Prove 26.3, 26.4, and 26.5.

26B. Find a vectorfield on $\mathbf{R}^2$ and $m \in \mathbf{R}^2$ that is o^+-stable using the standard metric, but that is o^+-unstable using some other equivalent metric.

§27. STRUCTURAL STABILITY

Structural stability was an earlier candidate for a generic property of vectorfields. Although it turned out to be generic only in the two-dimensional case, it may be of considerable importance in the applications (see Conclusion). Some weaker notion of stability may be found to be generic eventually. In any case, we outline now some of the results of this program, initiated by Andronov and Pontriagin [1] in 1937.

27.1. Definition. *Let X be a vectorfield on M. Then X is* **C^r structurally stable** *iff there is a neighborhood $\mathcal{O}$ of $X \in \mathcal{X}(M)$ in the Whitney C^r topology, such that $Y \in \mathcal{O}$ implies X and Y have equivalent phase portraits* (23.2). *The set of C^r structurally stable vectorfields on M is denoted by $\Sigma^r(M)$.*

The first result in this program was optimistic, as Peixoto showed in 1959 [1], that structural stability was generic on the two-dimensional disk.

27.2. Definition. *A vectorfield $X \in \mathcal{X}(M)$ is said to be a* **Morse–Smale system** *iff it has properties* (G3), (G4), *and* (F)*: It has a finite number of closed orbits.* (See 25.4, 25.9, *and* 25.14.)

Actually, from (G3), the number of critical points is finite, as elementary critical points are isolated; so $\Gamma_X = \Gamma_X^c$ if (G_2) and (F), so for a Morse–Smale system (G4) is equivalent to $\Omega_X \subset \Gamma_X$ (M compact).

For the two-dimensional case note that (G3) is equivalent to: No orbit connects two saddle points.

27.3. Theorem (Peixoto). *If M is compact, two-dimensional and $1 \leq r < \infty$, then*

(*i*) *$X \in \Sigma^r(M)$ iff X is a Morse–Smale system;*

(*ii*) *Σ^r is an open, dense subset of $\mathcal{X}(M)$ in the C^r topology.*

For the proof see Peixoto [2].

For higher dimensions, the foregoing approach fails because of the following results.

27.4. Theorem (Smale [1]). *For every $n > 2$, there exists a compact n manifold M, a vectorfield X_0 on M, and an open neighborhood U of $X_0 \in \mathcal{X}(M)$ in the C^1 topology, such that every $X \in U$ has property* (G4) *but not property* (F).

27.5. Theorem (Anosov [1]). *For each $n > 2$, there is a compact n manifold M and $X \in \mathcal{X}(M)$ such that X is C^1 structurally stable but does not have property (F).*

27.6. Theorem (Smale [2]). *There is a manifold of dimension* 4 *such that in the C^1 topology, Σ^1 is not dense in $\mathcal{X}^1(M)$.*

Concerning the relations between properties $G\alpha$ and structural stability there are the following results.

27.7. Theorem. *Let M be a compact manifold. If $X \in \mathcal{X}(M)$ is C^1 structurally stable, then X has*

(*i*) *Property* (G2) (*Markus* [2]);
(*ii*) *Property* (G4) (*Pugh* [1, 2]);
(*iii*) *Property* (G5) (*Thom, see Peixoto* [3]).

Exercises

27A. Prove that in the two dimensional case, property (G3) is equivalent to: No orbit connects two saddle points.

27B. Characterize structural stability (27.1) in terms of continuity of a mapping (see 26.2).

Notes

For the local qualitative theory, Coddington–Levinson [1] and Hartmann [1] are the standard references. For the global theory occupying most of this chapter, there is no reference yet except for the original papers.

Peixoto [3] gives a similar survey, while Nemitskii [1] reviews other aspects of recent qualitative theory. Philosophical remarks on structural stability are found in Thom [1], and examples in Kupka [1], and in van Karman [1].

Another definition of structural stability is also in common use. For it and a proof of 27.7 (iii) with that definition as hypothesis, see Arraut [1]. Prototype Morse–Smale systems were introduced by Reeb [5], in 1952.

For diffeomorphisms there is an analogous and related qualitative theory; see Smale [4, 5].

I am grateful to Mauricio Peixoto for his comments on this chapter, and to Stephen Smale, Charles Pugh, and René Thom for helpful conversations.

CHAPTER VI

QUALITATIVE THEORY OF HAMILTONIAN SYSTEMS

In this chapter we explain why the main results of the general qualitative theory of the last chapter do not apply to the Hamiltonian case; outline what little is known for this case; and tell a science fiction story about the future of the subject. The main positive results, the LIAPOUNOV–KELLEY and KOLMOGOROV–ARNOLD–MOSER Subcenter Theorems, will be applied in the next chapter.

§28. CRITICAL ELEMENTS

In this section we consider the characteristic multipliers for critical elements of Hamiltonian vectorfields and explain why such a critical element cannot be expected to be elementary in general.

First we take up the case of a critical point. Suppose (M, ω) is a symplectic manifold, $H \in \mathscr{F}(M)$, and X_H is the Hamiltonian vectorfield with Hamiltonian H. Recall that $m \in M$ is a critical point of X_H iff $X_H(m) = 0$ (23.3), and obviously this occurs iff $dH(m) = 0$, or m is a critical point of H. The characteristic exponents of X_H at m are defined as the eigenvalues of the linear mapping $X'_H(m) \in L(T_mM, T_mM)$ (25.1), and T_mM is symplectic with the form $\omega(m)$ (13.8). The main restriction on the characteristic exponents in the Hamiltonian case results from the fact that $X'_H(m)$ is infinitesimally symplectic (13.13).

28.1. Proposition. *Let (M, ω) be a symplectic manifold $H \in \mathscr{F}(M)$ and $m \in M$ a critical point of X_H. Then $X'_H(m) \in sp(T_mM, \omega(m))$.*

Proof. Let (U, φ) be a symplectic chart at m, so that in local representation, ω is a constant section. Let $F: V \times (-a, a) \to U$ be a flow box at $0 = \varphi(m)$ of the local representative $X_{H,\varphi} = X_{H\circ\varphi}$. Then $a = X'_{H\circ\varphi}(0)$ is the tangent vector at $t = 0$ of the curve $A(t) = DF_t(0_t)$, where $0_t = F(0, t)$. But F_t is symplectic (16.4), so $A(t)$ is a curve in $Sp(\mathbf{R}^n, \omega_0)$, and therefore $X'_{H\circ\varphi}(0) \in sp(\mathbf{R}^n, \omega_0)$ (13.13). It then follows that $X'_H(m) = (T_m\varphi)^{-1} \circ X'_{H\circ\varphi} \circ T_m\varphi$ is infinitesimally symplectic. ∎

The restriction on the characteristic exponents now follows at once from the infinitesimally symplectic eigenvalue theorem (13.17).

28.2. Corollary. *The characteristic exponents of X_H at a critical point $m \in M$ occur in pairs $(\lambda, -\lambda)$ of the same multiplicity. Thus if λ is a characteristic exponent, so are $\bar{\lambda}, -\lambda, -\bar{\lambda}$, all of these* *having the same multiplicity. The exponent zero always has even multiplicity.*

We see now why a Hamiltonian critical point may not be elementary in general. For m is elementary iff there are no characteristic exponents on the imaginary axis (25.4). However, if there are exponents $\pm i\beta$ of multiplicity one, small perturbations in H, thus X_H and $X'_H(m)$, perturb the exponents only slightly, and the exponents $\pm i\beta$ are trapped on the imaginary axis. Moreover, it follows that the stable and unstable manifolds of the critical point $m \in M$ have the same dimension, and the center manifold is even dimensional (25.6). The center manifold cannot in general be removed by a small perturbation of H alone, although its dimension may be reduced by four if there is a purely imaginary exponent of multiplicity two.

In the remainder of the section we consider analogously the case of a closed orbit $\gamma \subset M$ of the Hamiltonian vectorfield X_H (23.3). The characteristic multipliers of X_H at γ (25.2) are the eigenvalues of the tangent $T_m\Theta$, where $m \in \gamma$, and Θ is a Poincaré map on a local transversal section (23.6). Alternatively, the characteristic multipliers are the eigenvalues (omitting one $+1$) of the tangent T_mF_τ, where $m \in \gamma$, F is a flow box around γ, and τ is the period of γ (23.5). As F_τ is a symplectic diffeomorphism and $F_\tau(m) = m$, we get the following restriction on the characteristic multipliers.

28.3. Proposition. *The characteristic multipliers of X_H at a closed orbit $\gamma \subset M$ occur in pairs $(\gamma, \bar{\lambda})$ of the same multiplicity. Thus if λ is a characteristic multiplier, so are $\bar{\lambda}, \lambda^{-1}, \bar{\lambda}^{-1}$, all having the same multiplicity. The multiplier one always occurs with odd multiplicity at least one.*

This is an immediate consequence of the symplectic eigenvalue theorem (13.16). We see first that γ can never be elementary, as there is always at least one multiplier equal to one, and thus of modulus one (25.4). Shortly we will discuss other reasons, but now we consider this phenomenon. The multiplier one corresponds to an eigenspace on which the Poincaré map is the identity in first approximation, suggesting the possibility of the existence of an entire cylinder of closed orbits $\{\gamma_s\}$ with a parameter s, in which γ is an element, $\gamma = \gamma_0$ say.

The following proposition gives some additional information about the Poincaré map (23.6) in the Hamiltonian case. Note that if γ is a closed orbit of X_H, then we may assume γ lies in some regular energy surface Σ_e, even though e need not be a regular value of H (16.22).

28.4. Proposition. *Let (M, ω) be a symplectic manifold, $H \in F(M)$ and γ a closed orbit of X_H lying in a regular energy surface Σ_e. Then there exists a local transversal section S at $m \in \gamma$ and a Poincaré map $\Theta: W_0 \to W_1$ on S, such that the following hold:*

(i) (W_0, ω_0) and (W_1, ω_1) are contact manifolds, where $\omega_0 = i_{0*}\omega$, $i_0: W_0 \to M$ being the inclusion (20.1);

(ii) Θ is a canonical transformation; that is, Θ preserves H, and there is a function $\delta \in \mathscr{F}(W_0)$ such that $\Theta_*\omega_1 = \omega_0 - \mathbf{d}\delta \wedge \mathbf{d}H$; moreover, δ is the period shift of the Poincaré map described in 23.6;

(iii) There exists $\varepsilon > 0$ and regular energy surfaces $\Sigma_{e'}$ for $e' \in (e - \varepsilon, e + \varepsilon)$, such that $(S_{e'}, \omega_{e'})$ is a symplectic submanifold of codimension two and $\Theta | W_0 \cap S_{e'}$ is a symplectic diffeomorphism onto $W_1 \cap S_{e'}$, where $S_{e'} = S \cap \Sigma_{e'}$, $i: S_{e'} \to M$ is the inclusion mapping, and $\omega_{e'} = i_*\omega$.

Proof. Let (U, φ) be a Hamiltonian flow box chart (21.10) at $m \in \gamma$ and S be defined by $t = 0$. Then, if $i: S \to M$ is inclusion,

$$i_*\omega = i_*\left(\mathbf{d}H \wedge dt + \sum_{i=2}^{n} dq^i \wedge dp_i\right) = \sum_{i=2}^{n} dq^i \wedge dp_i$$

as $t \cdot i = 0$ (10.9). Hence (i) is clear (compare 20.2). Also, since γ is compact, there is an open neighborhood V of γ on which $\mathbf{d}H \neq 0$. Hence $\Sigma_{e'} = V \cap H^{-1}(e')$ is a regular energy surface for e' in some interval $(e - \varepsilon, e + \varepsilon)$, and, restricted to $S \cap \Sigma_e$, ω becomes $\sum_{i=2}^{n} dq^i \wedge dp_i$, so the first part of (iii) is clear. For (ii), a simple computation shows that for $s \in S$,

$$T\Theta(s) \cdot Y = T_1 F(s, \tau - \delta(s)) \cdot Y - (\mathbf{d}\delta(s) \cdot Y) X_H,$$

where $\Theta(s) = F(s, \tau - \delta(s))$ as in 23.6. Also, as $F_{\tau - \delta(s)}$ is symplectic and $H \circ F_{\tau - \delta(s)} = H$, we have

$$\begin{aligned}\Theta_*\omega_1(s)(X, Y) &= \omega(\Theta(s))(T\Theta(s) \cdot X, T\Theta(s) \cdot Y) \\ &= \omega(s)(X, Y) - \tfrac{1}{2} X_H(Y)\, \mathbf{d}\delta(X)(s) + \tfrac{1}{2} X_H(X)\, \mathbf{d}\delta(Y)(s)\end{aligned}$$

so that (ii) follows. Finally, (ii) implies (iii) by restricting to $\Sigma_{e'}$. ∎

Thus, on $S_{e'}$, Θ preserves the volume element

$$i_*(\omega^{n-1}) = dq^2 \wedge \cdots \wedge dq^n \wedge dp_2 \wedge \cdots \wedge dp_n$$

a classical and useful fact (see, for example, Pars [1, p. 446]). In addition, the properties of 28.4 and this corollary hold for any transversal section S (sufficiently small). This follows from existence (28.4) and local conjugacy (23.7).

Using the implicit mapping theorem, we now show the existence of a cylinder of closed orbits if γ has the characteristic multiplier one with multiplicity one (see 29.4).

28.5. Theorem. *Let (M, ω) be a symplectic manifold, $H \in \mathscr{F}(M)$, and γ a closed orbit of X_H with characteristic multiplier one of multiplicity one. Then there is an $\varepsilon > 0$, such that for all $e' \in (e - \varepsilon, e + \varepsilon)$, where $H(\gamma) = e$, there is a closed orbit of energy e'. Moreover, this collection of closed orbits is diffeomorphic to a cylinder (see Figure 28-1).*

Proof. Consider the Hamiltonian flow box chart (U, φ), local transversal section, and Poincaré map defined in the previous proposition. By abuse of notation we work directly in this chart. Define

$$\psi: W_0 \to \mathbf{R}^{n-1} \times \mathbf{R}^{n-1}; (\mathbf{q}, e - H, \mathbf{p}) \rightsquigarrow \Theta(\mathbf{q}, e - H, \mathbf{p}) - (\mathbf{q}, \mathbf{p})$$

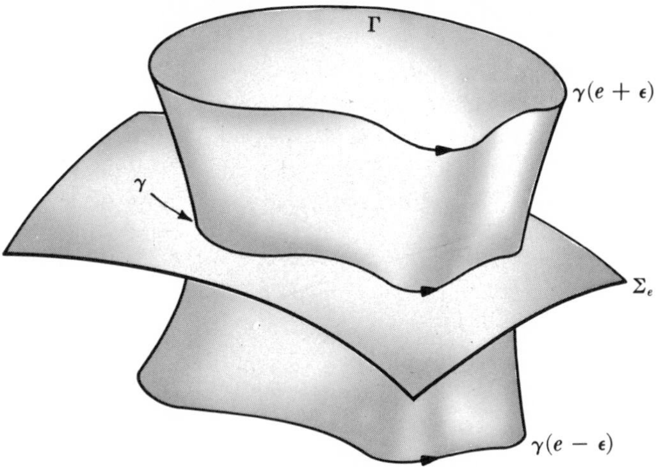

Figure 28-1

Now $\Theta|\Sigma_e$ is symplectic by 28.4, and since $D\Theta(\mathbf{0}, 0, \mathbf{0})$ has eigenvalue 1 occurring exactly once (see 23.7), $D(\Theta|\Sigma_e)(\mathbf{0}, \mathbf{0})$ has no eigenvalue 1, since this value must have even multiplicity (13.16, 14.13). Hence,

$$D(\psi|\Sigma_e)(\mathbf{0}, \mathbf{0}) = D(\Theta|\Sigma_e)(\mathbf{0}, \mathbf{0}) - I$$

has no eigenvalue zero, and hence, it is an isomorphism. Thus, by the implicit mapping theorem, 6.16, there are charts $\alpha_1\colon U_1 \times V_1 \subset S_e \times (e - \varepsilon, e + \varepsilon) \to U' \times V'$ and $\alpha_2\colon V \to U'$ so that $\alpha_2 \circ \psi \circ \alpha_1^{-1}((\mathbf{q}, \mathbf{p}), e') = (\mathbf{q}, \mathbf{p})$. Define a one-dimensional submanifold C in S by $\alpha_1^{-1}(\{(\mathbf{0}, \mathbf{0})\} \times V')$. Suppose $V' = (e - \varepsilon', e + \varepsilon')$, and $c = \alpha_1^{-1}|\{(\mathbf{0}, \mathbf{0})\} \times V'$. Then for $e' \in V'$, $\psi(c(e')) = (\mathbf{0}, \mathbf{0})$ or $\Theta(c(e')) = c(e')$, or Θ is the identity on C, and the orbit $\gamma_{e'}$ of $c(e')$ is closed. Clearly $\cup\{\gamma_{e'}\} = F(C \rtimes \mathbf{R})$ is diffeomorphic to a cylinder. ∎

In general, this cylinder cannot be extended for all energies without encountering a singularity, that is, a critical point or a closed orbit for which the hypotheses of the theorem fail.

Note that even restricted to the energy surface Σ_e, the Poincaré mapping must satisfy the symplectic eigenvalue theorem. Thus, as in the case of a critical point (28.2), we still expect in M (resp. in Σ_e) stable and unstable manifolds of the same dimension, and possibly a center manifold of even (resp. odd) dimension that cannot be eliminated by small perturbations of the Hamiltonian function.

Exercises

28A. Complete the proof of 28.4 by performing the indicated computations.

28B. Demonstrate 28.5 directly in the case of a Hamiltonian derived from a Riemannian metric (18.10).

§29. GENERIC PROPERTIES

As critical elements in the Hamiltonian case are not generically elementary, we propose an alternative notion of elementary critical element for this case. As this aspect of the theory is at the very beginning of its development, the suggested definition is not to be taken too seriously. Of many possibilities, we have proposed only those properties that appear in existing theorems and seem generic intuitively.

29.1. Definition. *Let* (M, ω) *be a symplectic manifold and* $H \in \mathscr{F}(M)$. *Then a critical point m of* X_H *is called* $\mathscr{H}$ **elementary** *iff each of the following conditions hold.*

(*i*) *Zero is not a characteristic exponent* (25.1).

(*ii*) *If* λ *is a characteristic exponent with real part zero, then* λ *has multiplicity one.*

(*iii*) *If* λ *and* μ *are characteristic multipliers with real part zero and imaginary part positive, then* λ *and* μ *are independent over the integers; that is, if* $n_1\lambda + n_2\mu = 0$ *for* $n_1, n_2 \in \mathbf{Z}$, *then* $n_1 = n_2 = 0$.

A Hamiltonian $H \in \mathscr{F}(M)$, *or its Hamiltonian vectorfield* $X_H \in \mathscr{X}_{\mathscr{H}}(M)$, *has* **property (H1)** *iff every critical point of* X_H *is* $\mathscr{H}$ *elementary.*

The property (H1) is actually generic. The meaning of generic in this context is expressed precisely by replacing $\mathscr{X}(M)$ by $\mathscr{X}_{\mathscr{H}}(M)$ in 25.10.

29.2. Theorem. *Property* (H1) *is* C^r *generic in* $\mathscr{X}_{\mathscr{H}}(M)$ *for all* $r \geq 1$.

The proof is quite beyond the methods of this book, but is listed as an exercise anyway, with an adequate hint. Using the transversality technique developed in Abraham–Robbin [1], it becomes quite easy.

Of course $\mathscr{H}$ *elementary* is not as elementary as *elementary* (25.4), and the qualitative behavior of orbits close to an $\mathscr{H}$ elementary critical point is much more complicated. In addition to the center manifold (25.6), which exists in any case, we get in the $\mathscr{H}$ elementary case an additional very important simplification in the behavior of nearby orbits, the splitting of the center manifold into the two-dimensional invariant *subcenter manifolds* discovered by Liapounov.

29.3. Theorem (Liapounov–Kelley subcenter stability). *Let* (M, ω) *be a symplectic manifold,* $H \in \mathscr{F}(M)$, *and* $m \in M$ *be an* $\mathscr{H}$ *elementary critical point of* X_H. *Then if* $i\beta$ *is a characteristic exponent of m* ($\beta \in \mathbf{R}$), *there is a two-dimensional submanifold* C_β *with* $m \in C_\beta$ *such that*

(*i*) $T_m C_\beta$ *is the eigenspace corresponding to the characteristic exponents* $i\beta$ *and* $-i\beta$;

(*ii*) C_β *is an invariant submanifold of* X_H (15.11);

(iii) C_β is a union of closed orbits γ_r such that there is a diffeomorphism $\varphi\colon C_\beta \to D_1$, ($D_1$ is the disk of radius one in $\mathbf{R}^2$) with $\varphi(\gamma_r)$ a circle of radius r about $0 = \varphi(m)$. Moreover, if τ_r denotes the period of γ_r, $\lim_{r\to 0} \tau_r = 2\pi/\beta$.

The proof is given in Appendix C by A. Kelley. Note that since $i\beta$ and $-i\beta$ have multiplicity one, C_β necessarily has dimension two. Also note that if the characteristic exponents on the imaginary axis are $\pm i\beta_\alpha$, $\alpha = 1, \ldots, k$, then $T_m C_{\beta_i} \oplus \cdots \oplus T_m C_{\beta_k} = T_m C$. In (*iii*), the linear case (in the coordinate system of eigenvectors) on the subcenter manifold C_β reduces to the equations

$$\frac{dx_1}{dt} = \beta x_2$$

$$\frac{dx_2}{dt} = -\beta x_1$$

with solutions

$$x_1(t) = c_1 \cos \beta t + c_2 \sin \beta t$$

$$x_2(t) = -c_1 \sin \beta t + c_2 \cos \beta t$$

which are circular closed orbits with period $2\pi/\beta$, and radius $r = (c_1^2 + c_2^2)^{1/2}$. Thus the phase portrait of $X_H|C_{\beta_\alpha}$ is equivalent to that of the linear case, on each of the subcenter manifolds.

Recall that for closed orbits in the Hamiltonian case the ever present characteristic multiplier one may correspond to stability of the closed orbit under perturbations of the energy. The remaining multipliers are multipliers of the vectorfield restricted to the energy surface (28.4). We now pose an elementary condition for these.

29.4. Definition. *Let (M, ω) be a symplectic manifold, $H \in \mathscr{F}(M)$ and γ a closed orbit of X_H. Then γ is called $\mathscr{H}$* **elementary** *iff each of the following holds.*

(i) The characteristic multiplier one has multiplicity one (multiplicity two as an eigenvalue of $TF_\tau(m)$).

(ii) If λ is a characteristic multiplier with $|\lambda| = 1$, then λ has multiplicity one.

(iii) If λ, μ are characteristic multipliers with $|\lambda| = 1$, $|\mu| = 1$, $\lambda \neq 1/\mu$, then λ and μ are multiplicatively independent over $\mathbf{Z}$; that is, if $\lambda = e^{i\alpha}$, $\mu = e^{i\beta}$, $\alpha, \beta > 0$, then $n_1\alpha + n_2\beta = 0$ implies $n_1 = n_2 = 0$.

The Hamiltonian $H \in \mathscr{F}(M)$ and the vectorfield $X_H \in \mathscr{X}(M)$ have **property (H2)** *iff every closed orbit is $\mathscr{H}$ elementary.*

At present we do not know if property (H2) is generic in $\mathscr{X}_{\mathscr{H}}(M)$. Some optimism on this question is possible as (H2) is generic on a small subspace of $\mathscr{X}_{\mathscr{H}}(T^*W)$ corresponding to Hamiltonians of the Riemannian metric type (18.11), if W is compact (Abraham [1]). In addition, the full analogue of the subcenter theorem (29.3) is false. The Moser subcenter theorem (30.4) is a partial analogue.

29.5. Conjecture. *Property* (H2) *is* C^r *generic in* $\mathscr{X}_{\mathscr{H}}(M)$ *for all* $r \geq 1$.

It is easier to guess generic properties than to prove them, so we will offer two more.

29.6. Definition. *A Hamiltonian vectorfield* $X_H \in \mathscr{X}_{\mathscr{H}}(M)$ *has* **property (H5)** *iff* $X_H|\Sigma_e$ *has property* (G5) *for all regular energy surfaces* $\Sigma_e \subset M$ *of* H, *and has* **property (H6)** *iff* $X_H|\Sigma_e$ *has property* (G6) *for all* Σ_e.

29.7. Conjecture. *Properties* (H5) *and* (H6) *are* C^r *generic in* $\mathscr{X}_{\mathscr{H}}(M)$ *for all* $r \geq 1$.

We may have a (very limited) optimism for this conjecture as (G5) and (G6) are generic in $\mathscr{X}(M)$ if M is compact, and a little more perhaps in the case of (H6), as this is known to be generic in the subspace of $\mathscr{X}_{\mathscr{H}}(T^*W)$ of Riemannian metric Hamiltonians if W is compact (see Abraham [1]).

Exercises

29A. Prove 29.2. (Hint: Follow Abraham–Robbin [1, §29].)

29B. Construct an example of a Hamiltonian vectorfield on $T^*\mathbf{R}^2$ that does not have any of the properties (H1), (H2), (H5), or (H6).

§30. STABILITY OF ORBITS

We consider now the question of orbital stability of critical elements in the Hamiltonian case. We have seen (§28) that if a critical element has a stable manifold, it also has an unstable manifold, and is therefore α^+ unstable for all cases, $\alpha = o, a, L$ (26.8). Thus there is the possibility of stability only if all of the characteristic multipliers have modulus one. This case, in which the entire manifold is a center manifold for the critical element, is called a **pure center**, or the **oscillatory case**. If the characteristic multipliers are expressed $(1, e^{\pm i\alpha_1}, \ldots, e^{\pm i\alpha_{n-1}})$ for a closed orbit, or $(e^{\pm i\alpha_1}, \ldots, e^{\pm i\alpha_n})$ for a critical point, $\alpha_i \in [0, 2\pi)$, the real numbers $\{\alpha_i/2\pi\}$ are called the **frequencies** for the reason discussed in §29. Thus the critical element is $\mathscr{H}$ elementary iff the frequencies are independent over the rationals. The nonelementary case is sometimes called the **problem of small divisors** in celestial mechanics.

In the oscillatory case, the flow is a rotation in linear approximation, so asymptotic Liapounov stability (26.3) is not to be expected. Orbital stability is natural, however, and always occurs in the case of a critical point in two dimensions (29.3). Thus the natural question for a Hamiltonian vectorfield is this: *When is a critical element of pure center type* o^+*-stable?* Certainly this has an obvious importance in celestial mechanics, for example, in

Laplace's problem of the stability of the solar system. For the case of an $\mathscr{H}$ elementary critical point, the subcenter stability theorem (29.3) gives a splitting of the center into two dimensional invariant manifolds that are o^+-stable. Thus a very important question is: Under what conditions does stability on all subcenter manifolds imply stability of the center? This is somewhat similar to the center-stable stability theorem (26.7), but at present, we do not even have a plausible conjecture to offer.

In the case of a closed orbit of oscillatory type, the analogous questions are still important, and in addition we do not even know the existence of subcenter manifolds. Stability in a given subcenter manifold is, however, the subject of Moser's theorem.

Consider the case of *two degrees of freedom*, $M = T^*W$ where W is a two-dimensional manifold. If Σ_e is a regular energy surface, $\gamma \subset \Sigma_e$ a closed orbit, and S a local transversal section, in Σ_e; then Σ_e is three dimensional, and S is two dimensional. A Poincaré map Θ on S can be considered a diffeomorphism in the plane $\mathbf{R}^2$ keeping the origin fixed. Then γ is a pure center iff $T_0\Theta$ is a rotation. In this case the entire 3-manifold Σ_e is a center (or subcenter) manifold for $\gamma \subset \Sigma_e$. Moser's theorem gives a sufficient condition for the existence of a very dense set of invariant circles in S, thus invariant tori in Σ_e, implying $o^{\pm}$-stability of γ. In the remainder of this section we describe Moser's results without proofs. These results are applied, in §36, to the restricted three-body problem, which has, in fact, two degrees of freedom.

30.1. Definition. *Let $U \subset \mathbf{R}^2$ be an open neighborhood of the origin. A C^∞ mapping $F: U \to \mathbf{R}^2$ is an (α, β)-**normal form**, $\alpha \in [0, 2\pi)$ and $\beta = -1, 0,$ or 1, iff $F(\mathbf{u}) = \mathbf{u}e^{i(\alpha + \beta|\mathbf{u}|^2)} + R_4(\mathbf{u})$ (in complex notation, $\mathbf{R}^2$ identified with the complex plane) where for some $K > 0, |R_4(\mathbf{u})| \leq K|\mathbf{u}|^4$ for all $\mathbf{u} \in U$. A C^∞ mapping $F: U \to \mathbf{R}^2$ is an α-**twist mapping** iff $F(\mathbf{0}) = \mathbf{0}$, and $DF(\mathbf{0})$ has eigenvalues $e^{\pm i\alpha}$.*

We consider $\mathbf{R}^2$ a symplectic manifold with symplectic form $dx \wedge dy$.

30.2. Theorem (Birkhoff-Moser normal form). *If $F: U \subset \mathbf{R}^2 \to \mathbf{R}^2$ is an α-twist mapping with α not zero or an integral multiple of $\pi/2$ or $2\pi/3$, then there is a symplectic chart at $\mathbf{0} \in \mathbf{R}^2$ such that the local representative of F is an (α, β)-normal form, and β is the same for all symplectic charts having this property.*

For the proof, see Siegel [1, Chapter 21] and Moser [10]. The excluded values of the eigenvalues of $DF(\mathbf{0})$ are illustrated in Figure 30-1.

30.3. Definition. *An α-twist mapping is an **elementary twist mapping** iff α is not zero or an integral multiple of $\pi/2$ or $2\pi/3$, and the invariant β of* 30.2 *is not zero. A **cycle** in U is a homeomorphic image of the circle S^1.*

30.4. Theorem (Moser twist stability). *If $F: U \subset \mathbf{R}^2 \to \mathbf{R}^2$ is an elementary twist mapping, then*

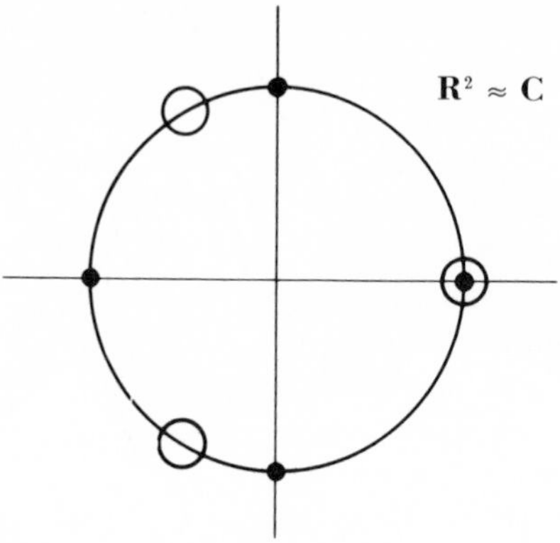

Figure 30-1

(*i*) *In every neighborhood of* $\mathbf{0} \in U$, *there is an invariant cycle* σ *having no periodic points. That is,* $F(\sigma) = \sigma$, *and for all* $\mathbf{u} \in \sigma$ *and integers* k, $F^k(\mathbf{u}) \neq \mathbf{u}$;

(*ii*) *For all* $\varepsilon > 0$ *there is a* $\delta > 0$ *such that the set of invariant cycles in* $D_\delta(\mathbf{0})$ *has measure greater than* $(1 - \varepsilon)(2\pi\delta^2)$;

(*iii*) *For every neighborhood* V *of* $\mathbf{0} \in U$ *and integer* k *there are infinitely many distinct points* $\mathbf{v} \in V$ *such that* $F^k(\mathbf{v}) = \mathbf{v}$.

For the proof of (*i*) and (*ii*) see Moser [2, 4].

The proof of (*iii*) has not been published, but a similar theorem with related hypotheses is proved in Siegel [1, Chapter 22].

By applying this theorem to the Poincaré map Θ on a local transversal section S within the energy surface Σ_e, we obtain a condition for $o^\pm$-stability of $\gamma \subset \Sigma_e$ in the case of two degrees of freedom.

30.5. Corollary. *Suppose* X_H *is a Hamiltonian vectorfield on a symplectic 4-manifold* M, γ *is a closed orbit of* X_H *in a regular energy surface* Σ_e, *and* Θ *is a Poincaré map of* $X_H|\Sigma_e$ *at* $\gamma \subset \Sigma_e$. *Then in the oscillatory case (characteristic multipliers* $1, e^{\pm i\alpha}$), *if* Θ *is an elementary twist mapping,* γ *is* $o^\pm$*-stable within* Σ_e *and within* M.

Proof. It follows at once from 30.4 that $\gamma \subset \Sigma_e$ is $o^\pm$-stable. To show that $\gamma \subset M$ is $o^\pm$-stable, we consider a local transversal section $\tilde{S}$ for $\gamma \subset M$. Let $\Gamma = U\{\gamma_{e'} | e - \varepsilon < e' < e + \varepsilon\}$ be a cylinder of closed orbits through $\gamma = \gamma_e$, $H(\gamma_{e'}) = e'$ (28.5). Then if $\Sigma_{e'}$ is a regular energy surface containing $\gamma_{e'}$, $S_{e'} = \tilde{S} \cap \Sigma_{e'}$ is a local transversal section for $\gamma_{e'}$. We may suppose in addition that $\tilde{S}$ and Θ are constructed as in 28.4, so $\Theta|S_{e'} = \Theta_{e'}$ is a Poincaré map on $S_{e'}$. Then Θ_e is an elementary twist mapping by hypothesis, and the derivatives of $\Theta_{e'}$ of all orders are continuous functions of e'. So for e' sufficiently close to e, $\Theta_{e'}$ is an elementary twist mapping also. Thus for some $\varepsilon' > 0$, $\gamma_{e'}$ is $o^\pm$-stable for all $e' \in (e - \varepsilon', e + \varepsilon')$. Then it follows easily that $\gamma \subset M$ is $o^\pm$-stable, as γ is compact and H is invariant. ∎

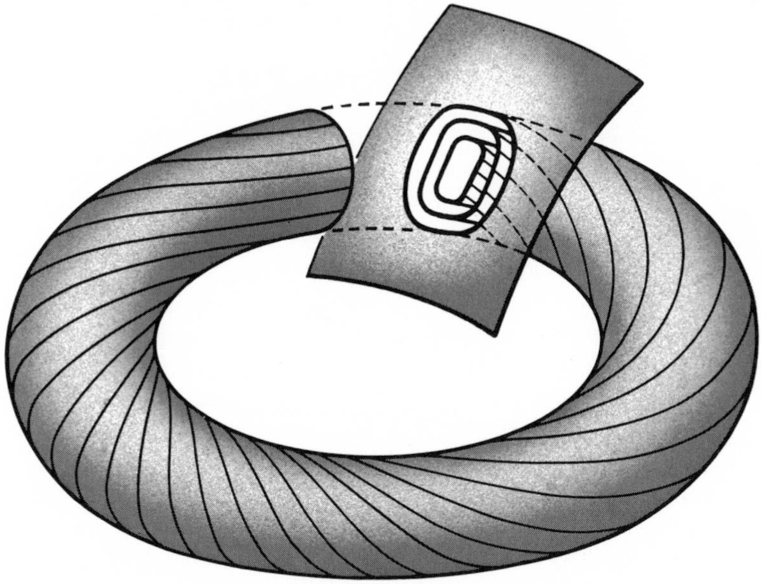

Figure 30-2

The conclusion of Moser's twist stability theorem is illustrated in Figure 30-2. We might add to the definition (29.4) of $\mathscr{H}$ elementary closed orbit and property (H2), the condition that the Poincaré map of the closed orbit, restricted to each subcenter manifold, be an elementary twist mapping, and then conjecture that *this property is generic.*

The Moser theorem admits a generalization to systems of three or more degrees of freedom (see Moser [4] and Arnold [1, 2]), but the generalization does not imply $o^{\pm}$-stability. This leaves open the central problem: *When does stability on the subcenter manifolds imply stability on the complete center manifold?*

Exercises

30A. Compute Taylor's formula (2.8) to order 4 for an α-twist mapping both in complex and in real notations.

30B. Find necessary conditions, on the second and third derivatives at the origin of a chart, that an α-twist mapping be changed to an (α, β)-normal form.

30C. Show that if Θ and Θ' are Poincaré maps on local transversal sections S and S' of dimension 2, and Θ is an elementary twist mapping, then so is Θ'.

30D. Show that if X_H is a Hamiltonian vectorfield, $\tilde{S}$ is a local transversal section, Σ is a regular energy surface, and $S = \tilde{S} \cap \Sigma$, then S is a local transversal section of $X_H|\Sigma$.

§31. STRUCTURAL STABILITY

We have seen several reasons why a Hamiltonian vectorfield cannot be structurally stable. For example, compare the stability of closed orbits under perturbation of the energy (28.5) with the necessity of property (G2), or the necessity of (G5) (27.7), which is violated by the Hamiltonian function itself.

From the point of view of the *stability dogma*, we may substitute other versions of structural stability that are more appropriate to the Hamiltonian case. For if we assume that the mathematical model of a theory is a conservative Hamiltonian system, the uncertainty of the experimental domain is represented by perturbations of the Hamiltonian function. That is, we arbitrarily exclude non-Hamiltonian and nonautonomous perturbations. Then for stability of the phase portrait under perturbations within $\mathscr{X}_{\mathscr{H}}(M)$, we get an appropriate analogue of the previous definition (27.1) by restricting it to the subspace $\mathscr{X}_{\mathscr{H}}(M) \subset \mathscr{X}(M)$, with the Whitney C^r topology.

31.1. Definition. *A Hamiltonian vectorfield X_H on a symplectic manifold (M, ω) is $\mathscr{H}^r$* **structurally stable** *(or the Hamiltonian H is $\mathscr{H}^{r+1}$ structurally stable) iff there is a neighborhood $\mathscr{O}$ of $X_H \in \mathscr{X}_{\mathscr{H}}(M)$ in the Whitney C^r topology* (§25) *such that $X_K \in \mathscr{O}$ implies X_K and X_H have equivalent phase portraits* (23.2).

We dare not conjecture that this stability is generic, and we have no idea of the connection between this and the $\mathscr{H}$ elementary properties (H1), (H2), (H5), and (H6) of §29.

It appears in the applications, especially to celestial mechanics, that orbital stability (26.2) and critical stability (26.9) may be more important than this very strong type of structural stability which involves the entire phase portrait. Perhaps an intermediate notion requiring stability of the phase portrait on a single energy surface Σ_e under perturbations of the Hamiltonian and the energy e is more appropriate.

31.2. Definition. *Suppose $X_H \in \mathscr{X}_{\mathscr{H}}(M)$ and $\Sigma_e = H^{-1}(e)$ is a regular energy surface* (16.22). *Then $X_H|\Sigma_e$ is Σ^r* **structurally stable** *iff there is a neighborhood $\mathscr{O}$ of $X_H \in \mathscr{X}_{\mathscr{H}}(M)$ in the Whitney C^r topology, and an $\varepsilon > 0$, such that if $X_K \in \mathscr{O}$ and $e' \in (e - \varepsilon, e + \varepsilon)$, then $K^{-1}(e')$ is a regular energy surface, and there is a homeomorphism $h: H^{-1}(e) \to K^{-1}(e')$ that maps orbits of $X_H|H^{-1}(e)$ into orbits of $X_K|K^{-1}(e)$.*

It seems plausible that $\mathscr{H}^r$ structural stability implies Σ^r structural stability on any regular energy surface. Perhaps this would actually be the case if in 31.1 we had required in addition that the phase portrait homeomorphism $h: M \to M$ preserve the energy surfaces, or in other words there exists a function $h_0 : \mathbf{R} \to \mathbf{R}$ such that the diagram

$$\begin{array}{ccc} M & \xrightarrow{\;h\;} & M \\ {\scriptstyle H}\downarrow & & \downarrow{\scriptstyle K} \\ \mathbf{R} & \xrightarrow{\;h_0\;} & \mathbf{R} \end{array}$$

commutes, and if in 31.2 we had permitted $\varepsilon = 0$. In any case, Σ^r structural stability is weaker in some sense, and close in spirit to the applications. In addition, we expect generically that X_H has property (H5), or $X_H|\Sigma_e$ has no first integrals, and this avoids the conflict between structural stability and the existence of first integrals.

31.3. Conjecture. *Suppose $X_H \in \mathscr{X}_{\mathscr{H}}(M)$ and $\Sigma_e = H^{-1}(e)$ is a compact regular energy surface of H. Then arbitrarily close to X_H (in the Whitney C^r topology) there is an X_K such that $K^{-1}(e)$ is close to Σ_e (in the Hausdorff topology) and $X_K|K^{-1}(e)$ is Σ^r structurally stable.*

Another stability definition has been proposed by Thom [1, Chapter 2]. This calls for a stronger type of equivalence of phase portraits. A symplectic diffeomorphism replaces the homeomorphism, and in addition, it is required to preserve parameterization of the integral curves, not just the orbits.

Recall that if $\varphi: (M, \omega_0) \to (N, \omega_1)$ is a symplectic diffeomorphism and $H \in \mathscr{F}(M)$, then $\varphi^* X_H = X_{\varphi^* H}$.

31.4. Definition. *A Hamiltonian vectorfield $X_H \in \mathscr{X}_{\mathscr{H}}(M)$ is T^r* **structurally stable** *iff there is a neighborhood $\mathscr{O}$ of $X_H \in \mathscr{X}_{\mathscr{H}}(M)$ (in the Whitney C^r topology) such that $X_K \in \mathscr{O}$ implies there is a symplectic diffeomorphism $\varphi: M \to M$ such that $\varphi^* X_H = X_K$.*

If M is connected, the last condition is equivalent to the commutativity of the diagram:

$$\begin{array}{ccc} M & \xrightarrow{\;\varphi\;} & M \\ {\scriptstyle H}\downarrow & & \downarrow{\scriptstyle K} \\ \mathbf{R} & \xrightarrow{\;c\;} & \mathbf{R} \end{array}$$

where c is translation by a constant. This implies preservation of energy surfaces, a natural condition. Although this is an extremely strong notion of stability, Thom states that the nested tori configuration around a closed orbit of elementary twist type in a system of two degrees of freedom (30.5) is stable in this sense.

Finally, we might consider the structural stability of a Hamiltonian vectorfield X_H restricted to an energy surface Σ_e. That is, the phase portrait in Σ_e should be stable under perturbation by arbitrary vectorfields tangent to Σ_e. Only this form seems to have been studied in the Hamiltonian case, and there is a surprising result.

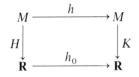

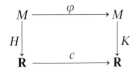

31.5. Theorem (Markus). *Suppose Σ_e is a compact regular energy surface of $H \in \mathscr{F}(M)$ and $X_H|\Sigma_e \in \mathscr{X}(\Sigma_e)$ is C^1 structurally stable* (27.1). *Then*

$$\Gamma^c_{X_H|\Sigma_e} = \Sigma_e$$

Thus almost every point in Σ_e is in a closed orbit. The proof follows from Pugh's theorem (27.7 (*ii*)). See Markus [3].

Exercise

31A. Characterize all types of structural stability in terms of continuity of a mapping (see 26.2).

Notes

Some of the local qualitative theory in the Hamiltonian case is discussed briefly in Whittaker [1] and Pars [1]. The standard sources for the earlier global theory are Poincaré [2], Birkhoff [1], and Siegel [1]. Related results are found in Reeb [6].

A prototype for the Liapounov–Kelley theorem (29.3) is found in Siegel [1].

The Moser twist theorem (30.4) was suggested by Kolmogorov [1], and similar results were obtained independently by Arnold [1].

The stability of closed orbits (28.5) is a recent folk theorem; I first heard of it from René Thom in 1961. Although I have not found it in the literature, a partial result in the same direction is mentioned by Pars [1, p. 446].

Concerning structural stability in the Hamiltonian case, some interesting conjectures have been made by Peixoto [3].

I am grateful to Al Kelley and Jurgen Moser for several very profitable conversations about this chapter.

CHAPTER VII

THE THREE-BODY PROBLEM

In the preceding chapters, we have not presented a single nontrivial example illustrating the general theory of Hamiltonian systems or the important qualitative results. In this chapter we give a complete discussion of the most important system to which the theory has been applied, the *restricted three-body problem.* The analysis requires the full power of the theory we have developed, and uses nearly every major result of the book.

In this program we follow the method of BARRAR [1, 2] based on the *Poincaré variables*, with minor modifications. We begin with the two-body problem, which is used in the definition of the Poincaré variables.

§32. MODELS FOR TWO BODIES

In this section we consider several mathematical models for the two-body problem and their interrelationships. The experimental domain might be the Earth and Sun, a binary star, etc. As the heuristic derivation of the models from Newton's gravitational theory is well known, we shall not discuss it or the experimental domain or interpretation.

32.1. Definition. *The* **first model for the two-body problem (I)** *is a system* (M, H^{μ}, m, μ), *where*

(*i*) $M = T^*W, W = \mathbf{R}^3 \times \mathbf{R}^3 \setminus \mathbf{\Delta}, \mathbf{\Delta} = \{(\mathbf{q}, \mathbf{q}) | \mathbf{q} \in \mathbf{R}^3\}$;
(*ii*) $m \in M$ (initial conditions);
(*iii*) $\mu \in \mathbf{R}$, $\mu > 0$, *and*
(*iv*) $H^{\Gamma} \in \mathscr{F}(M)$ *defined by*

$$H^{\mu}(\mathbf{q}, \mathbf{q}', \mathbf{p}, \mathbf{p}') = \frac{\|\mathbf{p}\|^2}{2\mu} + \frac{\|\mathbf{p}'\|^2}{2} - \frac{1}{\|\mathbf{q} - \mathbf{q}'\|}$$

where $\mathbf{q}, \mathbf{q}' \in \mathbf{R}^3$, $\mathbf{p}, \mathbf{p}' \in \mathbf{R}^{3*}$, *and* $\| \ \|$ *denotes the standard norm in* $\mathbf{R}^3$.

The **predictions** *of the model are the integral curve of* X_H *through* m, *and the orbits* m_σ *of* m $(\sigma = +, -, \pm)$, *where we use the natural symplectic structure on* M (14.14).

Note that $\mathbf{\Delta}$ is excluded from $\mathbf{R}^3 \times \mathbf{R}^3$ so that $H^{\mu} \in \mathscr{F}(M)$. Also, $X_{H^{\mu}}$ is not complete as integral curves can "run off the manifold" in finite time (collisions).

32.2. Proposition (Conservation of linear momentum). *In model* I (32.1) *the components of* $\mathbf{p} + \mathbf{p}'$ (*relative to the standard dual basis*) *are constants of the motion.*

Proof. Consider the Lie group $(\mathbf{R}^3, +)$ with action Φ on W (32.1) given by $\Phi(\mathbf{r})\colon (\mathbf{q}, \mathbf{q}') \rightsquigarrow (\mathbf{q} + \mathbf{r}, \mathbf{q}' + \mathbf{r})$ (22.8). Note that the diagonal $\boldsymbol{\Delta} \subset \mathbf{R}^3 \times \mathbf{R}^3$ is invariant. According to 14.16, the action Φ^*, $\Phi^*(\mathbf{r}) = \Phi(\mathbf{r})^*$ given by $(\mathbf{q}, \mathbf{q}', \mathbf{p}, \mathbf{p}') \rightsquigarrow (\mathbf{q} + \mathbf{r}, \mathbf{q}' + \mathbf{r}, \mathbf{p}, \mathbf{p}')$ is symplectic (which is obvious in this case). Consider $(\mathbf{0}, \mathbf{r}_0) \in \ell_G$ (22.3) so that $X \in \mathscr{L}_G$; $X(\mathbf{r}) = (\mathbf{r}, \mathbf{r}_0)$ is the corresponding left invariant vectorfield. Clearly the flow of X is $F_X(t, \mathbf{r}) = \mathbf{r} + t\mathbf{r}_0$. This induces on M the flow H_X given by $H_X(t, \mathbf{q}, \mathbf{q}', \mathbf{p}, \mathbf{p}') = (\mathbf{q} + t\mathbf{r}_0, \mathbf{q}' + t\mathbf{r}_0, \mathbf{p}, \mathbf{p}')$ (22.9) so that the infinitesimal transformation of X is given by

$$Y_X(\mathbf{q}, \mathbf{q}', \mathbf{p}, \mathbf{p}') = (\mathbf{q}, \mathbf{q}', \mathbf{p}, \mathbf{p}'; \mathbf{r}_0, \mathbf{r}_0, \mathbf{0}, \mathbf{0})$$

We know, from 22.11, that this is locally Hamiltonian. Indeed we see at once that $Y_X^\flat = \mathbf{d}(\mathbf{p} \cdot \mathbf{r}_0 + \mathbf{p}' \cdot \mathbf{r}_0)$, so that Φ^* is a Hamiltonian action. Thus, as H is invariant under Φ^*, $\mathbf{p} \cdot \mathbf{r}_0 + \mathbf{p}' \cdot \mathbf{r}_0$ is a constant of the motion by 22.13. This gives the result. ∎

The next proposition is the analogue of using *coordinates relative to the center of mass.*

32.3. Proposition. *There is a symplectic diffeomorphism* $F\colon M \to N$ *where* M *is as in* 32.1 *and* $N = T^*V$, $V = \mathbf{R}^3 \times (\mathbf{R}^3 \setminus \mathbf{R}\{\mathbf{0}\})$ *such that*

$$H^\mu \circ F^{-1}(\mathbf{q}, \mathbf{q}', \mathbf{p}, \mathbf{p}') = \frac{\|\mathbf{p} + \mathbf{p}'\|^2}{2\mu} + \frac{\|\mathbf{p}'\|^2}{2} - \frac{1}{\|\mathbf{q}'\|}$$

where H^μ *is given in* 32.1.

Proof. Consider the diffeomorphism $f\colon W \to V$; $(\mathbf{q}, \mathbf{q}') \rightsquigarrow (\mathbf{q}, \mathbf{q} - \mathbf{q}')$. The induced symplectic diffeomorphism $F = f^*\colon T^*W \to T^*V$ (14.16) is easily seen to be $(\mathbf{q}, \mathbf{q}', \mathbf{p}, \mathbf{p}') \rightsquigarrow (\mathbf{q}, \mathbf{q} - \mathbf{q}', \mathbf{p} + \mathbf{p}', -\mathbf{p}')$ with inverse $F^{-1}\colon T^*V \to T^*W$; $(\mathbf{q}, \mathbf{q}', \mathbf{p}, \mathbf{p}') \rightsquigarrow (\mathbf{q}, \mathbf{q} - \mathbf{q}', \mathbf{p} + \mathbf{p}', -\mathbf{p}')$. This gives the result. ∎

In 32.3, the components of $\mathbf{p}$ are constants of the motion for $'H^\mu = H \circ F^{-1}$. If $n \in N$ represents the initial conditions and $n = (\mathbf{q}_0, \mathbf{q}_0', \mathbf{p}_0, \mathbf{p}_0')$, then using the symplectic diffeomorphism $(\mathbf{q}, \mathbf{q}', \mathbf{p}, \mathbf{p}') \rightsquigarrow (\mathbf{q} - \mathbf{q}_0, \mathbf{q}', \mathbf{p} - \mathbf{p}_0, \mathbf{p}')$ we may assume $\mathbf{q}_0 = \mathbf{0}$, $\mathbf{p}_0 = \mathbf{0}$. Thus

$$'H^\mu(\mathbf{q}, \mathbf{q}', \mathbf{p}, \mathbf{p}') = \left(\frac{1}{\mu} + 1\right)\frac{\|\mathbf{p}'\|^2}{2} - \frac{1}{\|\mathbf{q}'\|}$$

along the integral curve, where

$$\left(\frac{1}{\mu} + 1\right)^{-1}$$

is called the **reduced mass**.

This leads naturally to another model which is "equivalent" in some sense (the one-body problem). This is an example of *reduction of degree by first integrals.*

32.4. Definition. *The second model* **for the two-body problem (II)** *is a system* (M, H, m), *where*

(*i*) $M = T^*U, U = \mathbf{R}^3 \setminus \{\mathbf{0}\}$;
(*ii*) $m \in M$ (*initial conditions*); *and*
(*iii*) $H \in \mathscr{F}(m)$, *defined by* $H(\mathbf{q}, \mathbf{p}) = \dfrac{\|\mathbf{p}\|^2}{2} - \dfrac{1}{\|\mathbf{q}\|}$.

Note that the μ *scale has again been changed.*

32.5. Proposition (Conservation of angular momentum). *In model* II *the following quantities are constants of the motion*

$$(q^2 p_3 - q^3 p_2, q^3 p_1 - q^1 p_3, q^1 p_2 - q^2 p_1) = (G_1, G_2, G_3)$$

where $\mathbf{q} = (q^1, q^2, q^3)$, $\mathbf{p} = (p_1, p_2, p_3)$.

Proof. Consider the Lie group $G = SO(3)$ of rotations of $\mathbf{R}^3$. Then $SO(3)$ acts on $\mathbf{R}^3 \setminus \{\mathbf{0}\}$ by restriction. This induces a symplectic action on $T^*(\mathbf{R} \setminus \{\mathbf{0}\})$ as given in 14.16. Consider the one parameter subgroup $t \rightsquigarrow e_t =$ rotation through an angle t about the z axis. This generates a left invariant vectorfield on G. The corresponding infinitesimal transformation on $\mathbf{R}^3 \setminus \{\mathbf{0}\}$ is

$$X(\mathbf{q}) = (\mathbf{q}; q^2, -q^1, 0)$$

where $\mathbf{q} = (q^1, q^2, q^3)$, while that on $T^*(\mathbf{R}^3 \setminus \{\mathbf{0}\})$ is given by

$$Y(\mathbf{q}, \mathbf{p}) = (\mathbf{q}, \mathbf{p}; q^2, -q^1, 0, p_2, -p_1, 0)$$

as

$$\mathbf{p} = p_1\, dq^1 + p_2\, dq^2 + p_3\, dq^3$$

and

$$\varphi^*\mathbf{p} = p_1 \circ \varphi^{-1}\, \mathbf{d}(q^1 \circ \varphi^{-1}) + p_2 \circ \varphi^{-1}\, \mathbf{d}(q^2 \circ \varphi^{-1}) + p_3 \circ \varphi^{-1}\, \mathbf{d}(q^3 \circ \varphi^{-1}) \qquad (10.9)$$

Then we differentiate the resultant flow. See §22 and compare 32.3.

But $Y^\flat = \mathbf{d}(q^1 p_2 - q^2 p_1)$ (§13). Hence the action is Hamiltonian and $q^1 p_2 - q^2 p_1$ is a constant of the motion. The other components are similar. ∎

Note that G is two-dimensional and hence admits two independent constants of the motion. The other is obtained from the Poisson bracket of these (see §14, §22).

Thus, 32.5 tells us that the orbit of $(\mathbf{q}, \mathbf{p})$ lies in the hyperplane perpendicular to $(G_1, G_2, G_3, G_1, G_2, G_3)$ at $(\mathbf{q}, \mathbf{p})$, in the standard metric. A rotation in $\mathbf{R}^3 \setminus \{\mathbf{0}\}$ together with the same one in the phase variables is, as we have seen, a symplectic diffeomorphism (compare 32.3). Thus we may orient the above hyperplane to obtain the following "equivalent" model.

32.6. Definition. The **third model for the two-body problem** (**III**) *is a system* (M, H, m) *where*

(*i*) $M = T^*(\mathbf{R}^2 \setminus \{\mathbf{0}\})$;

(*ii*) $m \in M$ *(initial conditions), and*

(*iii*) $H \in \mathscr{F}(m)$ *defined by* $H(\mathbf{q}, \mathbf{p}) = \dfrac{\|\mathbf{p}\|^2}{2} - \dfrac{1}{\|\mathbf{q}\|}$.

Again, $\| \ \|$ *denotes the Euclidean norm.*

From 18.16, the above Hamiltonian is hyperregular with Lagrangian L on $T(\mathbf{R}^2 \setminus \{\mathbf{0}\})$ given by

$$L(\mathbf{q}, \dot{\mathbf{q}}) = \frac{\|\dot{\mathbf{q}}\|^2}{2} + \frac{1}{\|\mathbf{q}\|}$$

Thus, in this case the Lagrangian equations become

$$\frac{d^2 q^i}{dt^2}(t) = -\frac{q^i(t)}{\|\mathbf{q}(t)\|^3} \qquad i = 1, 2$$

where $\mathbf{q}: I \to \mathbf{R}^2 \setminus \{\mathbf{0}\}: t \rightsquigarrow \mathbf{q}(t) = (q^1(t), q^2(t))$ denotes the base integral curve (17.21). We also have conservation of energy:

$$\tfrac{1}{2}\|\dot{\mathbf{q}}\|^2 - \frac{1}{\|\mathbf{q}\|} = H$$

and angular momentum (area integral):

$$q^1\dot{q}^2 - q^2\dot{q}^1 = G$$

The fiber derivative of H (or L) relates these constants of the motion since it is symplectic, and relates X_H to X_E as we have seen in §18. Moreover $\mathbf{F}H: T^*(\mathbf{R}^2 \setminus \{\mathbf{0}\}) \to T(\mathbf{R}^2 \setminus \{\mathbf{0}\}): (\mathbf{q}, \mathbf{p}) \rightsquigarrow (\mathbf{q}, \mathbf{p})$ (relative to the standard bases), so we may freely pass between the two formulations.

The well-known solution to these equations (a base integral curve of X_H in model III) is a conic section, possibly degenerate. In fact, if $G = 0$, the solution is a straight line (degenerate case), whereas if $G \neq 0$, the path is an ellipse, parabola, or hyperbola, according as $H < 0$, $H = 0$, or $H > 0$, the sense of rotation being determined by the sign of G.

It is not so simple to obtain the flow explicitly. For the details and a discussion of the use of the Jacobi metric, see Wintner [2, Chapter IV].

We shall be mainly interested in the case of closed orbits ($H < 0$, $G \neq 0$), which we discuss in the next section.

Exercise

32A. Prove the analogue of 32.2 for a translation invariant Hamiltonian on the torus (§A9).

§33. CLOSED ORBITS AND POINCARÉ VARIABLES

In model III for the two-body problem a large open subset of the phase space is filled with closed orbits. In this section we study this region, primarily because it is basic to the closed orbits of the restricted three-body problem.

In model III (32.6) we found the following equations for the base integral curves:

$$\frac{d^2q^i(t)}{dt^2} = -\frac{q^i(t)}{r(t)^3} \qquad r = \|\mathbf{q}\|$$

with constants of the motion

$$\frac{1}{2}\left\|\frac{dq(t)}{dt}\right\|^2 - \frac{1}{r(t)} = H$$

and

$$q^1(t)\frac{dq^2(t)}{dt} - q^2(t)\frac{dq^1(t)}{dt} = G$$

33.1. Proposition. *If, in the above model, $H < 0$ and $G \neq 0$ on the base integral curve (computed from initial conditions $\mathbf{q}_0$, $\mathbf{p}_0$), then the curve is an ellipse with eccentricity $e = (1 + 2HG^2)^{1/2}$, semimajor axis $a = (-2H)^{-1}$ and one focus at the origin. Also the rate of sweeping out of area by $\mathbf{q}(t)$ is constant and the period of the closed orbit is $\tau = 2\pi a^{3/2}$.*

Proof. It readily follows that

$$G\frac{d^2q^2(t)}{dt^2} = \frac{d}{dt}\left(\frac{q^1(t)}{r(t)}\right)$$

so that

$$G\frac{dq^2(t)}{dt} = \frac{q^1(t)}{r(t)} + A$$

Similarly,

$$G\frac{dq^1(t)}{dt} = -\frac{q^2(t)}{r(t)} - B$$

which gives $A^2 + B^2 = 1 + 2HG^2$ and $G^2 = Aq^1(t) + Bq^2(t) + r(t)$. Note $1 + 2HG^2 \geq 0$. In polar "coordinates" we see at once that if $H < 0$, we have an ellipse with e and a as given, and one focus at the origin. Finally, the rate of sweeping out area by the vector $\mathbf{q}(t)$ is $G/2$, and hence the period is

$$\tau = \frac{\pi a \cdot a(1 - e^2)^{1/2}}{G/2} = 2\pi a^{3/2}$$

Note also the compatibility condition $0 \leq 1 + 2HG^2 < 1$. ■

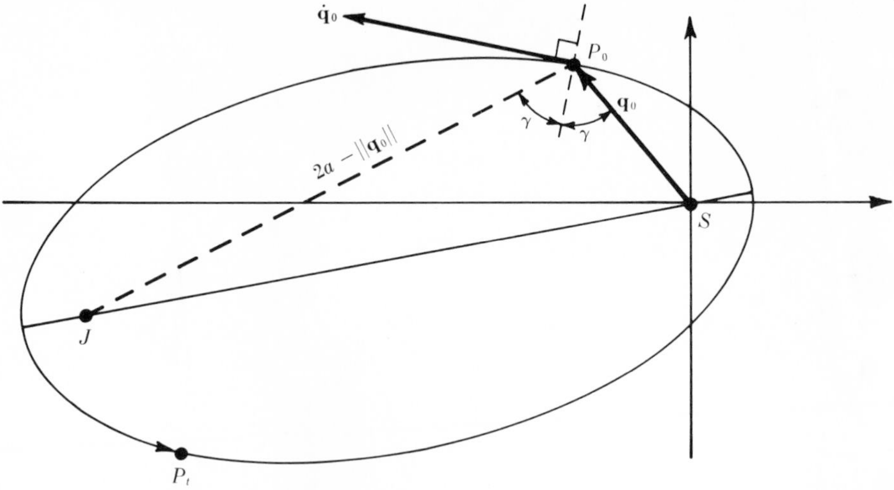

Figure 33-1
Construction of the apocenter J, from initial conditions $(\mathbf{q}_0, \dot{\mathbf{q}}_0)$, with $H < 0$ and $G > 0$.

Given initial conditions $\mathbf{q}_0, \mathbf{p}_0$ (or $\mathbf{q}_0, \dot{\mathbf{q}}_0$) the orbit may be easily reconstructed by geometrical means as indicated in Figure 33-1. Recall that the sum of the distances to the foci is always $2a$. (We assume $H < 0, G \neq 0$.)

The position of $P = (q^1, q^2)$ on the elliptical orbit is described by the various "anomalies" or angular parameters in $[0, 2\pi)$.

33.2. Definition. *Consider a point, P_t, moving on the ellipse described in* 33.1, *in accordance with the equations of motion, and P_0 at perihelion. Then the following quantities are defined in Figure* 33-2, *all in $[0, 2\pi)$:*

$\alpha(t)$, *the* **polar angle**;

$f(t)$, *the* **true anomaly**;

$u(t)$, *the* **eccentric anomaly**.

We also define, in case $e \neq 0$,

$g(t)$, *the* **argument of the perihelion**, *and*

$l(t) = (2\pi/\tau)t = a^{-3/2}t$, *the* **mean anomaly**.

That this diagram can be constructed follows at once from the equations of the ellipse.

33.3. Proposition (Kepler's law). *In the situation described above, we have: for all $t \in [0, \tau)$*

(*i*) $r(t) = a(1 - e \cos u(t))$, *and*

(*ii*) $l(t) = u(t) - e \sin u(t)$.

Proof. (i) In Figure 33-2, if $PA = \|P - A\|$, etc.,

$$r^2 = (PA)^2 + (\mathbf{0}A)^2$$

$$= (a\sqrt{1-e^2}\sin u)^2 + a^2(\cos u - e)^2$$
$$= a^2(1 - e\cos u)^2$$

As $r > 0$, the result follows. For (ii) we have, from the law of areas

$$\frac{l}{2\pi} = \frac{\text{area } P_0\mathbf{0}P}{\text{area ellipse}}$$

Now the ratio $P'A/PA$ is constant, being $(1-e^2)^{-1/2}$ times that of $\mathbf{0}P$. Hence

$$\frac{\text{area } P_0\mathbf{0}P}{\text{area ellipse}} = \frac{\text{area } P_0\mathbf{0}P'}{\text{area circle}}$$
$$= \frac{1}{\pi a^2}\left(\frac{a^2 u}{2} - \frac{a}{2}ae\sin u\right)$$

which gives the result. ∎

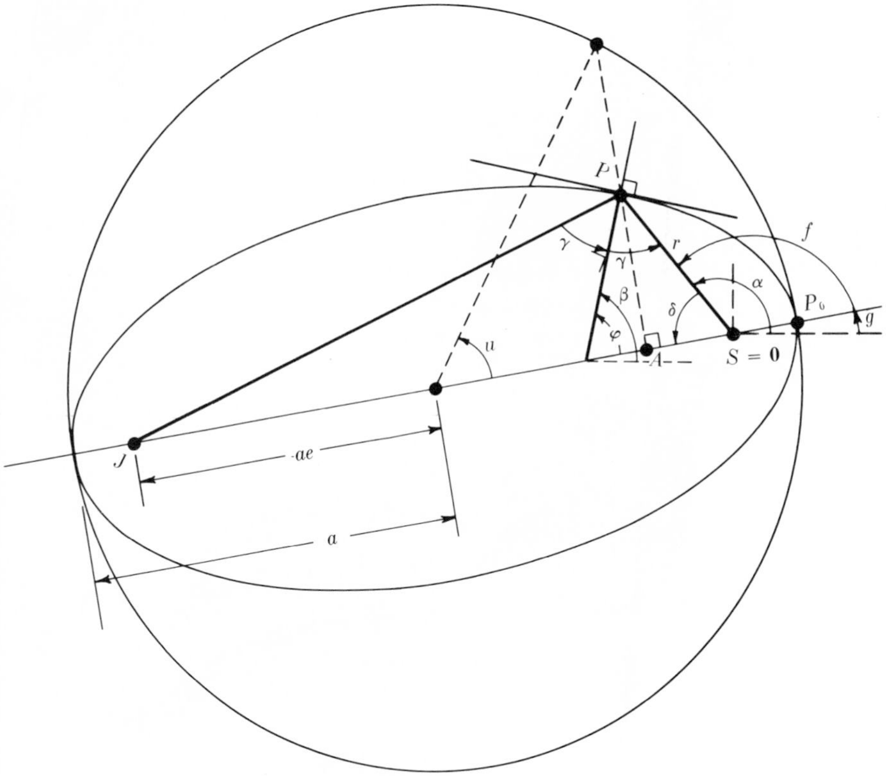

Figure 33-2
Definition of the anomalies, and related parameters.

For the three body problem it will be important to introduce coordinates that follow these elliptical orbits. We now define these *Delaunay variables.* Consider the third model for the two-body problem. The Hamiltonian

$$H(\mathbf{q}, \mathbf{p}) = \frac{\|\mathbf{p}\|^2}{2} - \frac{1}{\|\mathbf{q}\|}$$

is defined on $M = T^*W$, $W = \mathbf{R}^2 \setminus \{\mathbf{0}\}$. We map a subset of M into $T^*\mathbf{T}^2$, where $\mathbf{T}^2$ denote the 2-torus obtained as the quotient space of $\mathbf{R}^2$ by the subgroup of points whose components are integral multiples of 2π (compare with §A9).

*33.4. **Definition.** The* **elliptical domain** *of M is the subset*

$$M_0 = \{m \in M | H(m) < 0 < e(m) < 1\}$$

The **Delaunay domains** *in $T^*\mathbf{T}^2 \approx \mathbf{T}^2 \times \mathbf{R}^2$ are the subsets*

$$\mathscr{D} = \{(g, l, G, L) | L > |G| > 0\}$$

$$\mathscr{D}' = \{(g, l, G, -L) | L > |G| > 0\}$$

The **Delaunay mappings** *are defined by*

$$F: M_0 \to T^*\mathbf{T}^2 : m \rightsquigarrow (g(m), l(m), G(m), -L(m))$$

and

$$\Delta: M_0 \to T^*\mathbf{T}^2 : m \rightsquigarrow (g(m), l(m), G(m), L(m))$$

where $L(m) = [-2H(m)]^{-1/2}$.

The Delaunay domain is illustrated in Figure 33-3, for each fiber of $\mathscr{D}$.

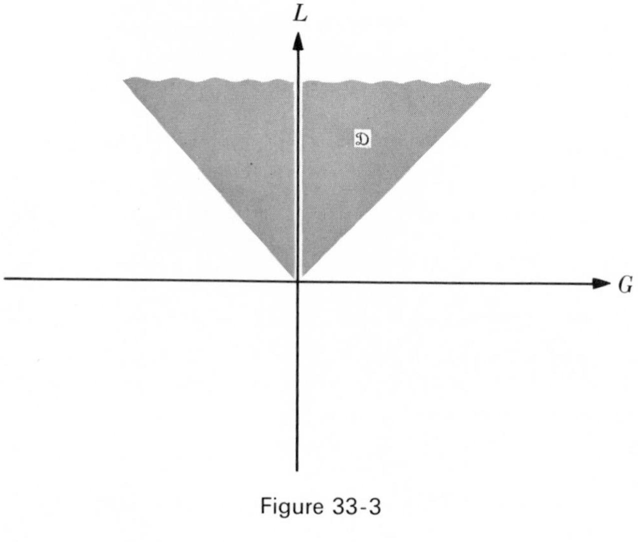

Figure 33-3

33.5. Proposition. *(i) $M_0 \subset M$ is an open submanifold, (ii) $\mathscr{D}, \mathscr{D}' \subset T^*T^2$ are open submanifolds, (iii) $\Delta: M_0 \to \mathscr{D}$ and $F: M_0 \to \mathscr{D}'$ are diffeomorphisms.*

The proof is left to the reader (Exercise 33A).

The Delaunay mapping Δ was introduced by Delaunay [1] in the study of the lunar problem, and was used in the present context by Poincaré under the name "Keplerian variables." Poincaré called (g, l, G, L) canonical coordinates, although they are not canonical in the sense of 21.9. But Poincaré apparently meant that $F_*X_H = X_K$ for a single H, and not all H. Our global Delaunay mapping F, which involves the actual mean anomaly l, cannot be symplectic, as it may be shown that the Poisson bracket $\{g, l\}$ does not vanish (Exercise 33B). We show in the next section that this does not interfere with the applications of §36. There the main tool will be a precise knowledge of $F^*\omega_0$, which we now develop.

Let ω_0 denote the natural symplectic form on $M_0 \subset T^*W$. In $\mathscr{D} \subset T^*T^2$ let (x^1, x^2, y_1, y_2) be the standard "coordinate functions," and $\omega_1 = dx^1 \wedge dy_1 + dx^2 \wedge dy_2$ the natural symplectic form.

33.6. Lemma. *If $m \in M_0$, there exists an open neighborhood U of $m \in M_0$ and a function $\lambda \in \mathscr{F}(U)$ such that*

(i) $F_*\omega_1 = \omega_0 + \mathbf{d}\lambda \wedge \mathbf{d}L$;

(ii) λ is independent of l, or $\mathbf{L}_{X_H}\lambda = 0$, and

(iii) λ is independent of g, or $\mathbf{L}_{X_G}\lambda = 0$.

Proof. Our program for the proof will be as follows. (a) We consider a Hamiltonian flow box chart (U_0, α_0) at $m \in M_0$ with coordinates $(q, s, p, -H)$, then (b) change to a nonsymplectic chart (U_0, α_1) with coordinates $(g, s, G, -H)$, and (c) using the relative Poincaré lemma (10.19) we find a new chart (U, α_2) with coordinates $(g, t, G, -H)$ where $t = s + \mu$, which is again a Hamiltonian flow box chart. Next (d) we obtain a new symplectic chart (U, α_3) by changing $(t, -H)$ to $(k, -L)$, which is similar to F, and (e) comparing α_3 to F we obtain (*i*) and (*ii*), with $\lambda = l - k$. Finally, (f) we show that λ satisfies (*iii*) by computing the Poisson bracket $\{l, G\}$.

(a) Let (U_0, α_0) be a Hamiltonian flow box chart at $m \in M_0$. Thus

$$\alpha_0: U_0 \subset M_0 \to U_0' \subset T^*\mathbf{R}^2: (q^1, q^2, p_1, p_2) \rightsquigarrow (q, s, p, -H)$$

where H is the Hamiltonian and s is a *natural parameter* on the orbits of X_H; that is, mapping $s \rightsquigarrow \alpha_0^{-1}(q, s, p, -H)$ is an integral curve of X_H at $\alpha_0^{-1}(q, 0, p, -H)$. Note that there is no unique natural parameter s; it depends on the initial hypersurface defined by $s = 0$.

(b) First, consider the mapping

$$\alpha_1: U_0 \to T^*\mathbf{R}^2: (q^1, q^2, p_1, p_2) \rightsquigarrow (g, s, G, -H)$$

where g, G are as before, H is the Hamiltonian, and s is defined by α_0. Then there exists a 1-form θ such that

(b1) $\alpha_{1*}\omega_1 = \omega_0 + \theta \wedge \mathbf{d}H$;
(b2) $\mathbf{i}_{X_H}\theta = 0$, and
(b3) $\mathbf{L}_{X_H}\theta = 0$.

This is proved by direct computation as follows. Obviously

$$\omega_0 = \mathbf{d}q \wedge \mathbf{d}p - \mathbf{d}s \wedge \mathbf{d}H$$

as α_0 is symplectic, and

$$\alpha_{1*}\omega_1 = \mathbf{d}g \wedge \mathbf{d}G - \mathbf{d}s \wedge \mathbf{d}H$$

so it suffices for (b1) to show

$$\mathbf{d}g \wedge \mathbf{d}G = \mathbf{d}q \wedge \mathbf{d}p + \theta \wedge \mathbf{d}H$$

Computing $\mathbf{d}g$, $\mathbf{d}G$, and $\mathbf{d}g \wedge \mathbf{d}G$ in terms of the basic 1-forms $\{\mathbf{d}g, \mathbf{d}s, \mathbf{d}p, -\mathbf{d}H\}$ of the chart α_0 we have, as g and G are constants of the motion,

$$\mathbf{d}g = g_q\mathbf{d}q + g_p\mathbf{d}p + g_H\mathbf{d}H$$

$$\mathbf{d}G = G_q\mathbf{d}q + G_p\mathbf{d}p + G_H\mathbf{d}H$$

where subscripts indicate partial derivatives in α_0. Hence

$$\mathbf{d}g \wedge \mathbf{d}G = (g_qG_p - g_pG_q)\mathbf{d}q \wedge \mathbf{d}p + \theta \wedge \mathbf{d}H$$

where

$$\theta = (g_qG_H - g_HG_q)\mathbf{d}q + (g_pG_H - g_HG_p)\mathbf{d}p$$

As θ satisfies (b2) and (b3) (Exercise 33C), it suffices to show the coefficient of $\mathbf{d}q \wedge \mathbf{d}p$ is 1 to prove (b). Computing the Poisson bracket $\{g, G\}$ in the symplectic chart α_0 we find, as $g_s = G_s = 0$ (g and G are constants of motion) that

$$\{g, G\} = g_qG_p - g_pG_q$$

so we need finally to show only $\{g, G\} = 1$ to complete (b). However, $\{g, G\} = \mathbf{L}_{X_G}g$, and returning to the symplectic chart (q^1, q^2, p_1, p_2) in M_0, we have $G = q^1p_2 - q^2p_1$, so $X_G(q, p)$ has components $(-q^2, q^1, -p_2, p_1)$. Thus, if we consider $G \in \mathscr{F}(T^*\mathbf{R}^2)$ we see X_G is complete, and its flow $\varphi: \mathbf{R} \times T^*\mathbf{R}^2 \to T^*\mathbf{R}^2$ is such that its one-parameter group of diffeomorphisms $\{\varphi_t\}$ consists of simultaneous rotations in the $\mathbf{q}$ and $\mathbf{p}$ planes by the same angle t. In fact, this is a Hamiltonian action of the additive group $(\mathbf{R}, +)$ on M with infinitesimal generator X_G, as we saw in 32.5. From Figure 33-2 it is clear that in M_0, which is invariant under φ_t,

$$g \circ \varphi_t = g + t$$

so by 8.20,

$$\mathbf{L}_{X_G} g = \frac{d}{dt}(g \circ \varphi_t)_{t=0} = 1$$

completing (b).

We now modify α_1 to cancel out the nonsymplectic term $\theta \wedge \mathbf{d}H$ in $\alpha_{1*}\omega_1$.

(c) We have $\alpha_{1*}\omega_1 = \omega_0 + \theta \wedge \mathbf{d}H$ and both ω_0 and ω_1 are closed, so $\mathbf{d}(\theta \wedge \mathbf{d}H) = \mathbf{d}\theta \wedge \mathbf{d}H = 0$. As α_1 is a diffeomorphism into a product $V \times \mathbf{R}$ with H the projection onto the second factor, θ is relatively closed (10.18) and by (b2) it is horizontal, so by the relative Poincaré lemma (10.19) there exists a neighborhood U of $m_0 \in U_0$ and a function $\mu \in \mathscr{F}(U)$, namely, $\mu = \mathbf{H}_V\theta$ (as in 10.19) such that $d_V\mu = \theta$, or $\theta = \mathbf{d}\mu - \mu_H \mathbf{d}H$, in U. Thus we have also

$$\alpha_{1*}\omega_1 = \omega_0 + \mathbf{d}\mu \wedge \mathbf{d}H$$

in U. As θ is independent of s, that is, $\mathbf{L}_{X_H}\theta = 0$ (b3), θ is horizontal (b2), θ closed mod H, and $\mu = \mathbf{H}_V\theta$, we find $\mathbf{L}_{X_H}\mu = 0$ (Exercise 10E). To eliminate the nonsymplectic term $\mathbf{d}\mu \wedge \mathbf{d}H$, we change the initial points of the natural parameter s by defining $t = s + \mu$. That is, we consider the mapping

$$\alpha_2 \colon U \to T^2\mathbf{R}^2 \colon (q^1, q^2, p_1, p_2) \rightsquigarrow (g, t, G, -H)$$

where $t(u) = s(u) + \mu(u)$ for $u \in U$, with $\mu = \mathbf{H}_V\theta$ as above. This is obviously a diffeomorphism onto an open subset, and

$$\begin{aligned} \alpha_{2*}\omega_1 &= \mathbf{d}g \wedge \mathbf{d}G - \mathbf{d}t \wedge \mathbf{d}H \\ &= \mathbf{d}g \wedge \mathbf{d}G - \mathbf{d}s \wedge \mathbf{d}H - \mathbf{d}\mu \wedge \mathbf{d}H \\ &= \alpha_{1*}\omega_1 - \mathbf{d}\mu \wedge \mathbf{d}H = \omega_0 \end{aligned}$$

Thus α_2 is a symplectic chart. Furthermore, $\mu_s = 0$ (or $\mathbf{L}_{X_H}\mu = 0$), so that t is a natural parameter on the orbits of X_H in U, and thus (U, α_2) is a Hamiltonian flow box chart.

(d) Let $\alpha_3 \colon U \to T^*\mathbf{R}^2$ be defined by

$$\alpha_3(q^1, q^2, p_1, p_2) = (g, k, G, -L)$$

where L is the same as in the Delaunay mapping, $L = (-2H)^{-1/2}$, and k is *analogous* to the mean anomaly, $k = L^{-3}t$. This is obviously a diffeomorphism onto an open subset of $T^*\mathbf{R}^2$, and in addition is symplectic. For

$$\alpha_{3*}\omega_1 = \mathbf{d}g \wedge \mathbf{d}G - \mathbf{d}k \wedge \mathbf{d}L$$

and

$$\alpha_{2*}\omega_1 = \mathbf{d}g \wedge \mathbf{d}G - \mathbf{d}t \wedge \mathbf{d}H = \omega_0$$

so $\alpha_{3*}\omega_1 = \omega_0$ if $\mathbf{d}t \wedge \mathbf{d}H = \mathbf{d}k \wedge \mathbf{d}L$. But $\mathbf{d}k = L^{-3}\mathbf{d}t - 3L^{-4}t\mathbf{d}L$, $\mathbf{d}L = (-2H)^{-3/2}\mathbf{d}H = L^3\mathbf{d}H$, and so $\mathbf{d}k \wedge \mathbf{d}L = \mathbf{d}t \wedge \mathbf{d}H$. Thus α_3 is symplectic. Note that k is proportional to a natural parameter on each orbit, but the ratio depends on the energy H. Therefore α_3 is not a Hamiltonian flow box chart.

(e) Comparing $F|U$ with α_3, which is symplectic, we have

$$F_*\omega_1 = \mathbf{d}g \wedge \mathbf{d}G - \mathbf{d}l \wedge \mathbf{d}L$$

$$\alpha_3\omega_1 = \mathbf{d}g \wedge \mathbf{d}G - \mathbf{d}k \wedge \mathbf{d}L = \omega_0$$

so if $\lambda = k - l$, we have

$$\alpha_{3*}\omega_1 = F_*\omega_1 - \mathbf{d}\lambda \wedge \mathbf{d}L = \omega_0$$

or

$$F_*\omega_1 = \omega_0 + \mathbf{d}\lambda \wedge \mathbf{d}L$$

Now if T is the natural time parameter on orbits measured from perihelion ($l = 0$), we have for a fixed orbit (by 33.2) $\lambda = L^{-3}t - L^{-3}T$, which is constant on the orbit as both t and T are natural parameters, so λ is independent of l. Consider now $\mathbf{L}_{X_G}l$, which is in fact the Poisson bracket $\{l, G\}$. The computation of $\{l, G\}$ in M_0 is similar to the evaluation of $\{g, G\}$ carried out in (b) above. There we observed that X_G is the infinitesimal generator of an action of $\mathbf{R}$ on M_0, $t \rightsquigarrow \varphi_t$, where φ_t is a simultaneous rotation of configuration and momentum variables by angle t. It is clear from the geometrical determination of orbits, Figure 33-2, that $l \circ \varphi_t = l$ so $\mathbf{L}_{X_G}l = 0$. Since $\mathbf{L}_{X_G}k = 0$, we have the result. ∎

Note that from 33.6, we have for every point $m \in M_0$ an open neighborhood U and a function $\nu \in \mathscr{F}(U)$ such that

$$F_*\omega_1 = \omega_0 + \nu\mathbf{d}G \wedge \mathbf{d}L$$

as we take $\nu = \lambda_G$. By a computation analogous to that of Exercise 14E, we see that $\underset{\sim}{e}_3 = -X_g$. Thus

$$\nu = \lambda_G = -L_{X_g}\lambda = L_{X_g}l = \{l, g\}$$

But this is globally defined, so we have proved the following.

33.7. Theorem. *For the Delaunay mappings F, Δ we have, throughout M_0,*

(i) $F_*\omega_1 = \omega_0 + \{l, g\}\mathbf{d}G \wedge \mathbf{d}L$

$= \mathbf{d}g \wedge \mathbf{d}G - \mathbf{d}l \wedge \mathbf{d}L + \{l, g\}\mathbf{d}G \wedge \mathbf{d}L$, *and*

(ii) $\Delta_*\omega_1 = \mathbf{d}g \wedge \mathbf{d}G + \mathbf{d}l \wedge \mathbf{d}L - \{l, g\}\mathbf{d}G \wedge \mathbf{d}L$.

Although the Delaunay mappings are not symplectic (as $\{l, g\} \neq 0$), they nevertheless preserve the canonical form of the Hamiltonian system X_H in model III. In fact, from 33.7, F is *symplectic mod G and L*, so F preserves Hamiltonian systems for which the Hamiltonian is a function of G and L only. This may be expressed more precisely as follows.

33.8. Corollary. *(i) If $K \in \mathscr{F}(\mathscr{D}')$ depends on (y_1, y_2) only, that is, $\mathbf{L}_{\underline{x}^1}K = \mathbf{L}_{\underline{x}^2}K = 0$, then $F_*X_K = X_{F_*K}$, where $F_*K = K \circ F$.*

(ii) If $K \in \mathscr{F}(\mathscr{D})$ depends on y_2 only, then $\Delta_*X_K = X_{-\Delta_*K}$.

(iii) If $K \in \mathscr{F}(\mathscr{D})$ depends on y_1 only, then $\Delta_*X_K = X_{\Delta_*K}$.

The proof will be left as an exercise.

Returning now to the third model for the two body problem, we see that $L = (-2H)^{-1/2}$, so $H = -1/2L^2$ on M_0, and

$$F: M_0 \to \mathscr{D}': (q^1, q^2, p_1, p_2) \rightsquigarrow (g, l, G, -L), \text{ so } L \circ F^{-1} = y_2$$

if (x^1, x^2, y_1, y_2) are the coordinates in $\mathscr{D}' \subset T^*\mathbf{T}^2 \approx \mathbf{T}^2 \times \mathbf{R}^2$ (x^1, x^2 are "cyclic coordinates" in $[0, 2\pi]$). Thus $F^*H = H \circ F^{-1} = K' = -1/2y_2^2$. As $F^*X_H = X_{K'}$ by 33.8, we obtain a new model, which is "equivalent" to III restricted to M_0, namely, $(\mathscr{D}', K')$. We may also cancel two offensive minus signs as follows. By 33.8 (*ii*), as $H = -1/2L^2$, $H \circ \Delta^{-1} = -1/2y_2^2$ depends on y_2 only, so $\Delta_*X_K = X_H$ if $K(x^1, x^2, y_1, y_2) = +1/2y_2^2$. To recall the relation to model III via the Delaunay map Δ, we may now relabel the coordinates (x^1, x^2, y_1, y_2) in $\mathscr{D}$ by (g, l, G, L). Then the natural symplectic form on $\mathscr{D}$ becomes $\omega_1 = \mathbf{d}g \wedge \mathbf{d}G + \mathbf{d}l \wedge \mathbf{d}L$, *but* in 33.7 (*ii*), $\Delta_*\omega_1 = \mathbf{d}g \wedge \mathbf{d}G + \mathbf{d}l \wedge \mathbf{d}L - \{l, g\}\mathbf{d}G \wedge \mathbf{d}L$. The first two terms on the right *are not* ω_1. We shall use these notations in $\mathscr{D}$ for historical reasons, in spite of this danger.

33.9. Definition. *The* **Delaunay model for the two-body problem (IV)** *is $(\mathscr{D}, K, \mathscr{A})$, where $\mathscr{D}$ is the Delaunay domain* (33.4), *$K(g, l, G, L) = 1/2L^2$, and $\mathscr{A} \in \mathscr{D}$ (initial condition).*

Warning. *The variables (g, l, G, L) are not canonical variables for model III* (see 33.7).

This model is related to model III, and thus to the experimental domain, by the Delaunay mapping Δ. As Δ is defined by the integral of X_H in model III, the Delaunay model, which is itself trivially integrable, is not of much use in studying the two body problem.

The main weakness of the Delaunay model is that it does not contain the circular Kepler orbits ($e = 0$ or $G = L$). The inverse $\Delta^{-1}: \mathscr{D} \to M_0$ of the Delaunay map can be extended so that its image contains the circular orbits, but the extension is no longer injective. This situation is analogous to the polar coordinates in the plane, $\rho: \mathbf{R}^2 \backslash \{\mathbf{0}\} \to T^*S^1$ in Figure 33-4, in which ρ^{-1} can be extended by mapping the entire θ "axis" ($r = 0$) into the origin.

For the purpose of studying the circular orbits (in §36) the Poincaré model is helpful, and is obtained from the Delaunay model by an additional symplectic diffeomorphism Π_+. The mapping $P_+ = \Pi_+ \circ \Delta$ relating the new model to M_0 in model III then extends to a diffeomorphism on M_1, the *domain of counterclockwise elliptical and circular orbits* in model III. This *Poincaré diffeomorphism*, P_1, preserves integral curves, so the Poincaré model is "equivalent" to model III restricted to M_1.

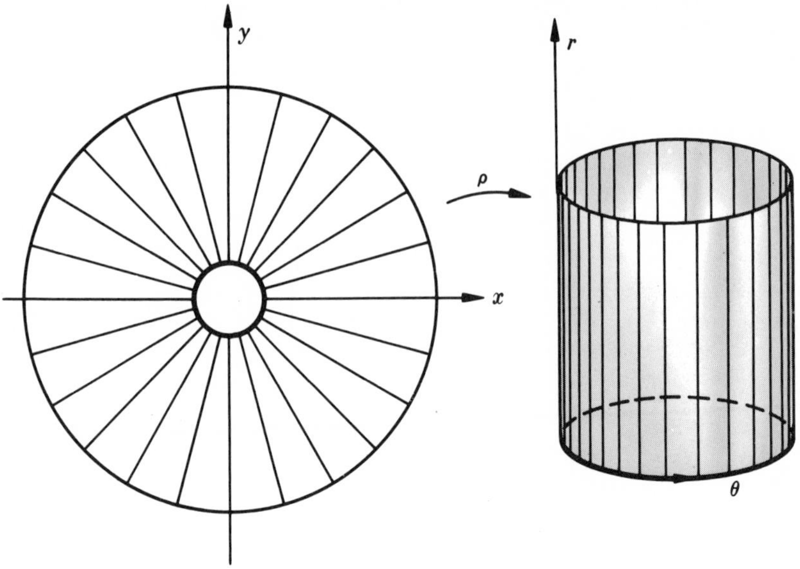

Figure 33-4

The two components of the Delaunay domain are distinguished by $G > 0$ or $G < 0$. As G is in fact the angular momentum, the integral curves in each domain are identical, except that the planet moves clockwise in one component and counterclockwise in the other. Thus nothing is lost in restricting the model to the domain $\mathscr{D}_+ \subset \mathscr{D}$ on which G is positive (counterclockwise motion).

We begin by constructing Π_+ on a larger domain $N \subset T^*\mathbf{T}^2$, which contains $\mathscr{D}_+$; we shall call this mapping Π. Let (x^1, x^2, y_1, y_2) be "coordinate functions" in $T^*\mathbf{T}^2 \approx \mathbf{T}^2 \times \mathbf{R}^2$, with (x^1, x^2) cyclic (mod 2π) in $\mathbf{T}^2$. Note the "coordinate functions" (x^1, x^2) are really coordinates in $\mathbf{R}^2$, which covers $\mathbf{T}^2$. Then we define $N \subset T^*\mathbf{T}^2$ by $N = \{(x^1, x^2, y_1, y_2) | y_2 - y_1 > 0\}$, which is obviously an open subset. Let $\mathbf{T}^1$ denote the circle S^1 parameterized $[0, 4\pi)$; that is, $\mathbf{T}^1$ is the quotient space of $\mathbf{R}$ (mod 4π) (see §A9), and in $T^*(\mathbf{R} \times \mathbf{T}^1)$ we use "coordinate functions" $(\alpha^1, \alpha^2, \beta_1, \beta_2)$, with α^2 cyclic (mod 4π). Then define

$$\Pi: N \to T^*(\mathbf{R} \times \mathbf{T}^1): (x^1, x^2, y_1, y_2) \rightsquigarrow (\alpha^1, \alpha^2, \beta_1, \beta_2)$$

where

$$\alpha^1(x^1, x^2, y_1, y_2) = -(2(y_2 - y_1))^{1/2} \sin x^1$$

$$\alpha^2 = x^1 + x^2$$

$$\beta_1 = (2(y_2 - y_1))^{1/2} \cos x^1$$

$$\beta_2 = y_2$$

33.10. Proposition. *The image* $\Pi(N) = N' \subset T^*(\mathbf{R} \times \mathbf{T}^1)$ *is an open subset, and* $\Pi\colon N \to N'$ *is a symplectic diffeomorphism (with respect to the natural symplectic forms).*

The proof is an exercise at the end of this section.

We may now apply this symplectic diffeomorphism to the counter-clockwise Delaunay model $(\mathscr{D}_+, K)$ to obtain the Poincaré model $(\mathscr{P}_1, \Omega)$. We let $\mathscr{P}_+ = \Pi(\mathscr{D}_+) \subset T^*(\mathbf{R} \times \mathbf{T}^1)$. Then as $\Pi_+ = \Pi|\mathscr{D}_+$ is a symplectic diffeomorphism we have $\Pi^*_+ X_K = X_{\Pi^*_+ K}$. But $K(x^1, x^2, y_1, y_2) = 1/2y_2^2$ and $\beta_2 \circ \Pi_+ = y_2$, so $\Pi^*_+ y_2 = \beta_2$, and $\Pi^*_+ K = 1/2\beta_2^2$. Now this new model is related to the third model (M_0, H) by the Delaunay mapping $\Delta|M_+$, where $M_+ = \Delta^{-1}(\mathscr{D}_+)$, composed with the mapping $\Pi_+ : \mathscr{D}_+ \to \mathscr{P}_+$. The composite mapping $P_+ = \Pi_+ \circ \Delta\colon M_+ \to \mathscr{P}_+$ is the *Poincaré mapping*, and traditionally the component functions of this mapping are denoted by

$$P_+(q^1, q^2, p_1, p_2) = (\eta, \lambda, \xi, \Lambda)$$

Then as $P_+ = \Pi_+ \circ \Delta$, and $\Delta(q^1, q^2, p_1, p_2) = (g, l, G, L)$, we may write

$$\eta = -(2(L - G))^{1/2} \sin g$$

$$\lambda = g + l$$

$$\xi = (2(L - G))^{1/2} \cos g$$

$$\Lambda = L$$

As these equations express the connection between the new model and model III, and thus the experimental domain, it is suggestive to relabel the coordinates $(\alpha^1, \alpha^2, \beta_1, \beta_2)$ by $(\eta, \lambda, \xi, \Lambda)$. Then the new Hamiltonian becomes $\Omega = 1/2\Lambda^2$.

We now extend this model slightly so as to include the circular orbits. In model III, the domain M includes all orbits, $M_0 \subset M$ contains elliptical orbits only ($e \neq 0$), and M_+ contains the counterclockwise elliptical orbits only.

As $e = (1 - G^2/L^2)^{1/2}$, M_+ is defined by the condition $0 < G < L$. Thus the enlarged domain $M_1 \subset M$ defined by $0 < G \leq L$ contains all elliptical and circular orbits. It does not follow immediately that M_1 is an open subset of M; however, this seems plausible if we recall that a circular orbit may be completely surrounded by elliptical orbits, as illustrated in Figure 33-5.

On the other hand, in the Poincaré model, (ξ, η) are polar coordinates in the plane, with radius $r = (2(L - G))^{1/2}$. As $0 < G < L$ in M_+, $r = 0$ is excluded from $\mathscr{P}_+ = \Pi_0(\mathscr{D}_+)$. Thus we may extend $\mathscr{P}_+$ to a larger set $\mathscr{P}_1 \subset T^*(\mathbf{R} \times T^1)$ by adding the points $\{(0, \lambda, 0, \Lambda)|\lambda \in T^1, \Lambda > 0\}$. Obviously $\mathscr{P}_1$ is open.

We now extend the Poincaré mapping $P_+ : M_+ \to \mathscr{P}_+$ to a mapping $P_1 : M_1 \to \mathscr{P}_1$ so as to include the circular orbits. From Figure 33-2 we see

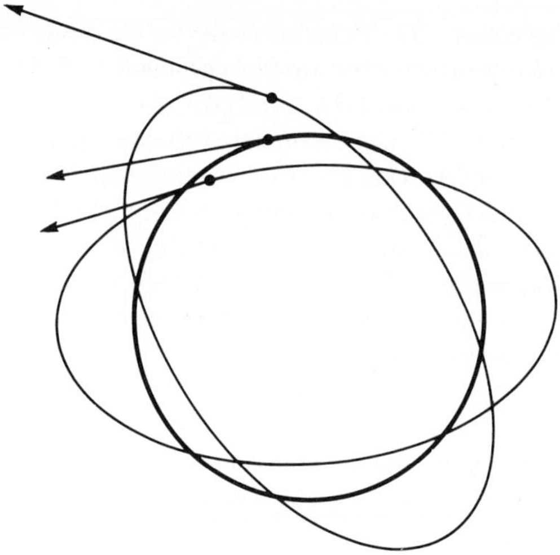

Figure 33-5

that for a circular orbit, the polar coordinate α replaces the sum $g + l = \lambda$. We may therefore define

$$P_1(q^1, q^2, p_1, p_2) = (0, \lambda, 0, \Lambda)$$

if

$$m = (q^1, q^2, p_1, p_2) \in M_1$$

with $G = L$, or $m \in M_1 \setminus M_+$, by defining $\lambda = \alpha$ and $\Lambda = L = G$. This is clearly a bijection on $M_1 \setminus M_+$. We now summarize the properties of the Poincaré mappings. Let ω_2 denote the natural symplectic form on $T^*(\mathbf{R} \times \mathbf{T}^1)$.

33.11. Theorem. *The subsets $M_1 \subset T^*(\mathbf{T}^2)$ and $\mathscr{P}_1 \subset T^*(\mathbf{R} \times \mathbf{T}^1)$ are open. The Poincaré mapping $P_1 : M_1 \to \mathscr{P}_1$ defined by $P_1(m) = (\eta, \lambda, \xi, \Lambda)$ for $m \in M_+$, where*

$$\eta = -(2(L - G))^{1/2} \sin g$$

$$\lambda = g + l$$

$$\xi = (2(L - G))^{1/2} \cos g$$

$$\Lambda = L$$

and $P_1(m) = (0, \lambda, 0, \Lambda)$ for $m \in M_1 \setminus M_+$, where $\lambda = \alpha$, the polar angle of Figure 33-2, and $\Lambda = L$, is a diffeomorphism. Also,

$$P_{1*}\omega_2 = dg \wedge dG + dl \wedge dL - \{l, g\} dG \wedge dL$$

The proof is left as an exercise.

Note that in the model $(\mathscr{P}_+, \Omega)$ with $\Omega = 1/2\Lambda^2$, Ω may be extended to $\mathscr{P}_1$ without singularity. Thus our last model is the following.

33.12. *Definition.* *The* **Poincaré model for the counterclockwise elliptical and circular orbits of the two-body problem** *is* $(\mathscr{P}_1, \Omega, \not{h})$ *where* $\mathscr{P}_1 = P_1(M_1)$, $\Omega(\eta, \lambda, \xi, \Lambda) = 1/2\Lambda^2$, *and* $\not{h} \in \mathscr{P}_1$.

This model is related to III by the Poincaré diffeomorphism P_1. Although not symplectic, P_1 preserves Hamiltonian systems depending on G and L only, analogous to the Delaunay mapping. Finally, the "equivalence" of the restricted models (M_1, H, m) and $(\mathscr{P}_1, \Omega, \not{h})$ can be expressed as follows.

33.13. *Proposition.* *The Poincaré diffeomorphism* $P_1 : M_1 \to \mathscr{P}_1$ *maps integral curves of* X_H *into integral curves of* X_Ω.

The proof is left as an exercise.

Exercises

33A. Prove 33.5 by exhibiting formulas. For example, if $m = (\mathbf{q}, \mathbf{p})$ show that $g(m)$ is determined by the following sequence of formulas (see Figure 33-2):

$$\tan \alpha = q^2/q^1, \qquad \tan \beta = -p_1/p_2, \qquad \gamma = \alpha - \beta;$$

$$\sin \delta = \frac{2a - r}{2ae} \sin 2\gamma; \qquad g = \alpha + \delta - \pi$$

33B. Show explicitly that $\{l, g\} \neq 0$, as follows. From Kepler's law (33.3), show that

$$a^2 e \sin u \{l, g\} = r\{r, g\} - \frac{rG}{e} (\cos u) + aG \sin^2 u$$

Evaluate this at a specific point, say $q^1 = \frac{1}{2}$, $q^2 = 0$, $p_1 = p_2 = 1$, to show $\{l, g\} \neq 0$.

33C. Complete the proof of (b2) and (b3) in the proof of 33.6 as follows: in symplectic coordinates $(q, s, p, -H)$ show

$$\mathbf{L}_{X_H} g_q = \mathbf{L}_{X_H} \mathbf{L}_{X_p} g = \mathbf{L}_{X_p} \mathbf{L}_{X_H} g + \mathbf{L}_{[X_H, X_p]} g$$

and note $[X_H, X_p] = \{p, H\}$. The other terms are handled similarly.

33D. Prove 33.8. Hint: Show $\mathbf{i}_{X_K} \omega_1 = \mathbf{d}K$ and

$$\mathbf{i}_{F_* X_K} F_* \omega_1 = F_*(\mathbf{i}_{X_K} \omega_1) = \mathbf{d}(K \circ F) = \mathbf{i}_{F_* X_K} \omega_1$$

Compare with $\mathbf{i}_{F_* X_K} \omega_0$ to deduce $\mathbf{i}_{F_* X_K}(\mathbf{d}G \wedge \mathbf{d}L) = 0$.

33E. Prove 33.10 by computation. See also Exercise 14F.

33F. In Figure 33-2, let φ denote the angle $\mathbf{0}AP'$, that is, $\varphi = \beta - g$ with α, β defined as in Exercise 33A. Prove that if u is the mean anomaly, then:

$$\tan u = \frac{|G|}{L} \tan \varphi$$

and $f - u = \alpha - \beta$.

33G. Complete the proof of 33.11 by proving that P_1 is a C^∞ mapping. Note this need only be proved near the circular orbits, $G = L$.

Hints: (i) Show λ is a smooth mapping as follows. Let θ denote the usual polar coordinate in the (q^1, q^2) plane $\mathbf{R}^2\setminus\{\mathbf{0}\}$. Using θ, show that the function $g + f$ defined on M_0 extends to a smooth function on M_1. Using Exercise 33F, show the function $f - u$ on M_0 extends to a smooth function on M_1. Then show $g + u$ extends to M_1, and using Kepler's law (33.3) so does $\lambda = g + l$. Note that $e \cos u = 1 - (r/a)$, and $e \sin u = e(1 - \cos^2 u)^{1/2}$.

(ii) Show ξ is smooth by considering the equation

$$(\tfrac{1}{2}(L + G))^{1/2}\xi = Le \cos g$$

(iii) Show η is smooth similarly.

(iv) Show Λ is smooth (trivial).

In fact this argument shows P_1 is analytic (§2).

33H. Show directly that $\Delta_*\omega_1$ is symplectic.

§34. MODELS FOR THREE BODIES

We consider two bodies S and J with mass ratio μ moving in circles about their center of mass (§32). The problem is to determine the motion of a small third body P moving under the influence of the first two, and lying in the same plane. For example, the experimental domain might be the Sun, Jupiter, and a small asteroid, or the Earth, the Moon, and a space vehicle, etc.

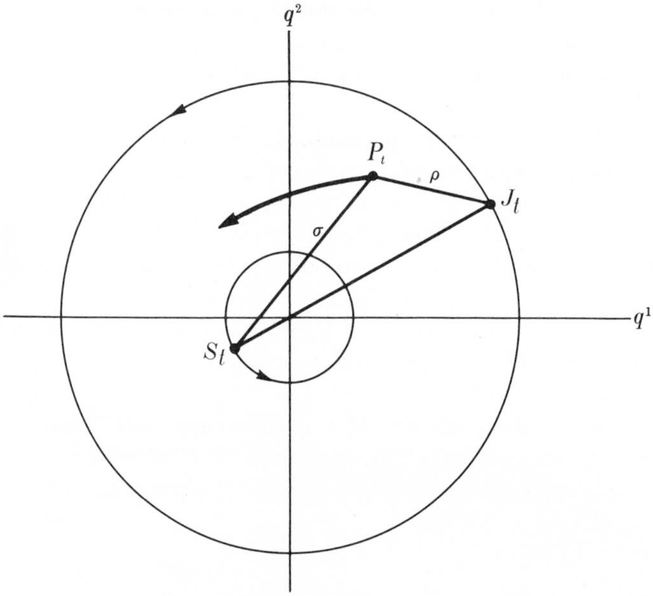

Figure 34-1

As in the two-body problem we omit those points where the potential is singular. Thus, we consider the following model.

34.1. Definition. *For $t \in \mathbf{R}$, $\mu \in \mathbf{R}$, $\mu > 0$, let*

$$S_t = (-\mu \cos t, -\mu \sin t) \in \mathbf{R}^2$$

$$S_* = \bigcup\{(t, S_t) | t \in \mathbf{R}\}$$

$$J_t = ((1 - \mu)\cos t, (1 - \mu)\sin t) \in \mathbf{R}^2$$

and

$$J_* = \bigcup\{(t, J_t) | t \in \mathbf{R}\}$$

The **first model for the restricted three-body problem (3BI)** *is a system (M, H, m, μ), where*

(*i*) $M \subset \mathbf{R} \times T^*\mathbf{R}^2$ **(phase space)** *defined by*

$$M = \mathbf{R} \times [\mathbf{R}^2 \times (\mathbf{R}^2)^* \setminus (S_* \cup J_*) \times (\mathbf{R}^2)^*]$$

with the standard contact structure;

(*ii*) $m \in M$ **(initial conditions)**;

(*iii*) $\mu \in \mathbf{R}$, $\mu > 0$ **(mass ratio)**, *and*

(*iv*) $H \in \mathscr{F}(M)$, *the* **Hamiltonian**, *defined by*

$$H(t, \mathbf{q}, \mathbf{p}) = \frac{\|\mathbf{p}\|^2}{2} - \frac{\mu}{\rho(t, \mathbf{q})} - \frac{1 - \mu}{\sigma(t, \mathbf{q})}$$

where $\| \; \|$ denotes the Euclidean norm, $\rho(t, \mathbf{q}) = \|\mathbf{q} - J_t\|$, and $\sigma(t, \mathbf{q}) = \|\mathbf{q} - S_t\|$.

The **prediction** *consists of the orbit of m in the time dependent Hamiltonian system $\tilde{X}_H$.*

As in the two-body problem, to obtain $H \in \mathscr{F}(M)$ we sacrifice completeness of $\tilde{X}_H$ (collisions). The assumptions that the three bodies lie in one plane and that P does not contribute to the gravitational potential are made to simplify the problem (*restricted* problem of three bodies). Note that H is not invariant under rotations and so we do not have conservation of angular momentum.

The above model is a time dependent Hamiltonian system, but we can obtain an "equivalent" conservative model by using a *rotating coordinate system* as follows.

34.2. Proposition. *Let M and H be as in* 34.1. *Then there is a canonical transformation $F: M \to \mathbf{R} \times T^*W$, $W = \mathbf{R}^2 \setminus \{(-\mu, 0), (1 - \mu, 0)\}$ such that $H' = H \circ F^{-1} + K_{F^{-1}}$ is given by*

$$H'(t, \mathbf{q}, \mathbf{p}) = \frac{\|\mathbf{p}\|^2}{2} + q^1 p_2 - q^2 p_1 - \frac{\mu}{\rho(\mathbf{q})} - \frac{1 - \mu}{\sigma(\mathbf{q})}$$

where $\rho(\mathbf{q}) = \|\mathbf{q} - (1 - \mu, 0)\|$ and $\sigma(\mathbf{q}) = \|\mathbf{q} - (-\mu, 0)\|$.

Proof. Consider the clockwise rotation mapping

$$F\colon M \to \mathbf{R} \times T^*W\colon (t, q^1, q^2, p_1, p_2) \rightsquigarrow (t, x^1, x^2, y_1, y_2)$$

where

$$x^1 = (q^1 \cos t + q^2 \sin t) \qquad y_1 = (p_1 \cos t + p_2 \sin t)$$

$$x^2 = (-q^1 \sin t + q^2 \cos t) \quad y_2 = (-p_1 \sin t + p_2 \cos t)$$

It is clear that F satisfies (C1) and (C2) of 21.1. For (C3) we have, by 10.9,

$$F_*\bar{\omega} = F_*(\mathbf{d}q^1 \wedge \mathbf{d}p_1 + \mathbf{d}q^2 \wedge \mathbf{d}p_2) = \mathbf{d}x^1 \wedge \mathbf{d}y_1 + \mathbf{d}x^2 \wedge \mathbf{d}y_2$$

and by direct computation we see that

$$F_*\tilde{\omega} = \tilde{\omega} + \mathbf{d}(q^1 p_2 - q^2 p_1) \wedge \mathbf{d}t$$

The proposition easily follows. ∎

Thus $F^*\tilde{X}_H = \tilde{X}_{H'}$ as we saw in 21.9. Hence we obtain the following model.

34.3. Definition. *The* **second model for the restricted three-body problem** (3BII) *is a system* (M, H, m, μ) *where*

(*i*) $M \subset T^*\mathbf{R}^2$ **(phase space)** *is defined by* $M = T^*W$, $W = \mathbf{R}^2 \setminus \{(-\mu, 0), (1 - \mu, 0)\}$, *together with the natural symplectic structure;*

(*ii*) $m \in M$ **(initial conditions)**;

(*iii*) $\mu \in \mathbf{R}$, $\mu > 0$ **(mass ratio)**, *and*

(*iv*) $H \in \mathscr{F}(M)$ (*the* **Hamiltonian**) *is defined by*

$$H(\mathbf{q}, \mathbf{p}) = \frac{\|\mathbf{p}\|^2}{2} + q^1 p_2 - q^2 p_1 - \frac{\mu}{\rho(\mathbf{q})} - \frac{1 - \mu}{\sigma(\mathbf{q})}$$

(*see* 34.2).

The extra term in H may be considered the rotational energy or angular momentum introduced by the rotating coordinate system.

34.4. Proposition. *The Hamiltonian H in model* 3BII (34.3) *is hyperregular* (§18). *The corresponding Lagrangian on TW is given by*

$$\mathscr{L}(\mathbf{q}, \dot{\mathbf{q}}) = \frac{\|\dot{\mathbf{q}}\|^2}{2} + \dot{q}^1 q^2 - \dot{q}^2 q^1 + \frac{\|\mathbf{q}\|^2}{2} + \frac{\mu}{\rho(\mathbf{q})} + \frac{1 - \mu}{\sigma(\mathbf{q})}$$

with ρ, σ as in 34.2 *and notation as in* 17.5.

Proof. For $H\colon T^*W \to \mathbf{R}$, $FH\colon T^*W \to TW$ is given by (see §17) $(q^1, q^2, p_1, p_2) \rightsquigarrow (q^1, q^2, p_1 - q^2, p_2 + q^1)$ which is a diffeomorphism. Hence H is hyperregular with inverse

$$(\mathbf{F}H)^{-1}\colon (q^1, q^2, \dot{q}^1, \dot{q}^2) \rightsquigarrow (q^1, q^2, \dot{q}^1 + q^2, \dot{q}^2 - q^1)$$

From 18.8, the action of H is

$$B = p_1 \frac{\partial H}{\partial p_1} + p_2 \frac{\partial H}{\partial p_2} = \|\mathbf{p}\|^2 + q^1 p_2 - q^2 p_1$$

Hence $\mathscr{L} = A - E$, where $E = H \circ (FH)^{-1}$ and $A = B \circ (FH)^{-1}$, so that after simplification:

$$E(\mathbf{q}, \dot{\mathbf{q}}) = \frac{\|\dot{\mathbf{q}}\|^2}{2} - \frac{\mu}{\rho(\mathbf{q})} - \frac{1-\mu}{\sigma(\mathbf{q})} - \frac{\|\mathbf{q}\|^2}{2}$$

and $A(\mathbf{q}, \dot{\mathbf{q}}) = \|\dot{\mathbf{q}}\|^2 + \dot{q}^1 q^2 - \dot{q}^2 q^1$. This gives the desired form for $\mathscr{L}$. ∎

Formally then, this transition to the Lagrangian formulation may be regarded as giving another "equivalent" model.

34.5. Definition. *The* **third model for the restricted three-body problem** (3BIII) *is* $(TW, \mathscr{L}, x, \mu)$ *where*

(*i*) $W = \mathbf{R}^2 \setminus \{(-\mu, 0), (1-\mu, 0)\}$;
(*ii*) $x \in TW$;
(*iii*) $\mu > 0$, *and*
(*iv*) $\mathscr{L} \in \mathscr{F}(TW)$ *the* **Lagrangian**, *is defined by*

$$\mathscr{L}(\mathbf{q}, \dot{\mathbf{q}}) = \frac{\|\dot{\mathbf{q}}\|^2}{2} + \dot{q}^1 q^2 - \dot{q}^2 q^1 + \frac{\mu}{\rho(\mathbf{q})} + \frac{1-\mu}{\sigma(\mathbf{q})} + \frac{\|\mathbf{q}\|^2}{2}$$

The **prediction** *of the model is the integral curve of* X_E *at* x.

The prediction is obtained from the Lagrangian equations (§17) which in this case become:

$$\frac{d^2 q^1(t)}{dt^2} + \frac{2dq^2(t)}{dt} = q^1(t) - (1-\mu)\frac{(q^1(t)+\mu)}{\sigma(\mathbf{q}(t))^3} - \mu\frac{(q^1(t)-1+\mu)}{\rho(\mathbf{q}(t))^3}$$

$$\frac{d^2 q^2(t)}{dt^2} - \frac{2dq^1(t)}{dt} = q^2(t) - (1-\mu)\frac{q^2(t)}{\sigma(\mathbf{q}(t))^3} - \frac{\mu q^2(t)}{\rho(\mathbf{q}(t))^3}$$

together with the energy integral (see the proof of 34.4):

$$E = \frac{\|\dot{\mathbf{q}}\|^2}{2} - \frac{\|\mathbf{q}\|^2}{2} - \frac{\mu}{\rho(\mathbf{q})} - \frac{1-\mu}{\sigma(\mathbf{q})}$$

We obtain additional models for the restricted three-body problem by applying the Delaunay and Poincaré mappings to model 3BII. The latter yields a very convenient model for the application of the Moser center theorem (§36).

Recall that the third two-body model (32.6) had phase space $M = T^*(\mathbf{R}^2 \setminus \{\mathbf{0}\})$ with natural symplectic form ω_0 and Hamiltonian $H(\mathbf{q},\mathbf{p}) = \|\mathbf{p}\|^2/2 - 1/\|\mathbf{q}\|$. We will now denote this Hamiltonian by H_{2B}. The Delaunay mapping (33.4) is a diffeomorphism

$$\Delta\colon M_0 \to \mathscr{D} \subset T^*T^2\colon (q^1, q^2, p_1, p_2) \rightsquigarrow (g, l, G, L)$$

where $M_0 \subset M$ is an open subset. This mapping is not symplectic with respect to the natural symplectic form ω_1 in $\mathscr{D} \subset T^*T^2$ for two reasons (§33). However we may take it symplectic trivially by introducing an unnatural symplectic structure in $\mathscr{D}$, $\omega_D = \Delta^*\omega_0$. Then if $K \in \mathscr{F}(\mathscr{D})$ and the Hamiltonian vectorfield X_K is constructed with the symplectic form ω_D, we will have $\Delta_* X_K = X_{\Delta_* K}$ as usual. If however we express the local representative of X_K with respect to the natural chart on $\mathscr{D}$, the Hamiltonian equations will have a slightly unusual form because the natural chart is not a symplectic chart with respect to ω_D (see Exercise 14E). We now derive the equations X_K for an arbitrary $K \in \mathscr{F}(\mathscr{D})$.

First we shall express ω_D in the natural chart (x^1, x^2, y_1, y_2). Recall that

$$\begin{aligned}
\omega_1 &= \mathbf{d}x^1 \wedge \mathbf{d}y_1 + \mathbf{d}x^2 \wedge \mathbf{d}y_2 \\
\omega_0 &= \mathbf{d}q^1 \wedge \mathbf{d}p_1 + \mathbf{d}q^2 \wedge \mathbf{d}p_2 \\
\Delta_*\omega_1 &= \mathbf{d}g \wedge \mathbf{d}G + \mathbf{d}l \wedge \mathbf{d}L
\end{aligned}$$

and from theorem 33.7

$$\Delta_*\omega_1 = \omega_0 + 2\,\mathbf{d}l \wedge \mathbf{d}L + \{l, g\}\,\mathbf{d}G \wedge \mathbf{d}L$$

Thus

$$\Delta_*(\omega_1 - 2\mathbf{d}x^2 \wedge \mathbf{d}y^2 - \{x^2, x^1\}\,\mathbf{d}y_1 \wedge \mathbf{d}y_2) = \omega_0$$

where $\{x^2, x^1\}$ is the Poisson bracket with respect to ω_D, so

$$\omega_D = \mathbf{d}x^1 \wedge \mathbf{d}y_1 - \mathbf{d}x^2 \wedge \mathbf{d}y_2 + \{x^1, x^2\}\,\mathbf{d}y_1 \wedge \mathbf{d}y_2$$

Now we see, with the notations of 14.1, we have

$$\begin{aligned}
(\underline{x}^1)^\flat &= \mathbf{i}_{\underline{x}^1}\omega_D = \mathbf{d}y_1 \\
(\underline{x}^2)^\flat &= -\mathbf{d}y_2 \\
\underline{y}_1^\flat &= -\mathbf{d}x^1 + \{x^1, x^2\}\,\mathbf{d}y_2 \\
\underline{y}_2^\flat &= \mathbf{d}x^2 - \{x^1, x^2\}\,\mathbf{d}y_1
\end{aligned}$$

and therefore

$$\begin{aligned}
(\mathbf{d}x^1)^\sharp &= -\underline{y}_1 - \{x^1, x^2\}\underline{x}^2 \\
(\mathbf{d}x^2)^\sharp &= \underline{y}_2 + \{x^1, x^2\}\underline{x}^1 \\
(\mathbf{d}y_1)^\sharp &= \underline{x}^1 \\
(\mathbf{d}y_2)^\sharp &= -\underline{x}^2
\end{aligned}$$

Hence if $K \in \mathscr{F}(\mathscr{D})$, $X_K = (\mathbf{d}K)^\sharp$ is given by:

$$X_K = (K_{y_1} + \{x^1, x^2\}K_{x^2})\underline{x}^1 + (-K_{y_2} - \{x^1, x^2\}K_{x^1})\underline{x}^2 - K_{x^1}\underline{y}_1 + K_{x^2}\underline{y}_2$$

Thus a curve $t \rightsquigarrow (x^1(t), x^2(t), y_1(t), y_2(t))$ is an integral curve of X_K iff it satisfies the system of equations:

$$\frac{dx^1}{dt} = \frac{\partial K}{\partial y_1} + \{x^1, x^2\}\frac{\partial K}{\partial x^2}$$

$$\frac{dx^2}{dt} = -\frac{\partial K}{\partial y_2} - \{x^1, x^2\}\frac{\partial K}{\partial x^1}$$

$$\frac{dy_1}{dt} = -\frac{\partial K}{\partial x^1}$$

$$\frac{dy_2}{dt} = \frac{\partial K}{\partial x^2}$$

These equations are actually Hamiltonian with respect to ω_D, although they are not in "canonical form" because (x^1, x^2, y_1, y_2) are not "canonical coordinates," as $\{x^1, x^2\} \neq 0$. Recall that in model 3BII we have the phase space $M^\mu = T^*W^\mu$, $W^\mu = \mathbf{R}^2 \diagdown \{(-\mu, 0), (1 - \mu, 0)\}$, so Δ may be defined on $M_0 \diagdown (\{(-\mu, 0), \ (1 - \mu, 0)\} \times \mathbf{R}^2) = M_0 \cap M^\mu \subset T^*\mathbf{R}^2$ (33.4) Let $\mathscr{D}^\mu = \Delta(M_0 \cap M^\mu)$ which is an open subset of $\mathscr{D}$. Also we have

$$H^\mu = \frac{\|\mathbf{p}\|}{2} + G + \frac{\mu}{\rho} + \frac{1-\mu}{\sigma} = H_{2B} + G + \mu\left(\frac{1}{\rho} - \frac{1}{\sigma}\right) + \left(\frac{1}{\sigma} - \frac{1}{\|\mathbf{q}\|}\right)$$

or $H^\mu = -1/2L^2 + G + S_\mu$ where

$$S_\mu = \mu\left(\frac{1}{\rho} - \frac{1}{\sigma}\right) + \left(\frac{1}{\sigma} - \frac{1}{\|\mathbf{q}\|}\right)$$

and H_{2B} is the Hamiltonian of the third two-body model (32.6). Thus $H^\mu = H^0 + S_\mu$ where $H^0 = -1/2L^2 + G$. If $K^\mu = \Delta^* H^\mu$, then $K^\mu = K^0 + R_\mu$, where $K^0 = \Delta^* H^0 = -1/2y_2^2 + y_1$, and $R_\mu = \Delta^* S_\mu$. Note R_0 and S_0 are zero.

We may now summarize this new model. For historical reasons we again relabel the coordinates (x^1, x^2, y_1, y_2) by (g, l, G, L) in spite of the danger of confusion.

34.6. Definition. *The* **Delaunay model for the restricted three-body problem** *is the system* $(\mathscr{D}^\mu, \omega_D, K^\mu, \mathscr{A}, \mu)$ *where* $\mathscr{D}^\mu = \Delta(M_0 \cap M^\mu)$, $\omega_D = \mathbf{d}g \wedge \mathbf{d}G - \mathbf{d}l \wedge \mathbf{d}L + \{g, l\}\mathbf{d}G \wedge \mathbf{d}L$, $\mu > 0$, $\mathscr{A} \in \mathscr{D}^\mu$; *and* $K(g, l, G, L) = -1/2L^2 + G + R_\mu(g, l, G, L)$. *The* **prediction** *in this model is the integral curve at* $\mathscr{A}$ *of the Hamiltonian vectorfield* X_K *of* K *with respect to* ω_D.

Thus in the Delaunay model the equations of motion are

$$\frac{dg}{dt} = 1 + \left[\frac{\partial R_\mu}{\partial G} + \{g, l\}\frac{\partial R_\mu}{\partial l}\right]$$

$$\frac{dl}{dt} = -\frac{1}{L^3} - \left[\frac{\partial R_\mu}{\partial L} - \{g, l\}\frac{\partial R_\mu}{\partial g}\right]$$

$$\frac{dG}{dt} = -\frac{\partial R_\mu}{\partial g}$$

$$\frac{dL}{dt} = \frac{\partial R_\mu}{\partial l}$$

Warning. *Because of the notations, it seems as if* $F_*\omega_1 = \omega_D$, *which is false. Also, the equations of motion differ from those of authors who suppose that* $\{g, l\} = 0$.

Except for this difference, this model agrees with the one in common use, and the extra terms disappear for $\mu = 0$.

Note that in this model the domain $\mathscr{D}^\mu$ and the Hamiltonian K^μ depend on the parameter μ. The model is "equivalent" to the second model restricted to an open subset (not necessarily invariant) of the phase space, by a symplectic diffeomorphism preserving the Hamiltonian vectorfield and therefore the predictions. For $\mu = 0$, the model corresponds to the elliptical closed orbit domain of the two-body problem in a rotating coordinate system. The domain does not contain the circular orbits, nor can the model be extended in a straightforward fashion so as to include them.

For the study of the circular orbits in the case $\mu \cong 0$, the model obtained from the Poincaré mapping is more useful. As the derivation of this model is very similar to the case of the Delaunay mapping treated above, we will simply state the model and leave the relationship to 3BII as an exercise.

34.7. Definition. *The* **Poincaré model for the restricted three-body problem** *is* $(\mathscr{P}^\mu, \omega_P, \Omega^\mu, \not{h}, \mu)$ *where* $\mu > 0$, $\not{h} \in \mathscr{P}^\mu$, $\mathscr{P}^\mu = P_1(M_1 \cap M^\mu)$, *considered a symplectic manifold with the symplectic form:*

$$\omega_P = \mathbf{d}\eta \wedge \mathbf{d}\xi + \mathbf{d}\lambda \wedge \mathbf{d}\Lambda + \{\xi, \lambda\}\mathbf{d}\eta \wedge \mathbf{d}\Lambda + \{\lambda, \eta\}\mathbf{d}\xi \wedge \mathbf{d}\Lambda$$

and Ω^μ *is the Hamiltonian function defined by* $\Omega^\mu = \Omega_0 + \Omega_\mu^*$, *where*

$$\Omega_0(\eta, \lambda, \xi, \Lambda) = -\frac{1}{2\Lambda^2} + \Lambda - \tfrac{1}{2}(\xi^2 + \eta^2)$$

and

$$\Omega_\mu^* = P_1^* S_\mu$$

The **prediction** *in this model is the integral curve at* $\not p \in \mathscr{P}$ *of the Hamiltonian vectorfield*

$$X_{\Omega^\mu} = X_{\Omega^0} + X_{\Omega^*_\mu}$$

of Ω^μ *with respect* ω_P.

Note that the equations of motion for $\mu = 0$ are, as $\Omega^*_0 = 0$:

$$\frac{d\eta}{dt} = -\xi$$

$$\frac{d\lambda}{dt} = \frac{1}{\Lambda^3} + 1$$

$$\frac{d\xi}{dt} = \eta, \quad \frac{d\Lambda}{dt} = 0$$

The equivalence of this model and 3BII (restricted to the domain $M_1 \cap M^\mu$) is given by the following.

34.8. Proposition. *If* P_1 *is the Poincaré diffeomorphism, then* $P_1^*\omega_0 = \omega_P$, $P_1^*H^\mu = \Omega^\mu$, *and* P_1 *maps integral curves of* X_{H^μ} *into integral curves of* X_{Ω^μ}.

The proof is left as an exercise. The construction of this model is summarized in the following diagram.

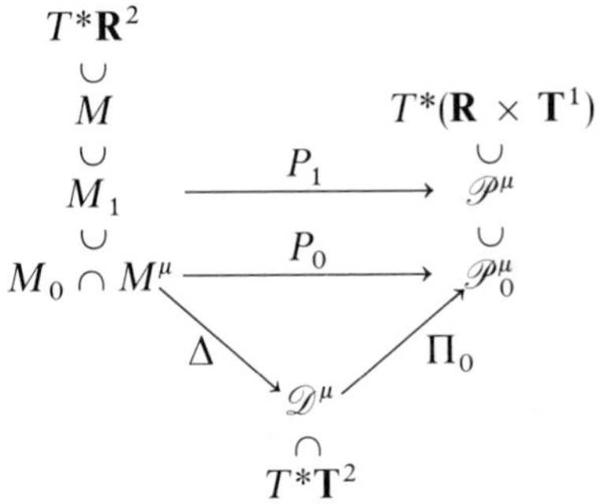

Exercises

34A. To prove 34.8, show that

$$\omega_P = P_1^*\omega_0 = \omega_2 + f(x^1 dx^1 \wedge dy_2 + y^1 dy_1 \wedge dy_2)$$

for some function f, by direct computation. Then, as in Exercise 14E, show that $fx^1 = \{y_1, x^2\}$ and $fy^1 = \{x^1, x^2\}$, where the Poisson brackets are computed with ω_P. Hint: Note that $y^1\,(fx^1) = x^1(fy^1)$.

34B. In 33A it is evident that $\{y_1, x^2\}y_1 - \{x^2, x^1\}x^1 = 0$. Prove this directly, using the facts that $\{x^2, \quad\}$ is a derivation, and $\xi^2 + \eta^2 = 2(L - G)$ is a constant of motion.

34C. Derive the Lagrangian equations stated after 34.5. Hint: Compute $\mathbf{F}\mathscr{L}$, and show that:

$$\omega_{\mathscr{L}} = \mathbf{d}q^1 \wedge \mathbf{d}\dot{q}^1 + \mathbf{d}q^2 \wedge \mathbf{d}\dot{q}^2 + 2\mathbf{d}q^1 \wedge \mathbf{d}q^2$$

$$E = \tfrac{1}{2}(\|\dot{\mathbf{q}}\|^2 - \|\mathbf{q}\|^2) - \frac{\mu}{\rho} - \frac{1-\mu}{\sigma}$$

Then compute the raising and lowering operation of $\omega_{\mathscr{L}}$, and find X_E with respect to $\omega_{\mathscr{L}}$.

§35. CRITICAL POINTS IN THE RESTRICTED THREE-BODY PROBLEM

In this section we examine the critical points in the restricted three-body problem using model 3BIII (34.5). These correspond to periodic orbits of period 2π in the time dependent model 3BI (34.1).

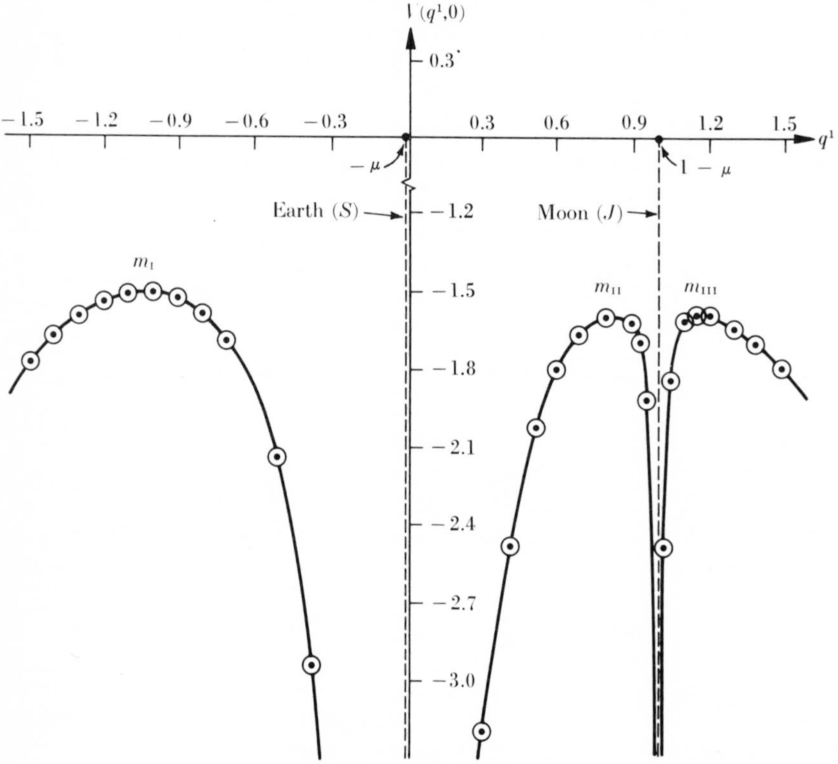

Figure 35-1 (a)

The potential V for $q^2 = 0$, showing the three collinear solutions of Euler in the Earth-Moon system: $\mu = 0.012277471$.

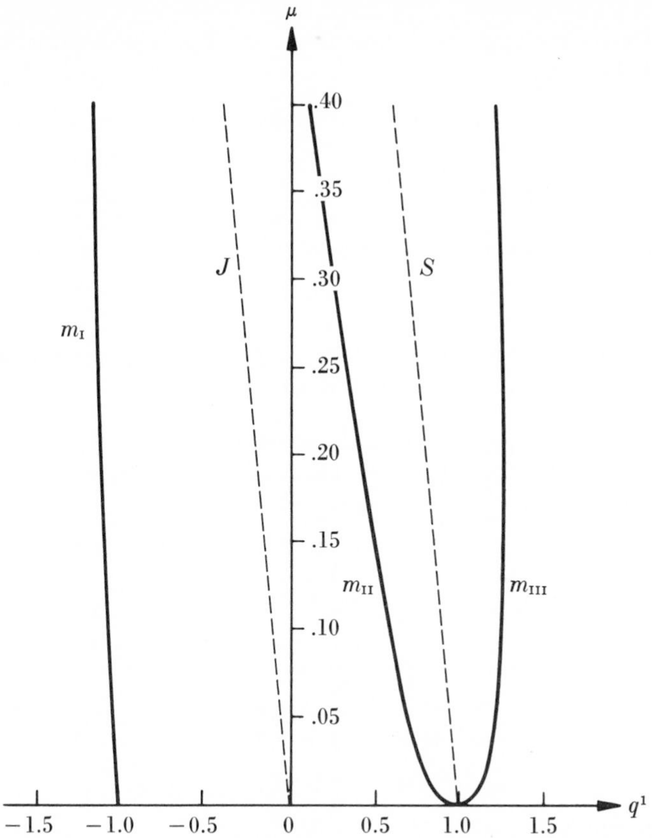

Figure 35-1 (b)
Positions of the three collinear solutions of Euler as functions of the mass ratio, μ.

Recall that $m \in TW$ (34.5) is a critical point iff $X_E(m) = 0$ iff $dE(m) = 0$. Carrying out the differentiation yields the following.

35.1. Proposition. *The point $(q^1, q^2, \dot{q}^1, \dot{q}^2) \in TW$ is a critical point of X_E iff $\dot{\mathbf{q}} = \mathbf{0}$, and $\mathbf{q}$ is a critical point of the function $V \in \mathscr{F}(W)$ defined by*

$$V(q^1, q^2) = -\tfrac{1}{2}[(q^1)^2 + (q^2)^2] - \frac{\mu}{\rho} - \frac{1-\mu}{\sigma}$$

or equivalently:

(*i*) $\dot{q}^1 = \dot{q}^2 = 0$

(*ii*) $-V_{q^1} = q^1\left(1 - \dfrac{1-\mu}{\sigma(\mathbf{q})^3} - \dfrac{\mu}{\rho(\mathbf{q})^3}\right) + \mu(1-\mu)\left(\dfrac{1}{\rho(\mathbf{q})^3} - \dfrac{1}{\sigma(\mathbf{q})^3}\right) = 0$

and

$$(iii) \quad -V_{q^2} = q^2\left(1 - \frac{1-\mu}{\sigma(\mathbf{q})^3} - \frac{\mu}{\rho(\mathbf{q})^3}\right) = 0$$

The critical points with $q^2 = 0$ are three in number, called the **collinear solutions** (Euler, 1767). The graph of V is shown in Figure 35-1a, with $q^2 = 0$, and the positions of the critical points as functions of μ in Figure 35-1b.

The other critical points, with $q^2 \neq 0$, occur when $\sigma = \rho$, which is satisfied only in the two cases: $q^1 = \frac{1}{2} - \mu$ and $q^2 = \pm 3^{1/2}/2$ (Lagrange's **equilateral triangle solutions**, 1773). See Figure 35-2.

There are no other critical points. The graph of V is shown in Figure 35-3.

We now study the stability of these five critical points by means of the theory of §30. Recall that the Lagrangian system X_E is a Hamiltonian vectorfield (§17) so the theorems of §30 apply. In fact, the characteristic exponents may be computed in either the Hamiltonian (3BII) or the Lagrangian (3BIII) model, according to the following.

35.2. Proposition. *Let H be a hyperregular Hamiltonian on T^*M and E the energy of the corresponding Lagrangian $\mathcal{L}$ on TM* (§18). *Then the characteristic multipliers of a critical element $m \in T^*M$ with respect to X_H are the same as those of $FH(m) \in TM$ with respect to X_E.*

Proof. Suppose F is the integral of X_H and $m \in T^*M$ is a critical point. Then the integral of X_E at $FH(m)$ is given by

$$G(t, FH(m)) = FH \circ F_t \circ FH^{-1}(m)$$

as we saw in §18. Since the flows are related by similarity, the result readily follows. (See 22.6 and Exercise 35A.) ∎

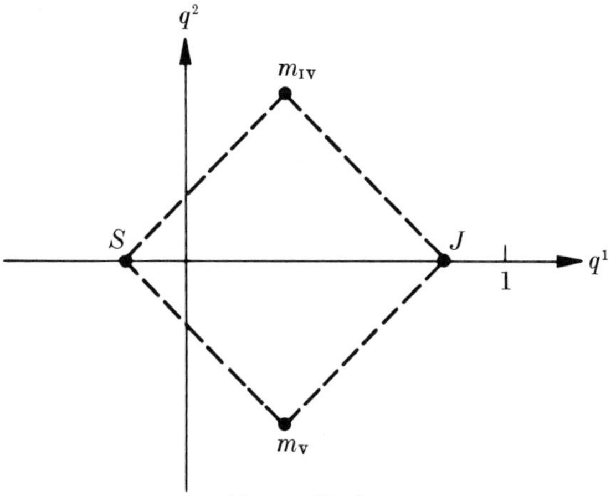

Figure 35-2
The equilateral triangle solutions of Lagrange.

From the Lagrangian equations in model 3BIII (§34) we see that the components of X_E relative to the natural chart are

$$X^1(\mathbf{q}, \dot{\mathbf{q}}) = \dot{q}^1$$

$$X^2(\mathbf{q}, \dot{\mathbf{q}}) = \dot{q}^2$$

$$X^3(\mathbf{q}, \dot{\mathbf{q}}) = -2\dot{q}^2 - V_1(\mathbf{q}, \dot{\mathbf{q}})$$

$$X^4(\mathbf{q}, \dot{\mathbf{q}}) = 2\dot{q}^1 - V_2(\mathbf{q}, \dot{\mathbf{q}})$$

where

$$V_1(\mathbf{q}, \dot{\mathbf{q}}) = V_{q^1}(\mathbf{q}, \dot{\mathbf{q}}) = q^1 - \frac{\mu(q^1 - 1 + \mu)}{[\rho(\mathbf{q})]^3} - \frac{(1 - \mu)(q^1 + \mu)}{[\sigma(\mathbf{q})]^3}$$

and

$$V_2(\mathbf{q}, \dot{\mathbf{q}}) = V_{q^2}(\mathbf{q}, \dot{\mathbf{q}}) = q^2 - \frac{(1 - \mu)q^2}{[\sigma(\mathbf{q})]^3} - \frac{\mu q^2}{[\rho(\mathbf{q})]^3}$$

(See 34.4.)

Thus the characteristic exponents are eigenvalues of the matrix representing $X'_E(m)$:

$$\begin{bmatrix} 0 & 0 & -V_{11} & -V_{12} \\ 0 & 0 & -V_{21} & -V_{22} \\ 1 & 0 & 0 & 2 \\ 0 & 1 & -2 & 0 \end{bmatrix}$$

where $V_{ij} = V_{q^iq^j}$. The characteristic polynomial is then

$$P(\lambda) = \lambda^4 + (4 + V_{11} + V_{22})\lambda^2 + (V_{11}V_{22} - V_{12}^2)$$

(Note that $det\begin{pmatrix} A & B \\ C & D \end{pmatrix} = det(AD - BC)$ if $CD = DC$.)

This is quadratic in λ^2 so that solutions have the form $\alpha_1, -\alpha_1, \alpha_2, -\alpha_2$, as they must according to the general theory (§28).

35.3. Proposition. *The collinear critical points of X_E for the restricted three-body problem are α^σ-unstable for all types α^σ* (26.2).

Proof. In this case $V_2 = V_{12} = 0$ so that $P(\lambda) = \lambda^4 + (4 + V_{11} + V_{22})\lambda^2 + V_{11}V_{22}$. It is easily verified directly that $V_{11} < 0 < V_{22}$ at these critical points. Hence $P(\lambda)$ has two real roots, and so the stable and unstable manifolds are both present. ∎

For the equilateral triangle solutions,

$$P(\lambda) = \lambda^4 + \lambda^2 + \tfrac{27}{4}\mu(1 - \mu) = 0$$

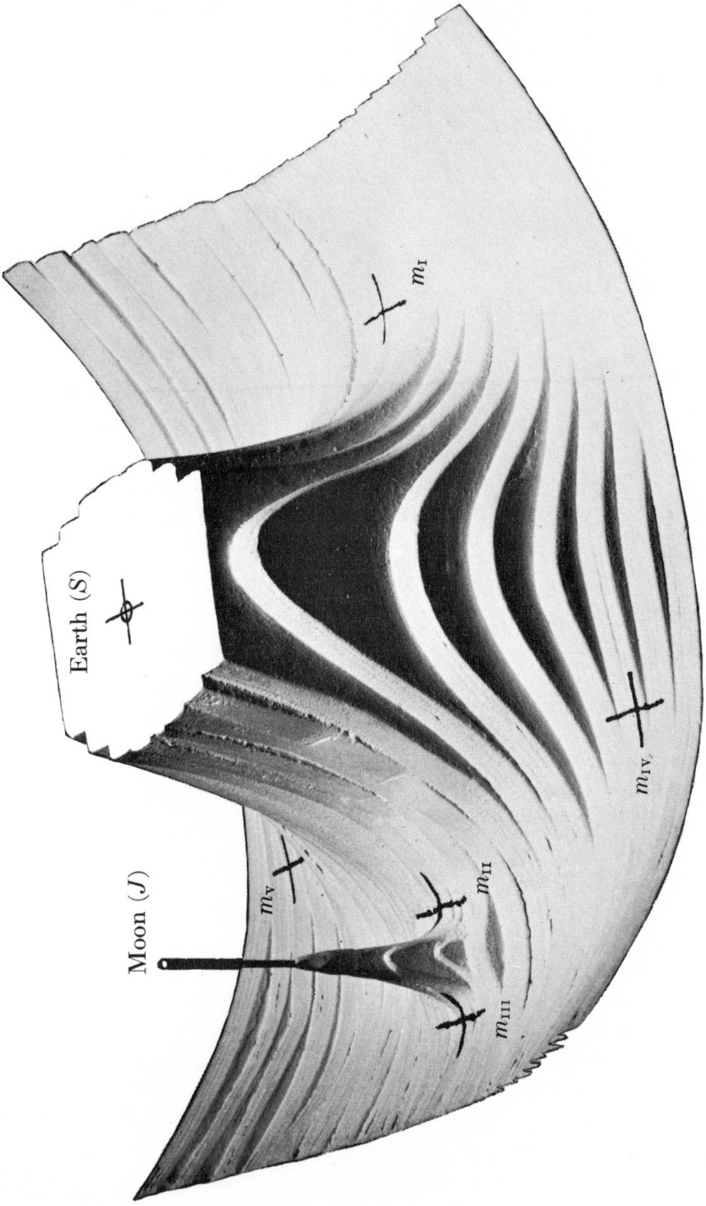

Figure 35-3

The graph of the potential $-V(q^1, q^2)$ of the Earth and Moon in rotating coordinates, $\mu = 0.012277471$, showing the five critical points.

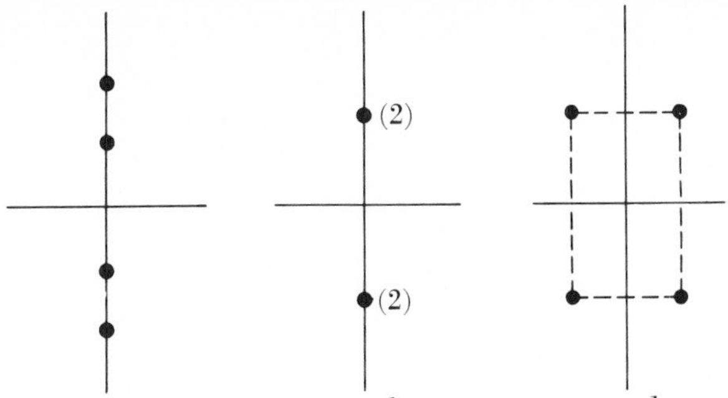

$0 < \mu < \frac{1}{27}$ $\quad$ $\mu \sim \frac{1}{27}$ (stable?) $\quad$ $\mu \gtrsim \frac{1}{26}$ (unstable)

Figure 35-4

and so $\lambda^2 = -\frac{1}{2} \pm \frac{1}{2}\{1 - 27\mu(1 - \mu)\}^{1/2}$, thus, if $0 < \mu < \frac{1}{27}$ then there are four eigenvalues on the imaginary axis. The Kelley center theorem (29.3) assures orbital stability $(0+)$ on the two subcenter manifolds, but not globally. This problem of stability remains unsolved, and experimental evidence indicates that they are indeed stable, as satellites have been observed in such positions. (See van de Kamp [1; p. 114].) On the other hand, nothing has been observed in the collinear critical points.

For the triangle case, the locations of the characteristic exponents for three values of μ are indicated in Figure 35-4.

Exercises

35A. Prove 35.2 for closed orbits. See Exercise 25A.

35B. Complete the details for 35.3 and succeeding remarks.

35C. Prove 35.1. (See Exercise 34C.)

§36. CLOSED ORBITS IN THE RESTRICTED THREE-BODY PROBLEM

In this section we will obtain some of the well-known closed orbits and periodic orbits in the restricted three-body problem.

Recall that in 3BI, the first model for the restricted three-body problem (34.1), the two bodies rotate around the origin and the Hamiltonian is time dependent. The system is a vectorfield on $M_{\mathrm{I}} \subset \mathbf{R} \times T^*\mathbf{R}^2$ with a constant upward vertical component, and the orbits are always rising. The "trajectory" in the phase space is obtained by projecting an integral curve into $T^*\mathbf{R}^2$. Thus an orbit in this model can never be closed (that is, a cycle), but the integral curve might be periodic in the sense that the projected trajectory is a closed curve (not necessarily simple, see Figure 36-1), say $t \rightsquigarrow (t, m_t)$, and $m_{t+\tau} = m_t$ for all t.

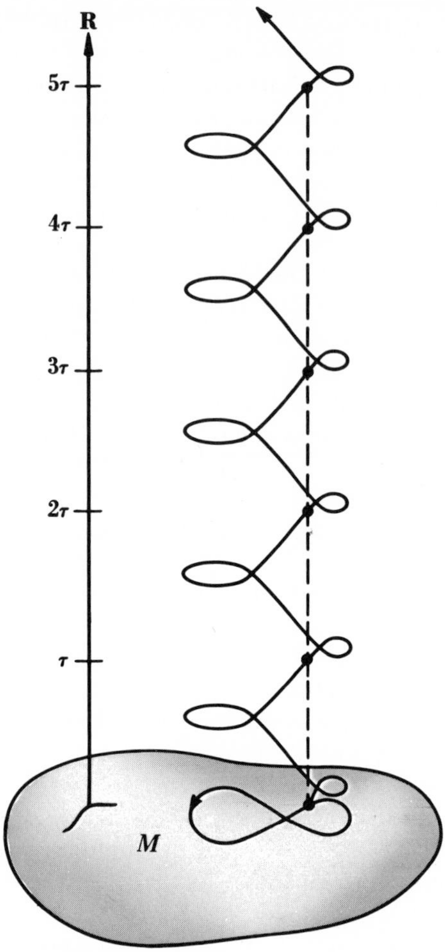

Figure 36-1

A *periodic orbit* in this sense, which spirals up covering a closed curve in phase space, is the analogue of a closed orbit for the time-dependent case. The projection into the phase space is called a *closed orbit*, but remember that it is not an orbit of an autonomous vectorfield, and may have self-intersections.

Recall also that 3BII, the second model (34.3), has the two bodies transformed to rest on the q^1 axis, and the Hamiltonian is conservative. The models are related by a canonical transformation $M_{\mathrm{I}} \to \mathbf{R} \times M_{\mathrm{II}}$ which preserves integral curves. Thus critical points in M_{II} become periodic orbits in M_{I} with period 2π, hence "closed orbits" in the phase space of M_{I}.

In the last section we showed the existence of exactly five critical points in the second model, the collinear solutions m_1, m_2, m_3 of Euler and the triangular solutions m_4 and m_5 of Lagrange. These critical points are mapped into periodic orbits $\gamma_1, \ldots, \gamma_5$ of period 2π in the first model by the canonical transformation relating the two models. As m_1, m_2 and m_3 are unstable critical points, γ_1, γ_2 and γ_3 are unstable periodic orbits (in a sense we have not made precise). The stability of m_4 and m_5, so also γ_4 and γ_5, remains an open question.

Also m_1, m_2 and m_3 have one-dimensional stable and unstable manifolds and a two-dimensional center manifold (35.3). The critical points m_4 and m_5 have imaginary characteristic exponents for $\mu < 1/27$ (§35), and for almost all $\mu \in (0, 1/27)$ the two exponents on the positive imaginary axis are independent over the integers. Applying the subcenter stability theorem (29.3) we have in these cases one-parameter families of closed orbits γ_{II}^s with periods τ_s depending continuously on s. For nearly all s we have $\tau_s = 2p\pi/q$ for relatively prime integers p and q, and γ_{II}^s is mapped into a closed orbit γ_{I}^2 in 3BI of period $2p\pi$. These are the closed orbits discovered by Liapounov [1] in 1882.

36.1. Theorem (Liapounov). *In M_{I} there are five closed orbits of period 2π corresponding to the critical points in M_{II}, and if $\mu < 1/27$, every neighborhood of any of these contains infinitely many closed orbits of arbitrarily high period.*

Next we turn to the closed orbits which are obtained by "analytic continuation" from $\mu = 0$. These are of two types. The *closed orbits of the first kind*, discovered by Poincaré [1, t. 1] in 1892, are close to the circular Keplerian orbits in the second model. The *closed orbits of the second kind*, discovered by Arenstorf [1], in 1963, are close to Keplerian orbits of arbitrary (positive) eccentricity. We shall treat both types simultaneously, using the Poincaré model (34.7), in a program suggested by Barrar [1].

The first step in this program is a trivial but very convenient criterion for closed orbits in model 3BII, apparently discovered by Birkhoff [2; v. I, p. 713] in 1914. If the initial condition m_0 is a symmetric conjunction at time $t = 0$, that is, a point of the form $m_0 = (q^1, q^2, p_1, p_2) = (q^1, 0, 0, p_2)$, and again at time $t = \tau/2$, $m_{\tau/2} = ('q^1, 0, 0, 'p_2)$, then $m_\tau = m_0$, so m_0 is in a closed orbit whose period divides τ. This is simply due to the fact that model 3BII is invariant under reflection through the (q^1, p_1) plane, which is true for all values of μ. Translating Birkhoff's criterion to the Poincaré model, we obtain the following. See 34.7 for notations.

36.2. Proposition. *In the Poincaré model for the restricted three-body problem if an initial condition $\not{h}_0$ is in symmetric conjunction, $\not{h}_0 = (0, 0, \xi_0, \Lambda_0)$ at time $t = 0$, and again at time $t = \tau/2$, that is $\not{h}_{\tau/2} = (0, n\pi, \pm\xi_0, \Lambda_0)$ for some integer n, then $\not{h}_0$ is a closed orbit of X_{Ω^μ} (for any μ) whose period divides τ, or $\not{h}_\tau = (0, 2n\pi, \xi_0, \Lambda_0)$.*

The proof is left for an exercise. Note that in $(0, 0, \xi_0, \Lambda_0)$ we have $\xi_0 = (2(L - G))^{1/2}$.

The second step in the program is to find a closed orbit in the case $\mu = 0$, using this criterion. Even though $\mu = 0$ corresponds to the two-body problem, not all orbits are closed because the coordinate system is rotating. In fact we only find closed orbits when Λ_0^3 is rational, and the period is a multiple of π.

36.3. Corollary. *In the Poincaré model with $\mu = 0$, initial conditions of the form $\not{p}_0 = (0, 0, \xi_0, \Lambda_0)$ with $\Lambda_0^{-3} = m/k$ (m, k integers) are in closed orbits of X_{Ω^0} whose period divides $2k\pi$. If m and k are relatively prime, the period equals $2k\pi$.*

Proof. From 34.7 we have $X_{\Omega^0} = (-\xi, \Lambda^{-3} + 1, \eta, 0)$ so the flow is

$$(\eta_0, \lambda_0, \xi_0, \Lambda_0; t) \rightsquigarrow (\eta_0 \cos t - \xi_0 \sin t, \lambda_0 + (\Lambda^{-3} + 1)t, \eta_0 \sin t - \xi_0 \cos t, \Lambda_0)$$

In the case of symmetric conjunction, this becomes

$$(\not{p}_0, t) = (0, 0, \xi_0, \Lambda_0; t) \rightsquigarrow \not{p}_t = (-\xi_0 \sin t, (\Lambda^{-3} + 1)t, \xi_0 \cos t, \Omega_0)$$

so if $\Lambda_0^{-3} = m/k$ and $t = k\pi$ we have $\not{p}_{k\pi} = (0, (m + k)\pi, \pm\xi_0, \Lambda_0)$, which satisfies the criterion (36.2). The proof of the last statement is left as an exercise. ∎

Note that above we obtain $+\xi_0$ or $-\xi_0$ in $\not{p}_{k\pi}$ according as k is even or odd. In any case the period is a rational multiple of 2π, and thus gives rise to a "closed orbit" or periodic orbit in the first model 3BI.

The third step in the program consists of showing that these particular closed orbits are preserved under small perturbations of μ away from zero. This requires the consideration of the domain $\mathscr{P}^\mu$, Hamiltonian Ω^μ, vectorfield X_{Ω^μ}, and integral F^μ, all depending on the parameter μ. It is important that all vary smoothly with μ. We let $\mathscr{D}^\mu = \mathscr{D}_{X_{\Omega^\mu}} \subset \mathscr{P}^\mu \times \mathbf{R}$ denote the domain of the integral F^μ of X_{Ω^μ} (7.10). Also, we extend all of our models for the restricted three-body problem by allowing μ to take on negative values, thus any real value. For each μ we have $\mathscr{P}^\mu \subset T^*(\mathbf{R} \times \mathbf{T}^1)$, and thus

$$\mathscr{P}^\# = \bigcup_{\mu \in \mathbf{R}} (\{\mu\} \times \mathscr{P}^\mu) \subset \mathbf{R} \times T^*(\mathbf{R} \times \mathbf{T}^1)$$

Let

$$\mathscr{D}^\# = \bigcup_{\mu \in \mathbf{R}} (\{\mu\} \times \mathscr{D}^\mu) \subset \mathscr{P}^\# \times \mathbf{R}$$

Note that we may consider the family of vectorfields $\{X_{\Omega^\mu} | \mu \in \mathbf{R}\} = X^\#$ itself as a vectorfield on $\mathscr{P}^\#$.

36.4. Lemma. *In the context above,*

(i) the function $\Omega^\#: \mathscr{P}^\# \to \mathbf{R}$ defined by $\Omega^\# | \mathscr{P}^\mu = \Omega^\mu$ is of class C^∞; $\mathscr{P}^\# \subset \mathbf{R} \times T^*(\mathbf{R} \times \mathbf{T}^1)$ and $\mathscr{D}^\# \subset \mathscr{P}^\# \times \mathbf{R}$ are open sets; the vectorfield $X^\#$ is C^∞; the mapping $F^\#: \mathscr{D}^\# \to \mathscr{P}^\#$ defined by

$F^{\#}|\mathscr{D}^{\mu} = F^{\mu}$ (the integral of $X_{\Omega^{\mu}}$) is none other than the integral of $X^{\#}$; and $F^{\#}$ is of class C^{∞};

(ii) If γ is a closed orbit of $X_{\Omega^{\mu_0}}$ in $\mathscr{P}^{\mu_0}$ with period τ, then there is a neighborhood U of $\gamma \subset \mathscr{P}^{\mu_0}$ and $\delta, \varepsilon > 0$ such that $U \subset \mathscr{P}^{\mu}$ for all $\mu \in I = (\mu_0 - \delta, \mu_0 + \delta)$, $U \times J \subset \mathscr{D}^{\mu}$ for all $\mu \in I$, where $J = (-\varepsilon, \tau + \varepsilon)$, and the mapping

$$F : I \times U \times J \to \mathscr{P}^{\mu_0} : (\mu, \not{p}, t) \rightsquigarrow F^{\mu}(\not{p}, t)$$

is of class C^{∞}.

The proof is left for an exercise.

To show the closed orbits of 36.3 are preserved under small perturbations of μ around zero, we will separate the two cases of elliptic ($\xi_0 \neq 0$) and circular ($\xi_0 = 0$) orbits. We consider first the circular case, to obtain the closed orbits of the first kind of Poincaré.

We begin with a circular closed orbit γ_0 of X_{Ω^0} with initial condition $\mathscr{P}_0 = (0, 0, 0, \Lambda_0)$, $\Lambda_0^{-3} = m/k$, and period $2k\pi$, m and k relatively prime (36.3). Thus in the notations of 36.4, we have the C^{∞} local integral

$$F : I \times U \times J \to \mathscr{P}^0 : (\mu, \not{p}, t) \rightsquigarrow F^{\mu}(\not{p}, t)$$

and for $\mu = 0$, we have

$$F^0(0, 0, 0, \Lambda_0 ; k\pi) = (0, n\pi, 0, \Lambda_0)$$

where $n = k + m$, the *order* of γ_0. According to the criterion (36.2) we seek (μ, t, Λ) near $(0, k\pi, \Lambda_0)$ such that

$$F^{\mu}(0, 0, 0, \Lambda ; t) = (0, n\pi, 0, \Lambda)$$

as well, so that $\not{p} = (0, 0, 0, \Lambda)$ is in a closed orbit γ_{μ} of period $2(1 + \sigma)k\pi$. Obviously we have a job for the implicit mapping theorem, which we may use because everything depends smoothly on μ as well as the other variables (36.4).

36.5. Theorem (Poincaré). *In the Poincaré model for the restricted three-body problem, the closed orbit γ_0 of X_{Ω^0} containing the initial conditions $\not{p}_0 = (0, 0, 0, \Lambda_0)$, with $\Lambda_0^{-3} = m/k$ and period $2k\pi$, is preserved under perturbation of the mass ratio μ away from zero. That is, there is an $\varepsilon > 0$ and a C^{∞} function f: $(-\varepsilon, \varepsilon) \to \mathbf{R}$ such that if $\mu \in (-\varepsilon, \varepsilon)$, then $\not{p}^{\mu}$ is in a closed orbit γ_{μ} of $X_{\Omega^{\mu}}$ of period $2k\pi$, where $\not{p}^{\mu} = (0, 0, 0, f(\mu))$, and $f(0) = \Lambda_0$.*

Proof. We consider the mapping

$$G \colon I \times K \to T^1 \colon (\mu, \Lambda) \rightsquigarrow G(\mu, \Lambda)$$

where $K \subset U$ is the intersection of U and the Λ axis, $K = \{(0, 0, 0, \Lambda) \in U\}$, and $G(\mu, \Lambda)$ is the λ-component of $F^{\mu}(0, 0, 0, \Lambda; k\pi)$. By the discussion above, we seek to "solve" the implicit equation $G(\mu, \Lambda) = n\pi$ for Λ as a function of

μ, where $n = m + k$, and we have

$$G(0, \Lambda_0) = n\pi$$

when $\Lambda_0^{-3} = m/k$. As

$$\frac{\partial G}{\partial \Lambda} = \frac{\partial}{\partial \Lambda}\left(\frac{-3t_0}{\Lambda^4}\right) \neq 0$$

the implicit mapping theorem (5.16) shows there is an $\varepsilon > 0$ and a mapping $f: (-\varepsilon, \varepsilon) \to \mathbf{R}$ such that $G(\mu, f(\mu)) = n\pi$ for all $\mu \in (-\varepsilon, \varepsilon)$. The result follows at once from the criterion (36.2). ∎

Note that we also obtain the smoothness of the energy, or $\Lambda(\gamma_\mu) = f(\mu)$, of the closed orbit γ_μ. In addition, we could have obtained by a similar argument a closed orbit γ'_μ of the same energy as γ_0, $\Lambda(\gamma'_\mu) = \Lambda_0$, for each μ, but then the period of γ'_μ depends on μ. Even more, there is a curve $s \rightsquigarrow \gamma^s_\mu$ of closed orbits for each μ, of which these are but two examples (see exercise 36D).

We turn now to the second case, the elliptical orbits. We begin with an elliptical closed orbit γ_0 of X_{Ω^0} of the type given by 36.3. Thus we have $\not{p}_0 = (0, 0, \xi_0, \Lambda_0)$ with $\Lambda_0^{-3} = m/k$, where m and k are relatively prime integers, and $F^G(\not{p}_0, k\pi) = (0, n\pi, \pm\xi_0, \Lambda_0)$, where $n = m + k$, so $\not{p}_0 \in \gamma_0$ has period $2k\pi$. For simplicity we suppose k even so that $(+\xi_0)$ is obtained in the third component. Note that $\xi_0 \neq 0$ in this case. As in the circular case $(\xi_0 = 0)$ we seek (μ, t, Λ) near $(0, k\pi, \Lambda_0)$ such that $F^\mu(0, 0, \xi_0, \Lambda; t) = (0, n\pi, \xi_0, \Lambda)$. That is, we keep ξ_0 fixed (but not zero).

36.6. Theorem (Arenstorf). *In the Poincaré model for the restricted three-body problem, the closed orbit γ_0 containing $\not{p}_0 = (0, 0, \xi_0, \Lambda_0)$ (where $\Lambda_0^{-3} = m/k$, m and k being relatively prime integers, $\xi_0 \neq 0$, and the period is $2k\pi$) is preserved under perturbation of the mass ratio μ away from zero. That is, there is an $\varepsilon > 0$ and C^∞ functions $f, g: (-\varepsilon, \varepsilon) \to \mathbf{R}$ such that if $\mu \in (-\varepsilon, \varepsilon)$, then $\not{p}^\mu$ is in a closed orbit γ_μ of period $g(\mu)$, where $\not{p}^\mu = (0, 0, \xi_0, f(\mu))$, $f(0) = \Lambda_0$, and $g(0) = 2k\pi$.*

The proof is very analogous to the previous one (which was inspired by this one of Arenstorf and Barrar rather than the original of Poincaré) and is relegated to the exercises.

A typical example of a closed orbit of the second kind of Arenstorf is illustrated in Figure 36-2, both in the inertial frame of the Sun (similar to 3BI) and rotating coordinates (configuration space of 3BII).

Here E and M replace S and J, as the orbit is computed for $\mu = 0.012277471$, corresponding to the Earth and the Moon. The orbit shown was computed electronically at the G. G. Marshall Space Flight Center of the National Aeronautics and Space Administration and is reproduced here through the courtesy of Dr. Arenstorf. The interest in these "bus orbits" is evident from the fact that they pass very close to the Earth and to the Moon.

Note that for the ε range in theorems 36.5 and 36.6 no collisions occur. Through lemma 36.4 (*ii*) we have chosen a domain in which the orbits do not run off the manifold in the times involved, hence do not arrive at S or J in these times. Also, the last theorem (elliptical case) can be proved very similarly in the Delaunay model (34.6) (see Barrar [1]), but the circular case cannot be attacked in that model because it does not contain circular orbits.

Finally, we shall show the existence of the *closed orbits of the second kind of Moser* and the o^+ stability of the closed orbits of the first kind of Poincaré. We obtain these two results of Moser simultaneously by applying the twist theorem (30.4) to the closed orbits of the first kind. The program of the proof is quite analogous to a proof by Barrar [2] of the existence of the Moser orbits.

Let γ_0 be a circular closed orbit for $\mu = 0$, as in theorem 36.5, with $\Lambda_0^{-3} = m/k$, and period $2k\pi$. By Lemma 36.4 (*ii*) we may choose an open neighborhood U of $\gamma \subset \mathscr{P}^0$ such that for $\mu \in (-\delta, \delta)$ we have $U \subset \mathscr{P}^\mu$ as well, and $U \times J \subset \mathscr{D}^\mu$, $J = (-\varepsilon, 2k\pi + \varepsilon) \subset \mathbf{R}$. Thus the integral F^μ of X_{Ω^μ} is defined for points $(t, \not{p}) \in J \times U$, or especially $F^\mu(\not{p}, 2k\pi)$ is defined for $\not{p} \in U$ and $|\mu| < \delta$. As above, there are no "collisions" in this range. Let

$$\not{p}^0 = (0, 0, 0, \Lambda_0) \in \gamma_0$$

so

$$F^0(\not{p}^0, 2k\pi) = (0, 2n\pi, 0, \Lambda_0) = (0, 0, 0, \Lambda_0) = \not{p}^0$$

From 36.5, the Poincaré orbits γ_μ for sufficiently small μ are defined by initial conditions $\not{p}^\mu = (0, 0, 0, f(\mu))$, and we have $F^\mu(\not{p}^\mu, 2k\pi) = \not{p}^\mu$.

To apply the Moser twist theorem, we must construct a local transversal section S^μ for γ_μ, and Poincaré section map Θ^μ on S^μ, such that S^μ, and its derivatives up to order four at least, depend continuously on the parameter μ. We may then verify the elementary twist hypothesis (30.3) for $\mu = 0$, and assert it is satisfied also for $\mu \approx 0$. Note that the local transversal section should be tangent to the energy surface $\Sigma^\mu_{e(\mu)}$ defined by $\Omega^\mu = \Omega^\mu(\not{p}^\mu)$, which depends on μ in two different ways. This construction is the heart of the proof of the following.

36.7. Theorem (Moser). *In the Poincaré model for the restricted three-body problem, let γ_0 be a closed orbit of X_{Ω^0} containing $\not{p}^0 =$ $(0, 0, 0, \Lambda_0)$, with $\Lambda_0^{-3} = m/k$, m and k relatively prime integers. Let γ_μ denote the closed orbit of the first kind of X_{Ω^μ} containing $\not{p}^\mu =$ $(0, 0, 0, \Lambda_\mu)$ given by 36.5 ($\Lambda_\mu = f(\mu)$). Then if $k/(m + k) \neq p/q$ for $q = 1, 2, 3, 4$ or any integer p, there is an $\varepsilon > 0$ such that*

(i) if $|\mu| < \varepsilon$, γ_μ is $o^\pm$-stable, and

(ii) if $|\mu| < \varepsilon$, V is a neighborhood of $\gamma_\mu \subset \mathscr{P}^\mu$, and N is a positive integer, there exists a closed orbit of X_{Ω^μ} in V with period greater than N.

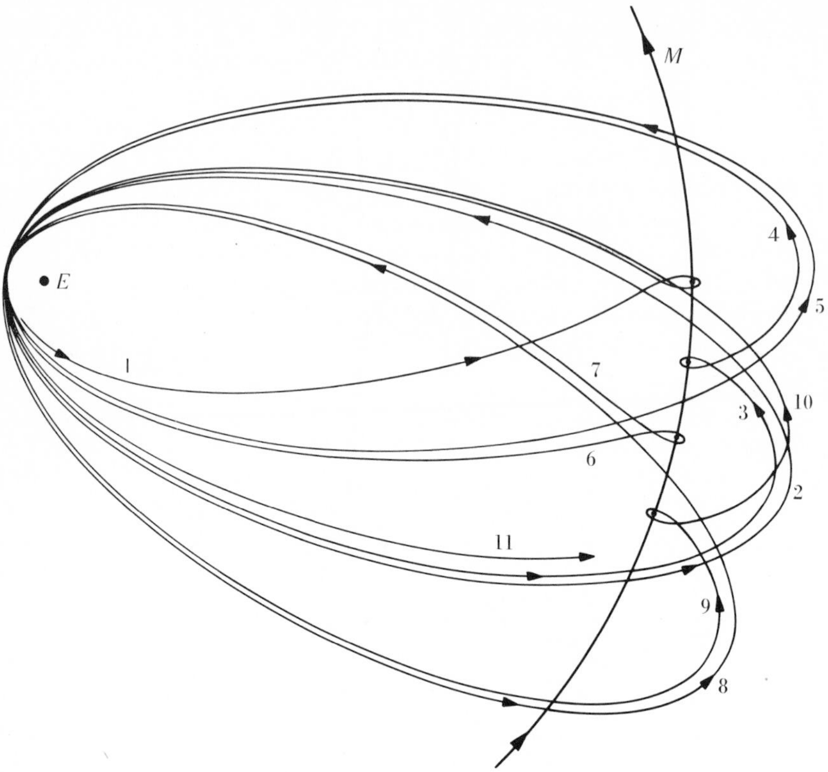

Figure 36-2(a)
Inertial frame.

Proof. We first construct the Poincaré section map Θ^μ on the local transversal section S^μ (see 23.6 for definitions). Let $e(\mu) = \Omega^\mu(\not{p}^\mu) = \Omega^\mu(\gamma_\mu)$ denote the energy of the closed orbits of the first kind, and $\Sigma_0^\mu = (\Omega^\mu)^{-1}(e(\mu))$ be the corresponding energy surfaces. Restricting to the neighborhood U of $\gamma_0 \subset \mathscr{P}^0$ of the preceding discussion, $F^\mu(\not{p}, 2k\pi)$ is defined for all $\not{p} \in U$. If U is taken sufficiently small, it contains none of the five critical points of X_{Ω^μ}, so $\Sigma^\mu = \Sigma_0^\mu \cap U$ is a regular energy surface. Let $\tilde{S}$ denote the intersection of U and the coordinate hyperplane in $\mathscr{P}^0$ defined by $\lambda = 0$ (in the Poincaré variables: η, λ, ξ, and Λ). Then for $\mu = 0$, the second (λ) component of X_{Ω^0} is not zero on $\tilde{S}$ (see the discussion after 34.7) so $\tilde{S}$ is a local transversal section of X_{Ω^0}. As X_{Ω^μ} depends continuously on μ (36.4), there is an $\varepsilon_1 > 0$ such that $\tilde{S}$ is a local transversal section of X_{Ω^μ} if $|\mu| < \varepsilon_1$. Hereafter we suppose $|\mu| < \varepsilon_1$ and $\varepsilon_1 < \varepsilon_0$ (the ε of 36.5).

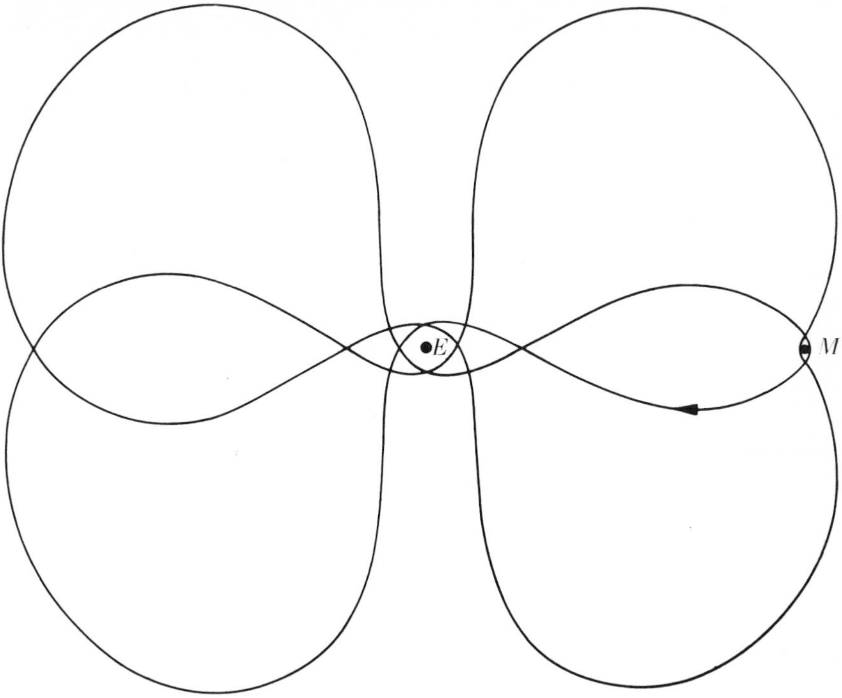

Figure 36-2(b)
Rotating frame

Note that the initial condition $\not{p}^\mu$ is in $\tilde{S}$ for all μ. Let $S^\mu = \tilde{S} \cap \Sigma^\mu$. As $\tilde{S}$ is a local transversal section and Σ^μ an energy surface, S^μ is a submanifold, necessarily of dimension two, and is a local transversal section of $X_{\Omega^\mu}|\Sigma^\mu$ (exercise 30D). As $\not{p}^\mu \in S^\mu$, there is a (locally) unique Poincaré map Θ^μ of $X_{\Omega^\mu}|\Sigma^\mu$ at $\not{p}^\mu \in S^\mu$.

This finishes the construction, and we now study the map Θ^0 corresponding to the unperturbed orbit γ_0, to establish the elementary twist hypothesis of Moser's theorem (30.4). Recall (34.7) that

$$\Omega^0(\eta, \lambda, \xi, \Lambda) = -\frac{1}{2\Lambda^2} + \xi - \tfrac{1}{2}(\xi^2 + \eta^2)$$

so

$$e(0) = \Omega^0(\not{p}^0) = -\frac{1}{2\Lambda_0^2} + \Lambda_0$$

We may thus solve the equation $\Omega^0(\not{p}) = e(0)$ (even explicitly if we wish), for Λ as a function of $(\xi^2 + \eta^2)$. That is, we have a C^∞ (in fact analytic) function $v: U \to \mathbf{R}$ such that

$$\Omega^0(\eta, \lambda, \xi, v(\xi^2 + \eta^2)) = e(0)$$

for all (η, λ, ξ). Thus a point $\not{p} = (\eta, \lambda, \xi, \Lambda)$ is in the local transversal section Σ^0 iff $\lambda = 0$ and $\Lambda = v(\xi^2 + \eta^2)$. Consider the integral $F^0(\not{p}, t)$ of X_{Ω_0} restricted to Σ^0. By integrating the equations X_{Ω^0} explicitly, we find (see the proof of 36.3)

$$F^0(\eta, 0, \xi, \Lambda; t) = (\eta \cos t - \xi \sin t, (\Lambda^{-3} + 1)t, \eta \sin t + \xi \cos t, \Lambda)$$

As $\not{p} \in \Sigma^0$ we have $\Lambda = v(\xi^2 + \eta^2)$, and we may choose for each $\not{p} \in \Sigma^0$ a time $t = \chi(\not{p})$ so that the point $F^0(\eta, 0, \xi, \mu; \chi)$ is again in Σ^0, as in the definition of the Poincaré section map. Namely, let $\chi(\xi, 0, \eta, v) = 2\pi(v^{-3} + 1)^{-1}$. Then we have

$$\begin{aligned} &F^0(\eta, 0, \xi, v(\xi^2 + \eta^2); \chi(\xi^2 + \eta^2)) \\ &\quad = (\eta \cos \chi - \xi \sin \chi, 2k\pi, \eta \sin \chi + \xi \sin \chi, v) \end{aligned}$$

This is in fact the Poincaré map on the local transversal section S^0. By choosing (η, ξ) as a coordinate chart in S^0, we obtain

$$\Theta^0(\eta, \xi) = (\eta \cos \chi - \xi \sin \chi, \eta \sin \chi + \xi \cos \chi)$$

where $\chi(\eta, \xi) = \chi(\xi^2 + \eta^2)$ is determined above. Looking back through the construction above, we have $\chi(\eta, \xi) = 2\pi(v^{-3} + 1)^{-1}$ where $v(\eta, \xi)$ is defined implicitly by

$$\frac{-1}{2v^2} + v - \tfrac{1}{2}(\xi^2 + \eta^2) = \frac{-1}{2\Lambda_0^2} + \Lambda_0$$

and $\Lambda_0^{-3} = m/k$. Luckily, *the section map is already in* (α, β)*-normal form.* For Θ^0, in complex notation, is $\Theta(v) = ve^{iv(|v|^2)}$. It only remains to expand $v(|v|^2)$ in a Taylor formula (2.8) to order 4, which we leave as an exercise (36G). The result is

$$\chi(|v|^2) = \alpha + \beta|v|^2 + |v|^4\mathscr{R}(v)$$

where $\mathscr{R}(0) = 0$,

$$\alpha = \chi(0) = \frac{2k\pi}{m + k} = \frac{k}{n}2\pi$$

and

$$\beta = \frac{-3k\pi\Lambda_0^2}{(\Lambda_0^{-3} + 1)^3} = \frac{-3k^4\pi\Lambda_0}{(m + k)^3}$$

As $\beta \neq 0$, this is an elementary twist iff α is not zero or an integral multiple of $\pi/2$ or $3\pi/2$. But this is the case iff $k/n \neq p/q$ for $q = 1, 2, 3, 4$ or any integer p.

This completes the proof that Θ^0 is stable, and the result follows from the continuity of Θ^μ in μ. ∎

Concerning this theorem, it is possible to prove the existence of the closed orbits of the second kind (ii) without the "order of resonance" assumption $k/n \neq p/q$ (see Moser [1] or Barrar [2]) by using the Birkhoff fixed point theorem (Siegel [1, ch. 22]), in place of the Moser twist theorem. For stability (i) the assumption $k/n \neq p/q$ with $q = 1, 2, 3$ is known to be necessary ("order of resonance ≤ 3") but Moser [4] states that the assumption $k/n \neq p/q$ with $q = 4$ can be removed.

It is tempting to apply the method of this proof to the closed orbits of the second kind of Arenstorf, to prove their stability. However the Poincaré section map Θ^0 in that case ($\xi_0 \neq 0$) is not in (α, β)-normal form, so one is faced with a difficult problem in computing the invariants α and β.

Finally, it is clear that the proof of 36.7 actually demonstrates a most important fact: the twist configuration (and $o^{\pm}$ stability) of the circular γ_0 is *preserved under any Hamiltonian perturbation of* Ω^0 *which is symmetric with respect to the* (q^1, p_1) *plane*

Exercises

36A. Prove 36.2. Hint: Let $i: \mathbf{R}^2 \to \mathbf{R}^2 : (q^1, q^2) \rightsquigarrow (q^1, -q^2)$, and $I = T^*i$. Show I is a symplectic diffeomorphism and $I^*H^\mu = H^\mu$ in 3BII, to obtain Birkhoff's criterion in the second model. Then apply the Poincaré diffeomorphism $P_1 : M_1 \to \mathscr{P}$.

36B. Prove 36.4. Hint: See Lang [1, p. 94], for (*i*). For (*ii*), see the proof of 23.7, use $\mathscr{D}^{\mathrm{II}}$ open and γ compact.

36C. Prove the last assertion of 36.3.

36D. In 36.5, show that in fact the perturbed orbit γ_μ is in a one-parameter family of closed orbits (as expected because of 28.45) by considering the mapping $G: (\mu, t, \Lambda) \rightsquigarrow \lambda$ component of $F^\mu(0, 0, 0, \Lambda; t)$ as in the proof of 36.5.

36E. Prove 36.6. Hint: Consider the mapping $G: (\mu, t, \Lambda) \rightsquigarrow (\eta, \lambda)$, the first two components of $F^\mu(0, 0, \xi_0, \Lambda; t)$.

36F. Relate the Poincaré and Arenstorf orbits (36.5 and 36.6) to the inertial frame, that is, model 3BI. Show that for $\mu = 0$, the period is $2n\pi$, where $n = m + k$ is the order of γ_0 in the Poincaré model. (See Figure 36-1.)

36G. Complete the proof of 36.7 by computing the Taylor formula to order 4 of $v(\xi^2 + \eta^2)$. Hint: See Barrar [2, p. 368], watch out for the difference in signs.

36H. Prove the last statement of the section. See Exercise 36A.

36I. Find a numbered proposition in the book which is not used in this chapter.

Notes

The elliptical orbits of the two-body problem are treated adequately in the standard works on celestial mechanics, e.g., Moulton [1]. For a full discussion of all orbits, see Wintner [2]. The Delaunay variables are introduced in Delaunay [1], and used subsequently by Poincaré [1], Wintner [1], and Barrar [1]. Poincaré gives the impression that the variables are symplectic, which is false, and some authors have taken this for granted. The Poincaré variables were introduced by Poincaré [1], and used by Wintner [1] and Barrar [2].

The critical points are discussed in standard references on celestial mechanics, e.g., Pars [1], Whittaker [1], Moulton [1].

For closed orbits in related problems, see Hill [1], Koopman [1], Conley [1], Jeffrys [1], and Arenstorf [2, 3, 4].

I am grateful to Jurgen Moser for several very helpful conversations about this material, to R. F. Arenstorf for contributing Figure 36-2, which was plotted by computer at the NASA G. C. Marshall Space Flight Center, and to R. H. Cushman for Figures 35-1 and 35-3, which were plotted by computer at Princeton University.

CONCLUSION

Looking back through these chapters from a practical viewpoint, perhaps the most impressive result of the qualitative theory of Hamiltonian systems initiated by POINCARÉ in 1889 is the stability of the near-circular orbits in the restricted three-body problem. The proof of this result, due to KOLMOGOROV, ARNOLD, and MOSER, requires nearly all of the theory in the preceding sections. Its importance is due to the two-hundred-year-old question of LAPLACE concerning the permanence of the solar system, for which it can be interpreted as a partial resolution. But this interpretation is subject to the problems of physical theories that were briefly discussed in the Introduction. With the help of the intervening chapters these problems may now be expressed more precisely, and applied to the context of this result to clarify its interpretation.

Recall that, according to DUHEM, a physical theory consists of an experimental domain and a mathematical model, connected by a conventional interpretation. The usefulness of the theory depends on its adequacy and stability. Adequacy refers to the agreement between the predictions of the model and the observations of the experimental domain, and is determined simply by comparison. Stability is a property of the mathematical model, which was described vaguely in the Introduction as the preservation of predictions under small perturbations of some parameters in the model. The parameters correspond, via the interpretation, to observed values of physical parameters in the experimental domain. The crucial importance of stability for the usefulness of the theory is based on the fact that these observed values can be known only approximately. We may now give a precise statement of this property which, although not of the greatest generality, includes all of the various types of stability discussed in the preceding chapters.

The experimental domain presents a set of observed values of physical parameters, which may be considered to be a point in a topological space D. For each value of the parameter $d \in D$ is constructed a mathematical model $\mathscr{M}_d$, and thereby a mathematical prediction $p(d)$. We may suppose that $p(d)$ is a point in a common topological space P. The system $\mathscr{F} = \{d, \mathscr{M}_d, p(d)\}$ is a **family of models**. Then a particular model $\mathscr{M}_{d_0}$ is a **stable model**, relative to the family $\mathscr{F}$, iff the mapping $p: D \to P: d \rightsquigarrow p(d)$ is continuous at the point $d_0 \in D$. For simplicity we consider only the case in which both D and P

are metric spaces. Then $\mathscr{M}_{d_0}$ is a stable model iff for every $\varepsilon > 0$ there is a $\delta > 0$ such that whenever the observable parameter d is actually within a distance (**experimental error**) δ of d_0, then the prediction $p(d)$ is within ε of $p(d_0)$. This notion of stability is a special case of the one considered by BOULIGAND [1] and DESTOUCHES [1].

Of course a model may be useful without satisfying this condition of stability. More important, a model may be stable and adequate without being useful, as this form of stability depends on special choices, for example, the topologies of D and P, the extent of the family $\mathscr{F}$, and the precise prediction p. Perhaps the most serious limitations are the following two problems.

Suppose that the prediction $p(d_0)$ is known precisely, and is relatively adequate. We may agree upon a positive real number ε such that if $p(d)$ is within ε of $p(d_0)$, then $p(d)$ is adequate also. If $\mathscr{M}_{d_0}$ is stable, we may in principle determine a maximum allowable experimental error δ such that if d is within δ of d_0, then $p(d)$ is within ε of $p(d_0)$ and therefore is adequate. The first problem, which we call the **problem of error**, is the difficulty of actually determining δ, and that d is within δ of d_0.

The second limitation, which we call the **problem of extent**, is more serious. We may never account for the full complexity of the experimental domain in the family of mathematical models $\mathscr{F} = \{d \in D, \mathscr{M}_d, p(d) \in P\}$. The choice of observables represented by points $d \in D$ excludes many that might be incorporated. If we enlarge the family $\mathscr{F}$ to another $\mathscr{F}' = \{d \in D', \mathscr{M}_d, p(d)\}$ where D is a subspace of D', then a particular model $\mathscr{M}_{d_0}$ might be stable relative to $\mathscr{F}$ but not stable relative to $\mathscr{F}'$. In this case the prediction is approximately preserved by some variations of the observable parameter and wildly disturbed by other variations. For example, the orbit of a harmonic oscillator is slightly changed if the mass is varied, and is seriously distorted by the introduction of friction.

The inescapability of these problems can be seen clearly in the context of LAPLACE's problem for the solar system. To study the permanence of the Earth's orbit, for example, we construct first a very idealized family of models which ignores: all the heavenly bodies except the Sun and Jupiter, their asphericities, the mass of the Earth, the deviation of the motion of these three bodies from a plane, and the eccentricity of the orbit of Jupiter. Thus the observed parameter is as restricted as possible; we put $D_1 = \{(\mu, m) | m \in M^\mu\}$, where μ is the *mass ratio*, M^μ is the *phase space* of model 3BII, and $m \in M^\mu$ is the *initial condition*. Then the *prediction* $p(\mu, m)$ can be taken to be $m^+ \in T^*\mathbf{R}^2$, the positive orbit of m in the Hamiltonian system X_{H^μ}. For a given m_0, $p(0, m_0)$ is a circle, and permanence of the Earth's orbit can be interpreted as the condition $\bar{\rho}(p(\mu, m), p(0, m_0)) < \varepsilon$ for a suitable ε, where $\bar{\rho}$ is the Hausdorff metric. Thus LAPLACE's question becomes: Is the orbit $p(\mu, m)$ in an ε neighborhood of the circle $p(0, m_0)$? And the answer is affirmative, for according to the theorems of POINCARÉ (36.5) and MOSER (36.7), the model $\mathscr{M}_{(0, m_0)}$ is stable, with respect to this family of models. Thus, given ε, there is a δ such that if $0 \leq \mu < \delta$, and m is within δ of m_0, or equivalently, the eccentricity of the orbit $p(0, m)$ is sufficiently small, then $\bar{\rho}(p(\mu, m), p(0, m_0)) < \varepsilon$. The error problem is easily resolved by a decision for ε, a mathematical computation of δ, and some faith in the accuracy of the astronomical determination of μ.

At this stage the problem of extent is acute, and we may try to alleviate it by successive enlargements of the family of models.

Recall that in model 3BII the Hamiltonian function has the form $H^\mu = H^0 + K^\mu$, so $X_{H^\mu} = X^0 + Y_\mu$, where $X^0 = X_{H^0}$, corresponding to the two-body problem in rotating coordinates, and $Y_\mu = X_{K^\mu}$. Thus we have studied the stability of orbits of X^0 under perturbations Y_μ contained, roughly speaking, in a continuous curve of Hamiltonian vectorfields parameterized by μ, and $Y_0 = 0$. In fact we might consider Y_μ, rather than μ itself, as the parameter in the family of models 3BII. Then we may enlarge the family of models simply by increasing the space of vectorfields, or Hamiltonians, that are to be allowed as perturbations of X^0, and using these perturbations themselves as parameters of the family.

For the second family of models, we allow perturbation by other heavenly bodies in a limited way. Let

$$\begin{aligned} D_2 = \{(\mu, H^*, m) | m \in M^\mu, H^* \in \mathscr{F}(M^\mu), H^*(q^1, q^2, p_1, p_2) \\ = H(q^1, -q^2, p_1, -p_2)\} \end{aligned}$$

and let $p(\mu, H^*, m) = m^+$, the positive orbit of m in the Hamiltonian system $X^0 + X_{H^*}$. The proofs of the theorems of POINCARÉ and MOSER show that for $d_0 = (0, 0, m_0)$, the corresponding model is stable with respect to this family.

This answers LAPLACE's question affirmatively again, within this family of models. But the problem of error becomes more difficult, for it is necessary to verify (for the extended proofs) that the H^* corresponding to the entire solar system is within δ of zero on some neighborhood of the original circular orbit $p(0, 0, m_0)$ (in the C^4 topology). Also, the extent problem, although alleviated, is still severe in that the orbits are still required to lie in a plane and be symmetric about the line through the Sun and Jupiter.

For the third family of models, we allow perturbation of X^0 by external influences of very arbitrary type, subject only to the limitation that they preserve the Hamiltonian character of the model. Thus let

$$D_3 = \{(\mu, H^*, m) | m \in M^\mu, H^* \in \mathscr{F}(M^\mu)\}$$

and let $p(\mu, H^*, m)$ be the orbit m^+ of m in $X^0 + X_{H^*}$, as in the second family. It is not known at present that the model $\mathscr{M}_{d_0}$ corresponding to $d_0 = (0, 0, m_0)$ is stable with respect to this family. It seems very likely, however, that this could be proved, using MOSER's theorem and the new methods of ARENSTORF [2]. Assuming for the moment that this is true, the problem of extent is now of smaller proportions, and the problem of error correspondingly increased. This problem has been dealt with quite forcefully by ARENSTORF, who actually computes a δ-range of error in a related context. Thus in this family, we may have in $\mathcal{M}_{d_0}$ a significant example of a model that is useful in the sense we have described. If so, and the δ-range is sufficiently large, LAPLACE's question is answered affirmatively in a theoretical system very plausibly related to the real world. This interpretation is subject to an important qualification, as it assumes the **doctrine of Maupertuis, the universe is a Hamiltonian system**. For stability of $\mathcal{M}_{d_0}$ in the third family means that the circular orbit of m_0 in X^0 is preserved by an arbitrary small *Hamiltonian* perturbation. This establishes a link between the doctrine of MAUPERTUIS and the tacit *dogma of stability* that underlies so much physical theory, and that has been elevated to the rank of a legitimate axiom by THOM [1].

For comparison, consider a fourth and final family of models in which X^0 can be perturbed by an arbitrary smooth vectorfield, not necessarily Hamiltonian. Thus, let

$$D_4 = \{(\mu, Y, m) | m \in M^\mu, Y \in \mathscr{X}(M^\mu)\}$$

and let the prediction $p(\mu, Y, m)$ be the orbit m^+ of m in the vectorfield $X^0 + Y$. Then very probably the model $\mathcal{M}_{d_0}$, where $d_0 = (0, 0, m_0)$, is unstable. If this is in fact the case, Laplacian stability fails in this family of models, which does not assume the doctrine of MAUPERTUIS.

If we assume these mathematical conjectures, which seem very near to being theorems, we are led to an identification (in this particular context) between the tenets of LAPLACE and MAUPERTUIS. Theoretically speaking, this means that the solar system is stable if and only if the universe is a conservative Hamiltonian system. We must recall, however, that the existence of an unstable (and therefore, according to DUHEM, useless) model for the solar system does not preclude the possibility that the Sun will rise every morning.

Hopefully, the position of this senior mathematical model with regard to the general question of stability and usefulness will clarify the problems faced by scientific theories in general.

APPENDIX A

TOPICS FROM TOPOLOGY

Probably the greatest difficulty this book presents to the nonmathematician is the reliance on point set topology. Although excellent references are available, the topics required cannot all be found in a single text, and the variation of notations and order in the different books presents a difficult challenge to an inexperienced reader. We assemble here for reference the topics needed, in a consistent notation used throughout this book. Some elementary direct proofs usually found as corollaries of more difficult theorems are also included. References to other texts are given instead of proofs, when this presents no problem to the reader. The exercises at the end also develop methods that are used in the text.

§A1. TOPOLOGICAL SPACES

A1.1. Definition. *A* **topological space** *is a set S together with a collection of subsets $\mathcal{O}$ called* **open sets** *such that*

(T1) $\phi \in \mathcal{O}$ *and* $S \in \mathcal{O}$;

(T1) *If* $U_1, U_2 \in \mathcal{O}$ *then* $U_1 \cap U_2 \in \mathcal{O}$;

(T3) *The union of any collection* U_α *of open sets is open.*

For such a topological space the **closed sets** *are the elements of*

$$\Gamma = \{A | \mathscr{C}A \in \mathcal{O}\}$$

where $\mathscr{C}$ denotes the complement, $\mathscr{C}A = S \setminus A = \{s \in S | s \notin A\}$. (The closed sets then obey rules dual to those for open sets.)

An **open neighborhood of a point** *u in a topological space S is an open set U such that $u \in U$. Similarly, for a subset A of S, U is an* **open neighborhood of** *A iff U is open and $A \subset U$.*

If A is a subset of a topological space S, the **relative topology** *on A is defined by*

$$\mathcal{O}_A = \{U \cap A | U \in \mathcal{O}\}$$

(which is clearly a topology on A).

Let S be a topological space. Then a **basis** *for the topology is a collection $\mathscr{B}$ of open sets such that every open set of S is a union of elements of $\mathscr{B}$. The topology is called* **first countable** *iff for each*

$u \in S$, there is a countable collection $\{U_n\}$ of neighborhoods of u such that for any neighborhood U of u, there is an N so $U_N \subset U$. The topology is called **second countable** *iff it has a countable basis.*

Let S and T be topological spaces and $S \times T = \{(u, v) | u \in S$ and $v \in T\}$. The **product topology** *on $S \times T$ consists of all subsets that are unions of sets of the form $U \times V$ where U is open in S and V is open in T. Thus, these* **open rectangles** *form a basis for the topology.*

Let S be a topological space and $\{u_n\}$ a sequence of points in S. The sequence is said to **converge** *iff there is a point $u \in S$ such that for every neighborhood U of u, there is an N such that $n \geq N$ implies $u_n \in U$. We say that $\{u_n\}$* **converges to** *u, or u is a* **limit point** *of $\{u_n\}$.*

A1.2. Example. On the real line **R**, the *standard topology* consists of the sets that are unions of open intervals (a, b). Then **R** is second countable, and hence first countable with a basis

$$\left\{\left(r_n - \frac{1}{m}, r_n + \frac{1}{m}\right) \middle| r_n \text{ is rational, } m \in \mathbf{N}, \text{ the positive integers}\right\}$$

The topology on the plane $\mathbf{R}^2$ is the product topology $\mathbf{R} \times \mathbf{R}$. In **R**, the sequence $\{1/n\}$ converges to 0, but in the subspace $(0, 1]$, the sequence does not converge.

A1.3. Definition. *Let S be a topological space and $A \subset S$. Then the* **closure** *of A, denoted A^c, is the intersection of all closed sets containing A. The* **interior** *of A, denoted A^o is the union of all open sets contained in A. The* **boundary** *of A, denoted $bd(A)$ is defined by*

$$bd(A) = A^c \cap (\mathscr{C}A)^c$$

Thus, $bd(A)$ is closed, and $bd(A) = bd(\mathscr{C}A)$. Note A open iff $A = A^o$, and A closed iff $A = A^c$.

A1.4. Proposition. *Let S be a topological space and $A \subset S$. Then*

(i) *$u \in A^c$ iff for every neighborhood U of u, $U \cap A \neq \phi$;*

(ii) *$u \in A^o$ iff there is a neighborhood U of u such that $U \subset A$;*

(iii) *$u \in bd(A)$ iff for every neighborhood U of u, $U \cap A \neq \phi$ and $U \cap (\mathscr{C}A) \neq \phi$.*

This proposition follows at once from the definitions.

A1.5. Definition. *Let S be a topological space. A point $u \in S$ is called* **isolated** *iff $\{u\}$ is open. The unique topology in which every point is isolated is called the* **discrete topology** *($\mathscr{O} = 2^S$, the collection of all subsets). The topology in which $\mathscr{O} = \{\phi, S\}$ is called the* **trivial topology**.

A subset A of S is called **dense** *in S iff $A^c = S$ and is called* **nowhere dense** *iff $\mathscr{C}(A^c)$ is dense in S.*

Thus, A is nowhere dense iff $(A^c)^0 = \phi$.

A1.6. Definition. *A topological space S is called* **Hausdorff** *iff each two distinct points have disjoint neighborhoods (that is, with empty intersection). Similarly, S is called* **normal** *iff each two disjoint closed sets have disjoint neighborhoods.*

Equivalent forms of Hausdorff are the following.

A1.7. Proposition. (*i*) *A space S is Hausdorff iff $\Delta_S = \{(u, u) | u \in S\}$ is closed in $S \times S$ in the product topology.*

(*ii*) *A first countable space S is Hausdorff iff all sequences have at most one limit point.*

Proof. If Δ_S is closed and u_1, u_2 are distinct, there is an open rectangle $U \times V$ containing (u_1, u_2) and $U \times V \subset \mathscr{C}\Delta_S$. Then in S, U and V are disjoint. The converse is similar, and we leave (*ii*) as an exercise. ∎

§A2. METRIC SPACES

A2.1. Definition. *Let $\hat{\mathbf{R}}^+$ denote the nonnegative real numbers with a point $\{+\infty\}$ adjoined, and topology generated by the open intervals of the form (a, b) or $(a, +\infty]$. Let M be a set. A* **metric** *on M is a function $\rho: M \times M \to \hat{\mathbf{R}}^+$ such that*

(M1) $\rho(m_1, m_2) = 0$ *iff* $m_1 = m_2$;

(M2) $\rho(m_1, m_2) = \rho(m_2, m_1)$;

(M3) $\rho(m_1, m_3) \leq \rho(m_1, m_2) + \rho(M_2, m_3)$, *triangle inequality.*

r $\varepsilon \in \hat{\mathbf{R}}^+$, $\varepsilon > 0$, *and $m \in M$, the ε* **disk** *about m is defined by*

$$D_\varepsilon(m) = \{m' \in M | d(m', m) < \varepsilon\}$$

The collection of subsets of M that are unions of such disks is the **metric topology** *at (M, ρ). (It is easily verified that it is a topology on M.)*

Two metrics on a set are **equivalent** *iff they induce the same metric topology.*

Let M be a metric space with metric ρ and $\{u_n\}$ a sequence in M. Then $\{u_n\}$ is a **Cauchy sequence** *iff for all $\varepsilon > 0$, $\varepsilon \in \hat{\mathbf{R}}^+$, there is an $N \in \mathbf{N}$ such that $n, m \geq N$ implies $\rho(u_n, u_m) < \varepsilon$. (It is easily seen that a convergent sequence is a Cauchy sequence.) The space M is called* **complete** *iff every Cauchy sequence converges.*

A **pseudometric** *on a set M is a function $\rho: M \times M \to \hat{\mathbf{R}}^+$ that satisfies* (M2), (M3), *and*

$$\text{(PM1)} \qquad \rho(m, m) = 0 \qquad \text{for all } m$$

The **pseudometric topology** *is defined exactly as the metric space topology.*

If M is a metric space (or pseudometric space) and $u \in M$, $A \subset M$ we define $\rho(u, A) = \inf\{\rho(u, v) | v \in A\}$, if $A \neq \phi$ and $\rho(u, \phi) = \infty$.

Clearly, metric spaces are first countable and Hausdorff.

A2.2. Proposition. *Every metric space is normal.*

Proof. Let A and B be closed, disjoint subsets of M, and let

$$U = \{u \in M | \rho(u, A) < \rho(u, B)\}$$

$$V = \{v \in M | \rho(v, A) > \rho(v, B)\}$$

It is easily verified that U and V are open, disjoint, and $A \subset U$, $B \subset V$. ∎

A2.3. Definition. *The* **standard metric** *on* $\mathbf{R}^n$ *is defined by*

$$\rho(\mathbf{x}, \mathbf{y}) = \left(\sum_{i=1}^{n} (x^i - y^i)^2 \right)^{1/2}$$

where $\mathbf{x} = (x^1, \ldots, x^n)$.

§A3. CONTINUOUS MAPPINGS

A3.1. Definition. *Let S and T be topological spaces and $\varphi: S \to T$ be a mapping. Then φ is* **continuous at u ∈ S** *iff for every neighborhood V of $\varphi(u)$ there is a neighborhood U of u such that $\varphi(U) \subset V$. If, for every open set V of T, $\varphi^{-1}(V) = \{u \in S | \varphi(u) \in V\}$ is open in S, φ is* **continuous**. *(Thus, φ is continuous iff φ is continuous at each $u \in S$.)*

If $\varphi: S \to T$ is a **bijection** *(that is, one-to-one and onto), φ and φ^{-1} are continuous, then φ is a* **homeomorphism** *and S and T are* **homeomorphic**.

It follows at once that $\varphi: S \to T$ is continuous iff the inverse image of every closed set is closed. The following is also useful.

A3.2. Proposition. *Let S and T be topological spaces and $\varphi: S \to T$. Then φ is continuous iff for every $A \subset S$, $\varphi(A^c) \subset \varphi(A)^c$.*

Proof. If φ is continuous, then $\varphi^{-1}(\varphi(A)^c)$ is closed. But $A \subset \varphi^{-1}(\varphi(A)^c)$ and hence $A^c \subset \varphi^{-1}(\varphi(A)^c)$, or $\varphi(A^c) \subset \varphi(A)^c$. Conversely, let $B \subset T$ be closed and $A = \varphi^{-1}(B)$. Then $A^c \subset \varphi^{-1}(B) = A$, so A is closed. ∎

From A1.4 we obtain the following.

A3.3. Proposition. *Let S be a first countable space and $A \subset S$. Then $u \in A^c$ iff there is a sequence of points of A that converge to u (in the topology on S).*

Continuity may be expressed in terms of sequences as follows:

A3.4. Proposition. *Let S and T be topological spaces with S first countable and $\varphi: S \to T$. Then φ is continuous iff for every sequence $\{u_n\}$ converging to u, $\{\varphi(u_n)\}$ converges to $\varphi(u)$, for all $u \in S$.*

We leave this to the reader. In the case that φ is continuous, note that the result follows at once from A3.2 and A3.3.

For metric spaces, note that $\varphi: M_1 \to M_2$ is continuous at $u_1 \in M_1$ iff for all $\varepsilon > 0$ there is a $\delta > 0$ such that $\rho(u_1, u_1') < \delta$ implies $\rho(\varphi(u_1), \varphi(u_1')) < \varepsilon$.

A3.5. Proposition. *Let M and N be metric spaces with N complete. Then the collection $C(M, N)$ of all continuous maps $\varphi: M \to N$ forms a complete metric space with the metric*

$$\rho^0(\varphi, \psi) = sup\{\rho(\varphi(u), \psi(u)) | u \in M\}$$

We leave this as an exercise. Note that ∞ is an allowed value.

§A4. COMPACT SPACES

A4.1. Definition. *Let S be a topological space. Then S is called* **compact** *iff for every covering of S by open sets U_α (that is, $\bigcup_\alpha U_\alpha = S$) there is a finite subcovering. A subset $A \subset S$ is called* **compact** *iff A is compact in the relative topology. A space is called* **locally compact** *iff each point has a neighborhood whose closure is compact.*

It follows easily that a closed subset of a compact space is compact and that the continuous image of a compact space is compact.

The following is often convenient.

A4.2. Theorem (Bolzano–Weierstrass). *If S is a first countable space and is compact, then every sequence has a convergent subsequence.*

(The converse is also true in a metric space.)

Proof. Suppose $\{u_n\}$ contains no convergent subsequences. Then we may assume all points are distinct. Each u_n has a neighborhood $\mathcal{O}_n$ that contains no other u_m. From A3.3 $\{u_n\}$ is closed, so that $\{\mathcal{O}_n\}$ together with $\mathscr{C}\{u_n\}$ forms an open covering of S, with no finite subcovering. ∎

In a metric space, every compact subset is closed and bounded. In $\mathbf{R}^n$, the converse is also true (Dieudonné [1, §3.16]).

A4.3. Proposition. *Let S be a Hausdorff space. Then every compact subset of S is closed. Also, every compact Hausdorff space is normal.*

Proof. Let $u \in \mathscr{C}A$ and $v \in A$, where A is compact in S. There are disjoint neighborhoods of u and v and, since A is compact, there are disjoint neighborhoods of u and A. Thus $\mathscr{C}A$ is open. We leave the second part as an exercise. ∎

A4.4. Proposition. *Let S be a Hausdorff space that is locally homeomorphic to a locally compact Hausdorff space (that is, for each $u \in S$, there is a neighborhood of S homeomorphic, in the subspace topology, to an open subset of a locally compact Hausdorff space). Then S is locally compact. In particular, manifolds are locally compact. (The Hausdorff assumption is essential.)*

Proof. Let $U \subset S$ be homeomorphic to $\varphi(U) \subset T$. There is a neighborhood V of $\varphi(u)$ so $V^c \subset \varphi(U)$ and V^c is compact. (We leave this as an exercise; locally compact Hausdorff spaces are regular.) Then $\varphi^{-1}(V^c)$ is compact, and hence closed in S. By A3.2 $\varphi^{-1}(V^c) \subset (\varphi^{-1}V)^c$. Thus $\varphi^{-1}(V)$ has compact closure $\varphi^{-1}(V)^c = \varphi^{-1}(V)^c$. ∎

§A5. PARACOMPACT SPACES

A5.1. Definition. *Let S be a topological space. A covering $\{U_\alpha\}$ of S is called a* **refinement** *of a covering $\{V_i\}$ iff for every U_α there is a V_i such that $U_\alpha \subset V_i$. A covering $\{U_\alpha\}$ of S is called* **locally finite** *iff each point $u \in S$ has a neighborhood U such that U intersects only a finite number of U_α. A space is called* **paracompact** *iff every open covering of S has a locally finite refinement of open sets, and S is Hausdorff.*

A5.2. Theorem. *Second countable, locally compact Hausdorff spaces are paracompact. In particular, manifolds are paracompact.*

Proof. S is the countable union of open sets U_n such that U_n^c is compact and $U_n^c \subset N_{n+1}$. If W_α is a covering of S by open sets, and $K_n = U_n^c - U_{n-1}$ then we can cover K_n by a finite number of open sets each of which is contained in some $W_\alpha \cap U_{n+1}$, and is disjoint from U_{n-2}^c. The union of such collections yields the desired refinement of $\{W_\alpha\}$. ∎

A minor modification yields the following.

A5.3. Corollary. *Let M be an n manifold and $\{W_\alpha\}$ be an open covering. Then there is a locally finite refinement consisting of charts $\{V_i, \varphi_i\}$ such that $\varphi_i(V_i)$ is the disk of radius 3, and such that φ_i^{-1} $(D_1(\mathbf{0}))$ cover M.*

This is the critical lemma for C^∞ partitions of unity (§A6).

A5.4. Theorem. *Every paracompact space is normal. In particular, manifolds are normal.*

Proof. We first show that if A is closed and $u \in \mathscr{C}A$, there are disjoint neighborhoods of u and A (regularity). For each $v \in A$ let U_u, V_v be disjoint neighborhoods of u and v. Let W_α be a locally finite refinement of the covering $V_v, \mathscr{C}A$, and $V = \bigcup W_\alpha$, the union over those α so $W_\alpha \cap A \neq \phi$. A neighborhood U_0 of u meets a finite number of W_α. Let U denote the intersection of U_0 and the corresponding U_v. Then V and U are the required neighborhoods. The case for two closed sets proceeds somewhat similarly, so we leave the details for the reader. ∎

§A6. PARTITIONS OF UNITY

We wish to give here some proofs of theorems in the text.

A6.1. Proof of 11.3. Let $\mathscr{A}$ be an atlas on M and let $\{V_i, \varphi_i\}$ be a locally finite refinement with the properties of A5.3. From 8.6 we have a function $h_i \in \mathscr{F}(M)$ whose support lies in V_i. Let

$$g_i(u) = \frac{h_i(u)}{\Sigma_i h_i(u)}$$

(the sum is finite). These are the required functions. ∎

A6.2. Proof of 8.7. More generally, let A and B be two closed sets. Then by normality, there is an atlas $\{U_\alpha, \varphi_\alpha\}$ such that $U_\alpha \cap A \neq \phi$ implies $U_\alpha \cap B = \phi$. Let $\{V_i, \varphi_i, g_i\}$ be a subordinate partition of unity and $h = \Sigma g_i$, where the sum is over those i for which $V_i \cap A \neq \phi$. Then h is one on A and zero on B. ∎

This theorem is a smooth version of a topological theorem for normal spaces (Urysohn's lemma; see J. Kelley [1, p. 115]). For a more general discussion of partitions of unity, see Lang [1, pp. 25 ff.], and J. Kelley [1, p. 171].

§A7. CONNECTEDNESS

A7.1. Definition. *A topological space S is* **connected** *iff ϕ and S are the only subsets of S that are both open and closed. A subset of S is connected iff it is connected in the relative topology. A* **component** *A of S is a nonempty connected subset of S such that the only connected subset of S containing A is A; S is called* **locally connected** *iff each point has a connected neighborhood.*

It follows easily that the continuous image of a connected set is connected. Equivalent forms of the definition follow at once.

A7.2. Proposition. *A space S is not connected iff either of the following holds.*

(*i*) *There is a nonempty proper subset of S that is both open and closed.*

(*ii*) *S is the disjoint union of two nonempty open sets.*

(*iii*) *S is the disjoint union of two nonempty closed sets.*

Also, we have the following.

A7.3. Proposition. *Let S be a connected space and $f: S \to \mathbf{R}$ be continuous. Then f assumes every value between any two values $f(u)$, $f(v)$.*

Proof. Suppose $f(u) < a < f(v)$ and f does not assume the value a. Then $U = \{u_0 | f(u_0) < v\}$ is both open and closed. ∎

It is also true that disks in $\mathbf{R}^n$ are connected. See Dieudonné [1, §19 and §20].

A7.4. Proposition. *Let S be a topological space and $B \subset S$ be connected. Then*

(*i*) *if $B \subset A \subset B^c$, then A is connected;*

(*ii*) *if B_α are connected and $B_\alpha \cap B \neq \phi$, then $B \cup (\bigcup_\alpha B_\alpha)$ is connected.*

Proof. If A is not connected, A is the disjoint union of $U_1 \cap A$ and $U_2 \cap A$ where U_1 and U_2 are open on S. Then from A1.4 (*i*), $U_1 \cap B \neq \phi$, $U_2 \cap B \neq \phi$, so B is not connected. We leave (*ii*) as an exercise. ∎

A7.5. Corollary. *The components of a topological space are closed. Also, S is the disjoint union of its components. If S is locally connected, the components are open as well as closed.*

Note that manifolds are locally connected.

A7.6. Proposition. *Let S be a first countable compact Hausdorff space and $\{A_n\}$ a sequence of closed, connected subsets of S with $A_n \subset A_{n-1}$. Then $A = \bigcap_1^\infty A_n$ is connected.*

Proof. As S is normal, if A is not connected, A lies in two disjoint open subsets U_1 and U_2 of S. If $A_n \cap \mathscr{C}U_1 \cap \mathscr{C}U_2 \neq \phi$ for all n, then there is a sequence $u_n \in A_n \cap \mathscr{C}U_1 \cap \mathscr{C}U_2$ with a subsequence converging to u. As $A_n, \mathscr{C}U_1, \mathscr{C}U_2$ are closed, $u \in A \cap \mathscr{C}U_1 \cap \mathscr{C}U_2$, a contradiction. Hence some A_n is not connected. ∎

In A7.6, the first countable assumption is not essential.

An intuitively more appealing, but less convenient, definition of connectedness is the following.

A7.7. Definition. *Let S be a topological space and $I = [0, 1] \subset$ **R**. An* **arc** *φ in S is a continuous mapping $\varphi: I \to S$. If $\varphi(0) = u$, $\varphi(1) = v$ we say φ* **joins** *u and v; S is called* **arcwise connected** *iff every two points in S can be joined by an arc in S. A space is called* **locally arcwise connected** *iff each point has an arcwise connected neighborhood (in the relative topology).*

The relationship with connectedness is the following.

A7.8. Proposition. *Every arcwise connected space is connected. If a space is connected and locally arcwise connected, it is arcwise connected. In particular, a manifold is connected iff it is arcwise connected.*

Proof. If S is arcwise connected and not connected, write $S = U_1 \cup U_2$, where U_1 and U_2 are nonempty, disjoint, and open. Let $u_1 \in U_1$ and $u_2 \in U_2$ and let φ be an arc joining u_1 and u_2. Now $\varphi(I)$ is connected, and since $\varphi(I) \cap U_i \neq \phi$, $\varphi(I) \cap U_1 \cap U_2 \neq \phi$. Hence $U_1 \cap U_2 \neq \phi$, a contradiction. For the second part, let $u \in S$ and U denote all points that can be joined to u by an arc. An easy argument shows U and $\mathscr{C}U$ are open and so $U = S$, by A7.2. ∎

It is often convenient to use the following.

A7.9. Theorem. *Every manifold is metrizable. That is, there is a metric that induces the manifold topology.*

This can be proven in several ways. First, manifolds can be embedded in Euclidean space (3.5), and the metric on $\mathbf{R}^{2n+1}$ induces one on the manifold. Second, as we saw in 11.13, every manifold possesses a Riemannian metric, and it can be shown that the metric $\rho(m_1, m_2) = \inf\{\text{length } \varphi | \varphi \text{ is a piecewise smooth curve joining } m_1 \text{ and } m_2\}$ induces the manifold topology (Milnor [1, p. 62]). Finally, the result also follows from general metrization theorems, such as: A second countable space is metrizable iff it is normal. See J. Kelley [1, p. 125] and A5.4.

§A8. HAUSDORFF METRICS

A8.1. Definition. *Let S be a metric space with metric ρ, and 2^S denote the set of all subsets of S. For $a \in S$ and $B \subset S$, $B \neq \phi$, define*

$$\rho(a, B) = \inf\{\rho(a, b) | b \in B\}$$

and for $A, B \subset S$, $A, B \neq \phi$

$$\vec{\rho}(A, B) = \sup\{\rho(a, B) | a \in A\}$$

As this is not symmetric, we further define

$$\bar{\rho}(A, B) = \sup\{\vec{\rho}(A, B), \vec{\rho}(B, A)\}$$

If $A \neq \phi$ and $B = \phi$ we define $\rho(a, B) = \infty$ and $\bar{\rho}(A, B) = \infty$. Finally, define $\bar{\rho}(\phi, \phi) = 0$. We call $\bar{\rho}$ the **Hausdorff metric**.

A8.2. Proposition. *If ρ is a metric on S, then $\bar{\rho}$ is a pseudo-metric on 2^S.*

Proof. Clearly, $\bar{\rho}: 2^S \times 2^S \to \hat{\mathbf{R}}^+ = [0, \infty]$, $\bar{\rho}(A, A) = 0$ and $\bar{\rho}$ is symmetric. For the triangle inequality, it is sufficient to show $\vec{\rho}(A, C) \leq \vec{\rho}(A, B) + \vec{\rho}(B, C)$ for $A, B, C \in 2^S$. But $\rho(a, c) \leq \rho(a, b) + \rho(b, c)$ implies $\rho(a, C) \leq \rho(a, b) + \rho(b, C) \leq \rho(a, b) + \vec{\rho}(B, C)$. Hence $\rho(a, C) \leq \rho(a, B) + \vec{\rho}(B, C)$, which yields the result. The cases A, B, or $C = \phi$ are easily checked. ∎

As metric spaces are normal, it follows easily that on the closed subsets of S, $\bar{\rho}$ is a metric. The Hausdorff metric provides a measure of the uniform closeness of sets, as noted in §26. For further details, see Hausdorff [1], J. Kelley [1, p. 131], or Michael [1, p. 152].

Continuity of a map $f: S \to 2^S$ can be rephrased as follows.

A8.3. Proposition. *Let S be a metric space and $\bar{\rho}$ the Hausdorff metric on 2^S. Then $f: S \to 2^S$ is continuous at $u_0 \in S$ iff for all $\varepsilon > 0$ there is a $\delta > 0$ such that $\rho(u, u_0) < \delta$ implies:*

(i) *for all $a \in f(u)$, there is a $b \in f(u_0)$ so $\rho(a, b) < \varepsilon$; that is*

$$f(u) \subset \bigcup_{b \in f(u_0)} D_\varepsilon(b)$$

and

(ii) *for all $b \in f(u_0)$, there is an $a \in f(u)$ such that $\rho(b, a) < \varepsilon$; that is, $f(u_0) \subset \bigcup_{a \in f(u)} D_\varepsilon(a)$.*

This proposition follows at once from the definitions of continuity and the Hausdorff metric.

§A9. QUOTIENT TOPOLOGIES; THE TORUS AND KLEIN BOTTLE

A9.1. Definition. *Let S be a set. An* **equivalence relation** $\sim$ *on S is a binary relation such that for all $u, v, w \in S$,*

(i) $u \sim u$,

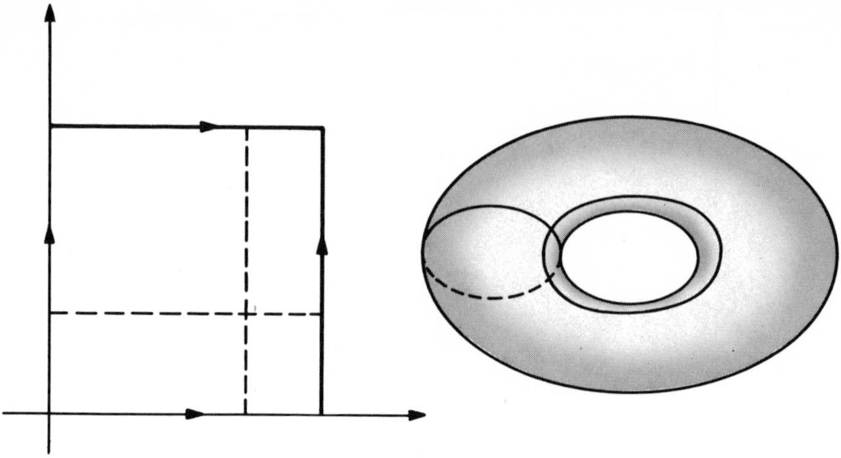

Figure A-1

(ii) $u \sim v$ *iff* $v \sim u$, *and*
(iii) $u \sim v$ *and* $v \sim w$ *implies* $u \sim w$.

The **equivalence class** *containing* u, *denoted* $[u]$, *is defined by*

$$[u] = \{v \in S | u \sim v\}$$

The set of equivalence classes is denoted $S/\sim$, *and the mapping* $\pi: S \to S/\sim; u \to [u]$ *is called the* **canonical projection**

It follows easily that S is the disjoint union of its equivalence classes.

A9.2. Definition. *Let S be a topological space and* $\sim$ *an equivalence relation on S. Then* $\{U \subset S/\sim | \pi^{-1}(U)$ *is open in* $S\}$ *is called the* **quotient topology** *on* $S/\sim$. *Similarly, if* $S/\sim$ *has a topology, we can induce one on S by* $\{\pi^{-1}(U) | U$ *is open in* $S/\sim\}$. *These are clearly topologies.*

A9.3. Example. Consider $\mathbf{R}^2$ and the relation $\sim$ defined by

$$(a_1, a_2) \sim (b_1, b_2) \quad \text{iff} \quad a_1 - b_1 \in \mathbf{Z}$$

and $a_2 - b_2 \in \mathbf{Z}$ ($\mathbf{Z}$ denotes the integers).

Then $\mathbf{T}^2 = \mathbf{R}^2/\sim$ is called the 2-**torus.** In addition to the quotient topology, it inherits a group structure in the usual way:

$$[(a_1, a_2)] + [(b_1, b_2)] = [(a_1, a_2) + (b_1, b_2)]$$

The n-dimensional torus $\mathbf{T}^n$ is defined in a similar manner.

The torus $\mathbf{T}^2$ may be obtained in two other ways. First, let $\square$ be the unit square in $\mathbf{R}^2$ with the subspace topology. Define $\sim$ by $\mathbf{x} \sim \mathbf{y}$ iff any of the following hold:

(i) $\mathbf{x} = \mathbf{y}$;
(ii) $x_1 = y_1, x_2 = 0, y_2 = 1$;

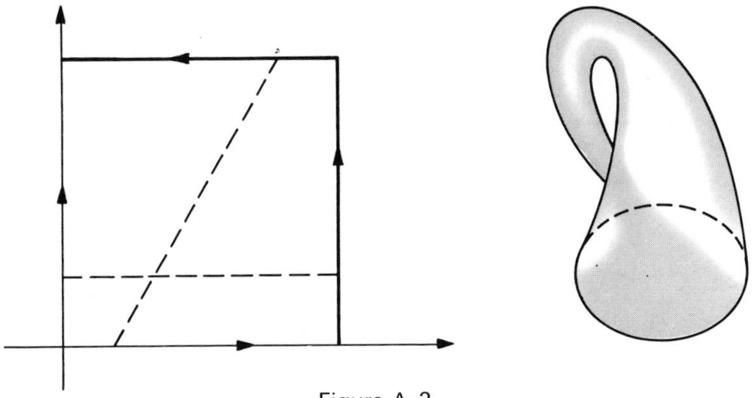

Figure A-2

(iii) $x_1 = y_1, x_2 = 1, y_2 = 0$;
(iv) $x_2 = y_2, x_1 = 0, y_1 = 1$; or
(v) $x_2 = y_2, x_1 = 1, y_1 = 0$;
as indicated in Figure A-1.

Then $\mathbf{T}^2 = \square/\sim$.

Second, define $T^2 = S^1 \times S^1$, as shown in Figure A-1.

A9.4. Example. The Klein bottle is obtained by reversing one of the orientations on $\square$, as indicated in Figure A-2.

Then $\mathbf{K}^2 = \square/\sim$ (the equivalence relation indicated) is the Klein bottle. Although it is realizable as a submanifold of $\mathbf{R}^4$, it is convenient to picture it in $\mathbf{R}^3$ as shown. Notice that $\mathbf{K}^2$ is not orientable and does not inherit a group structure from $\mathbf{R}^2$, as did $\mathbf{T}^2$.

§A10. SIMPLY CONNECTED SPACES

A10.1. Definition. *Let Z be a topological space and $c: [0, 1] \to Z$ a continuous map such that $c(0) = c(1) = p \in Z$. We call c a* **loop** *in Z based at p. The loop c is called* **contractible** *if there is a continuous map $H: [0, 1] \times [0, 1] \to Z$ such that $H(t, 0) = c(t)$ and $H(t, 1) = p$ for all $t \in [0, 1]$. (See Figure A-3.)*

Roughly speaking, a loop is contractible when it can be shrunk continuously to p. The study of loops leads naturally to homotopy theory. In fact the loops at p can easily be made into a group called the **fundamental group**.

A10.2. Definition. *A space Z is called* **simply connected** *iff every loop in Z is contractible.*

In the plane $\mathbf{R}^2$ there is an alternate approach to simple connectedness, by way of the Jordan curve theorem: namely, that every simple (nonintersecting) loop in $\mathbf{R}^2$ divides $\mathbf{R}^2$ (that is, its complement has two components). The unbounded component of the complement is called the interior, and a

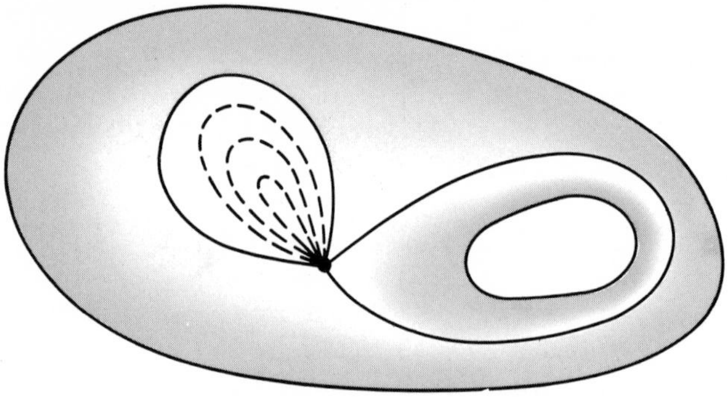

Figure A-3

subset A of $\mathbf{R}^2$ is simply connected iff the interior of every loop in A lies in A.

For manifolds it can be shown that a connected manifold is simply connected iff every closed one form is exact. (The proof is a long story.)

§A11. RESIDUAL SETS

A11.1. Definition. *Let X be a topological space and $A \subset X$. Then A is called* **residual** *iff A is the intersection of a countable family of open dense subsets of X. A space X is called a* **Baire space** *iff every residual set is dense.*

Recall that $B \subset X$ is nowhere dense iff $(B^c)^o = \phi$, so that $X \backslash A$ is residual iff A is the union of a countable collection of nowhere dense closed sets. Clearly, a countable intersection of residual sets is residual.

A11.2. Lemma. *Let X be a locally Baire space; that is, each point $x \in X$ has a neighborhood U such that U^c is a Baire space. Then X is a Baire space.*

Proof. Let $A \subset X$ be residual;

$$A = \bigcap_1^\infty O_n$$

where $O_n^c = X$. Then

$$A \cap U^c = \bigcap_1^\infty (O_n \cap U^c)$$

Now $O_n \cap U^c$ is dense in U^c for if $u \in U^c$ and $u \in O$ then $O \cap U \neq \phi$ and $O \cap U \cap O_n \neq \phi$. Hence $U^c \subset A^c$ and so $A^c = X$. ∎

Then the *Baire category theorem* is as follows.

A11.3. Theorem. *Every complete pseudometric space is a Baire space.*

Proof. Let $U \subset X$ be open and $A = \bigcap_1^\infty O_n$ be residual. By A1.4 (i) we must show $U \cap A \neq \phi$. Now as $O_n^c = X$, $U \cap O_n \neq \phi$ and so we can choose a disk of diameter less than one, say V_1, such that $V_1^c \subset U \cap O_1$. Proceed inductively to obtain $V_n^c \subset U \cap O_n \cap V_{n-1}$ where V_n has diameter $<1/n$. Let $x_n \in V_n^c$. Clearly $\{x_n\}$ is a Cauchy sequence, and by completeness has a convergent subsequence with limit point x. Then

$$x \in \bigcap_1^\infty V_n^c \quad \text{and} \quad U \cap O_n \neq \phi \qquad \blacksquare$$

For the case of a locally compact regular space, see J. Kelley [1, p. 200].

A11.4. Corollary. *Every manifold is a Baire space.*

This follows at once from A11.2 and A11.3 (see A4.4).

Exercises

AA. Let S and T be sets and $f: S \to T$. Show that f is a bijection iff there is a mapping $g: T \to S$ such that $f \circ g$ and $g \circ f$ are the identity mappings on T and S, respectively.

AB. Let X and Y be topological spaces with Y Hausdorff. Then show that, for any continuous maps $f, g: X \to Y$, $\{x \in X | f(x) = g(x)\}$ is closed. Hint: Consider the mapping $x \rightsquigarrow (f(x), g(x))$.

AC. (i) Prove A3.4 and A3.5.
(ii) Prove A1.7 (*ii*), A4.3, and A4.4. Also, in a Hausdorff space, single points are closed.
(iii) Complete the proofs for A5.2, A5.3, and A5.4.

AD. Define a *topological manifold* as a space locally homeomorphic to $\mathbf{R}^n$. Find a topological manifold that is not Hausdorff and not locally compact. Hint: Consider $\mathbf{R}$ with "extra origins."

AE. Prove A7.2, A7.4 (*ii*) and a corresponding statement for arcwise connected spaces. Show that the continuous image of a connected (resp. arcwise connected) space is connected (resp. arcwise connected).

AF. Let M be a topological space and $H: M \to \mathbf{R}$ continuous. Suppose $e \in H(M)$. Then show $H^{-1}(e)$ divides M; that is, $M \setminus H^{-1}(e)$ has at least two components.

AG. (i) Show that $\vec{\rho}$ in A8.1 is not symmetric, by an example.
(ii) Prove that $\bar{\rho}$ is a metric on the closed subsets (including ϕ).
(iii) Express the definition of uniform convergence of a sequence of (real) functions in terms of the Hausdorff metric.
(iv) If X is a compact metric space and ρ and ρ' are equivalent metrics, then show $\bar{\rho}$ and $\bar{\rho}'$ are equivalent.
(v) In case X is not compact show that (iv) can fail.

APPENDIX B

This appendix is an original research article by Al Kelley that has not been published previously. It is reproduced here from the author's manuscript, with his Introduction and Bibliography, and without editing.

STABILITY OF THE CENTER-STABLE MANIFOLD

AL KELLEY*

The Institute for Advanced Study, Princeton, and the University of California, Santa Cruz

1. INTRODUCTION

For a real, autonomous, smooth system of ordinary differential equations in a neighborhood of a critical point (the origin)

$$\dot{p} = Fp + P(p) \tag{1}$$

where F is a constant matrix, P and its first-order derivatives vanish at the origin; the matrix F settles the question of stability of the origin negatively if at least one eigenvalue of F has positive real part. On the other hand, if at least one eigenvalue of F has negative real part, there exists for (1) a smooth invariant manifold, the stable manifold, which contains the origin and such that on this manifold the origin is asymptotically stable. The purpose of this paper is to extend a result of PLISS [5] which describes the case when some of the eigenvalues of F have zero real parts.

Let $F = \text{diag}(A, B, C)$, where A, B, C are constant square matrices (not necessarily of the same dimension); A has eigenvalues with zero real parts ($A = 0$ (zero matrix) is allowed); B has eigenvalues with negative real parts; C has eigenvalues with positive real parts. The invariant manifolds of (1) associated with A, B, C, $\text{diag}(A, B)$ are called, respectively, the center manifold, the stable manifold, the unstable manifold, the center-stable manifold. For a proof of the existence and smoothness of these manifolds see KELLEY [3]. Using the techniques of [3], section 7, one can show that any solution of (1) which does not start on the center-stable manifold at $t = 0$ (and therefore is never on the center-stable manifold) must eventually (for $t > T$, T sufficiently large) remain outside any sufficiently small neighborhood of the origin. Thus the question of stability of the origin is really of interest

* Research supported in part by the National Science Foundation through grant GP-2439.

only on the center-stable manifold, and on this manifold system (1) reduces to

$$\dot{x} = Ax + X(x, y)$$
$$\dot{y} = By + Y(x, y) \tag{2}$$

where X and Y and their first-order derivatives vanish at the origin. With respect to (2), the center manifold is given by

$$M^* = \{(x, y) | \, |x| < \delta, y = v^*(x)\}$$

where v^* and its first-order derivatives vanish at $x = 0$. The theorem of PLISS [5] states that the stability of the origin in (2) is completely determined by the stability of the origin on the center manifold: if the origin is stable (asymptotically stable) (unstable) for the system

$$\dot{x} = Ax + X(x, v^*(x))$$

then the origin is also stable (asymptotically stable) (unstable) for system (2).

Our purpose is to give an extension of the theorem of Pliss to systems of ordinary differential equations in a neighborhood of a periodic orbit or periodic surface. However, we consider only smooth (C^2) systems of equations, whereas Pliss proved his theorem for Lipschitzian systems. Our procedure will be to use the center manifold to put our system of equations in a convenient form, and then by means of a technique of HARTMAN [2] (see also [4]) our result will follow.

Finally it should be mentioned that even though the center and center-stable manifolds in general may not be unique, this in no way affects our discussion of stability. (See [3], section 4 for a discussion of possible non-uniqueness for the center and center-stable manifolds.) This is because stability of the center-stable manifold implies its uniqueness, so that our main result below is in no way dependent upon uniqueness. If there should exist more than one center manifold, the theorem of Pliss and our extension holds for any center manifold and therefore for all center manifolds.

2. NOTATION

If $G = G(p)$ is a smooth vector valued function of the vector p, then G_p will represent the usual Jacobian matrix of partial derivatives. The norm $|\cdot|$ will represent the euclidean norm on vectors and the operator norm on matrices. The notation $\langle \cdot, \cdot \rangle$ will represent the usual inner product on pairs of vectors.

3. MAIN RESULT

Consider the real, C^2 system of ordinary differential equations

$$\dot{\theta} = \tilde{a} + \Theta(\theta, p, q)$$

$$\dot{p} = \tilde{A}p + P(\theta, p, q)$$

$$\dot{q} = Bq + Q(\theta, p, q) \tag{3}$$

where $\tilde{A}$ and B are constant matrices in real canonical form; $\tilde{A}$ has eigenvalues with zero real parts; B has eigenvalues with negative real parts; θ, p, etc., are vectors; $\tilde{a}$ is a constant vector; Θ, P, Q are defined and C^2 in

$$N_\delta = \{(\theta, p, q) | \theta \text{ arbitrary}, |p| + |q| < \delta\}$$

and have multiple period ω in θ; Θ, P, Q, $(P, Q)_{(p,q)} \equiv 0$ when $(p, q) = 0$. System (3) can represent a system of ordinary differential equations in a neighborhood of a critical point, periodic orbit, or periodic surface depending on whether θ is absent ($\dim \theta = 0$), $\dim \theta = 1$, or $\dim \theta > 1$, respectively. The (p, q)-origin, which we now define as

$$\{(\theta, p, q) | \theta \text{ arbitrary}, (p, q) = 0\}$$

represents the critical point, periodic orbit, or periodic surface, as the case may be, around which system (3) is defined.

Let the center manifold for (3) be given by

$$M^* = \{(\theta, p, q) | \theta \text{ arbitrary}, |p| < \delta_0, q = v^*(\theta, p)\}$$

where v^* has multiple period ω in θ; v^*, $v_p^* \equiv 0$ when $p = 0$. In [3] it is shown that v^* exists and is C^2.

Theorem 1. *The stability of the (p, q)-origin in (3) is completely determined by the stability of the p-origin on the center manifold: if the p-origin for the system*

$$\dot{\theta} = \tilde{a} + \Theta(\theta, p, v^*(\theta, p))$$

$$\dot{p} = \tilde{A} + P(\theta, p, v^*(\theta, p))$$

is stable (asymptotically stable) (unstable), then the (p, q)-origin for (3) is also stable (asymptotically stable) (unstable).

Proof. By introducing the variable

$$r = q - v^*(\theta, p) \tag{4}$$

system (3) becomes

$$\dot{\theta} = \tilde{a} + \tilde{\Theta}(\theta, p, r)$$

$$\dot{p} = \tilde{A}p + \tilde{P}(\theta, p, r)$$

$$\dot{r} = Br + \tilde{Q}(\theta, p, r) \tag{5}$$

where

$$\tilde{\Theta}(\theta, p, r) = \Theta(\theta, p, r + v^*(\theta, p))$$

$$\tilde{P}(\theta, p, r) = P(\theta, p, r + v^*(\theta, p))$$

$$\begin{aligned}\tilde{Q}(\theta, p, r) = {} & Q(\theta, p, r + v^*(\theta, p)) - Q(\theta, p, v^*(\theta, p)) \\ & - v_\theta^*(\theta, p)\{\Theta(\theta, p, r + v^*(\theta, p)) - \Theta(\theta, p, v^*(\theta, p))\} \\ & - v_p^*(\theta, p)\{P(\theta, p, r + v^*(\theta, p)) - P(\theta, p, v^*(\theta, p))\}\end{aligned}$$

Hence $\tilde{\Theta}$, $\tilde{P}$, $\tilde{Q}$ are defined and C^1 in N_{δ_1}, δ_1 sufficiently small, and have multiple period ω in θ; $\tilde{\Theta}$, $\tilde{P}$, $\tilde{Q}$, $(\tilde{P}, \tilde{Q})_{(p,r)} \equiv 0$ when $(p, r) = 0$; $\tilde{Q}(\theta, p, 0) \equiv 0$ so that the center manifold in (3) is described by $r = 0$ in (5). By introducing a scalar change of variables

$$(p, r) \to (\lambda p, \lambda r) \tag{6}$$

where λ is a small positive scalar, and then multiplying $\tilde{\Theta}$, $\tilde{P}$, $\tilde{Q}$ by $\phi(|p|^2 + |r|^2)$ where $\phi(t)$ is a C^∞, real valued function of t such that $\phi \equiv 1$ for $0 \le t \le \frac{1}{2}$ and $\phi \equiv 0$ for $1 \le t < \infty$; we obtain

$$\begin{aligned}\dot{\theta} &= \tilde{a} + \phi(|p|^2 + |r|^2)\tilde{\Theta}(\theta, \lambda p, \lambda r) \\ \dot{p} &= \tilde{A}p + \phi(|p|^2 + |r|^2)\lambda^{-1}\tilde{P}(\theta, \lambda p, \lambda r) \\ \dot{r} &= Br + \phi(|p|^2 + |r|^2)\lambda^{-1}\tilde{Q}(\theta, \lambda p, \lambda r)\end{aligned} \tag{7}$$

By choosing λ sufficiently small, the functions $\phi\tilde{\Theta}$, $\phi\lambda^{-1}\tilde{P}$, $\phi\lambda^{-1}\tilde{Q}$ exist and are C^1 for all (θ, p, r), vanish outside $|p|^2 + |r|^2 \ge 1$, and these functions and their first-order derivatives go to zero uniformly in (θ, p, r) as $\lambda \to 0$.

Let $x = (\theta, p)$, $y = r$, $a = (\tilde{a}, 0)$, $A = \mathrm{diag}(0, \tilde{A})$, $X = (\phi\tilde{\Theta}, \phi\lambda^{-1}\tilde{P})$, $Y = \phi\lambda^{-1}\tilde{Q}$ so that (7) can be written

$$\begin{aligned}\dot{x} &= a + Ax + X(x, y) \\ \dot{y} &= By + Y(x, y)\end{aligned} \tag{8}$$

where we have suppressed the dependence of X and Y on λ. Since $\tilde{Q}(\theta, p, 0) \equiv 0$ in (5),

$$Y(x, 0) \equiv 0 \tag{9a}$$

Since A and B are constant matrices in real canonical form, there exist positive constants γ and μ, $\gamma \ll \mu$, such that

$$\langle Ex, x\rangle = 0 \tag{9b}$$

$$|F| \le \gamma \tag{9c}$$

$$\langle By, y\rangle \le -\mu|y|^2 \tag{9d}$$

for all (x, y) where $A = E + F$. In particular, if A is a diagonalizable matrix, then F is the zero matrix. The constant μ may be chosen as one-half the maximum of the real parts of the eigenvalues of B. (See [1], page 341 for details.) By choosing λ in (6) sufficiently small, we obtain

$$\sup_{(x,y)} |(X, Y)| \leq \gamma$$

$$\sup_{(x,y)} |(X, Y)_{(x,y)}| \leq \gamma \tag{9e}$$

Since system (3) in a neighborhood of the (p, q)-origin is related to system (8) by means of a scalar change of variables, our theorem will be proved if we can show that stability for (8) is completely determined by the behavior of the solutions of

$$\dot{x} = a + Ax + X(x, 0) \tag{10}$$

that is, stability for (8) is completely determined by behavior on the center manifold.

Let $(\xi(t), \eta(t))$ with $\xi(t) = \xi(t, x, y)$, $\eta(t) = \eta(t, x, y)$, designate the unique solution of (8) with initial condition (x, y) at $t = 0$. By (9e) the solution exists for all (t, x, y). The main idea of the proof is to show that ξ has a representation

$$\xi(t) = u(t) + v(t)$$

where $u(t) = u(t, z)$ is the unique solution of (10) with initial condition z at $t = 0$, and where $v(t) \to 0$ as $t \to +\infty$. If such a representation exists, then v must satisfy

$$\dot{v} = Av + X(u + v, \eta) - X(u, 0)$$

or

$$\dot{v} = (E + F)v + X(u + v, \eta) - X(u, 0) \tag{11}$$

Introducing the new variable

$$f = e^{-Et}v \tag{12}$$

we have from (11)

$$\dot{f} = Ff + e^{-Et}\{X(u + e^{Et}f, \eta) - X(u, 0)\} \tag{13}$$

It follows from (9b) that for all t,

$$|e^{Et}| = 1 \tag{14}$$

and therefore by (12), $|f| = |v|$. To obtain a solution of (13) satisfying $f(t) \to 0$ as $t \to +\infty$, we will solve the system of integral equations

$$f(t) = \int_{+\infty}^{t} \{Ff(\tau) + e^{-E\tau}X(u(\tau) + e^{E\tau}f(\tau), g(\tau)) - e^{-E\tau}X(u(\tau), 0)\}\, d\tau$$

$$g(t) = e^{Bt}\left\{y + \int_{0}^{t} e^{-B\tau}Y(u(\tau) + e^{E\tau}f(\tau), g(\tau))\right\} d\tau \tag{15}$$

Since $u(t) = u(t, z)$, we will have $f(t) = f(t, z, y)$, $g(t) = g(t, z, y)$. We proceed to solve (15) by recursion (or a slight variation thereof). Let $f^{-1} \equiv 0$, $f^0 \equiv 0$, and define

$$f^{n+1}(t) = \int_{+\infty}^{t} \{Ff^n(\tau) + e^{-E\tau}X(u(\tau) + e^{E\tau}f^n(\tau), g^n(\tau)) - e^{-E\tau}X(u(\tau), 0)\}\, d\tau$$

$$g^n(t) = e^{Bt}\left\{y + \int_0^t e^{-B\tau}Y(u(\tau) + e^{E\tau}f^{n-1}(\tau), g^n(\tau))\right\} d\tau \qquad (n = 0, 1, 2, \ldots) \tag{16}$$

Observe that

$$\frac{d}{dt}g^n(t) = Bg^n(t) + Y(u(t) + e^{Et}f^{n-1}(t), g^n(t))$$

and therefore

$$\frac{d}{dt}|g^n(t)|^2 = 2\langle Bg^n(t), g^n(t)\rangle + 2\langle Y(u(t) + e^{Et}f^{n-1}(t), g^n(t)), g^n(t)\rangle \tag{17}$$

Using the mean value theorem with (9a) and (9e), we obtain

$$|Y(u(t) + e^{Et}f^{n-1}(t), g^n(t))| \leq \gamma |g^n(t)| \tag{18}$$

Then (9d) and (18) yield from (17)

$$\frac{d}{dt}|g^n(t)|^2 \leq 2(-\mu + \gamma)|g^n(t)|^2 \tag{19}$$

and this inequality holds irrespective of the behavior of $f^{n-1}(t)$. In a similar manner we obtain

$$\frac{d}{dt}|g^{n+1}(t) - g^n(t)|^2 \leq 2(-\mu + \gamma)|g^{n+1}(t) - g^n(t)|^2 + 2\gamma|f^n(t) - f^{n-1}(t)|\,|g^{n+1}(t) - g^n(t)| \tag{20}$$

Since $g^n(0) = y$, we have from (19)

$$|g^n(t)| \leq |y|e^{(-\mu+\gamma)t} \qquad (n = 0, 1, 2, \ldots) \tag{21}$$

and assuming γ sufficiently small relative to μ, one shows by induction that

$$|f^n(t)| \leq \tfrac{1}{2}|y|e^{(-\mu+\gamma)t} \qquad (n = 1, 2, \ldots) \tag{22}$$

From (16), (9c), and the mean value theorem with (9e),

$$|f^{n+1}(t) - f^n(t)| \leq \int_t^{+\infty} \{2\gamma|f^n(\tau) - f^{n-1}(\tau)| + \gamma|g^n(\tau) - g^{n-1}(\tau)|\}\, d\tau \tag{23}$$

and assuming γ sufficiently small relative to μ, one shows by induction from (20) and (23) that

$$|f^n(t) - f^{n-1}(t)| \leq 2^{-n}|y|e^{(-\mu+3\gamma)t} \qquad (n = 1, 2, \ldots)$$

$$|g^n(t) - g^{n-1}(t)| \leq 2^{-n}|y|e^{(-\mu+3\gamma)t} \qquad (n = 1, 2, \ldots)$$

Thus

$$v(t) = v(t, z, y) = \lim_{n \to \infty} e^{Et} f^n(t, z, y)$$

Because solutions of (8) are unique,

$$\begin{aligned} \xi(t, x, y) &= u(t, z) + v(t, z, y) \\ \eta(t, x, y) &= g(t, z, y) \end{aligned} \tag{24}$$

when $x = z + v(0, z, y)$. Let T represent the mapping of (z, y) space into (x, y) space given by

$$T: \begin{aligned} x &= z + v(0, z, y) \\ y &= y \end{aligned}$$

Clearly T is a continuous map. To show that T is one-to-one, suppose that $z^1 \neq z^2$, but

$$x = z^1 + v(0, z^1, y) = z^2 + v(0, z^2, y)$$

for some fixed y. Let $u^j(t) = u(t, z^j)$, $v^j(t) = v(t, z^j, y)$, $(j = 1, 2)$. Because solutions of (8) are unique, it follows from (24) that

$$u^1(t) - u^2(t) = v^2(t) - v^1(t) \tag{25}$$

holds for all t. Introducing the new variables

$$w^j(t) = e^{-Et} u^j(t) \qquad (j = 1, 2)$$

we have

$$\frac{d}{dt}\{w^1 - w^2\} = F\{w^1 - w^2\} + e^{-Et}\{X(e^{Et}w^1, 0) - X(e^{Et}w^2, 0)\}$$

$$\begin{aligned} \frac{d}{dt}|w^1 - w^2|^2 &= 2\langle F\{w^1 - w^2\}, \{w^1 - w^2\}\rangle \\ &\quad + 2\langle e^{-Et}\{X(e^{Et}w^1, 0) - X(e^{Et}w^2, 0)\}, \{w^1 - w^2\}\rangle \end{aligned}$$

and from (9c) and (9e)

$$\frac{d}{dt}|w^1 - w^2|^2 \geq -4\gamma|w^1 - w^2|^2$$

Therefore

$$|u^1(t) - u^2(t)| = |w^1(t) - w^2(t)| \geq e^{-2\gamma t}|z^1 - z^2| \tag{26}$$

Inequality (22) implies that

$$|v^j(t)| \leq \tfrac{1}{2}|y|e^{(-\mu+\gamma)t} \qquad (j = 1, 2)$$

Hence

$$\exp(\tfrac{1}{2}\mu t)|v^1(t) - v^2(t)| \to 0 \qquad \text{as} \qquad t \to +\infty$$

whereas (26) implies

$$\exp(\tfrac{1}{2}\mu t)|u^1(t) - u^2(t)| \to +\infty \qquad \text{as} \qquad t \to +\infty$$

but from (25) this is a contradiction. Therefore T is one-to-one. From (22)

$$|v(t, z, y)| \leq \tfrac{1}{2}|y|e^{(-\mu+\gamma)t}$$

Thus the range of T is closed. T is an open map by invariance of domain. Therefore T is onto, and T is a homeomorphism, from which it follows that all solutions of (8) have a unique representation (24). This completes the proof of our theorem.

BIBLIOGRAPHY

[1] E. CODDINGTON and N. LEVINSON, *Theory of Ordinary Differential Equations*, McGraw-Hill, New York, 1955.

[2] P. HARTMAN, *On the local linearization of differential equations*, Proc. Amer. Math. Soc. **14** (1963), 568–573.

[3] A. KELLEY, *The stable, center-stable, center, center-unstable, unstable manifolds*. An appendix in *Transversal Mappings and Flows* by R. ABRAHAM and J. ROBBIN, Benjamin, New York, 1967.

[4] A. KELLEY, *Linearization near a periodic surface or integral manifold* (an unpublished note).

[5] V. A. PLISS, *Principal reduction in the theory of the stability of motion* (in Russian), Izv. Akad. Nauk S.S.S.R., Mat. Ser. **28** (1964), 1297–1324.

APPENDIX C

This Appendix is an original research article by Al Kelley that has not been published previously. It is reproduced here from the author's manuscript, with his Introduction and Bibliography, and without editing.

ON THE LIAPOUNOV SUB-CENTER MANIFOLD

AL KELLEY*

The Institute for Advanced Study, Princeton, and the University of California, Santa Cruz

1. INTRODUCTION

For a real, C^1, Hamiltonian system of ordinary differential equations in a neighborhood of a critical point, let A be the matrix associated with the linear approximation to this system. Let $\pm i\lambda_j$ $(j = 1, \ldots, m)$ represent the purely imaginary eigenvalues of A, and let μ_j $(j = 1, \ldots, 2n)$ represent the remaining eigenvalues of A all of which have non-zero real parts. If $\lambda_j\lambda_k^{-1} \neq$ integer $(1 \leq j, k \leq m; j \neq k)$, then Theorem 1 (below) shows that the Hamiltonian system has m distinct, local, C^1, two-dimensional, invariant manifolds M^{λ_j} $(j = 1, \ldots, m)$; each manifold is composed of a nested, 1-parameter $(r \geq 0)$ family of closed orbits, and as $r \to 0$ the corresponding closed orbit goes to the origin (critical point) and its period goes to $2\pi|\lambda^{-1}|$.

The invariant manifold associated with all the purely imaginary eigenvalues of A is designated M^* and called the center manifold. (See [3].) (The existence of M^* does not require an integral for the system of differential equations.) In view of this we call M^{λ_j} a two-dimensional sub-center manifold, and Theorem 1 in this language shows that for Hamiltonian systems in a neighborhood of a critical point, the center manifold contains two-dimensional sub-center manifolds composed of nested periodic orbits; a two-dimensional sub-center manifold being associated with each pair of purely imaginary eigenvalues for which a certain restriction holds (see Theorem 1 below).

If we consider system (1) below with the added hypothesis of being analytic, then Liapounov [6] proved the existence of M^λ but did not investigate the smoothness of the manifold. With the method of Liapounov it is not imme-

* Research supported in part by the Office of Naval Research and the National Science Foundation through grant GP-2439.

diately evident that M^λ is more than C^0 at the origin even though (1) is analytic. If (1) is analytic, Hamiltonian, and the eigenvalues of the linear part of (1) are distinct, then C. L. SIEGEL [7] proved that M^λ is analytic. J. Moser has recently informed us that J. LAVITA [4] has also proved Theorem 1. His proof, however, is different.

2. NOTATION

If $P = P(p)$ is a smooth vector valued function of the vector p, then P_p will designate the usual Jacobian matrix of partial derivatives. In particular, if p is a scalar variable then $P_p = \partial P/\partial p$. The norm $|\cdot|$ will always represent the euclidean norm on vectors.

3. MAIN THEOREM

Consider the real C^1 system of ordinary differential equations

$$\begin{aligned} \dot{x} &= \lambda y + X(x, y, z) \\ \dot{y} &= -\lambda x + Y(x, y, z) \\ \dot{z} &= Az + Z(x, y, z) \end{aligned} \tag{1}$$

where x and y are scalars, z is a vector, etc.; λ is a non-zero real number; A is a square matrix with constant coefficients; X, Y, Z are defined and C^1 on some neighborhood of the origin; $X, Y, Z, (X, Y, Z)_{(x,y,z)} = 0$ when $(x, y, z) = 0$. Let

$$H = \tfrac{1}{2}\lambda(x^2 + y^2) + F(z) + G(x, y, z) \tag{2}$$

be an integral for (1) (a real valued function that is constant along any given solution of (1)) where F is a quadratic form in the components of z; G is defined and C^2 in some neighborhood of the origin; G and its first- and second-order derivatives vanish at the origin.

Theorem 1. *If no eigenvalue of A is equal to $i\lambda n$ ($i = \sqrt{-1}$) for any integer n, then system (1) has a locally unique, C^1, two-dimensional, invariant manifold.*

$$M^\lambda = \{(x, y, z) \,|\, |x| + |y| < \delta, z = w(x, y)\}$$

where w is a real vector valued function defined and C^1 is some neighborhood of the origin; $w, w_{(x,y)} = 0$ when $(x, y) = 0$; M^λ is composed of a nested, 1-parameter ($r \geq 0$) family of periodic orbits of (1), and as $r \to 0$ the corresponding periodic orbit goes to the origin and its period goes to $2\pi|\lambda^{-1}|$.

Proof. Since H is an integral for (1), the equation

$$H = \tfrac{1}{2}\lambda r^2 \tag{3}$$

implicitly defines a 1-parameter ($r \geq 0$) family of invariant manifolds for (1). Introducing the variables

$$x = r(1 + R)\cos\theta$$

$$y = r(1 + R)\sin\theta$$

$$z = ru \tag{4}$$

we obtain from (2), (3), (4)

$$\tfrac{1}{2}\lambda r^2(1 + R)^2 + F(ru) + \tilde{G} = \tfrac{1}{2}\lambda r^2 \tag{5}$$

where

$$\tilde{G} = \tilde{G}(\theta, r, u) = G(r(1 + R)\cos\theta, r(1 + R)\sin\theta, ru)$$

From (5)

$$2R + R^2 + 2\lambda^{-1}\{F(u) + r^{-2}\tilde{G}\} = 0 \tag{6}$$

Define

$$N_\delta = \{(\theta, r, u) | \theta \text{ arbitrary}, 0 \leq r \leq \delta, |u| \leq \delta\}$$

$$N'_\delta = \{(\theta, r, u) | (\theta, r, u) \in N_\delta, r \neq 0\}$$

Lemma 1. *Equation (6) has a unique solution $R = R(\theta, r, u)$ where R is defined and continuous on N_δ, δ sufficiently small, and is C^1 in (θ, u) on N_δ; R has period 2π in θ; $R(\theta, 0, 0) \equiv 0$; $R_\theta(\theta, 0, u) \equiv 0$; R is C^1 in (θ, r, u) on N'_δ; $rR_r(\theta, r, u) \to 0$ uniformly in θ and $|u| \leq \delta$ as $r \to 0$.*

Proof of Lemma 1. Since $G(x, y, z)$ and its first- and second-order derivatives vanish at the origin,

$$r^{-2}\tilde{G}, \frac{\partial}{\partial R}\{r^{-2}\tilde{G}\} \to 0$$

uniformly in θ and $|u| \leq \delta$ as $r \to 0$. At $r = 0$ define $r^{-2}\tilde{G} = 0$, then the implicit function theorem is applicable to equation (6). (See [1] Theorem 2 on page 138 and the paragraph below (2:8) on page 139.) The implicit function theorem asserts the existence of $R = R(\theta, r, u)$ defined and continuous on N_δ and C^1 in (θ, r, u) on N'_δ for δ sufficiently small where $R(\theta, 0, 0) \equiv 0$ and $R(\theta + 2\pi, r, u) = R(\theta, r, u)$. The remaining properties listed for R are easily deduced by differentiating (6). This completes the proof of Lemma 1.

Let

$$a = a(\theta, r, u) = r(1 + R(\theta, r, u)) \tag{7}$$

From (1) and (4)

$$\dot{\theta} = -\lambda - a^{-1}\{\tilde{X}\sin\theta - \tilde{Y}\cos\theta\} \tag{8a}$$

$$\dot{a} = \tilde{X}\cos\theta + \tilde{Y}\sin\theta \tag{8b}$$

$$\dot{u} = Au + r^{-1}\tilde{Z} \tag{8c}$$

where

$$\tilde{X} = \tilde{X}(\theta, r, u) = X(r(1 + R)\cos\theta, r(1 + R)\sin\theta, ru)$$

etc. Since (7) gives a in terms of (θ, r, u), we may consider equation (8b) superfluous or redundant. From (8a, c)

$$\frac{du}{d\theta} = Bu + U(\theta, r, u) \tag{9}$$

where

$$B = -\lambda^{-1}A$$

$$U(\theta, r, u) = \lambda^{-1}Au - \{\lambda + a^{-1}\{\tilde{X}\sin\theta - \tilde{Y}\cos\theta\}\}^{-1}\cdot\{Au + r^{-1}\tilde{Z}\}$$

Using Lemma 1 it is easy to check that U is defined and continuous on N_δ and is C^1 in (θ, u) on N_δ; $U(\theta, 0, u) \equiv 0$ and hence $U_{(\theta,u)}(\theta, 0, u) \equiv 0$; U is C^1 in (θ, r, u) on N'_δ; $rU_r(\theta, r, u) \to 0$ uniformly in θ and $|u| \leq \delta$ as $r \to 0$.

Since A has no eigenvalue equal to $i\lambda n$ ($i = \sqrt{-1}$) for any integer n, it follows that B has no eigenvalue equal to in for any integer n, and hence we can use perturbation theory, where r is considered the perturbation parameter, to solve (9) for the unique solution $u = v(\theta, r)$ having period 2π in θ. As is well known, v satisfies the following integral equation (see [2] Chapter 5).

$$v(\theta, r) = \{e^{-B2\pi} - 1\}^{-1}\int_0^{2\pi} e^{-B\sigma}U(\theta + \sigma, r, v(\theta + \sigma, r))\,d\sigma \tag{10}$$

Lemma 2. *The solution $v = v(\theta, r)$ has the following properties.*

(*i*) *For δ sufficiently small v is defined and continuous for all θ and $0 \leq r \leq \delta$; v has period 2π in θ; $v(\theta, 0) \equiv 0$.*

(*ii*) *v is C^1 in θ and $v_\theta(\theta, 0) \equiv 0$.*

(*iii*) *v is C^1 in (θ, r) for all θ and $0 < r \leq \delta$; $rv_r(\theta, r) \to 0$ uniformly in θ as $r \to 0$.*

Proof of Lemma 2. The fact that v exists with property (*i*) is well known; one merely solves (10) by iteration. From (10), if v_θ exists it must satisfy

$$v_\theta(\theta, r) = \{e^{-B2\pi} - 1\}^{-1}\int_0^{2\pi} e^{-B\sigma}\{U_\theta(\theta + \sigma, r, v(\theta + \sigma, r)) + U_u(\theta + \sigma, r, v(\theta + \sigma, r))v_\theta(\theta + \sigma, r)\}\,d\sigma$$

Consider the equation

$$p(\theta, r) = \{e^{-B2\pi} - 1\}^{-1}\int_0^{2\pi} e^{-B\sigma}\{U_\theta(\theta + \sigma, r, v(\theta + \sigma, r)) + U_u(\theta + \sigma, r, v(\theta + \sigma, r))p(\theta + \sigma, r)\}\,d\sigma$$

where dim p = dim v_θ. Using the properties we listed for U and starting with $p^0 \equiv 0$, one easily solves this equation by iteration. The solution $p = p(\theta, r)$ is defined and continuous for all θ and $0 \le r \le \delta$ for δ sufficiently small. It is not difficult to show that for h a real scalar,

$$h^{-1}\{v(\theta + h, r) - v(\theta, r)\} \to p(\theta, r)$$

as $h \to 0$. Thus v_θ exists and $v_\theta(\theta, r) = p(\theta, r)$. A similar argument shows that v_r exists and is continuous for all θ and $m^{-1} \le r \le \delta$ where m is any large positive integer. Therefore v_r exists and is continuous for all θ and $0 < r \le \delta$. The fact that $rv_r(\theta, r) \to 0$ uniformly in θ as $r \to 0$ follows by computing rv_r from (10) and using the properties listed for U. This completes the proof of Lemma 2.

An immediate consequence of Lemmas 1 and 2 is that the two products $rR(\theta, r, v(\theta, r))$ and $rv(\theta, r)$ are C^1 in (θ, r) for all θ and $0 \le r \le \delta$, and that

$$\frac{d}{dr}\{rR(\theta, r, v(\theta, r))\}_{r=0} = 0$$

$$\frac{d}{dr}\{rv(\theta, r)\}_{r=0} = 0$$

Let

$$b = b(\theta, r) = r(1 + R(\theta, r, v(\theta, r))) \tag{11}$$

The inverse function theorem applied to (11) yields $r = r(\theta, b)$ where r is defined and C^1 for all θ and $0 \le b \le \gamma$ for γ sufficiently small; r has period 2π in θ; $r(\theta, 0) \equiv 0$; $r_\theta(\theta, 0) \equiv 0$; $r_b(\theta, 0) \equiv 1$. Via the polar coordinates

$$x = b \cos \theta$$

$$y = b \sin \theta \tag{12}$$

the manifold M^λ is easily described. Let

$$w(x, y) = r(\theta, b)v(\theta, r(\theta, b))$$

where θ and b are functions of x and y obtained by inverting (12). Then

$$M^\lambda = \{(x, y, z) \,\big|\, |x| + |y| < \delta, z = w(x, y)\}$$

The changes of variables (12) is non-singular except at the origin. To show that w is C^1 in (x, y) at the origin, we compute

$$\begin{aligned}\frac{\partial}{\partial x} w(x, y) &= \frac{\partial}{\partial x}\{rv(\theta, r)\} \\ &= \left\{\cos\theta \frac{\partial}{\partial b} - b^{-1} \sin\theta \frac{\partial}{\partial \theta}\right\} rv(\theta, r) \\ &= \cos\theta\{r_b v(\theta, r) + rv_r(\theta, r) r_b\} \\ &\quad - b^{-1} \sin\theta\{r_\theta v(\theta, r) + rv_\theta(\theta, r) + rv_r(\theta, r) r_\theta\}\end{aligned}$$

Therefore $w_x(x, y) \to 0$ as $(x, y) \to 0$. A similar computation shows that $w_y(x, y) \to 0$ as $(x, y) \to 0$. It is easy to see that

$$w(x, y) = o(|x| + |y|)$$

as $(x, y) \to 0$. Hence w is C^1 in (x, y) in a neighborhood of the origin and $w, w_{(x,y)} = 0$ when $(x, y) = 0$.

The parameterization

$$\begin{aligned} x &= r(1 + R(\theta, r, v(\theta, r))) \cos \theta \\ y &= r(1 + R(\theta, r, v(\theta, r))) \sin \theta \\ z &= rv(\theta, r) \end{aligned} \tag{13}$$

exhibits M^λ as a nested, 1-parameter ($r \geq 0$) family of periodic orbits of (1). That this is so follows from having introduced new coordinates in (4), having computed R by means of the integral H in (5), and having computed v as the unique family of periodic solutions of (9) that was obtained by eliminating t between (8a) and (8c). From (13) it is clear that as $r \to 0$ the periodic orbit goes to the origin.

Let $\psi(t, r)$, $\psi(0, r) = 0$, represent the unique solution of the equation

$$\dot{\theta} = -\lambda - b^{-1}\{\hat{X} \sin \theta - \hat{Y} \cos \theta\} \tag{14}$$

with zero initial condition at $t = 0$, where $b = b(\theta, r)$ given in (11) and

$$\hat{X} = X(b \cos \theta, b \sin \theta, rv(\theta, r)) = X(r(1 + R(\theta, r, v(\theta, r))) \cos \theta, \ldots)$$

$$\hat{Y} = Y(b \cos \theta, \ldots)$$

Thus (14) is equation (8a) restricted to M^λ. Solutions of (1) on M^λ are obtained by replacing θ in (13) by $\psi(t + c, r)$, where c is any real constant. If there exists $\omega \neq 0$ such that

$$\psi(\omega, r) + 2\pi = 0$$

then for all t

$$\psi(t + \omega, r) - \psi(t, r) + 2\pi = 0$$

and the corresponding solution of (1) on M^λ will have period $|\omega|$. Clearly

$$\psi(2\pi\lambda^{-1}, 0) + 2\pi = 0$$

and

$$\dot{\psi}(2\pi\lambda^{-1}, 0) = -\lambda$$

Therefore by the implicit function theorem there exists a unique, real valued function $\omega(r)$ defined and continuous for $0 \leq r \leq \delta$, δ sufficiently small, such that $\omega(0) = 2\pi\lambda^{-1}$. Hence the nested family of periodic orbits of (1) on M^λ

have the property that as $r \to 0$ the corresponding periodic orbit goes to the origin and its period goes to $2\pi|\lambda^{-1}|$.

The uniqueness of M^λ follows from the uniqueness of the periodic solutions of (9). This completes the proof of our theorem.

BIBLIOGRAPHY

[1] L. M. GRAVES, *The Theory of Functions of Real Variables*, McGraw-Hill, New York, 1946.

[2] J. HALE, *Oscillations in Nonlinear Systems*, McGraw-Hill, New York, 1963.

[3] A. KELLEY, *The stable, center-stable, center, center-unstable, unstable manifolds*. An appendix in *Transversal Mappings and Flows* by R. ABRAHAM and J. ROBBIN, Benjamin, New York, 1967.

[4] J. LAVITA, *Concerning a theorem of Liapounov*, pp. 202–211 of *Hamiltonian Systems* by J. Moser (unpublished notes).

[5] S. LEFSCHETZ, *Differential Equations: Geometric Theory*, Wiley (Interscience), New York, 1957, pp. 160–163.

[6] A. LIAPOUNOV, *Problème général de la Stabilité du Mouvement*, Ann. Math. Studies No. 17, Princeton Univ. Press, Princeton, N.J., 1949, pp. 375–392.

[7] C. L. SIEGEL, *Vorlesungen uber Himmelsmechanik*, Springer, Berlin, 1956, pp. 82–92.

APPENDIX D

This appendix is an English translation of an address to the 1954 International Congress of Mathematicians by A. N. KOLMOGOROV [1, 2], in which the first version of the stability theorem (30.5) was stated.

THE GENERAL THEORY OF DYNAMICAL SYSTEMS AND CLASSICAL MECHANICS

A. N. KOLMOGOROV

INTRODUCTION

It came as a surprise to me that I would need to make an address at the final session of the Congress in this large hall, which up to now I had been familiar with more as a place for the performance of great musical masterpieces of the world under Mengelberg's conduction. The address that I have prepared, without taking into consideration the perspectives of such an esteemed position in the program of the present Congress, will be devoted to a rather specialized group of questions. My problem is to make clear the different paths that one may use to apply the basic ideas and results of present-day general measure theory and spectral theory of dynamical systems to the study of the conservative dynamical systems of classical mechanics. However, it seems to me that the theme that I have chosen can be of broader interest, since it is one of the examples of the birth of new, unexpected, and profound relationships between the different branches of classical and contemporary mathematics.

In his remarkable address at the Congress in 1900, Hilbert said that the unity of mathematics, the impossibility of dividing it into mutually independent branches, is a consequence of the very nature of our science. The most convincing confirmation of the validity of his view is the fact that, at every stage in the development of mathematics, there appear new joining points where, in the solution of quite specific problems, the concepts and methods of quite different mathematical disciplines become necessary and enter into a new interrelationship with each other. For the mathematics of the nineteenth century, one of these joining points was the complex question of integrating the systems of differential equations of classical mechanics, where the problems of mechanics and differential-equation theory were organically interwoven with the problems of the calculus of variations, many-dimensional differential geometry, the theory of analytic functions, and the theory of continuous groups.

After the appearance of Poincaré's works, the fundamental role of topology for this class of questions became clear. On the other hand, the Poincaré–Carathéodory recurrence theorem served as the starting point in the measure theory of dynamical systems, in the sense of the investigation of the properties of motions that take place at "almost all" initial states of a system. The "ergodic theory," which developed from this, has acquired various generalizations and has become an independent center of attraction and a junction in the web of methods and problems of various new divisions of mathematics (abstract measure theory, the theory of groups of linear operators in Hilbert and other infinite-dimensional spaces, the theory of random processes, etc.). At the preceding International Congress in 1950, the long address by KAKUTANI [23] was devoted to general questions in ergodic theory.

As we know, topological methods acquired significant applications in the theory of oscillations, in particular, in the solution of quite specific problems that arise in the study of automatic control systems, electrotechnology, etc. However, these real physical and technical applications deal primarily with nonconservative systems. Here, the problem usually reduces to finding individual asymptotically stable motions (in particular, stable rest points and stable limiting cycles) and to the study of pencils of integral curves that are attracted to these asymptotically stable motions.

In conservative systems, asymptotically stable motions are impossible. Therefore, the search for individual periodic motions, for example, has, for all its mathematical interest, only a restricted real physical interest in the case of conservative systems. Of special significance in the case of conservative systems is the measure-theoretic point of view, which enables us to study the properties of the basic set of motions. To this end, present-day general ergodic theory has produced a number of concepts that are extremely significant from a physical standpoint. However, our successes in an analytical sense from these contemporary points of view in handling the specific problems of classical mechanics have up to the present been more than restricted.

The question deals, in the first instance, with the following problem. Let us suppose that motion along an s-dimensional analytic manifold V^s is defined by a canonical system of differential equations with an analytic Hamiltonian function $H(q_1, \ldots, q_s, p_1, \ldots, p_s)$. Suppose also that there are k single-valued analytic first integrals $I_1, I_2, \ldots, I_k$ and that the conditions

$$I_1 = C_1, \ldots, I_k = C_k$$

define an analytic manifold M^{2s-k} in the phase space Ω^{2s}. As we know, for almost all values of $C_1, \ldots, C_k$, there arises in a natural way an analytic invariant density on M^{2s-k}, which makes it possible to apply to the motions on M^{2s-k} the general principles of the measure theory of dynamical systems. It is natural to turn to more modern tools in cases in which, besides $I_1, \ldots, I_k$, there are no single-valued analytic first integrals independent of them, or in which the problem of finding them is too difficult and other classical analytic methods of carrying out the integration of the system are also inapplicable. In such cases, one must, by use of quantitative considerations, solve the question as to whether motion on M^{2s-k} is transitive or not (that is, whether almost all the manifold M^{2s-k} consists of a single unique ergodic set) and, in the case in which it is transitive, to determine the nature of the spectrum or, when it is not, to study with accuracy up to a set of measure zero (or at least up to a set of small measure) the nature of the decomposition of M^{2s-k} into ergodic sets and the nature of the spectrum on these ergodic sets.

I know only two specific problems in classical mechanics in which this program has been completed to a greater or lesser degree:

1. For inertial motion along a closed surface V^2 with everywhere-negative curvature,* Hopf established in 1939 that motion on three-dimensional manifolds L_h^3 defined by the requirement that the energy $H = h$ be constant is transitive and that the spectrum is continuous (cf. [8]).

2. As will be shown later, in the case of inertial motion along an analytic surface that is sufficiently close to an ellipsoid in Euclidean 3-space, the motion on L_h^3 is nontransitive and, up to a set of small measure, it can be decomposed into two-dimensional tori T^2 on each of which the motion is transitive and the spectrum discrete (cf. end of §2).

It seems to me, however, that the time has come when it should be possible to advance much more rapidly.

§1. ANALYTIC DYNAMICAL SYSTEMS AND THEIR STABILITY PROPERTIES

The dynamical systems of classical mechanics constitute a special case of analytic dynamical systems with an integral invariant. The domain of such a dynamical system is an analytic n-dimensional manifold Ω^n (the phase space of the system). Accordingly, admissible transformations of the coordinates $x_1, \ldots, x_n$ of a point $x \in \Omega^n$ will always be analytic.

* Perhaps it might be worthwhile to note that, in ordinary Euclidean space, one can define a closed surface V^2 of genus 1 and to place close to it a finite number of centers of attraction or repulsion that create on V^2 a potential of forces in such a way that the motion of a point mass on V^2 under the influence of these external forces will be mathematically equivalent to inertial motion in a metric possessing everywhere a negative curvature.

The right-hand sides of the differential equations determining the motion

$$\frac{dx_\alpha}{dt} = F_\alpha(x_1, \ldots, x_n) \tag{1-1}$$

and the invariant plane generating the invariant measure

$$m(A) = \int_A M(x)\, dx_1 \cdots dx_n$$

will be assumed analytic functions of the coordinates.*

In line with what was said in the introduction, we shall concern ourselves primarily with canonical systems, systems in which $n = 2s$, with a partition of the coordinates of the point $(q, p) \in \Omega^{2s}$ into two sets $q_1, q_2, \ldots, q_s$ and $p_1, \ldots, p_s$, with contact transformations as admissible transformations of coordinates, with equations of canonical form

$$\frac{dq_\alpha}{dt} = \frac{\partial H}{\partial p_\alpha} \qquad \frac{dp_\alpha}{dt} = -\frac{\partial H}{\partial q_\alpha} \tag{1-2}$$

and with invariant density

$$M(p, q) = 1$$

Particular attention will be given to the question as to what properties of dynamical systems, with "arbitrary" F_α and M (or an "arbitrary" function $H(q, p)$ in the case of canonical systems), are "typical" and which properties may occur only "exceptionally." However, this is quite a delicate question. An approach from the standpoint of the category of the corresponding sets in functional spaces of systems of functions $\{F_\alpha, M\}$ (or functions H) is, despite the known successes obtained in this direction in the general theory of abstract dynamical systems, interesting more as a means for proving existence than as a direct answer to arbitrarily stylized and idealized real inquiries by investigators in physics or mechanics. The approach from the standpoint of measure, on the other hand, is quite a sound and natural approach from the physical point of view (as was argued in detail, for example, by von Neumann [1]), but it runs into the problem of absence of a natural measure in functional spaces.

We shall follow two paths. In the first place, to obtain positive results stating that this or that type of dynamical system must be accepted as one of the essential, not "exceptional," systems, that cannot be "neglected" from any sensible point of view (similar to the way in which we neglect sets of measure zero), we shall use the concept of stability in the sense of conservation of a given type of behavior of a dynamical system when there is a slight variation in the functions F_α and M or the function H. An arbitrary type of

* Whenever we speak simply of "measure" without any other qualification, we mean the measure m.

behavior of a dynamical system, for which there exists at least one example of its stable realization, must from this point of view be considered essential and may not be neglected. In accordance with the approach taken from the standpoint of analytic functions, "smallness" in the variation of the function $f_0(x)$ will be understood in the sense of change from a function $f_0(x)$ to a function of the form

$$f(x) = f_0(x) + \theta\varphi(x, \theta)$$

with a small value of the parameter θ, where the function φ is analytic with respect to the variables $x_1, x_2, \ldots, x_n, \theta$. Such an approach may be open to criticism, but by means of it one can obtain certain interesting results. When we may confine ourselves to closeness of the functions f_0 and f in the sense of closeness of their derivatives or arbitrary order, this will be pointed out.

To obtain negative results of the nonessential exceptional nature of a certain phenomenon, we shall apply only one somewhat artificial device: if on the class K of functions $f(x)$ it is possible to define a finite number of functionals

$$F_1(f), F_2(f), \ldots, F_r(f)$$

that in some sense or other may naturally be considered as assuming "generally speaking arbitrary" values

$$F_1(f) = C_1, \ldots, F_r(f) = C_r$$

in some region in the r-dimensional space of points $C = (C_1, \ldots, C_r)$, we shall consider an arbitrary phenomenon that takes place only when C is in a set of r-dimensional Lebesgue measure zero as exceptional and "negligible." I begin a survey of specific results with the application of this idea to the investigation of dynamical systems, the phase space of which is a two-dimensional torus.

§2. DYNAMICAL SYSTEMS ON A TWO-DIMENSIONAL TORUS AND CERTAIN CANONICAL SYSTEMS WITH TWO DEGREES OF FREEDOM

In all that follows, by points on a torus T^2 we shall mean given circular coordinates x_1, x_2 (the point x does not change in the shift from x_α to $x_\alpha + 2\pi$). The functions F_α in the right-hand members of the equations

$$\frac{dx_1}{dt} = F_1(x_1, x_2) \qquad \frac{dx_2}{dt} = F_2(x_1, x_2)$$

and the invariant density $M(x_1, x_2)$ will, in accordance with what was said above, be assumed analytic. We shall also assume that

$$F_1^2 + F_2^2 > 0 \qquad M > 0 \tag{2-1}$$

For simplicity, we assume that the normalization condition $m(T^2) = 1$ is satisfied. We introduce the mean frequencies of rotation

$$\lambda_1 = \int_{T^2} F_1(x)\,dm \qquad \lambda_2 = \int_{T^2} F_2(x)\,dm$$

A slight strengthening of the results of Poincaré, Denjoy, and Kneser lead in the present case to the conclusion that, by means of an analytic coordinate transformation, the equations of motion can be reduced to the form

$$\frac{dx_1}{dt} = \lambda_1 M(x_1, x_2) \qquad \frac{dx_2}{dt} = \lambda_2 M(x_1, x_2)$$

It is well known that in the case of an irrational ratio

$$\gamma = \frac{\lambda_1}{\lambda_2}$$

all the trajectories are everywhere dense and the measure m is transitive. In addition, one can easily show, following MARKOV [2], that for irrational γ, a dynamical system is strongly ergodic; that is, it contains exactly one ergodic set E the points of which have with the appropriate measure, measure

$$\mu_\varepsilon = cm$$

where c is a constant. The natural assertion that motions on a two-dimensional torus under conditions (2-1) possess "generally speaking" all the properties that we have just enumerated is already seen to apply to the principle, mentioned above, of neglecting cases in which some finite system of functionals (in the present case λ_1 and λ_2) assumes values in some set of measure 0 (in the present case, the set of points (λ_1, λ_2) with rational ratio γ).

In the article [3], I succeeded in proceeding somewhat further. Specifically, I showed that, under the assumption that there exist positive numbers c and h such that, for all integral r and s,

$$|r - s\gamma| \geqq ch^s \tag{2-2}$$

the equations of motion can be reduced by an analytic transformation of coordinates to the form

$$\frac{dx_1}{dt} = \lambda_1 \qquad \frac{dx_2}{dt} = \lambda_2 \tag{2-3}$$

As we know from the theory of Diophantine approximations, condition (2-2) is satisfied (for suitable c and h) for almost all irrational numbers γ. Thus, except for cases in which γ can be approximated "abnormally well" by fractions r/s, an analytic dynamical system with integral invariant on the torus T^2 under conditions (2-1) necessarily admits only almost-periodic and even more restrictively "conditionally periodic" motions with two independent frequencies λ_1 and λ_2.

As we know, many problems in classical mechanics with two degrees of freedom ($s = 2, n = 4$) in which the four-dimensional manifold Ω^4 is decomposed, with the exception of certain exceptional manifolds of no more than three dimensions, into the two-dimensional manifolds

$$L^2_{C_1C_2} = L^2(I_1 = C_1, I_2 = C_2)$$

because of the presence of two first integrals I_1 and I_2 that are single-valued on the entire manifold Ω^4. Since the four equations

$$\frac{\partial H}{\partial q_1} = \frac{\partial H}{\partial q_2} = \frac{\partial H}{\partial p_1} = \frac{\partial H}{\partial p_2} = 0$$

are satisfied at rest points, the set of these points in the case of an analytic function H is no more than countable. Therefore, they may fall into the manifold L^2 only as exceptions. From this we conclude that almost all compact manifolds L^2 are tori (since they are orientable, compact, two-dimensional manifolds admitting a vectorfield without zero vectors).

Problems of classical mechanics of the type that we have been considering are, as we know, always integrable. A qualitative investigation of the special problems of this type (motion under the influence of gravity along a surface of rotation, inertial motion along the surface of an ellipsoid in 3-space, etc., the motion of a point along a plane under the influence of the Newtonian attraction of two immovable centers, etc.) also leads us to a large number of examples of the decomposition of the space Ω^4 basically into tori T^2 with windings that fill them everywhere densely from the trajectories of conditionally periodic motions with two independent frequencies λ_1 and λ_2. Among these tori there is, generally speaking, an everywhere dense set of tori that are, by virtue of the commensurability of the frequencies, decomposed into closed trajectories and a discrete set of singular manifolds of dimension ≤ 3 on which, in particular, rest points are placed and so-called asymptotic motions are set up. Consideration of these integrable problems yields a number of interesting examples of rather complicated partitions of the phase space Ω into ergodic sets with a remainder consisting of "non-regular points" that lie on the trajectories of asymptotic motions.*

In my article [3] referred to above, it is shown that, for exceptional irrational values of γ (that is, not satisfying condition (2-2)), there are indeed a number of new possibilities, some of them rather unexpected for analytic systems (of this we shall speak later). However, in the problems of classical mechanics mentioned above, these exceptional cases fail to appear for an extremely simple reason: the transition to circular coordinates ξ_1, ξ_2 on the tori $\mathbf{T}^2$ and to the parameters C_1 and C_2 of these tori in these problems

* In connection with this, I mention that the extremely instructive qualitative analysis of the problem on the attraction by two immovable centers that was made in Charlier's well-known treatise has proven to be incomplete and partially erroneous. It has twice been corrected [4, 5].

is made by means of contact transformations. Therefore, the equations keep their canonical form

$$\frac{d\xi_\alpha}{dt} = \frac{\partial}{\partial C_\alpha} H \qquad \frac{dC_\alpha}{dt} = -\frac{\partial}{\partial \xi_\alpha} H$$

and since invariance of the tori $\mathbf{T}^2$ is obtained only in the case

$$\frac{dC_1}{dt} = \frac{dC_2}{dt} = 0$$

then H depends only on C_1 and C_2, which leads, on each torus $\mathbf{T}^2$, to equations (2-3) with constants λ_1 and λ_2 with no exceptions.

Therefore, the real significance for classical mechanics of the analysis that I have made of dynamical systems on $\mathbf{T}^2$ depends on whether there are sufficiently important examples of canonical systems with two degrees of freedom that cannot be integrated by classical methods and in which invariant (with respect to the transformations S^t) two-dimensional tori play a significant role.

To show that such examples exist, we shall, following the study made by BIRKHOFF [6] of a neighborhood of an elliptic periodic motion, examine the system with circular coordinates q_1, q_2 and with momenta p_1, p_2 for which

$$H(q, p) = W(p)$$

The equations of motion take the form

$$\frac{dq_\alpha}{dt} = \frac{\partial W}{\partial p_\alpha} \qquad \frac{dp_\alpha}{dt} = 0$$

Obviously, the tori $\mathbf{T}_c^2$ defined by the conditions

$$p_1 = c_1 \qquad p_2 = c_2$$

are invariant and on each of them a periodic motion

$$\frac{dq_\alpha}{dt} = \lambda_\alpha(c) = \frac{\partial}{\partial c_\alpha} W(c_1, c_2)$$

arises, with two frequencies that are independent of C. Let us suppose that the Jacobian of the frequencies λ_α with respect to the momenta p_α is nonzero:

$$\left|\frac{\partial \lambda_\alpha}{\partial p_\beta}\right| = \left|\frac{\partial^2 W}{\partial p_\alpha \partial p_\beta}\right| \neq 0 \tag{2-4}$$

It turns out that in this case, the partitioning of the region in question of the four-dimensional space Ω^4 into two-dimensional tori $\mathbf{T}^2$ is basically stable with respect to small changes in H of the form

$$H(q, p, \theta) = W(p) + \theta S(q, p, \theta)$$

To obtain a precise formulation, let us consider a region $G \subset \Omega^4$ determined by the condition $p \in B$, where B is a bounded region in the plane of points p. Assuming that the functions W and S are analytic and that condition (2-4) is satisfied, we can prove that, for arbitrary $\varepsilon > 0$, there exist a $\delta > 0$ such that, for $|\theta| < \delta$, in the dynamical system

$$\frac{dq_\alpha}{dt} = \frac{\partial}{\partial p_\alpha} H(q, p, \theta) \qquad \frac{dp_\alpha}{dt} = -\frac{\partial}{\partial p_\alpha} H(q, p, \theta)$$

the entire region G except for a set of measure less than ε consists of invariant two-dimensional tori $\mathbf{T}^2$ on each of which, in suitable (that is, depending analytically on (q, p)) circular coordinates ξ_1, ξ_2, the motion is determined by the equations

$$\frac{d\xi_1}{dt} = \lambda_1 \qquad \frac{d\xi_2}{dt} = \lambda_2$$

where λ_1 and λ_2 are constant on each $\mathbf{T}^2$, that is, they are conditionally periodic with two periods.

The proof consists in following the fate of the original tori $\mathbf{T}_c^2$ with frequencies $\lambda_\alpha(c)$ satisfying condition (2-2) with varying θ and in showing that each such torus is not destroyed when θ is sufficiently small but is merely displaced in Ω keeping on itself the trajectories of conditionally periodic motions with constant frequencies λ_α.

Very likely, many of my listeners have already guessed that it is basically a matter of working out an idea already widely discussed in the literature on celestial mechanics, namely, the possibility of avoiding "abnormally small denominators" in calculating the perturbations of orbits. In contrast with the usual theory of perturbations, however, I obtain precise results instead of a conclusion as to the convergence of series of this or that approximation of finite order (with respect to θ). This is due to the fact that, instead of calculating the disturbed motion under fixed initial conditions, I modify the initial conditions themselves in such a way as to have motions with normal (in the sense of condition (2-2)) frequencies λ_α at all times when θ varies.

I wish to make the following three remarks in connection with what has been said.

1. The theorem on the reducibility of motions on $\mathbf{T}^2$ to the form (2-3) can be proven even under conditions of sufficiently high order of finite differentiability of the functions F_α and M (naturally with a corresponding weakening of the conclusion). The theorem on the conservation of tori in Ω^4, on the other hand, obviously has to require either that the functions $W(p)$ and $S(q, p, \theta)$ be analytic or that these functions have infinitely many derivatives satisfying certain restrictions on the order of their growth.

2. The exceptional set of measure less than ε foreseen in the second theorem may actually prove to be everywhere dense and, very likely, of positive

measure for arbitrarily small θ. This is analogous to the "zones of instability" discovered by Birkhoff in his study of neighborhoods of elliptic periodic trajectories [6].

3. As one of the special cases to which all that has been said above applies, we may mention inertial motion along an analytic surface that is close to an ellipsoid in 3-space.

§3. ARE DYNAMICAL SYSTEMS ON COMPACT MANIFOLDS "GENERALLY SPEAKING" TRANSITIVE, AND SHOULD WE CONSIDER A CONTINUOUS SPECTRUM AS THE "GENERAL" CASE AND A DISCRETE SPECTRUM AS THE "EXCEPTIONAL" CASE?

The hypothesis of the predominant occurrence of the transitive case and the case of a continuous spectrum (mixing) have been asserted more than once in connection with the "ergodic" hypotheses in physics. As applied to canonical systems, it is natural to consider both these hypotheses only for $(2s - 1)$-dimensional invariant manifolds L_h^{2s-1}, which are defined by the requirement that the energy be constant:

$$H = h$$

and to apply them only to the case of compact manifolds L_h^{2s-1} since, on noncompact manifolds L_h^{2s-1}, in even the simplest problems there are "departing" trajectories (and they usually dominate from a standpoint of measure), of which we shall speak in §4. If the first hypothesis is relaxed, it is natural to apply the second not to the entire manifold Ω^n (or to L_h^{2s-1} in the case of canonical systems) but to those ergodic sets into which Ω^n is decomposed (neglecting, of course, ergodic sets the union of which is of measure zero).

In the application to analytic canonical systems, the answer to both questions is negative since the theorem on stability of the decomposition into tori that we asserted for theorems with two degrees of freedom remains valid for an arbitrary number of degrees of freedom. If the equation

$$H(q, p, \theta) = W(p) + \theta S(q, p, \theta)$$

holds in a $2s$-dimensional toroidal layer G of the phase space Ω^{2s}, then for $\theta = 0$ this layer can be decomposed in an obvious manner into invariant s-dimensional tori T_p^s on each of which the motion is conditionally periodic with s periods. Also, if

$$\left| \frac{\partial^2 W}{\partial p_\alpha \partial p_\beta} \right| \neq 0$$

on almost all tori $\mathbf{T}_p^s$, the periods are independent in the sense that

$$(n, \lambda) = \sum_\alpha n_\alpha \lambda_\alpha \neq 0$$

for arbitrary integers n_α. Therefore, the trajectories wind around the torus everywhere densely, the s-dimensional Lebesgue measure on $\mathbf{T}^s$ is transitive, and the entire torus constitutes a single ergodic set. Theorems 1 and 2 in my article [22] assert that, under the hypotheses described, this entire picture changes for small values of θ only in that certain tori corresponding to systems of frequencies for which the expressions (n, λ) decrease too rapidly with increasing

$$|n| = \sqrt{\Sigma n_\alpha^2}$$

may disappear. However, the majority of the tori $\mathbf{T}_p^s$ conserve the nature of the motions that arise on them and are only displaced in Ω^{2s}, continuing, for small values of θ, to fill G up to a set of small measure. Thus, for small changes in H, a dynamical system remains nontransitive and the region G remains, up to a remainder of small measure, partitionable into ergodic sets with discrete spectrum (with special nature mentioned).

In connection with this, it is interesting to note that certain physicists (see, for example, [7]) have made the hypothesis that the "general case" of a canonical dynamical system without departing trajectories is just the decomposition of Ω^{2s} into s-dimensional tori $\mathbf{T}^s$ on which there are conditionally periodic motions with s periods. Apparently, this idea is based only on the predominant attention that has been given to linear systems and to a restricted set of integrable classical problems. In any case, it should be noted that the methods of proving the theorem referred to above are connected in a very real way with just the problem of stratifying Ω^{2s} into tori $\mathbf{T}^s$ and are not applicable to stratifying it into tori of any other dimension $r > s$ or $r < s$.

The hypothesis stated above can hardly stand up in its general form since it is extremely likely that, for arbitrary s, there are examples of canonical systems with s degrees of freedom and with stable transitiveness and mixing on the manifolds L_h^{2s-1}. I have in mind motion along geodesics on compact manifolds V^s of constant negative curvature, that is, dynamical systems such that

$$H(q, p) = \sum_{\alpha\beta} g_{\alpha\beta}(q) p_\alpha p_\beta \tag{3-1}$$

where the q_α are coordinates on a compact manifold V^s of constant negative curvature and the $g_{\alpha\beta}$ are the components of a metric tensor on V^s.

The stability of negative curvature under small variations in the functions $g_{\alpha\beta}(q)$ requires no clarification. The difficulties consist only in the fact that variation of the functions $g_{\alpha\beta}(q)$ is not the only possible form of variation of the function $H(q, p)$, and the transitivity and mixing for $s > 2$ remains proven only for the case of constant curvature whereas, with varying $g_{\alpha\beta}$, the curvature ceases to be constant. The second difficulty disappears in the case $s = 2$, for which transitivity is proven even when the curvature is variable. However, the first of these is not significant if we confine ourselves to functions $H(q, p)$ of the form

$$H(q, p) = U(q) + \sum_{\alpha\beta} g_{\alpha\beta}(q) p_\alpha p_\beta \tag{3-2}$$

(with which classical mechanics is primarily concerned) since systems of the form (3-2) reduce to systems of the form (3-1) by a shift to a new metric.

If we remember what was said earlier regarding inertial motion along surfaces close to an ellipsoid in 3-space, we conclude that, in even the simplest problems of classical mechanics, we need to consider as stable and hence worthy of equal and fundamental attention, at least the two cases that we have considered, one of which is connected with the transitivity on manifolds of constant energy and with continuous spectrum, the other with the absence of transitivity and with a primarily discrete spectrum.

I do not know of any analogous results regarding the stability of one general type of behavior or another of noncanonical dynamical systems with integral invariant and compact Ω^n.

§4. SOME REMARKS ON THE NONCOMPACT CASE

The distinctive feature of the noncompact case is the possibility of the existence of trajectories that depart, as $t \to +\infty$ or as $t \to -\infty$, from every compact subset of Ω. Here, I shall expound certain general facts from ergodic theory that are applicable for arbitrary continuous flows S^t in locally compact spaces Ω. Since a one-sided approach to infinity is possible only for trajectories constituting a set of measure zero, we first define a departing point x by the requirement that, for an arbitrary compact set K, there exists a T such that all points S_x^t, where $|t| > T$, lie outside K. We denote by Ω'' the set of all departing points. For purposes of detailed analysis of specific classical dynamical systems, it is expedient to construct "an individual ergodic theory," not in the purely metric variant expounded in the book of Hopf [9], but by following the earlier works by Hopf and Stepanov [10, 11] and in certain places following directly the exposition in the memoir by Krylov and Bogolyubov [12], although this memoir deals also with the compact case.

In such an exposition, just as in the compact case, the concept of a regular point remains basic. A point x is said to be regular if there exists an invariant measure μ possessing the following properties:

1. $\mu(\Omega - I_x^c) = 0$, where I_x^c is the closure of the trajectory passing through x.
2. $\mu(V_y) > 0$ for an arbitrary neighborhood V_y of the point $y \in I_x$.

3. For arbitrary continuous functions $f(x)$ and $g(x)$ that are nonzero only on compact sets,

$$\lim \frac{\int_a^T f(S_x^t)\,dt}{\int_a^T g(S_x^t)\,dt} = \frac{\int_\Omega f\,d\mu}{\int_\Omega g\,d\mu}$$

provided

$$\int_\Omega g\,d\mu \neq 0$$

4. The measure μ is transitive.

Since there is no requirement of normalization, the measure μ is defined by a point only up to a constant factor. Nonetheless, we shall denote it by μ_x and shall call it the "individual measure" of the point x. Therefore, we make the following minor modification in the definition of ergodic sets: two points x and x' are said to belong to a single ergodic set if their individual measures coincide in the sense of coincidence up to a constant factor. Thus, the set Ω' of regular points can be represented as the sum of ergodic sets:

$$\Omega' = \sum \varepsilon$$

Of course, the measures μ_ε are defined by an ergodic set only up to a constant factor.

The individual ergodic theorem asserts that

$$\Omega = \Omega' + \Omega'' + N \qquad \text{where } \lambda(N) = 0$$

with respect to an arbitrary invariant measure λ. Basically, however, the only thing that is essential for us is that $m(N)$ always be zero.

An arbitrary transitive invariant measure μ either is a measure μ_ε of some ergodic set ε or is of the form

$$\mu(A) = r_I(A \cap I)$$

where r_I is the "time" measure on the departing trajectory I. In contrast with the second trivial case, it is natural to call measures of the first type ergodic since corresponding to them is a set ε_μ, where

$$\mu_{\varepsilon_\mu} = \mu$$

Those considerations that, in the case of a compact space Ω, can be used to support the view that a compact dynamical system "of general type" is transitive, lead, when applied to noncompact dynamical systems, to the hypothesis that "in general" one or the other of two situations exists: Either the system is dissipative (that is, almost all its points depart), or the measure

m is ergodic (obviously, in the second case, the departing points constitute only a set of measure zero).

Sometimes this hypothesis is also applied to individual classical problems in the following form. If a given problem has a certain number of first integrals and if there is no basis for expecting the discovery of new ones, then it seems likely that there is transitivity on the manifolds defined by giving the values of the known first integrals. In support of such a practice, it might be remarked that, from the investigations of Hedlund and Hopf, this alternative always holds for geodesic motions on spaces of constant negative curvature.

If it is known that a set of positive measure consisting of departing points exists, then, in accordance with what has been said, the hypothesis arises that the system is dissipative. Evidently, Birkhoff's assumption as to the dissipative nature of the three-body problem is based on considerations of this nature.

It seems probable, however, that it will prove possible to construct, by the methods indicated in §3 for canonical systems, examples of the stable simultaneous existence in Ω^{2s} of a dissipative subset of positive measure and a positive region G filled basically by s-dimensional invariant tori.

I mention the fact that, for the more elementary questions, specialists in the qualitative theory of differential equations have not occupied themselves to a great extent with specific problems dealing with departing trajectories of the different special types. A notable example of this is the fact that the refutation of Chazy's assertions regarding the impossibility of "exchange" and "capture" in the three-body problem [17, 18] was first done by the difficult (and logically unconvincing, without precise bounds for the errors!) method of numerical integration (cf. BECKER [19] and SHMIDT [20]) and only recently has an example of "capture" been constructed by Sitnikov quite simply and almost without numerical calculations [21].

§5. TRANSITIVE MEASURES, SPECTRA, AND EIGENFUNCTIONS OF ANALYTIC SYSTEMS

We shall say that a measure μ in Ω^n is analytic if it can be written in the form

$$\mu(A) = \int_{V^k \cap A} f(\xi)\, d\xi, \ldots, d\xi_k$$

where each V^k is an analytic manifold, locally closed in Ω^n, the dimension of which is $k \leq n$, and where f is an analytic function of the coordinates ξ_α on V^k (which depend analytically on the coordinates x_α in Ω^n).

The manifold V^k is uniquely determined by the measure μ (if it is not identically zero). Therefore, we may call the number k the dimension of the measure μ also.

We shall be especially interested in transitive measures. In this case, the manifold V^k must be invariant. Two invariant manifolds of the same dimension do not intersect, but two invariant manifolds of differing dimension can only be contained one in the other (specifically, the one of lower dimension in the one of higher dimension). Every invariant manifold carries on itself no more than one transitive measure. By virtue of what has been said, a system of analytic transitive measures has a relatively transparent structure.

Until a comparatively short time ago, only analytic transitive measures were known in analytic systems. Only recently, GRABAR' [13], by constructing an analytic analogue of an example of Markov (an analytic irreducible but not strictly ergodic dynamical system) gave an example of a nonanalytic transitive measure in an analytic system. However, it may prove that the union of all nonanalytic ergodic sets is always negligible in the sense of the basic measure m.

Ergodic sets are unambiguously defined by their measures μ_ε which, by their very definition, are transitive.

With regard to ergodic sets corresponding to analytical transitive measures (that do not reduce to the measure μ_ε of any trajectory), we know only that, in the case in which the measure μ_ε is analytic, an ergodic set is contained in the support V^r of the measure μ_ε since it is everywhere dense in it; however, even in certain simple classical examples, the difference $V^r - \varepsilon$ may also be everywhere dense in V^r.

The spectral properties of transitive measures on analytic systems have been only slightly studied.

Discrete spectra have as yet been obtained only with a finite basis of independent frequencies

$$\lambda_1, \lambda_2, \ldots, \lambda_x$$

Also, for analytic measures, the number of independent frequencies coincides in all known cases with the dimension.

A continuous spectrum has been completely determined only recently by GEL'FAND and FOMIN [14, 15] for certain cases of geodesic motions on surfaces of constant negative curvature. In these cases, it proved to be a Lebesgue spectrum of countable multiplicity.

The possibility is not excluded that only these cases (a discrete spectrum with a finite number of independent frequencies and a Lebesgue spectrum of countable multiplicity) are possible for analytic transitive measures or that they alone are the general typical cases in some sense or other.

For nonanalytic transitive measures, it is more likely that their structure is completely arbitrary. This would be the case without doubt if someone were to establish an analytic analogue of Kakutani's theorem [16] on isometric embedding of an arbitrary flow in the flow of a continuous dynamical system.

With regard to the eigenfunctions, we pause only for an example of an analytic dynamical system on a two-dimensional torus $\mathbf{T}^2$ with discrete spectrum and everywhere-continuous eigenfunctions. Of course, this example, associated with a ratio $\gamma = \lambda_1/\lambda_2$ of average frequencies that can be approximated abnormally well by rational fractions r/s, indicates by its very origin that we are dealing not with a typical but with an exceptional phenomenon.

To clarify the question in greater detail, let us again look at the equations of motion on a two-dimensional torus, introducing into these equations a parameter θ that varies in some interval $[\theta_1, \theta_2]$:

$$\frac{dx_\alpha}{dt} = F_\alpha(x_1, x_2, \theta)$$

We shall assume that the functions $F_\alpha(x_1, x_2, \theta)$ are analytic. Obviously, the ratio of mean frequencies $\gamma(\theta)$ is also an analytic function of θ. If $\gamma(\theta)$ is not constant, then the set R of all θ for which it is possible to reduce the system analytically to the form

$$\frac{d\xi_\alpha}{dt} = \lambda_\alpha$$

will occupy almost all the interval $[\theta_1, \theta_2]$. The eigenfunctions

$$\varphi_{mn} = e^{i(m\lambda_1 + n\lambda_2)}$$

when we return to the original coordinates x_1 and x_2 will, for $\theta \in R$, be analytic functions of x_1 and x_2. Generally speaking, however, even on R they will be everywhere discontinuous with respect to θ on that set. Also, this discontinuity cannot be removed by deleting from R a set of measure zero. These facts are considerably more significant than the fact that $\varphi_{mn}(x_1, x_2, \theta)$ can be defined even at certain points of the remainder set, $[\theta_1, \theta_2]\backslash R$ of measure zero, by virtue of the admissibility of their non-analyticity and discontinuity with respect to x_1 and x_2.

It is possible that the dependence of $\varphi_{mn}(x_1, x_2, \theta)$ on the parameter θ on the set R is related to the class of functions of the type of monogenic Borel functions [24] and, despite its everywhere-dicontinuous nature, will admit investigation by appropriate analytical tools.

CONCLUSION

I shall consider my purpose attained if I have succeeded in convincing my listeners that, despite the great difficulties and the restricted nature of the results obtained up to now, the problem posed of using general concepts of present-day ergodic theory for a qualitative analysis of motion in analytic and, in particular, canonical dynamical systems deserves considerable attention on the part of investigators who are capable of grasping the many-sided relationships with the most varied divisions of mathematics that are disclosed here. In conclusion, I wish to thank the organizing committee of the Congress for the opportunity presented to me of reading this paper and for the kind help in reproducing the abstract with formulas and bibliographic references, and all those present for the attention that they have shown me on this last day of our meetings, when everyone is already satiated with the enormous volume of addresses given on the preceding days.

BIBLIOGRAPHY

[1] J. von Neumann, *Mathematische Grundlagen der Quantenmechanik*, Berlin, 1932.
[2] A. A. Markov, *Trudy vtorogo vsesoyuznogo matematicheskogo s"yezda* [Proc. Second All-Union Math. Congr.], Vol. II, pp. 227–231 (1934).
[3] A. N. Kolmogorov, *Doklady Akad. nauk* **93,** No. 5, 763–766 (1953).
[4] H. J. Tallquist, *Acta Soc. Sci. Fennicae*, No. 3. A. T. 1, No. 5 (1927).
[5] G. K. Badalyan, *Trudy vtorogo vsesoyuznogo matematicheskogo s"yezda* [Proc. Second All-Union Math. Congr.], Vol. II, pp. 239–241 (1934).
[6] G. D. Birkhoff, *Dynamical Systems*. Colloq. Publ. IX, Second Ed., Amer. Math. Soc., Providence, R.I., 1966.
[7] L. Landau and L. Pyatigorskiy, *Mekhanika*, 1940.
[8] E. Hopf, *Ber. Verh. Sächs. Akad. Wiss. Leipzig* **91,** No. 3, 261–304 (1939).
[9] E. Hopf, *Ergodentheorie*, Berlin, 1937.
[10] E. Hopf, *Math. Ann.* **103,** 710 (1930).
[11] V. V. Stepanov, *Compositio Math.* No. 3, 239 (1936).
[12] N. M. Krylov and N. N. Bogolyubov, *Ann. of Math.* **38** (1937).
[13] M. I. Grabar', *Doklady Akad. nauk* **95,** No. 1, 9–12 (1954).
[14] I. M. Gel'fand and S. V. Fomin, *Doklady Akad. nauk* **76,** No. 6, 771–774 (1951).
[15] I. M. Gel'fand and S. V. Fomin, *Uspekhi matem. nauk* **7,** No. 1, 118–137 (1952).
[16] S. Kakutani, *Proc. Nat. Acad. Sci. U.S.A.* **28,** No. 1, 16–21 (1942).
[17] I. Chazy, *J. de Math.* **8,** 353 (1929).
[18] I. Chazy, *Bull. Astr.* **8** (1952).
[19] L. Becker, *Monthly Notices* **80,** No. 6 (1920).
[20] O. Yu. Shmidt, *Doklady Akad. nauk* **58,** No. 2, 213–216 (1947).
[21] K. A. Sitnikov, *Matematich. sbornik* **32,** No. 3, 693–705 (1953).
[22] A. N. Kolmogorov, *Doklady Akad. nauk* **98,** No. 4 (1954).
[23] S. Kakutani, *Proc. Intern. Congr. Math.* **2,** 128–142 (1950).
[24] E. Borel, *Leçons sur les fonctions monogènes uniformes d'une variable complexe*, Paris, 1917.

BIBLIOGRAPHY

(See also the bibliographies in Appendixes B, C, and D.)

ABRAHAM, R.

[1] *Generic properties of closed geodesics* (to be published).

ABRAHAM, R. and ROBBIN, J.

[1] *Transversal Mappings and Flows*, Benjamin, New York, 1967.

ANDRONOV, A. and PONTRIAGIN, L.

[1] *Systems grossiers*, Dokl. Akad. Nauk SSSR **14** (1937), 247–251.

ANOSOV, D.

[1] *Roughness of geodesic flows on compact Riemannian manifolds of negative curvature*, (Russian) Dokl. Akad. Nauk SSSR **145** (1962), 707–709; (English) Sov. Math. **3** (1962), 1068–1069.

APOSTOL, T.

[1] *Mathematical Analysis*, Addison-Wesley, Reading, Mass., 1957.

ARENSTORF, R. F.

[1] *Periodic solutions of the restricted three-body problem representing analytic continuations of Keplerian elliptic motion*, Amer. J. Math. **85** (1963), 27–35.

[2] *Periodic trajectories passing near both masses of the restricted three-body problem*, Proc. XIVth Intern. Astronautical Congr., Paris **4** (1963), 85–97.

[3] *New periodic solutions of the plane three-body problem*, Proc. Intern. Symp. on Differential Equations and Dynamical Systems (1965), Academic Press, New York, 1967.

[4] *A new method of perturbation theory and its application to the satellite problem of celestial mechanics*, J. Reine Angew. Math. **221** (1966), 113–145.

ARNOLD, V. I.

[1] *Proof of a theorem of A. N. Kolmogorov on the invariance of quasi-periodic motions under small perturbations of the Hamiltonian*, Russian Math. Surveys **18** (1963), 9–36.

[2] *Small denominators and problems of stability of motion in classical and celestial mechanics*, Russian Math. Surveys **18** (1963), 85–192.

ARNOLD, V. I. and AVEZ, A.

[1] *Théorie ergodique des Systèmes dynamiques*, Gauthier-Villars, Paris, 1967.

ARRAUT, J.

[1] *Note on structural stability*, Bull. Amer. Math. Soc. **72** (1966), 542–544.

ARTIN, E.

[1] *Geometric Algebra,* Wiley (Interscience), New York, 1957.

BARRAR, R. B.

[1] *Existence of periodic orbits of the second kind in the restricted problem of three bodies*, Astron. J. **70** (1965), 3–5.

[2] *A new proof of a theorem of J. Moser concerning the restricted problem of three bodies*, Math. Ann. **160** (1965), 363–369.

BIRKHOFF, G. D.

[1] *Dynamical Systems*, Colloq. Publ. IX, Second Ed., Amer. Math. Soc., Providence, R. I., 1966.

[2] *Collected Mathematical Papers*, Amer. Math. Soc., Providence, R. I., 1950.

BISHOP, R. and CRITTENDEN, R.

[1] *Geometry of Manifolds*, Academic Press, New York, 1964.

BOULIGAND, G.

[1] *Sur la stabilité des propositions mathématiques*, Acad. Roy. Belg. Bull. Cl. Sci. (5) **21** (1935), 277–282; 776–779.

BRUNET, P.

[1] *Etude historique sur le Principe de la moindre Action*, Hermann, Paris, 1938.

CARATHÉODORY, C.

[1] *Calculus of Variations and Partial Differential Equations*, Holden-Day, San Francisco, 1965.

CARTAN, E.

[1] *Leçons sur les Invariants intégraux*, Hermann, Paris, 1922.

CHEVALLEY, C.

[1] *Theory of Lie Groups*, Princeton University Press, Princeton, N. J., 1946.

CODDINGTON, E. and LEVINSON, N.

[1] *Theory of Ordinary Differential Equations*, McGraw-Hill, New York, 1955.

CONLEY, C.

[1] *On some new long periodic solutions of the plane restricted three-body problem*, Comm. Pure Appl. Math. **14** (1963), 449–467.

COPPEL, W.

[1] *Stability and Asymptotic Behavior of Differential Equations*, Heath, Boston (1965).

CORBIN, H. and STEHLE, P.

[1] *Classical Mechanics*, Second Ed., Wiley, New York, 1960.

DARBOUX, G.
[1] *Sur le problème de Pfaff*, Bull. Sci. Math. (2) **6** (1882), 14–36.
DELAUNAY, C.
[1] *Théorie du mouvement de la lune*, Mem. **28** (1860), **29** (1867), Acad. Sci. France, Paris.
DESTOUCHES, J.
[1] *Les espaces abstraits en logique et la stabilité des propositions*, Acad. Roy. Belg. Bull. Cl. Sci. (5) **21** (1935), 780–786.
DIEUDONNÉ, J.
[1] *Foundations of Modern Analysis*, Academic Press, New York, 1960.
DILIBERTO, S.
[1] *Formal Stability of Hamiltonian Systems with Two Degrees of Freedom*, Technical report, Univ. of Calif., Berkeley, Calif., 1966.
DUFF, G.
[1] *Partial Differential Equations*, University of Toronto Press, Toronto, 1956.
DUGAS, R.
[1] *A History of Mechanics*, Griffon, Neuchatel, Switzerland, 1955.
DUHEM, P.
[1] *The Aim and Structure of Physical Theory*, Princeton Univ. Press, Princeton, N. J., 1954.
EILENBERG, S. and CARTAN, H.
[1] *Foundations of fibre bundles*, Intern. Sym. on Algebraic Topology, UNAM, Mexico City, 1958, pp. 16–23.
FLANDERS, H.
[1] *Differential Forms, with Applications to the Physical Sciences*, Academic Press, New York, 1963.
FLEMING, W.
[1] *Functions of Several Variables*, Addison-Wesley, Reading, Mass., 1965.
GALLISSOT, F.
[1] *Application des formes extérieures du 2ᵉ ordre à la dynamique Newtonienne et relativiste,* Ann. Inst. Fourier (Grenoble) **3** (1951), 277–285.
[2] *Formes extérieures en mécanique*, ibid. **4** (1952), 145–297.
[3] *Formes extérieures et la mécanique des milieux continus*, ibid. **8** (1958), 291–335.
GELFAND, I. and FOMIN, S.
[1] *Calculus of Variations*, Prentice Hall, Englewood Cliffs, N. J., 1963.
GOFFMAN, C.
[1] *Calculus of Several Variables*, Harper and Row, New York, 1965.
GOLDSTEIN, H.
[1] *Classical Mechanics*, Addison-Wesley, Reading, Mass., 1950.
GRAY, J.
[1] *Some global properties of contact structures*, Ann. of Math. (2) **69** (1959), 421–450.

HARTMAN, P.
[1] *Ordinary Differential Equations*, Wiley, New York, 1964.
HELGASON, S.
[1] *Differential Geometry and Symmetric Spaces*, Academic Press, New York, 1962.
HERMANN, R.
[1] *Lectures on Hamilton-Jacobi-Lie Theory and the Calculus of Variations*, I, Notes, Univ. of Calif., Berkeley, Calif., 1962.
[2] *E. Cartan's geometric theory of partial differential equations*, Advances in Mathematics **1** (H. Busemann, ed.), Academic Press, New York, 1966.
[3] *Lie Groups for Physicists*, Benjamin, New York, 1966.
HAUSDORFF, F.
[1] *Set Theory*, Second English Ed., Chelsea, New York, 1962.
HICKS, N.
[1] *Notes on Differential Geometry*, Van Nostrand, Princeton, N. J., 1965.
HILL, G.
[1] *Researches in lunar theory,* Amer. J. Math., 1 (1878), 5–26, 129–147, 245–260.
HOCKING, J. and YOUNG, G.
[1] *Topology*, Addison-Wesley, Reading, Mass., 1960.
HOFFMAN, K. and KUNZE, R.
[1] *Linear Algebra*, Prentice Hall, Englewood Cliffs, N. J., 1961.
JEFFERYS, W.
[1] *Doubly symmetric periodic orbits in the three-dimensional restricted problem*, Astron. J. **70** (1965), 393–394.
JOST, R.
[1] *Poisson brackets (an unpedagogical lecture)*, Rev. Modern Phys. **36** (1964), 572–579.
KAPLAN, W.
[1] *Regular curve families filling the plane, I*, Duke Math. J. **7** (1940), 154–185.
[2] *Regular curve families filling the plane, II*, Duke Math. J. **8** (1941), 11–46.
[3] *Topology of the two-body problem*, Amer. Math. Monthly **49** (1942), 316–323.
KELLEY, A.
[1] *The stable, center-stable, center, center-unstable, and unstable manifolds*, Appendix C in Abraham and Robbin [1].
KELLEY, J.
[1] *General Topology*, Van Nostrand, Princeton, N. J., 1955.
KHILMI, G. F.
[1] *Qualitative Methods in the Many-Body Problem,* Gordon and Breach, New York, 1961.

KNESER, H.
[1] *Reguläre Kurvenscharen auf den Ringflächen*, Math. Ann. **91** (1924), 135–154.
KOOPMAN, B.
[1] *On rejection to infinity and exterior motion in the restricted problem of three bodies*, Trans. Am. Math. Soc. **29** (1927), 287–331.
KOLMOGOROV, A. N.
[1] *General theory of dynamical systems and classical mechanics*, Proc. 1954 Intern. Congr. Math., North Holland, Amsterdam, 1957, pp. 315–333 (Russian, see App. D. for an English translation).
[2] *Théorie générale des systèmes dynamiques de la mécanique classique*, Sém. Janet, 1957–58, no. 6, Fac. Sci., Paris, 1958 (Fr. transl. of preceding reference [1]).
KUPKA, I.
[1] *Stabilité structurelle*, Sém. Janet, 1960–61, no. 7 Fac. Sci., Paris, 1962.
[2] *Contribution à la théorie des champs génériques*, Contributions to Differential Equations **2** (1963), 457–484; also **3** (1964), 411–420.
LANG, S.
[1] *Introduction to Differentiable Manifolds*, Wiley (Interscience), New York, 1962.
[2] *A Second Course in Calculus*, Addison-Wesley, Reading, Mass., 1964.
[3] *Algebra*, Addison-Wesley, Reading, Mass., 1965.
[4] *Linear Algebra*, Addison-Wesley, Reading, Mass., 1966.
LESLIE, J.
[1] *On a differential structure for the group of diffeomorphisms* (to be published).
LIAPOUNOV, M.
[1] *Problème général de la Stabilité du Mouvement*, Princeton University Press, Princeton, N. J., 1949.
MACKEY, G.
[1] *The Foundations of Quantum Mechanics*, Benjamin, New York, 1963.
MARKUS, L.
[1] *Global structure of ordinary differential equations on the plane*, Trans. Amer. Math. Soc. **76** (1954), 127–148.
[2] *Structurally stable differential systems*, Ann. of Math. **73** (1961), 1–19.
[3] *Periodic solutions and invariant sets of structurally stable differential systems*, Bol. Soc. Mat. Mexicana **5** (1960), 190–194.
MICHAEL, E.
[1] *Topologies on spaces of subsets*, Trans. Amer. Math. Soc. **71** (1951), 151–182.
MILNOR, J.
[1] *Morse Theory*, Princeton Univ. Press, Princeton, N. J., 1963.

MORLET, C.

[1] *Le lemme de Thom et les théorèmes de plongement de Whitney*, Sém. H. Cartan (1961–62), no. 4, École Normale Supérieure, Paris, 1963.

MOSER, J.

[1] *Periodishe Lösungen des restringierten Dreikörperproblems, die sich erst nach vielen Umlaufen schliessen,* Math. Ann. **126** (1953), 325–335.

[2] *On invariant curves of area-preserving mappings of an annulus*, Nachr. Akad. Wiss. Gottingen, Math. Phys. K1.II (1962), 1–20.

[3] *Perturbation theory for almost periodic solutions for undamped nonlinear differential equations*, Intern. Sym. on Nonlinear Differential Equations and Nonlinear Mechanics (LaSalle and Lefschetz, ed.), Academic Press, New York, 1963, pp. 71–79.

[4] *Stability and nonlinear character of ordinary differential equations in nonlinear problems*, Nonlinear Problems (Langer, ed), Univ. Wisconsin Press, Madison, Wis., 1963, pp. 139–149.

[5] *A rapidly convergent iteration method and non-linear partial differential equations, I*, Ann. Scuola Norm. Sup. Pisa (3) **20** (1966), 265–316; II (to be published).

[6] *Convergent series expansions for quasi-periodic motions* (to be published).

[7] *On the theory of quasi-periodic motions*, Stanford Lectures, 1965 (to appear in SIAM Rev.).

[8] *Structurally stable systems on tori* (to be published).

[9] *On invariant manifolds of vector fields and symmetric partial differential equations*, Differential Analysis, Oxford Univ. Press, Oxford, 1964, pp. 227–236.

[10] *Stabilitätsverhalten kanonischer Differentialgleichungssysteme*, Nach. Akad. Wiss. Göttingen, Math. Phys. K1.II (1955), 87–120.

MOULTON, F.

[1] *An Introduction to Celestial Mechanics*, Macmillan, New York, 1902.

NOMIZU, K. and KOBAYASHI, S.

[1] *Foundations of Differential Geometry*, Wiley (Interscience), New York, 1963.

PALAIS, R.

[1] *A Global Formulation of the Lie Theory of Transportation Groups*, Mem. 22, Amer. Math. Soc., Providence, R. I., 1957.

PARS, L.

[1] *A Treatise on Analytical Dynamics*, Wiley, New York, 1965.

PAULI, W.

[1] *On the Hamiltonian structure of non-local field theories*, Nuovo Cimento **10** (1953), 648–667.

PEIXOTO, M.

[1] *On structural stability*, Ann. Math. **69** (1959), 199–222.

[2] *Structural stability on 2-dimensional manifolds*, Topology **2** (1962), 101–121.
[3] *Qualitative theory of differential equations and structural stability*, Intern. Sym. on Nonlinear Differential Equations and Nonlinear Mechanics, Academic Press, New York, 1967.
[4] *On an approximation theorem of Kupka and Smale* (to be published).
POINCARÉ, H.
[1] *Sur les courbes définies par les équations différentielles*, C. R. Acad. Sci., Paris **90** (1880), 673–675; see also J. Math. Pures Appl. (3) **7** (1881), 375–422; (3) **8** (1882), 251–286; (4) **1** (1885), 167–244; (4) **2** (1886), 151–217.
[2] *Les Méthodes nouvelles de la Mécanique céleste*, 1, 2, 3, Gauthier-Villars, Paris, 1892–99; Dover, New York, 1957.
POLLARD, H.
[1] *Introduction to Celestial Mechanics*, Prentice Hall, Englewood Cliffs, N. J., 1965.
PUGH, C.
[1] *The closing lemma* (to be published).
[2] *An improved closing lemma and a general density theorem* (to be published).
REEB, G.
[1] *Sur les mouvements périodiques de certains systèmes mécaniques*, C. R. Acad. Sci. Paris **227** (1948), 1331–1332.
[2] *Sur les solutions périodiques de certains systèmes différentiels canoniques*, C. R. Acad. Sci. Paris **228** (1949), 1196–1198.
[3] *Quelques propriétés globales des trajectoires de la dynamique dues à l'existence de l'invariant intégral de M. Elie Cartan*, C. R. Acad. Sci. Paris **229** (1949), 969–971.
[4] *Sur certaines propriétés globales des trajectoires de la dynamique, dues à l'existence de l'invariant intégral de M. Elie Cartan*, Colloque de Topologie de Strasbourg, 1951, no. III, Univ. de Strasbourg, Strasbourg, 1952.
[5] *Sur la nature et la distribution des trajectoires périodiques de certains systèmes dynamiques*, C. R. Congr. Soc. Savantes Paris (Grenoble, 1952), Section des Sci., pp. 35–39, Gauthier-Villars, Paris, 1952.
[6] *Sur certaines propriétés topologiques des trajectoires des systèmes dynamiques*, Acad. Roy. Belg. Cl. Sci. Mem. Coll. in 8° (2) **27** (1952), no. 9.
[7] *Remarques sur l'existence de mouvements périodiques de certains systèmes dynamiques excités*, Arch. Math. **3** (1952), 76–78.
[8] *Variétés symplectiques, variétés presque-complexes et systèmes dynamiques*, C. R. Acad. Sci. Paris **235** (1952), 776–778.
[9] *Sur certaines problèmes relatifs aux variétés presque-symplectiques et systèmes dynamiques*, Convegno Intern. di Geometria Differenziale (Italia, 1953) Cromonese, Rome, 1954, pp. 104–106.

ROYDEN, H.

[1] *Real Analysis*, Macmillan, New York, 1963.

SACKER, R.

[1] *A new approach to the perturbation theory of invariant surfaces*, Comm. Pure Appl. Math. **18** (1965), 717–732.

SCHWARTZ, A.

[1] *A generalization of a Poincaré–Bendixson theorem to closed two-dimensional manifolds*, Amer. J. Math. **85** (1963), 453–458.

SIEGEL, C.

[1] *Vorlesungen über Himmelsmechanik*, Springer-Verlag, Berlin, 1956.

SMALE, S.

[1] *Diffeomorphisms with many periodic points*, Differential and Combinatorial Topology, Sym. in Honor of Marston Morse, Princeton Univ. Press, Princeton, N. J., 1964.

[2] *Structurally stable systems are not dense*, Amer. J. Math. **88** (1966), 491–496.

[3] *Morse theory and a non-linear generalization of the Dirichlet problem*, Ann. of Math. (2) **80** (1964), 382–396.

[4] *Stable manifolds for differential equations and diffeomorphisms*, Topologia Differenziale, CIME., Cremonese, Rome, 1963; or Ann. Scuola Norm. Sup. Pisa (3) **17** (1963), 97–116.

[5] *Dynamical systems and the topological conjugacy problem for diffeomorphisms*, Proc. Intern. Congr. Math., Stockholm, 1963, pp. 490–496.

SPIVAK, M.

[1] *Calculus on Manifolds*, Benjamin, New York, 1965.

STERNBERG, S.

[1] *Lectures on Differential Geometry*, Prentice Hall, Englewood Cliffs, N. J., 1964.

[2] *Infinite Lie groups and the formal aspects of dynamical systems*, J. Math. Mech., **10** (1961), 451–474.

SUNDMAN, K.

[1] *Mémoire sur le problème des trois corps*, Acta. Math. **36** (1913), 105–179.

[2] *Theorie der Planeten*, Enzycl. Math. Wiss. (Astronomie) **6/2/1**, n. 15 (1915), 729–807.

THOM, R.

[1] *Stabilité structurelle et morphogenèse*, Benjamin, New York, 1967.

VAN DE KAMP, P.

[1] *Elements of Astromechanics*, Freeman, San Francisco, 1964.

VAN KARMAN, J.

[1] *The engineer grapples with nonlinear problems*, Bull. Amer. Math. Soc. **46** (1940), 615–675.

WHITTAKER, E.
[1] *A Treatise on the Analytical Dynamics of Particles and Rigid Bodies,* Fourth Ed., Cambridge Univ. Press, Cambridge, 1959.
WINTNER, A.
[1] *Uber eine Revision der Sortentheorie des restringierten Dreikorperproblems,* Sitzsber. Sachsischer Akad. Wiss. Leipzig **82** (1930), 3–56.
[2] *The Analytical Foundations of Celestial Mechanics,* Princeton Univ. Press, Princeton, N. J., 1941.
[3] *On the periodic analytic continuations of the circular orbits in the restricted problem of three bodies*, Proc. Nat. Acad. Sci., U.S.A. **22** (1936), 435–439.

INDEX